Instructor's Resource Manual with Tests

Patricia Foard — South Plains College

Cindy Gaddis — Tyler Junior College

Marilyn Platt — Gaston College

Jennifer Wilson — Tyler Junior College

With Contributions from

Kevin Bodden & Randy Gallaher — Lewis and Clark Community College

Beginning Algebra

FIFTH EDITION

Elayn Martin-Gay

PEARSON
Prentice Hall

Upper Saddle River, NJ 07458

Vice President and Editorial Director, Mathematics: Christine Hoag
Editor-in-Chief: Paul Murphy
Sponsoring Editor: Mary Beckwith
Assistant Editor: Georgina Brown
Senior Managing Editor: Linda Mihatov Behrens
Project Manager, Production: Robert Merenoff
Supplement Cover Manager: Paul Gourhan
Supplement Cover Designer: Victoria Colotta
Operations Specialist: Ilene Kahn
Senior Operations Supervisor: Diane Peirano

© 2009 Pearson Education, Inc.

Pearson Prentice Hall

Pearson Education, Inc.

Upper Saddle River, NJ 07458

Printed in the United States of America

10 9 8 7 6 5 4 3 2

ISBN-13: 978-0-13-603111-6

ISBN-10:   0-13-603111-0

Pearson Education Ltd., London
Pearson Education Singapore, Pte. Ltd.
Pearson Education, Canada, Inc.
Pearson Education—Japan
Pearson Education Australia Pty, Ltd.
Pearson Education North Asia, Ltd., Hong Kong
Pearson Educación de Mexico, S.A. de C.V.
Pearson Education Malaysia, Pte. Ltd.
Pearson Education Upper Saddle River, New Jersey

Instructor's Resource Manual with Tests

Beginning Algebra, Fifth Edition
Elayn Martin-Gay

TABLE OF CONTENTS

TEST FORMS

Mini-Lecture 1.1
Tips for Success in Mathematics

Learning Objectives:

1. Get ready for this course.
2. Understand some general tips for success.
3. Understand how to use this text.
4. Get help as soon as you need it.
5. Learn to prepare for and take exams.
6. Develop good time management.

Examples:

1. Getting ready for this course.
   a) Positive attitude   b) Allow adequate time for class arrival
   c) Bring all required materials

2. Understanding some general tips for success.
   a) Find a contact person   b) Choose to attend <u>all</u> classes
   c) Do your homework   d) Check your work and learn from mistakes
   e) Seek help when needed   f) Stay organized
   g) Ask questions   h) Hand in all assignments on time

3. Understanding how to use the text.
   a) Each example in every section has a Practice Problem associated with it.
   b) Refer to the Lecture Video CD's and the Test Prep Video CD's.
   c) Review the meaning of icons used in text.
   d) At beginning of each section, a list of icons shows availability of support materials.
   e) Each chapter ends with Chapter Highlights, Reviews, Practice Tests, and Cumulative Reviews.

4. Get help as soon as you need it.
   a) Try your instructor, a tutoring center, a math lab, or you may want to form as study group with fellow classmates.

5. Learning to prepare for and take exams.
   a) Review previous homework assignments, class notes, quizzes, etc.
   b) Read Chapter Highlights to review concepts and definitions.
   c) Practice working out exercises in the end-of-the-chapter Review and Test.
   d) When taking a test, read directions and problems carefully.
   e) Pace yourself. Use all available time. Check your work and answers.

6. Good time management.
   a) Make a list of all weekly commitments with estimated time needed.
   b) Be sure to schedule study time. Don't forget eating, sleeping, and relaxing!

Teaching Notes:

- Most developmental students have a high anxiety level with mathematics.
- Many developmental students are hesitant to ask questions and seek extra help.
- Be sure to include <u>your</u> individual expectations. Keep your expectations clear and concise.
- Each section in the text has 3 worksheets in the Extra Practice featuring differentiated learning.

Mini-Lecture 1.2
Symbols and Sets of Numbers

Learning Objectives:

1. Use a number line to order numbers.
2. Translate sentences into mathematical statements.
3. Identify natural numbers, whole numbers, integers, rational numbers, irrational numbers, and real numbers.
4. Find the absolute value of a real number.

Examples:

1. Insert $<, >,$ or $=$ in the space between the paired numbers to make each statement true.

   a) 2 ___ 8

   b) 41 ___ 14

   c) 2.12 ___ -2.12

   d) $\dfrac{3}{7}$ ___ $\dfrac{9}{21}$

   Determine whether each statement is true or false.

   e) $15 \leq 20$

   f) $3.002 \geq 3.202$

   g) $\dfrac{14}{18} \neq \dfrac{7}{9}$

   h) $\dfrac{6}{7} \geq \dfrac{11}{14}$

2. Translate each sentence into a mathematical statement.

   a) Negative eleven is less than or equal to negative four.

   b) Fourteen is greater than one

3. Tell which set or sets each number belongs to: natural numbers, whole numbers, integers, rational numbers, irrational numbers, and real numbers.

   a) 5

   b) -3

   c) $\dfrac{8}{3}$

   d) $\sqrt{5}$

   e) 0

4. Find each absolute value.

   a) $|6.2|$

   b) $|-14|$

   c) $\left| -\dfrac{2}{9} \right|$

   d) $|0.03|$

   e) $|0|$

Teaching Notes:

- Some students need to be reminded to read the expression and inequality symbols from left to right.
- Some students are not familiar with $<$ or $>$ and need to be told to point the symbol at the smaller value.
- Many students need to see value plotted on a number line to visually understand less than or greater than.
- Each section in the text has 3 worksheets in the Extra Practice featuring differentiated learning.

Answers: *1a) <; 1b) >; 1c) >; 1d) =; 1e) false; 1f) false; 1g) false; 1h) false; 2a) -11 ≤ -4; 2b) 14 > 1; 3a) N, W, ., Rat., Real; 3b) I, Rat., Real; 3c) Rat., Real; 3d) Irr., Real; 3e) W, I, Real; 4a) 6.2; 4b) 14; 4c) 2/9; 4d) 0.03; 4e) 0*

Mini-Lecture 1.3
Fractions

Learning Objectives:

1. Write fractions in simplest form.
2. Multiply and divide fractions.
3. Add and subtract fractions.

Examples:

1. Simplify by dividing the numerator by the denominator.

   a) $\dfrac{3}{3}$ b) $\dfrac{40}{4}$ c) $\dfrac{16}{1}$ d) $\dfrac{0}{7}$ e) $\dfrac{12}{0}$

2. Write each fraction as an equivalent fraction with the given denominator.

   a) $\dfrac{3}{10}$ with a denominator of 40 b) $\dfrac{4}{7}$ with a denominator of 56

3. Simplify the following fractions.

   a) $\dfrac{5}{10}$ b) $\dfrac{9}{15}$ c) $\dfrac{88}{66}$ d) $\dfrac{300}{550}$

4. Multiply or divide as indicated.

   a) $\dfrac{1}{3} \cdot \dfrac{5}{7}$ b) $\dfrac{28}{6} \cdot \dfrac{8}{21}$ c) $\dfrac{6}{19} \div \dfrac{9}{13}$ d) $\dfrac{9}{14} \div \dfrac{3}{10}$

5. Add or subtract as indicated.

   a) $\dfrac{1}{8} + \dfrac{3}{8}$ b) $\dfrac{1}{6} + \dfrac{7}{15}$ c) $\dfrac{5}{9} - \dfrac{1}{12}$ d) $\dfrac{7}{8} - \dfrac{5}{6}$

6. Perform the indicated operations on mixed numbers.

   a) $13\dfrac{2}{3} + 6\dfrac{5}{8}$ b) $5 - 2\dfrac{3}{7}$ c) $2\dfrac{1}{3} \cdot 6\dfrac{3}{7}$ d) $3\dfrac{4}{5} \div 1\dfrac{2}{5}$

Teaching Notes:

- Some students may need a visual review of the meaning of a fraction (i.e. pie drawing).
- Most students have experience with fractions but may have forgotten the procedures.
- Stress that all fractions must be written in simplified form.
- Each section in the text has 3 worksheets in the Extra Practice featuring differentiated learning.

Answers: *1a) 1; 1b) 10; 1c) 16; 1d) 0; 1e) undefined; 2a) 12/40; 2b) 32/56; 3a) ½; 3b) 3/5; 3c) 4/3; 3d) 6/11; 4a) 5/21; 4b) 16/9; 4c) 26/57; 4d) 15/7; 5a) ½; 5b) 19/30; 5c) 17/36; 5d) 1/24; 6a) 20 7/21; 6b) 2 4/7; 6c) 15; 6d) 19/7;*

Mini-Lecture 1.4
Introduction to Variable Expressions and Equations

Learning Objectives

1. Define and use exponents and the order of operations.
2. Evaluate algebraic expressions, given replacement values for variables.
3. Determine whether a number is a solution of a given equation.
4. Translate phrases into expressions and sentences into equations.

Examples:

1. Evaluate.

   a) 2^3
   b) 1^7
   c) $\left(\dfrac{6}{7}\right)^2$
   d) $(0.3)^3$

   Using order of operation, simplify each expression.

   e) $7 + 3 \cdot 2$
   f) $25 - 3^2 \cdot 2$
   g) $6[-5 + 6(-3 + 8)]$
   h) $\dfrac{20(-1) - (-4)(-3)}{2[-12 \div (-3 - 3)]}$

2. Evaluate each expression when $x = 3$, $y = 2$, and $z = 6$.

   a) $x + y + z$
   b) $3x - z$
   c) $|5x - 2z|$
   d) $\dfrac{5z}{x} - \dfrac{3y^2}{z}$

3. Determine whether the given number is a solution of the given equation.

   a) $x - 12 = 15$; 27
   b) $12 + y = 29$; 7
   c) $\dfrac{3}{4}x = \dfrac{15}{20}$; 5
   d) $y = 3y + 2$; 0

4. Write each phrase as an algebraic expression.

   a) The sum of a number and thirteen
   b) The quotient of forty-two and a number

   Write each sentence as an equation.

   c) The product of one-third and a number is nine
   d) A number added to twelve is fourteen.

Teaching Notes:

- Be sure to identify base and exponent when working with exponential notation.
- Most students find order of operations challenging.
- Many students will confuse expression and equation. Be sure students understand that you simplify an expression, but solve an equation.
- Many students have problems with translating sentences into equations.
- Each section in the text has 3 worksheets in the Extra Practice featuring differentiated learning.

Answers: 1a) 8; 1b) 1; 1c) 36/49; 1d) 0.027; 1e) 13; 1f) 7;1g) 150; 1h) -8; 2a) 11; 2b) 3; 2c) 3; 2d) 8; 3a) true; 3b) false; 3c) false; 3d) false; 4a) x + 13; 4b) 42/x; 4c) 1/3 x = 9; 4d) 12 + x = 14

Mini-Lecture 1.5
Adding Real Numbers

Learning Objectives:

1. Add real numbers with the same sign.
2. Add real numbers with unlike signs.
3. Solve problems that involve addition of real numbers.
4. Find the opposite of a number.

Examples:

1. Add the following real numbers with the same sign.

   a) $8 + 11$
   b) $(-3) + (-15)$
   c) $(-14) + (-35)$
   d) $\left(-\dfrac{3}{5}\right) + \left(-\dfrac{1}{2}\right)$

2. Add the following real numbers with different signs.

   a) $(-9) + 5$
   b) $16 + (-25)$
   c) $(-15.3) + 27.03$
   d) $\left(\dfrac{1}{2}\right) + \left(-\dfrac{5}{8}\right)$

   Mixed exercise of addition of signed numbers.

   e) $-7 + (-23)$
   f) $-42 + 38$
   g) $53 + (-22)$
   h) $\left(-\dfrac{5}{12}\right) + \left(\dfrac{3}{8}\right)$

3. Solve each of the following.

   a) At the beginning of a chemistry experiment, Amy measured the temperature of a liquid to be -5°C. During the experiment, the temperature rose 14°C. What was the liquid's temperature at the end of the experiment?

   b) A local restaurant reported net incomes of -$1,397, -$2,042, and -$809 for the past three months. What was its total net income for the three months?

4. Find the additive inverse or opposite.

   a) 8
   b) -9
   c) 0
   d) $\left|-17\right|$

Teaching Notes:

- Some students will need to see addition performed on a number line.
- Some students will need instruction with inputting negative numbers into a calculator.
- Review the definition of absolute value.
- Each section in the text has 3 worksheets in the Extra Practice featuring differentiated learning.

Answers: 1a) 19; 1b) -18; 1c) −49; 1d) -11/10; 2a) -4; 2b) -9; 2c) 11.73; 2d) -1/8; 2e) -30; 2f) -4; 2g) 31; 2h) -1/24; 3a) 9° C; 3b) -$4,248; 4a) -8; 4b) 9; 4c) 0; 4d) -17

Mini-Lecture 1.6
Subtracting Real Numbers

Learning Objectives:

1. Subtract real numbers.
2. Add and subtract real numbers.
3. Evaluate algebraic expressions using real numbers
4. Solve problems that involve subtraction of real numbers.

Examples:

1. Subtract.

   a) $-8 - 4$ b) $11 - 18$ c) $-15 - (-10)$ d) $-12 - 12$

   e) $22 - (-13)$ f) $-132 - (-207)$ g) $1.3 - (3.8)$ h) $\dfrac{15}{7} - \left(-\dfrac{9}{14}\right)$

2. Simplify each expression.
   a) $-3 - (-4) - 5 + (-2)$ b) $7 - 10 - 8 + (-7)$ c) $-2 + |-3 - 5| - 3^2$

3. Evaluate each expression when $x = -3$, $y = -7$, and $z = 9$

   a) $x - y$ b) $\dfrac{10 - x}{y - 2}$ c) $|x| + |y| - |z|$ d) $x^2 - y$

4. Solve:
   a) In a game of cards, Alicia won 11 chips, lost 6 chips, won 3 chips, lost 14 chips, and won 1 chip. What was her final count of chips?

   Find the complementary or supplementary angle.

   b)
   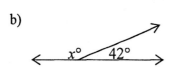

   c)
   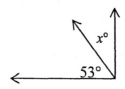

Teaching Notes:

- Remind students to always change subtraction to addition and "add the opposite".
- Some students forget to change the sign of the second value after changing to addition.
- Encourage students to take the time to write the steps: $3 - (-2) = 3 + (+2) = 5$
- Each section in the text has 3 worksheets in the Extra Practice featuring differentiated learning.

Answers: 1a) -12; 1b) -7; 1c) -5; 1d) -24; 1e) 35; 1f) 75; 1g) -2.5; 1h) 39/14; 2a) -6, 2b) -18, 2c) -3; 3a) 4; 3b) -13/9; 3c) 1; 3d) 16; 4a) -5; 4b) 138°; 4c) 37°

Mini-Lecture 1.7
Multiplying and Dividing Real Numbers

Learning Objectives

1. Multiply and divide real numbers.
2. Evaluate algebraic expressions using real numbers.

Examples

1. Multiply the real numbers.

   a) $-6(5)$

   b) $(-11)(-3)$

   c) $-\dfrac{3}{5}\left(\dfrac{10}{21}\right)$

   d) $2(-5)(-1)(-3)$

   Find the reciprocal of the real number.

   e) $\dfrac{3}{7}$

   f) 5

   g) $-\dfrac{5}{21}$

   h) 0.3

   Divide the real numbers.

   i) $\dfrac{27}{-3}$

   j) $-90 \div (-5)$

   k) $-\dfrac{1}{2} \div \left(-\dfrac{8}{15}\right)$

   l) $\dfrac{-22}{0}$

2. Evaluate each expression.

   a) $2x - y^2$, when $x = 4$, $y = -3$

   b) $\dfrac{-2-x}{y-5}$, when $x = -4, y = 6$

   c) $\dfrac{-6x - 4y}{-2z + 3 - (-10)}$ when $x = 5, y = -1 , z = 0$

   d) -8^2

   e) $(-7)^2$

   f) -1^8

   g) $(-1)^{87}$

Teaching Notes:

- Most students find multiplying and dividing real numbers relatively easy.
- Many students confuse $\dfrac{0}{5} = 0$ and $\dfrac{5}{0} =$ undefined.
- Many students have difficulty with the fact that $-5^2 \neq (-5)^2$
- Each section in the text has 3 worksheets in the Extra Practice featuring differentiated learning.

Answers: *1a) -30; 1b) 33; 1c) -2/7; 1d) -30; 1e) 7/3; 1f) 1/5; 1g) -21/5; 1h) 10/3; 1i) -9; 1j) 18; 1k) 15/16; 1l) undefined; 2a) -1, 2b) 2, 2c) -2, 2d) -64, 2e) 49, 2f) -1, 2g) -1*

Mini-Lecture 1.8
Properties of Real Numbers

<u>**Learning Objectives:**</u>

1. Use the commutative and associative properties.
2. Use the distributive property.
3. Use the identity and inverse properties.

<u>**Examples:**</u>

1. Use the commutative property of addition or multiplication to complete each statement.

   a) $3 + y =$ _____   b) $a + (-9) =$ _____   c) $-10 \cdot x =$ _____   d) $s \cdot t =$ ____

   Use the associative property of addition or multiplication to complete each statement.

   e) $(3 + x) + y =$ _____   f) $-2 \cdot (5x) =$ _____

   Use the commutative and associative properties to simplify each expression.

   g) $12 + (4 + x)$ h) $-7(5x)$ i) $\left(-\dfrac{1}{3} + x\right) + \dfrac{5}{12}$ j) $0.13(-1.2y)$

2. Use the distributive property to write each expression without parentheses. Then simplify the result, if possible.

   a) $8(x + y)$ b) $-3(7x - 9)$ c) $-2(-6y - 10)$ d) $6(4x - 3y - 9)$

   Use the distributive property to write each sum as a product.

   e) $6 \cdot x + 6 \cdot y$ f) $13 \cdot x + 13 \cdot 4$ g) $(-2)x + (-2)y$ h) $\dfrac{1}{3}a + \dfrac{1}{3} \cdot 6$

3. Name the property that is illustrated by each true statement.

   a) $0 + 11 = 11$ b) $3 \cdot \dfrac{1}{3} = 1$ c) $5 + (-5) = 0$ d) $12 \cdot 1 = 12$

<u>**Teaching Notes:**</u>

- Many students use the Properties of Real Numbers without realizing that they are using these properties.
- Some students, when using the distributive property, forget to multiply the second term.
- Each section in the text has 3 worksheets in the Extra Practice featuring differentiated learning.

Answers: *1a) y+3; 1b) -9+a; 1c) x·-10; 1d) t·s; 1e) 3 + (x + y); 1f) (-2 · 5) x; 1g) 16 + x; 1h) -35x; 1i) 1/12 + x; 1j) -0.156y; 2a) 8x + 8y; 2b) -21x + 27; 2c) 12y + 20; 2d) 24x - 18y - 54; 2e) 6(x + y); 2f) 13(x + 4); 2g) -2(x + y); 2h) 1/3 (a + 6); 3a) addition property of zero; 3b) inverse property of multiplication; 3c) inverse property of addition; 3d) multiplication property of one*

Mini-Lecture 2.1
Simplifying Algebraic Expressions

Learning Objectives:

1. Identify terms, like terms, and unlike terms.
2. Combine like terms.
3. Use the distributive property to remove parentheses.
4. Write word phrases as algebraic expressions.

Examples

1. Identify the numerical coefficient of each term.

   a) $9x$ b) $-3y$ c) $-x$ d) $2.7x^2y$

   Indicate whether the terms in each list are like or unlike.

   e) $6x, -3x$ f) $-xy^2, -x^2y$ g) $5ab, -\dfrac{1}{2}ba$ h) $2x^3yz^2, -x^3yz^3$

2. Simplify each expression by combining any like terms.

   a) $7x - 2x + 4$ b) $-9y + 2 - 1 + 6 + y - 7$ c) $1.6x^5 + 0.9x^2 - 0.3x^5$

3. Simplify each expression. Use the distributive property to remove any parentheses.

   a) $3(x + 6)$ b) $-(-5m + 6n - 2p)$ c) $\dfrac{1}{3}(6x - 9)$

   Remove parentheses and simplify each expression.

   d) $14(2x + 6) - 4$ e) $10a - 5 - 2(a - 3)$ f) $3(2x - 5) - (x + 7)$

4. Write each phrase as an algebraic expression. Simplify if possible.

   a) Add $-4y + 3$ to $6y - 9$ b) Subtract $2x - 1$ from $3x + 7$

   c) Triple a number, decreased by six   d) Six times the sum of a number and two

Teaching Notes:

- Students will need repeated practice with identifying terms and like terms.
- Some students do not know that a variable without a numerical coefficient actually has a coefficient of 1.
- Some students will forget to distribute the minus sign in 3b), 3e), and 3f). Some students might need to write a 1 in front of the parentheses in 3b) and 3f).
- Each section in the text has 3 worksheets in the Extra Practice featuring differentiated learning.

Answers: 1a) 9; 1b) -3; 1c) -1; 1d) 2.7; 1e) like; 1f) unlike; 1g) like; 1h) unlike; 2a) 5x+4; 2b) -8y; 2c) $1.3x^5$+0.9x²; 3a) 3x+18; 3b) 5m-6n+2p; 3c) 2x-3; 3d) 28x+80; 3e) 8a+1; 3f) 5x-22; 4a) (-4y+3) + (6y-9) = 2y-6; 4b) (3x+7) – (2x-1) = x + 8; 4c) 3x-6; 4d) 6(x + 2)

Mini-Lecture 2.2
The Addition Property of Equality

Learning Objectives:

1. Define linear equations and use the addition property of equality to solve linear equations
2. Write word phrases as algebraic expressions.

Examples:

1. Solve each equation. Check each solution.

   a) $y - 6 = 18$ b) $-18 = t - 5$ c) $8.1 + y = 13.9$ d) $a + \dfrac{2}{3} = -\dfrac{3}{4}$

   Solve each equation. If possible, be sure to first simplify each side of the equation. Check each solution.

   e) $5(y + 2) = 6(y - 3)$ f) $10x = 4x + 9 + 5x$

   g) $-8z + 5 + 6z = -3z + 10$ h) $-5x + 4 + 6x = 15 - 28$

   i) $-\dfrac{1}{6}x - \dfrac{1}{3} = \dfrac{5}{6}x + \dfrac{1}{2}$ j) $-14.9 + 4a - 2.7 + 2a = 5.1 + 7a + 1.5$

2. Write each algebraic expression described.

   a) Two numbers have a sum of 72. If one number is z, express the other number in terms of z.

   b) During a recent marathon, Tom ran 8 more miles than Judy ran. If Judy ran x miles, how many miles did Tom run?

   c) On a recent car trip, Raymond drove x miles on day one. On day two, he drove 170 miles more than he did on day one. How many miles, in terms of x, did Raymond drive for both days combined?

Teaching Notes:

- Some students need a quick review of "like terms".
- Advise students to write out each step until they have mastered this concept. Avoid shortcuts!
- Some students need to be taught how to work a problem in sequential order showing each step.
- Encourage students to take their time and organize their work. This will help when the problems become more complex.
- Each section in the text has 3 worksheets in the Extra Practice featuring differentiated learning.

Answers: 1a) 24; 1b) -13; 1c) 5.8; 1d) -17/12; 1e) 28; 1f) 9; 1g) 5; 1h) -17; 1i) -5/6; 1j) 11; 2a) 72 - z; 2b) x+8; 2c) 2x+ 170

Mini-Lecture 2.3
The Multiplication Property of Equality

Learning Objectives:

1. Use the multiplication property of equality to solve linear equations.
2. Use both the addition and multiplication properties of equality to solve linear equations.
3. Write word phrases as algebraic expressions.

Examples:

1. Use the multiplication property of equality to solve the following linear equations. Check each solution.

   a) $-8x = -24$ b) $7x = 0$ c) $-z = 19$ d) $3x = -22$

   e) $\dfrac{2}{5}a = 12$ f) $\dfrac{y}{-11} = 2.5$ g) $\dfrac{-3}{8}b = 0$ h) $-10.2 = -3.4c$

2. Use the addition property of equality and the multiplication property of equality to solve the following linear equations. Check each solution.

   a) $5x + 6 = 46$ b) $\dfrac{a}{9} - 7 = 11$ c) $-24 = -3x - 9$ d) $\dfrac{1}{3}y - \dfrac{1}{3} = -6$

   e) $-5.8z + 1.9 = -32.5 - 1.5z$ f) $8y + 7 = 6 - 2y - 10y$ g) $4(4x - 1) = (-8) - (-24)$

3. Write each algebraic expression described. Simplify if possible.

   a) If z represents the first of two consecutive even integers, express the sum of the two integers in terms of z.

   b) If x represents the first of three consecutive even integers, express the sum of the first and third integer in terms of x.

   c) Houses on one side of a street are all numbered using consecutive odd integers. If the first house on the street is numbered x, write an expression in x for the sum of five house numbers in a row.

Teaching Notes:

- Review "like terms" with students.
- Many students do not combine like terms before using one of the properties.
- Encourage students to always take the time to check their solution.
- Each section in the text has 3 worksheets in the Extra Practice featuring differentiated learning.

Answers: *1a) 3; 1b) 0; 1c) -19; 1d) -22/3; 1e) 30; 1f) -27.5; 1g) 0; 1h) 3; 2a) 8; 2b) 162; 2c) 5;*
2d) -17; 2e) 8; 2f) -1/20; 2g) 5/4; 3a) 2z+2; 3b) 2x+4; 3c) 5x+20

Mini-Lecture 2.4
Solving Linear Equations

Learning Objectives:

1. Apply a general strategy for solving a linear equation.
2. Solve equations containing fractions.
3. Solve equations containing decimals.
4. Recognize identities and equations with no solution.

Examples:

1. Solve the following linear equations.

   a) $6a - (5a - 1) = 4$

   b) $4(3b - 1) = 16$

   c) $4z = 8(2z + 9)$

   d) $2(x + 8) = 3(x - 5)$

   e) $3(2a - 3) = 5(a + 4)$

   f) $12(4c - 2) = 3c - 4$

2. Solve each equation containing fractions.

   a) $\dfrac{y}{6} - 4 = 1$

   b) $\dfrac{1}{4}x - \dfrac{3}{8}x = 5$

   c) $\dfrac{-6x + 5}{4} + 1 = -\dfrac{5x}{4}$

   Solve each equation containing decimals.

   d) $0.05x + 0.06(x - 1,500) = 570$

   e) $0.4(x + 7) - 0.1(3x + 6) = -0.8$

3. Solve each equation. Indicate if it is an identity or an equation with no solution.

   a) $6(z + 7) = 6z + 42$

   b) $3 + 12x - 1 = 8x + 4x - 1$

   c) $\dfrac{x}{3} - 3 = \dfrac{2x}{6} + 1$

Teaching Notes:

- Refer students to the beginning of this section in the textbook for steps: To Solve Linear Equations in One Variable.
- Most students find solving equations with fractions or decimals difficult.
- Common error: When multiplying equations with fractions by the LCD, some students multiply only the terms with fractions instead of all terms.
- Common error: When solving equations with decimals and parentheses (examples 2d and 2e), some students multiply terms both inside parentheses and outside parentheses by a power of 10.
- Each section in the text has 3 worksheets in the Extra Practice featuring differentiated learning.

Answers: *1a) 3; 1b) 5/3; 1c) -6; 1d) 31; 1e) 29; 1f) 4/9; 2a) 30; 2b) -40; 2c) 9; 2d) 6,000 2e) -30; 3a) identify; 3b) no solution; 3c) no solution*

Mini-Lecture 2.5
An Introduction to Problem Solving

Learning Objectives:

Apply the steps for problem solving as we

1. Solve problems involving direct translation.
2. Solve problems involving relationships among unknown quantities.
3. Solve problems involving consecutive integers.

Examples:

1. Solve.
   a) Eight is added to a number and the sum is doubled, the result is −11 less than the number. Find the number.

   b) Three times the difference of a number and 2 is equal to 8 subtracted from twice a number. Find the integers.

2. Solve.

   a) A college graduating class is made up of 450 students. There are 206 more girls than boys. How many boys are in the class?

   b) A 22-ft pipe is cut into two pieces. The shorter piece is 7 feet shorter than the longer piece. What is the length of the longer piece?

   c) A triangle has three angles, A, B, and C. Angle C is 18° greater than angle B. Angle A is 4 times angle B. What is the measure of each angle?
   (Hint: The sum of the angles of a triangle is 180°).

3. Solve.
   a) The room numbers of two adjacent hotel rooms are two consecutive odd numbers. If their sum is 1380, find the hotel room numbers.

   b) When you open a book, the left and right page numbers are two consecutive natural numbers. The sum of their page numbers is 349. What is the number of the page that comes first?

Teaching Notes:

- Many students find application problems challenging.
- Encourage students, whenever possible, to draw diagrams, charts, etc.
- Encourage students to use algebra to solve a problem even though they may be able to solve without it.
- Refer students to *General Strategy for Problem Solving* section 2.4.
- Each section in the text has 3 worksheets in the Extra Practice featuring differentiated learning.

Answers: *1a) -27; 1b) 21, 63; 2a) 122 boys; 2b) 14.5 feet; 2c) A=108°, B=27°, C=45°; 3a) 689, 691; 3b) 174*

Mini-Lecture 2.6
Formulas and Problem Solving

Learning Objectives:

1. Use formulas to solve problems.
2. Solve a formula or equation for one of its variables.

Examples:

1. Substitute the given values into each given formula and solve for the unknown variable, If necessary, round to one decimal place.

   a) Distance Formula
      $d = rt$; $t = 9, d = 63$

   b) Perimeter of a rectangle
      $P = 2l + 2w$; $P = 32, w = 7$

   c) Volume of a pyramid
      $V = \frac{1}{3} Bh$; $V = 40, h = 8$

   d) Simple interest
      $I = prt$; $I = 23, p = 230, r = 0.02$

   e) Convert the record high temperature of 102°F to Celsius. ($F = \frac{9}{5}C + 32$)

   f) You have decided to fence an area of your backyard for your dog. The length of the area is 1 meter less than twice the width. If the perimeter of the area is 70 meters, find the length and width of the rectangular area.

   g) For the holidays, Chris and Alicia drove 476 miles. They left their house at 7 a.m. and arrived at their destination at 4 p.m. They stopped for 1 hour to rest and re-fuel. What was their average rate of speed?

2. Solve each formula for the specified variable.

   a) Area of a triangle
      $A = \frac{1}{2}bh$ for b

   b) Perimeter of a triangle
      $P = s_1 + s_2 + s_3$ for s_3

   c) Surface area of a special rectangular box
      $S = 4lw + 2wh$ for l

   d) Circumference of a circle
      $C = 2\pi r$ for r

Teaching Notes:

- Most students will only need algebra reminders when working with a formula given values.
- Refer students to *Solving Equations for a Specified Variable* chart in the textbook.
- Most students have problems with applications. Refer them back to section 2.4 and the *General Strategy for Problem Solving* in the textbook.
- Each section in the text has 3 worksheets in the Extra Practice featuring differentiated learning.

Answers: 1a) 7; 1b) 9; 1c) 15; 1d) 5; 1e) 38.9°C; 1f) l=23, w=12; 1g) 59.5 mph; 2a) $b = \dfrac{2A}{h}$;

2b) $s_3 = P - s_1 - s_2$; 2c) $\dfrac{S - 2wh}{4w}$; 2d) $r = \dfrac{C}{2\pi}$

Mini-Lecture 2.7
Percent and Mixture Problem Solving

Learning Objectives:

1. Solve percent equations.
2. Solve discount and mark-up problems.
3. Solve percent increase and percent decrease problems.
4. Solve mixture problems.

Examples:

1. Find each number described.

   a) 5% of 300 is what number?   b) 207 is 90% of what number?
   c) 15 is 1% of what number?   d) What percent of 350 is 420?

2. Solve the following discount and mark-up problems. If needed, round answers to the nearest cent.

   a) A "Going-Out-Of-Business" sale advertised a 75% discount on all merchandise. Find the discount and the sale price of an item originally priced at $130.

   b) Recently, an anniversary dinner cost $145.23 excluding tax. Find the total cost if a 15% tip is added to the cost.

3. Solve the following percent increase and decrease problems.

   a) The number of minutes on a cell phone bill went from 1200 minutes in March to 1600 minutes in April. Find the percent increase. Round to the nearest whole percent.

   b) In 2004, a college campus had 8,900 students enrolled. In 2005, the same college campus had 7,600 students enrolled. Find the percent decrease. Round to the nearest whole percent.

   c) Find the original price of a pair of boots if the sale price is $120 after a 20% discount.

4. How much pure acid should be mixed with 4 gallons of a 30% acid solution in order to get a 80% acid solution? Use the following table to model the situation.

	Number of Gallons · Acid Strength = Amount of Acid		
Pure Acid			
30% Acid Solution			
80% Acid Solution Needed			

Teaching Notes:

- Most students find problem solving challenging. Encourage students to make a list of all appropriate formulas.
- Each section in the text has 3 worksheets in the Extra Practice featuring differentiated learning.

Answers: *1a) 15; 1b) 230; 1c) 1500; 1d) 120%; 2a) discount - $97.50, sale price - $32.50; 2b) $167.01;*
3a) 33%; 3b) 15%; 3c) $150; 4) 10 gallons

Mini-Lecture 2.8
Further Problem Solving

Learning Objectives:

1. Solve problems involving distance.
2. Solve problems involving money.
3. Solve problems involving interest.

Examples:

1. How long will it take a car traveling 60 miles per hour to overtake an activity bus traveling 45-miles per hour if the activity bus left 2 hours before the car?

	r	*D*	*t*
Car	60 mph	60x	*x*
Activity Bus	45 mph	45(*x* + 2)	*x* + 2

2. A collection of dimes and quarters and nickels are emptied from a drink machine. There were four times as many dimes as quarters, and there were ten less nickels than there were quarters. If the value of the coins was$19.50, find the number of quarters, the number of dimes, and the number of nickels.

	Number	**Value of each**	**Total value**	
Quarters	*x*	0.25	0.25x	40 @ 0.25=$10.00
Dimes	2*x*	0.10	0.10(2x)	80 @ 0.10=$$8.00
Nickels	*x* - 10	0.05	0.05(*x* − 10)	30 @ 0.05=$1.50
Entire Collection			$19.50	$19.50

3. Jeff received a year end bonus of $80,000. He invested some of this money at 8% and the rest at 10%. If his yearly earned income was $7,300, how much did Jeff invest at 10%? Use the following table to model the situation.

	Principal ·	Rate ·	Time =	Interest
8% Fund	x	0.08	1	0.08x
10% Fund	80,000 - x	0.1	1	0.01(50,000 − x)
Total	80,000			7,300

Teaching Notes:

- Most students find problem solving challenging. Encourage students to make a list of all appropriate formulas.
- Each section in the text has 3 worksheets in the Extra Practice featuring differentiated learning.

Answers: 1) 6 hours; 2) Number of Quarters = 40, Number of dimes = 80, number of nickels = 303; 3) $45,000

Mini-Lecture 2.9
Solving Linear Inequalities

Learning Objectives:

1. Define linear inequality in one variable, graph solution sets on a number line, and use interval notation.
2. Solve linear inequalities.
3. Solve compound inequalities.
4. Solve inequality applications.
5. Key Vocabulary: *inequality, <, ≤, >, ≥, addition property of inequality, multiplication property of inequality, at least, no less than, at most, no more than, is less than, is greater than.*

Examples:

1. Graph each inequality on a number line and write it in interval notation.

   a) $x \geq -5$ b) $y < 7$ c) $-\dfrac{3}{2} \geq m$ d) $x > -\dfrac{2}{5}$

2. Using the addition property of inequality, solve each inequality. Graph the solution set and write it in interval notation.

   a) $x + 7 \leq 12$ b) $x - 10 > -3$ c) $-4z - 2 > -5z + 1$ d) $18 - 2x \leq -3x + 24$

   Using the multiplication property of inequality, solve each inequality. Graph the solution set and write it in interval notation.

   e) $-8 \geq \dfrac{x}{3}$ f) $3x < 73$ g) $0 < \dfrac{y}{8}$ h) $-\dfrac{3}{5}z \leq 9$

   Using both properties, solve each inequality.

   i) $3(3x - 16) < 12(x - 2)$ j) $-18(z - 2) \geq -21z + 24$ k) $\dfrac{8}{21}(x + 2) > \dfrac{1}{7}(x + 3)$

3. Solve each inequality. Graph the solution set and write it in interval notation.
   a) $-5 < t \leq 0$ b) $-12 \leq 2x < -8$ c) $3 \leq 4x - 9 \leq 7$

4. Solve the following.
   a) Eight more than twice a number is less than negative twelve. Find all numbers that make this statement true.

   b) One side of a triangle is six times as long as another side and the third side is 8 inches long. If the perimeter can be no more than 106 inches, find the maximum lengths of the other two sides.

Teaching Notes:

- Remind students to reverse the direction of the inequality symbol when multiplying or dividing by a negative number.
- Suggest students keep the coefficient of the variable positive whenever possible.
- Each section in the text has 3 worksheets in the Extra Practice featuring differentiated learning.

Answers: *1a) – 3c) graph answers at end of mini-lectures; 1a) [-5,∞); 1b) (∞,7); 1c) $\left(-\infty, -\dfrac{3}{2}\right]$; 1d) (-2/5, ∞);*

2a) (−∞,5]; 2b) (7,∞); 2c) (3,∞); 2d) (−∞,6]; 2e) (−∞,−24]; 2f) (−∞,24⅓); 2g) (0,∞);

2h) [−15,∞); 2i) (−8,∞); 2j) [−4,∞); 2k) (−7/5,∞); 3a) (−5,0]; 3b) [−6, −4); 3c) [3,4]; 4a) x<−10;
4b) 14, 84

Mini-Lecture 3.1
Reading Graphs and the Rectangular Coordinate System

Learning Objectives:
1. Read bar and line graphs.
2. Define the rectangular coordinate system and plot ordered pairs of numbers.
3. Graph paired data to create a scatter diagram.
4. Determine whether an ordered pair is a solution of an equation in two variables.
5. Find the missing coordinate of an ordered pair solution, given one coordinate of the pair.

Examples:

1. a) The following bar graph shows points scored per quarter in a basketball game. Use the bar graph to find the final score.

   b) The following line graph shows the average monthly rent for people in Worcester. How much did monthly rent increase from 1980 – 2000.

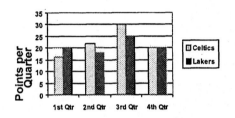
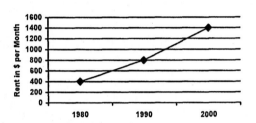

2. Plot each order pair. State in which quadrant or on which axis each point lies.

   a) (-2, -5)   b) (0, -4)   c) $\left(2\frac{2}{3}, 4\frac{1}{2}\right)$ d) (-1, 4)

3. The table gives a bookstore's net dollar sales for the period of 2000-2005.

Year (x)	2000	2001	2002	2003	2004	2005
Sales – in thousands (y)	19	22	21	23	25	26

   a. Write this paired data as a set of ordered pairs of the form (year, sales)
   b. In your own words, write the meaning of the order pair.
   c. Create a scatter diagram of the paired data.

4. Determine whether each ordered pair is a solution of the given linear equation.

   a) $5x + y = 15$; (1,4), (2,5), (0, 15)   b) $x = \frac{1}{4}y$; (1,4), (8,2), (0,0)

5. Complete each ordered pair so that it is a solution of the given linear equation.

   a) $x + 2y = 6$; (2,), (, -3)   b) $y = \frac{1}{3}x - 2$; (6,), $\left(, -\frac{1}{3}\right)$

Teaching Notes:
- Most students can read bar and line graphs successfully.
- Many students have trouble putting meaning to an ordered pair.
- Remind students that an ordered pair is (x, y) – alphabetical order.
- Each section in the text has 3 worksheets in the Extra Practice featuring differentiated learning.

Answers: 1a) 88 to 82; 1b) $1000; 2a) III; 2b) y-axis; 2c) I; 2d) II; 3a) { (2000,19), (2001,22), (2002, 21), (2003, 23), (2004, 25), (2005, 26)}; 3b) answers will vary; 4a) No, Yes, Yes; 4b) Yes, No, Yes;

5a) (2, 2), (12, -3); 5b) (6, 0), (5, $-\frac{1}{3}$)

Mini-Lecture 3.2
Graphing Linear Equations

Learning Objectives:

1. Identify linear equations.
2. Graph a linear equation by finding and plotting ordered pair solutions.

Examples:

1. For each equation, find three ordered pair solutions by completing the table. Then use the ordered pairs to graph the equation.

a) $x - y = 2$

x	y
3	
	-2
-1	

b) $y = -\dfrac{1}{3}x - 2$

x	y
6	
	-2
	0

c) $y = \dfrac{2}{3}x$

x	y
-3	
	0
	$\dfrac{10}{3}$

d) $y = -3$

x	y
2	
-1	
0	

Graph the following linear equations.

e) $x + y = 0$

f) $y = -2x - 1$

g) $x - 2 = 0$

2. Solve: The value of a house (y) increases in value x years after purchase by the formula $y = 7,500x + 120,000$.

   a) Graph the linear equation
   b) Complete the ordered pair (5,   )
   c) Write a sentence explaining the meaning of the ordered pair found in part b.

Teaching Notes:

- Problems 1a) – d) tend to pose the least amount of challenge.
- Some students become very confused when they can choose any value for x or y as a starting point for finding an ordered-pair solution.
- Many students do not understand problems 1d) and 1g) and must memorize the form for an equation for a horizontal or a vertical line.
- Each section in the text has 3 worksheets in the Extra Practice featuring differentiated learning.

Answers (for all graphs, see Mini-Lecture graphing answers at end of section) : 1a) (3,1), (0, -2), (-1, -3);
1b) (6, -4), (0, -2), (-6, 0); 1c) (-3, -2), (0,0), (5, $\frac{10}{3}$); 1d) (-2,-3), (-1, -3), (0, -3); 1e) – 1g) see graphing answers;
2a) see graphing answers; 2b) (5, $157,500); 2c) After 5 years, the house's value increased to $157,500.

Mini-Lecture 3.3
Intercepts

Learning Objectives:

1. Identify intercepts of a graph.
2. Graph a linear equation by finding and plotting intercepts.
3. Identify and graph vertical and horizontal lines.

Examples:

1. Identify the intercepts.

   a) 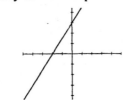   b) 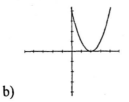   c)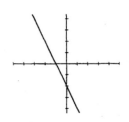

2. Graph each linear equation by finding and plotting its intercepts.

   a) $x - y = 2$ b) $x - y = -3$ c) $2x + 4y = 8$

   d) $x - 3y = 0$ e) $y = 3x + 3$ f) $y = -2x - 4$

3. Identify the type of equation (horizontal or vertical line) and graph the equation.

   a) $x = -3$ b) $y = 2$ c) $x + 3 = 5$

Teaching Notes:

- Sometimes, students will list the intercepts as a single number; not an ordered pair. For example: x-intercept: 3, y-intercept: 4.
- Remind students that any time (0, 0) is a point on a graph, then that is both its x- and y-intercept.
- Some students confuse horizontal and vertical lines. For example: if x = -5, have students mentally graph the line that would intersect the x axis at –5. This line could only be vertical, not horizontal.
- Each section in the text has 3 worksheets in the Extra Practice featuring differentiated learning.

Answers: 1a) (-2, 0), (0, 3); 1b) (2, 0), (0,4); 1c) (-1, 0), (0, -2); 2a) – 2f) see mini-lecture graphing answers; 3a) vertical; 3b) horizontal; 3c) vertical.

Mini-Lecture 3.4
Slope and Rate of Change

Learning Objectives:

1. Find the slope of a line given two points of the line.
2. Find the slope of a line given its equation.
3. Find the slopes of horizontal and vertical lines.
4. Compare the slopes of parallel and perpendicular lines.
5. Slope as a rate of change.

Examples:

1. Find the slope of the line that passes through the given points.

   a) $(6, 5)$ and $(1, 7)$ b)    c) $(-5, 0)$ and $(0, -3)$

2. Find the slope of each line.

   a) $x + y = 12$ b) $3x + y = 8$ c) $11x - 3y = 33$

   d) $9x + y = -12$ e) $y + 5 = 0$ f) $2x - 7 = 0$

3. Determine whether each pair of lines is parallel, perpendicular, or neither.

   a) $\begin{aligned} 3x &= 2y + 3 \\ 2x + 3y &= 2 \end{aligned}$ b) $\begin{aligned} x + 3y &= 4 \\ 8x + 2y &= 2 \end{aligned}$ c) $\begin{aligned} 9x &= 16 - 3y \\ 16 - 4y &= 12x \end{aligned}$

   Find the slope of a line that is **(a)** parallel and **(b)** perpendicular to the line passing through each pair of points.

   d) $(-5, -5)$ *and* $(-1, -1)$ e) $(-2, 10)$ *and* $(5, -4)$

4. An inclined ramp leading to a warehouse is to rise 16 inches for each horizontal distance of 17 feet. Write this slope as a grade. (Round to the nearest tenth of a percent, if necessary).

Teaching Notes:

- Many students confuse the change in y and change in x in the slope formula. Hint: if you can imagine a picnic table $(\overline{X \ \ X})$, the x is on the bottom. If the y is on the bottom $(\overline{Y \ \ Y})$, the picnic table will fall over!
- Remind students to "read" the slope of the line as it moves from left to right.
- Each section in the text has 3 worksheets in the Extra Practice featuring differentiated learning.

Answers: *1a)* $-\dfrac{2}{5}$; *1b)* $\dfrac{5}{4}$; *1c)* $-\dfrac{3}{5}$; *2a)* *-1,* *2b)* *-3;* *2c)* $\dfrac{11}{3}$; *2d)* *-9;* *2e)* *0;* *2f) undefined;*
3a) perpendicular; *3b) neither;* *3c) parallel;* *3d) a: 1, b: -1;* *3e) a: -2, b: 1/2 ;* *4) 4/51 or 7.8%*

Mini-Lecture 3.5
Equations of Lines

Learning Objectives

1. Use the slope-intercept form to write an equation of a line.
2. Use the slope-intercept form to graph a linear equation.
3. Use the point-slope form to find an equation of a line given its slope and a point on the line.
4. Use the point-slope form to find an equation of a line given two points on the line.
5. Find equations of vertical and horizontal lines.
6. Use the point-slope form to solve problems.

Examples:

1. Write an equation of the line with each given slope, m, and y-intercept, (0, b).

   a) $m = -9; b = 4$
   b) $m = -\frac{2}{3}; b = 7$
   c) $m = 0; b = \frac{1}{2}$
   d) $m = -\frac{5}{2}; b = \frac{31}{2}$

2. Use the slope-intercept form to graph each equation.

   a) $y = \frac{1}{2}x - 3$
   b) $y = -\frac{1}{4}x + 2$
   c) $y = -4x$
   d) $5x + 2y = 10$

3. Find an equation of each line with the given slope that passes through the given point. Write the equation in the form $Ax + By = C$.

   a) $m = 4; (10, 5)$
   b) $m = -\frac{7}{9}; (5, 2)$
   c) $m = -6; (-8, -10)$
   d) $m = \frac{1}{2}; (-4, 8)$

4. Find an equation of the line passing through each pair of points. Write the equation in the form Ax + By = C.

   a) (-7, -4) and (0, 5)
   b) (3, 7) and (-2, -6)
   c) (9, -9) and (6, -5)
   d) $\left(-\frac{1}{2}, \frac{3}{4}\right)$ and $\left(-\frac{5}{3}, \frac{1}{3}\right)$

5. Find an equation of each line.

   a) Vertical line through (0,5)
   b) Horizontal line through (4,3)

6. Solve.
   Assume the following describes a linear relationship. Write an equation in slope-intercept form. A faucet is used to add water to a large bottle that already contains some water. After it has been filling for 3 seconds, the gauge on the bottle indicates that it contains 10 ounces of water. After it has been filling for 20 seconds, the gauge indicates the bottle contains 24 ounces of water. Let y be the amount of water in the bottle x seconds after the faucet was turned on. Write a linear equation that models the amount of water in the bottle in terms of x.

Teaching Notes:

- Many students do not understand that you leave "*x and y*" in the final equation.
- Each section in the text has 3 worksheets in the Extra Practice featuring differentiated learning.

Answers: 1a) $y=-9x+4$; *1b)* $y = -\frac{2}{3}x + 7$; *1c)* $y = \frac{1}{2}$; *1d)* $y = -\frac{5}{2}x + \frac{31}{2}$; *2a)-2d) see mini-lecture graphing answers; 3a)* $4x-y=35$; *3b)* $7x+9y=53$; *3c)* $6x+y=-58$; *3d)* $x-2y=-20$; *4a)* $9x-7y=-35$; *4b)* $13x-5y=4$; *4c)* $4x+3y=9$; *4d)* $5x-14y=-13$; *5a)* $x =0$; *5b)* $y = 3$; *6)* $14x - 17y = -128$

Mini-Lecture 3.6
Functions

Learning Objectives:

1. Identify relations, domains, and ranges.
2. Identify functions.
3. Use the vertical line test.
4. Use function notation.

Examples:

1. Find the domain and range of each relation.

   a) $\{(2,3),(0,0),(-1,-5),(-2,6)\}$

   b) $\{(3,1),(3,-2),(3,0),(3,6)\}$

2. Determine whether each relation is also a function.

   a) $\{(10,5),(-3,-2),(2,-1),(6,5)\}$

   b) $\{(3,5),(-3,5),(-3,0),(2,4)\}$

3. Determine whether each graph is the graph of a function.

   a)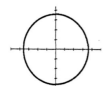

   b)

   c)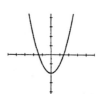

4. For each function (a – c), find the value of the f(-3,) f(2), and f(0).

   a) $f(x) = -\dfrac{1}{3}x - 5$

   b) $f(x) = 3x^2 - 2x - 2$

   c) $f(x) = |-3 - x|$

   d) If f(4) = 8, write a corresponding ordered-pair solution.

Teaching Notes:

- At first, students find the definition of relation and function confusing.
- Many students have trouble determining if a relation is a function.
- Some students struggle with the concept of domain and range.
- Each section in the text has 3 worksheets in the Extra Practice featuring differentiated learning.

Answers: *1a) D: {-2, -1, 0, 2}, R:{-5, 0, 3, 6}; 1b) D: {3}, R: {-2, 0, 1, 6}; 2a) yes; 2b) no; 3a) no; 3b) yes;*
3c) yes; 4a) $-4, -\dfrac{17}{3}, -5$; 4b) 31, 6, -2; 4c) 0, 5, 3; 4d) (4, 8)

Mini-Lecture 4.1
Solving Systems of Linear Equations by Graphing

Learning Objectives:

1. Determine if an ordered pair is a solution of a system of equations in two variables.
2. Solve a system of linear equations by graphing.
3. Without graphing, determine the number of solutions of a system.

Examples:

1. Determine whether the ordered pair is a solution of the system of linear equations.

   a) $(-4, -5) \begin{cases} x + y = -9 \\ x - y = 1 \end{cases}$

   b) $(-5, -3) \begin{cases} 2x + y = -7 \\ 3x + 2y = -9 \end{cases}$

   c) $(2, -4) \begin{cases} 4x = 4 - y \\ 2x = -12 - 4y \end{cases}$

   d) $(-3, 1) \begin{cases} 3x = 10 - y \\ 4x = 15 - 3y \end{cases}$

2. Solve each system of linear equations by graphing. Note: All systems have a solution.

   a) $\begin{cases} 4x + y = -4 \\ 5x + 2y = -2 \end{cases}$

   b) $\begin{cases} 3x + 2y = 22 \\ 2x + 4y = 28 \end{cases}$

   c) $\begin{cases} x = 6 \\ \dfrac{1}{6}x - y = 1 \end{cases}$

   d) $\begin{cases} 2x + 5y = 32 \\ 3y = 20 - 2x \end{cases}$

3. Without graphing, determine the number of solutions of a system.
   Note: the systems have no solution or an infinite number of solutions.

   a) $\begin{cases} 4x - 16y = 12 \\ y = \dfrac{1}{4}x - \dfrac{3}{4} \end{cases}$

   b) $\begin{cases} -x = y \\ x = 6 - y \end{cases}$

Teaching Notes:

- Many students need to be reminded to use graph paper and be very neat with their graphing skills.
- Remind students to substitute their solution into the original equations to check their results.
- Many students get confused between consistent and inconsistent systems and its meaning for the solution.
- Each section in the text has 3 worksheets in the Extra Practice featuring differentiated learning.

Answers: *1a) yes; 1b) no; 1c) yes; 1d) no; 2a) – 2d) see mini-lecture graphing answers; 3a) infinite; 3b) no solution*

Mini-Lecture 4.2
Solving Systems of Linear Equations by Substitution

Learning Objectives:

1. Use the substitution method to solve a system of linear equations.

Examples:

1. Solve each system of equations by the substitution method. Note: the following systems have one equation already solved for one variable.

a) $\begin{cases} x + y = 9 \\ y = 2x \end{cases}$

b) $\begin{cases} x = y - 2 \\ x + y = 6 \end{cases}$

Solve each system of equations by the substitution method.

c) $\begin{cases} x + 6y = 2 \\ 4x + 5y = -11 \end{cases}$

d) $\begin{cases} x - 3y = 3 \\ -5x - 2y = 2 \end{cases}$

e) $\begin{cases} x - 4y = -1 \\ 6x - 3y = -6 \end{cases}$

f) $\begin{cases} 6x + 7y = 33 \\ 3x - 3y = -42 \end{cases}$

g) $\begin{cases} 4x - 3y = 30 + x \\ 4x = -(y + 2) + 3x \end{cases}$

h) $\begin{cases} x - y = -4 \\ \dfrac{1}{2}x + \dfrac{1}{2}y = -3 \end{cases}$

i) $\begin{cases} 4x + y = 11 \\ 12x + 3y = 33 \end{cases}$

j) $\begin{cases} -6x - 24y = -10 \\ 5x + 20y = 0 \end{cases}$

Teaching Notes:

- Remind students to check their solution in the *original* equations.
- Many students write their final answer as x = a number and y = a number rather than an ordered pair (x, y).
- Many students find working with fractional coefficients challenging.
- Refer students to the textbook's summary "To Solve a System of Two Linear Equations by the Substitution Method".
- Each section in the text has 3 worksheets in the Extra Practice featuring differentiated learning.

Answers: 1a) (3, 6); 1b) (2, 4); 1c) (-4, 1); 1d) (0, -1); 1e) (-1, 0); 1f) (-5, 9) ; 1g) (4, -6); 1h) (-5, -1); 1i) infinite; 1j) no solution.

Mini-Lecture 4.3
Solving Systems of Linear Equations by Addition

Learning Objectives:

1. Use the addition method to solve a system of linear equations.

Examples:

1. Solve each system of equations by the addition method.

a) $\begin{cases} x+y=5 \\ x-y=11 \end{cases}$

b) $\begin{cases} -x+4y=28 \\ -6x-4y=-56 \end{cases}$

Solve each system of equation by the addition method. If a system contains fractions or decimals, you may want to first clear each equation of fractions or decimals.

c) $\begin{cases} x+5y=49 \\ -7x+4y=-31 \end{cases}$

d) $\begin{cases} x+3y=2 \\ 4x+2y=18 \end{cases}$

e) $\begin{cases} -2x-7y=-6 \\ 5x-3y=-26 \end{cases}$

f) $\begin{cases} 5x+8y=1 \\ 2x+3y=2 \end{cases}$

g) $\begin{cases} -x-2y=-4 \\ 5x+10y=8 \end{cases}$

h) $\begin{cases} 4x-6y=1 \\ 20x-30y=3 \end{cases}$

i) $\begin{cases} 3x+\dfrac{1}{3}y=10 \\ 2x+\dfrac{2}{3}y=4 \end{cases}$

j) $\begin{cases} 3.5x+0.3y=-18.7 \\ 0.7x+0.9y=-7.1 \end{cases}$

Teaching Notes:

- Encourage students to discuss which variable is the easiest to eliminate and what number an equation should be multiplied by to make the elimination possible.
- Remind students that there can be more than one way to solve a system.
- Remind students to check their solution.
- Each section in the text has 3 worksheets in the Extra Practice featuring differentiated learning.

Answers: *1a) (8, -3); 1b) (4, 8); 1c) (9, 8); 1d) (5, -1); 1e) (-4, 2); 1f) (13, -8); 1g) no solution;*
1h) no solution; 1i) (4, -6); 1j) (-5, -4)

Mini-Lecture 4.4
Systems of Linear Equations and Problem Solving

Learning Objectives:

1. Use a system of equations to solve problems.

Examples:

1. Solve .

a) *Finding Unknown Numbers:* The sum of two numbers is 7. Three times the first number equals 4 times the second number. Find the two numbers.

b) *Finding Unknown Numbers:* One number is four more than a second number. Two times the first number is 2 more than four times the second number.

c) *Solving a Problem about Prices:* Alicia purchased tickets to a local comedy club for 5 adults and 2 children. The total cost was $161. The cost of a child's ticket was $7 less than the cost of an adult's ticket. Find the price of an adult's ticket and a child's ticket.

d) *Solving a Problem about Prices:* Allison throws loose change found in the laundry into container. After one month, she finds it contains all nickels and dimes. In fact, there are 4 times as many dimes as nickels, and the value of the dimes is $3.50 more than the value of the nickels. How many nickels and dimes does Allison have?

e) *Finding Rates:* Kyle and Jason live 28 miles apart in Central Massachusetts. They decide to bicycle towards each other and meet somewhere in between. Kyle' rate of speed is 40% of Jason's. They start out at the same time and meet 2 hours later. Find Kyle's rate of speed.

f) *Finding Amounts of Solutions:* Amy has 3 liters of a 35% solution of sodium hydroxide in a container. What is the amount and concentration of sodium hydroxide solution she must add to this in order to end up with 7 liters of 27% solution?

Teaching Notes:

- Most students struggle with word problems.
- Refer students to the textbook's *Problem-Solving Steps* for guidance.
- Encourage students to draw and label diagrams or construct charts whenever possible.
- Entertain a discussion around which algebraic method, substitution or addition, is appropriate for the word problem.
- Remind students to always check their answer.
- Each section in the text has 3 worksheets in the Extra Practice featuring differentiated learning.

Answers: *1a) 4,3; 1b) 7,3; 1c) $25, $18; 1d) 10 nickels, 40 dimes; 1e) 4 mph; 1f) 4 liters of 21% solution*

Mini-Lecture 4.5
Graphing Linear Inequalities

Learning Objectives:

1. Graph a linear inequality in two variables.

Examples:

1. Determine whether the ordered pairs given are solutions of the linear inequality in two variables.

   a) $x - y > -2$; $(0, -1)$, $(1, 4)$ b) $2x + 4y \geq 6$; $(4, -1)$, $(-3, 3)$

   c) $x > -y$; $(0, 0)$, $(3, -2)$ d) $y > \dfrac{1}{3}x - 1$; $(0, 0)$, $(-3, -1)$

   Graph each inequality.

   e) $x + y \geq 2$ f) $y < -\dfrac{1}{5}x$ g) $x - y > -3$

   h) $2x + y \leq -5$ i) $-2x - 3y < 6$ j) $x > y$

   k) $y \geq 2$ l) $x < 5$ m) $y \geq 0$

Teaching Notes:

- Most students who are good at graphing equalities will find this section easy.
- Although many students do not understand the region they are testing in problems 1a) – 1d), most need practice in testing before they begin graphing inequalities.
- Remind students to always use a test point from their proposed solution region to check their work.
- Remind students that the boundary line is dashed for < or > and solid for ≤ or ≥ .
- Refer students to the gray instruction block: *To Graph a Linear Inequality in Two Variables.*
- Each section in the text has 3 worksheets in the Extra Practice featuring differentiated learning.

Answers: *1a) yes, no; 1b) no, yes; 1c) no, yes; 1d) yes, yes; 1e) – 1m) see mini-lecture graphing answers.*

Mini-Lecture 4.6
Systems of Linear Inequalities

Learning Objectives:

1. Graph a system of linear inequalities.

Examples:

1. Graph the solution to the following system.

a) $\begin{cases} 2x \le y \\ x + y \ge 2 \end{cases}$

b) $\begin{cases} x - y > 3 \\ y < 2 \end{cases}$

c) $\begin{cases} x \ge -3 \\ y < 2 \end{cases}$

d) $\begin{cases} 3x > -6 \\ x + y \le -2 \end{cases}$

Teaching Notes:

- Students may have difficulty finding the solution region even when both inequalities are graphed correctly. Have students shade each inequality with a different color pencil or shading each at a different angle.
- Each section in the text has three worksheets in the Extra Practice featuring differentiated learning.

Answers
1a-d) graph answers at end of mini-lectures

Mini-Lecture 5.1
Exponents

Learning Objectives:
1. Evaluate exponential expressions.
2. Use the product rule for exponents.
3. Use the power rule for exponents.
4. Use the power rule for products and quotients.
5. Use the quotient rule for exponents, and define a number raised to the 0 power.
6. Decide which rule(s) to use to simplify an expression.

Examples:

1. Evaluate each expression.

   a) 3^3
   b) $(-7)^2$
   c) -6^2
   d) $-4y^2$ when $y = -5$

2. Use the product rule to simplify each expression. Write the results using exponents.

   a) $x^5 \cdot x^3$
   b) $(4z^3)(9z^5)$
   c) $(-3x^3y^2)(-5x^4y^6)$
   d) $(9ab^2c^4)(-11a^3b)(-2b^2c^5)$

3. Use the power rules to simplify each expression.

   a) $(x^7)^3$
   b) $(y^3)^{11}$
   c) $(xy)^5$
   d) $(5x^3y^2z)^3$

4. Use the power rule for products and quotients.

   a) $(-7a^3b^3)^2$
   b) $\left(\dfrac{ab}{c}\right)^7$
   c) $\left(\dfrac{-3xy}{z^3}\right)^4$
   d) $\left(\dfrac{3x^2y^4}{-2z^3}\right)^2$

5. Use the quotient rule and simplify each expression.

   a) $\dfrac{x^5}{x^2}$
   b) $\dfrac{(-6)^{11}}{(-6)^9}$
   c) $\dfrac{x^{12}y^5}{x^8y^4}$
   d) $\dfrac{8a^3b^8c^3}{18ab^5c^2}$

   Simplify each expression.

   e) 8^0
   f) $\left(\dfrac{3}{7}\right)^0$
   g) $(5x^2y)^0$
   h) $x^0 + 9^0$

6. Mixed practice. Decide which rules to use and simplify each expression.

   a) $(8a^3b^2c^0)^2$
   b) $\left(\dfrac{-3x^2y^5}{2xz^2}\right)^3$
   c) $(-4a^2c^3)(-6a^3b^2c^7)$
   d) $\dfrac{(12ab)^4}{(6a^2b^2)^2}$

Teaching Notes:
- Most students need a lot of practice to master these rules.
- Each section in the text has 3 worksheets in the Extra Practice featuring differentiated learning.

Answers: 1a) 27; 1b) 49; 1c) -36; 1d) -100; 2a) x^8; 2b) $36z^8$; 2c) $15x^7y^8$; 2d) $198a^4b^5c^9$; 3a) x^{21}; 3b) y^{33}; 3c) x^5y^5; 3d) $125x^9y^6z^3$; 4a) $49a^6b^6$; 4b) $\dfrac{a^7b^7}{c^7}$; 4c) $\dfrac{81x^4y^4}{z^{12}}$; 4d) $\dfrac{9x^4y^8}{4z^6}$; 5a) x^3; 5b) 36; 5c) x^4y; 5d) $\dfrac{4a^2b^3c}{9}$; 5e) 1; 5f) 1; 5g) 1; 5h) 2; 6a) $64a^6b^4$; 6b) $\dfrac{-27x^4y^{15}}{4z^6}$; 6c) $24a^5b^2c^{10}$; 6d) 576

Mini-Lecture 5.2
Adding and Subtracting Polynomials

Learning Objectives:

1. Define polynomial, monomial, binomial, trinomial, and degree.
2. Find the value of a polynomial given replacement values for the variables.
3. Simplify a polynomial by combining like terms.
4. Add and subtract polynomials.

Examples:

1. Find the degree of each polynomial and determine whether it is a monomial, binomial, trinomial, or none of these.

   a) $x^2 + x - 6$ b) $3x + 10$ c) $10x^3y^2z$ d) $8z^5 + 9$

   Identify the degrees of the terms and degree of the polynomial.

   e) $2xy - 5x + 6xy$ f) $4a^3 - 3a + 6$ g) $x^3y - x^2y^2 + xy^3$ h) $s^5t^2 - 3s^4t + 5st$

2. Evaluate each polynomial when (a) $y = 0$; and (b) $y = -2$

   a) $4y - 7$ b) $y^3 - 4$ c) $3y^2 + 8y - 9$ d) $-13 - 4y - y^2$

3. Simplify each expression buy combining like terms.

   a) $3x - 10x$ b) $3y^3 - 6x^2 + 2x^2 - 5y^3$ c) $3.7x^3 - 6.3x + 11.6 + 1.8x - x^3 - 8.2$

4. Perform the indicated operation.

   a) $(4x - 3) + (2x - 7)$ b) $(5x^2 + 3x - 7) - (-5x - 3)$ c) Subtract $(3x + 2y)$ from $(5x - 7y)$

Teaching Notes:

- Most students find these objectives easy.
- Some students, when identifying the degree of a polynomial, get confused when one term is made of different variables.
- Each section in the text has 3 worksheets in the Extra Practice featuring differentiated learning.

Answers: 1a) 2, trinomial; 1b) 1, binomial; 1c) 3, monomial; 1d) 5, binomial; 1e) 2,1,2,2; 1f) 3, 1, 3; 1g) 4, 4, 4, 4; 1h) 7, 5, 2, 7; 2a) -7, -15; 2b) -4, -12; 2c) -9, -13; 2d) -13, -9; 3a) -7x; 3b) -2y²-4x²; 3c) 2.7x³-4.5x+3.4; 4a) 6x-10; 4b) 5x²+8x-4; 4c) 2x-9y

Mini-Lecture 5.3
Multiplying Polynomials

Learning Objectives

1. Use the distributive property to multiply polynomials.
2. Multiply polynomials vertically.

Examples:

1. Multiply the following monomials.

   a) $4x^3 \cdot 2x^6$ b) $(-3t^4)(5t^3)$ c) $(-4.2x^3)(5.1x^5)$ d) $\left(-\frac{2}{7}a^4\right)\left(\frac{7}{8}a^7\right)$

   Multiply the monomial by the polynomial.

   e) $5a(-12a - 6)$ f) $4x^3(-7x + 1)$

   g) $-6y^5(8y^4 - 12y^2)$ h) $3ab^7\left(3ab^3 - 12b^2 - 4a\right)$

   Multiply the following binomials.

   i) $(x + 3)(x - 5)$ j) $(3x^2 - 4)(2x^3 + 5)$ k) $\left(x + \frac{3}{4}\right)^2$ l) $(1 - 5x)(2 - 3x)$

   m) $(y - 12)(y^2 + 6y - 3)$ n) $(x - 8)(4 - 5x - x^2)$ o) $(8ab - b)^2$

2. Multiply vertically.

   a) $(x - 3y)(4x - 5y)$ b) $(y - 2)(3y^2 + 4y - 1)$ c) $(x^2 + x + 7)(x^2 + x + 1)$

Teaching Notes:

- Most students find this section relatively easy.
- Remind students to be cautious with signs when distributing.
- In 3c) and 3g), many students will "distribute" the exponent to each term in the base instead of squaring the binomial.
- Some students are very hesitant to work vertically.
- Each section in the text has 3 worksheets in the Extra Practice featuring differentiated learning.

Answers: 1a) $8x^9$; 1b) $-15t^7$; 1c) $-21.42x^8$; 1d) $-1/4a^{11}$; 1e) $-60a^2-30a$; 1f) $-28x^4+4x^3$; 1g) $-48y^9+72y^7$;

1h) $9a^2b^{10}-36ab^9-12a^2b^7$; 1i) $x^2-2x-15$; 1j) $6x^5-8x^3-15x^2-20$; 1k) $x^2 + \frac{6}{4}x + \frac{9}{16}$; 1l) $15x^2-13x+2$;

1m) $y^3-6y^2-75y+36$; 1n) $-x^3-13x^2-36x-32$; 1o) $64a^2b^2-16ab^2+b^2$; 2a) $4x^2-17xy+15y^2$; 2b) $3y^3-2y^2-9y+2$;
2c) $x^4 + 2x^3 + 9x^2 + 8x + 7$

Mini-Lecture 5.4
Special Products

Learning Objectives:

1. Multiply two binomials using the FOIL Method.
2. Square a binomial.
3. Multiply the sum and difference of two terms.

Examples:

1. Multiply using FOIL.

   a) $(x + 7)(x - 12)$ b) $(3x - 1)(2x + 5)$ c) $(a - 2b)(a + 12b)$ d) $\left(x + \dfrac{3}{7}\right)\left(x - \dfrac{1}{6}\right)$

2. Multiply. (Square a binomial).

   a) $(x + 4)^2$ b) $(3x - 5)^2$ c) $(5x - 3y)^2$ d) $(7a^3 - 4)^2$

3. Multiply the sum and difference of two terms.

   a) $(y - 3)(y + 3)$ b) $(5x - 1)(5x + 1)$ c) $\left(2x - \dfrac{3}{5}\right)\left(2x + \dfrac{3}{5}\right)$ d) $(10x - 7y)(10x + 7y)$

4. Mixed practice. Multiply using special products.

   a) $(n + 13)^2$ b) $(a - 4y)(a + 11y)$ c) $(t - 2)(t + 13)$ d) $(3x + 5)(3x - 5)$

   e) $\left(-5a^2 + 10b\right)\left(-5a^2 - 7b\right)$ f) $\left(2x - \dfrac{4}{7}\right)\left(2x + \dfrac{4}{7}\right)$ g) $(4x + 13y)^2$

Teaching Notes:

- Many students find FOIL easy.
- In examples 2, some students will incorrectly "distribute" the exponent rather than squaring the binomial. For example: $(x+4)^2 = x^2 + 4^2$.
- Encourage students to recognize the special products rather than just "FOIL"-ing them.
- Each section in the text has 3 worksheets in the Extra Practice featuring differentiated learning.

Answers: 1a) $x^2 - 5x - 84$; 1b) $6x^2 + 13x - 5$; 1c) $a^2 + 10ab - 24b^2$; 1d) $x^2 + \dfrac{11}{42}x - \dfrac{1}{14}$; 2a) $x^2 + 8x + 16$;

2b) $9x^2 - 30x + 25$; 2c) $25x^2 - 30xy + 9y^2$; 2d) $49a^6 - 56a^3 + 16$; 3a) $y^2 - 9$; 3b) $25x^2 - 1$; 3c) $4x^2 - \dfrac{9}{25}$;

3d) $100x^2 - 49y^2$; 4a) $n^2 + 26n + 169$; 4b) $a^2 + 7ay - 44y^2$; 4c) $t^2 + 11t - 26$; 4d) $9x^2 - 25$; 4e) $25a^4 - 15a^2b - 70b^2$;

4f) $4x^2 - \dfrac{16}{49}$; 4g) $16x^2 + 104xy + 169y^2$

Mini-Lecture 5.5
Negative Exponents and Scientific Notation

Learning Objectives:

1. Simplify expressions containing negative exponents.
2. Use all the rules and definitions for exponents to simplify exponential expressions.
3. Write numbers in scientific notation.
4. Convert numbers from scientific notation to standard form.

Examples:

1. Simplify each expression. Write each result using positive exponents only.

   a) 3^{-2}

   b) $8a^{-3}$

   c) $\dfrac{x^{-4}}{y^{-3}}$

   d) $4^{-2} + 4^0$

2. Simplify each expression. Write each result using positive exponents only.

   a) $a^{-6} \cdot a^{-3} \cdot a \cdot a^{-2}$

   b) $\dfrac{\left(2x^4\right)^3}{x^{15}}$

   c) $\left(x^{-2}y^8\right)^{-2}$

   d) $\dfrac{-6x^2 y^{-3}}{-12x^5 y^{-6}}$

   e) $\dfrac{m^2 \left(m^{-4}\right)^{-2}}{\left(m^{-2}\right)^5}$

   f) $\left(\dfrac{3xy^5}{2x^4 y^7}\right)^{-3}$

   g) $\left(\dfrac{3a^{-3}b^{-2}}{6a^{-2}b^{-5}}\right)^0$

   h) $\left(-2r^{-3}s^{-2}t\right)\left(-5t^{-4}\right)$

3. Convert the following numbers in standard form to scientific form.

   a) 83,000

   b) 1,250,000

   c) 0.000154

   d) 0.00000689

4. Convert the following numbers in scientific form to standard form.

   a) 1.03×10^6

   b) 8.7×10^{-5}

   c) 6.003×10^{10}

   d) 2.02×10^{-3}

Teaching Notes:

- Many students move the numerical coefficient along with the variable. For example, in 1b) a common incorrect answer is $8a^{-3} = \dfrac{1}{8a^3}$

- Overall, students need a lot of practice with these rules to master these objectives.

- Each section in the text has 3 worksheets in the Extra Practice featuring differentiated learning.

Answers: 1a) 1/9; 1b) $8/a^3$; 1c) y^3/x^4; 1d) 17/16; 2a) $1/a^{10}$; 2b) $8/x^3$; 2c) x^4/y^{16}; 2d) $y^3/2x^3$; 2e) m^{20};

2f) $\dfrac{8x^9 y^6}{27}$; 2g) 1; 2h) $\dfrac{10}{r^3 s^2 t^3}$; 3a) 8.3×10^4; 3b) 1.25×10^6; 3c) 1.54×10^{-4}; 3d) 6.89×10^{-6}; 4a) 1,030,000;

4b) 0.000087; 4c) 60,030,000,000; 4d) 0.00202

Mini-Lecture 5.6
Dividing Polynomials

Learning Objectives:

1. Divide a polynomial by a monomial.
2. Use long division to divide a polynomial by another polynomial.

Examples:

1. Perform each division.

   a) $\dfrac{10x^6 - 40x^3}{5x^2}$

   b) $\dfrac{6a^7 - 10a^5}{-2a^7}$

   c) $\dfrac{-14x^7 + 6x^6 - 6x^5}{-2x^5}$

2. Find each quotient using long division.

   a) $\dfrac{x^2 + 9x + 20}{x + 5}$

   b) $\dfrac{6m^3 + 26m^2 - 17m + 15}{m + 5}$

   c) $\dfrac{-20x^3 + 17x^2 + 15x + 13}{-5x - 2}$

   d) $\left(4m^3 + 14m^2 - 5m + 12\right) \div \left(m + 4\right)$

   Find each quotient using long division. Don't forget to write the polynomials in descending order and fill in any missing terms.

   e) $\left(x^4 + 81\right) \div \left(x - 3\right)$

   f) $\dfrac{9 - 5x - 25x^3 - 15x^2}{-5x + 2}$

Teaching Notes:

- Encourage students to write out each step before simplifying in 1a), 1b), 1c). Many students will "cancel" the monomial and one of the terms instead of dividing.
- Most students will need slow, methodical modeling to understand the concept of dividing by a monomial.
- Many students need to see a numerical long division done in parallel with long division of polynomials.
- Each section in the text has 3 worksheets in the Extra Practice featuring differentiated learning.

Answers: 1a) $2x^4$-8x; 1b) $-3 + \dfrac{5}{a^2}$; 1c) $7x^2$-3x+3; 2a) x+4; 2b) $6m^2$-4m+3; 2c) $4x^2$-5x-1$+ \dfrac{11}{-5x-2}$;

2d) $4m^2$-2m+3; 2e) x^3+3x^2+9x+27$+\dfrac{162}{x-3}$; 2f) $5x^2$+5x+3$+\dfrac{3}{-5x+2}$

Mini-Lecture 6.1
The Greatest Common Factor and Factoring by Grouping

Learning Objectives:

1. Find the greatest common factor of a list of integers.
2. Find the greatest common factor of a list of terms.
3. Factor out the greatest common factor from a polynomial.
4. Factor a polynomial by grouping.

Examples:

1. Find the greatest common factor for each list.

   a) $16, 6$ b) $18, 24$ c) $15, 21$ d) $12, 28, 40$

2. Find the GCF for each list.

   a) $15m^2, 25m^5$ b) $40x^2, 20x^7$ c) $-28x^4, 56x^5$ d) $21m^2n^5, 35mn^4$

3. Factor out the GCF from each polynomial.

   a) $5a + 15$ b) $56z + 8$ c) $y^3 + 2y$

   d) $5x^3 + 10x^4$ e) $16z^5 + 8z^3 - 12z$ f) $x(y^2 - 2) + 3(y^2 - 2)$

   g) $6a^8b^9 - 8a^3b^4 + 2a^2b^3 + 4a^5b^3$

4. Factor each four-term polynomial by grouping.

   a) $8y^2 - 12y + 10y - 15$ b) $15a^6 - 25a^3 - 6a^3 + 10$ c) $15x^3 - 25x^2y - 6xy^2 + 10y^3$

Teaching Notes:

- Many students remove common factors, not the *greatest* common factor.
- Encourage students to factor in a step-by-step manner: first factor out the GCF for the coefficients, then the GCF for each variable.
- Most students have trouble factoring by grouping when it entails factoring a negative from the second group. Encourage students to always write a sign and check by distributing. If the check has the correct terms but wrong sign; switch the sign.
- Remind students that they can check their work by multiplying.
- Each section in the text has 3 worksheets in the Extra Practice featuring differentiated learning.

Answers: 1a) 2; 1b) 6; 1c) 3; 1d) 4; 2a) $5m^2$; 2b) $20x^2$; 2c) $-28x^4$; 2d) $7mn^4$; 3a) $5(a+3)$; b) $8(7z+1)$; 3c) $y(y^2+2)$; 3d) $5x^3(1+2x)$; 3e) $4z(4z^4+2z^2-3)$; 3f) $(y^2-2)(x+3)$; 3g)$2a^2b^3(3a^6b^6-4ab+1+2a^3)$; 4a)$(2y-3)(4y+5)$; 4b) $(3a^3-5)(5a^3-2)$; 4c) $(3x-5y)(5x^2-2y^2)$

Mini-Lecture 6.2
Factoring Trinomials of the Form $x^2 + bx + c$

Learning Objectives:

1. Factor trinomials of the form $x^2 + bx + c$.
2. Factor out the greatest common factor and then factor a trinomial of the form $x^2 + bx + c$.

Examples:

1. Factor each trinomial completely. If a polynomial can't be factored, write "prime".

   a) $x^2 + 11x + 30$ 　　　　 b) $y^2 + 7y + 10$ 　　　　 c) $x^2 + 3x - 4$

   d) $x^2 - 4x - 21$ 　　　　 e) $x^2 - 13x + 30$ 　　　　 f) $x^2 - x + 32$

   g) $m^2 + 17m + 16$ 　　　　 h) $5x - 14 + x^2$ 　　　　 i) $a^2 + 13ab + 40b^2$

2. Factor each trinomial completely. Some of these trinomials contain a greatest common factor (other than 1). Don't forget to factor out the GCF first.

   a) $2x^2 - 18x + 28$ 　　　　 b) $3x^2 + 6x - 9$ 　　　　 c) $x^2 + 10x + 24$

   d) $2x^2 + 20x - 22$ 　　　　 e) $5x^2 + 20x + 15$ 　　　　 f) $-x^3 + 3x^2 + 10x$

   g) $4x^4 - 36x^3 + 56x^2$ 　　　　 h) $x^3y + 10x^2y^2 + 24xy^3$ 　　　　 i) $\frac{1}{3}y^2 - \frac{8}{3}y - 11$

Teaching Notes:

- When factoring trinomials of this form, many students find it helpful to make a table listing all possible factor pairs for c in the first column and their sums in the second column.
- Some students have trouble factoring a trinomial when the last term is negative.
- Remind students that when the last term (the constant) of a trinomial is positive, the factors have the same sign. When the last term (the constant) of a trinomial is negative, the factors have different signs.
- Refer students to: ***To Factor a Trinomial of the Form $x^2 + bx + c$*** in the textbook.
- Remind students that they can always check their work by multiplication.
- Each section in the text has 3 worksheets in the Extra Practice featuring differentiated learning.

Answers: *1a) (x+6)(x+5); 1b) (y+5)(y+2); 1c) (x+4)(x-1); 1d) (x-7)(x+3); 1e) (x-10)(x-3); 1f) prime; 1g) (m+16)(m+1); 1h) (x+7)(x-2); 1i) (a+8b)(a+5b); 2a) 2(x-7)(x-2); 2b) 3(x+3)(x-1); 2c) (x+6)(x+4); 2d) 2(x+11)(x-1); 2e) 5(x+3)(x+1); 2f) -x(x-5)(x+2); 2g) 4x²(x-7)(x-2); 2h) xy(x+6y)(x+4y);*

2i) $\frac{1}{3}(y-11)(y+3)$

Mini-Lecture 6.3
Factoring Trinomials of the Form $ax^2 + bx + c$ and Perfect Square Trinomials

Learning Objectives

1. Factor trinomials of the form $ax^2 + bx + c$, where $a \neq 1$.
2. Factor out the GCF before factoring a trinomial of the form $ax^2 + bx + c$.
3. Factor perfect square trinomials.

Examples;

1. Complete each factored form.

   a) $3x^2 + 8x + 4 = (3x + 2)($ $)$ b) $2y^2 + 7y - 15 = (2y - 3)($ $)$

   Factor each trinomial completely.

   c) $2x^2 + 7x + 3$ d) $5x^2 + 17x + 6$ e) $8x^2 + x - 7$

   f) $20r^2 + 31r - 7$ g) $6x^2 + 19x - 11$ h) $3x^2 - 7x - 20$

2. Factor each trinomial completely. If necessary, factor out the GCF first.

   a) $14x^2 + 4x - 10$ b) $9x^2 - 6x - 15$ c) $14x^3 + 66x^2 - 20x$

   d) $25x^3 - 15x^2 - 10x$ e) $4x^2y^2 - xy^2 - 105y^2$ f) $12x^2 - 25xt + 12t^2$

   g) $-7x^2 - 33x + 10$ h) $18x^4 - 3x^3 - 21x^2$ i) $2x^5 - x^3y^2 - 15xy^4$

3. Factor each Perfect Square Trinomial completely.

   a) $x^2 + 2x + 1$ b) $4x^2 - 12x + 9$ c) $25x^2 + 60xy + 36y^2$

   d) $16x^3 - 8x^2y + xy^2$ e) $5x^3 - 10x^2 + 5x$ f) $2a - 24ay + 72ay^2$

Teaching Notes:

- Some students remember factoring from high school and are able to use the trial-and-error method to factor.
- Some students may need to see Section 4.4, *Factoring Trinomials by Grouping* before being able to factor successfully.
- Encourage students to use strategies when factoring. For example, identify any prime numbers to reduce the number of combinations.
- Many students will forget to put the GCF in their final answer.
- Remind students that they can check their work by multiplying.
- Each section in the text has 3 worksheets in the Extra Practice featuring differentiated learning.

Answers *1a) (x+2); 1b) (y+5); 1c) (2x+1)(x+3); 1d) (5x+2)(x+3); 1e) (8x-7)(x+1); 1f) (5r-1)(4r+7); 1g) (3x+11)(2x-1); 1h) (3x+5)(x-4); 2a) 2(7x-5)(x+1); 2b) 3(3x-5)(x+1); 2c) 2x(7x-2)(x+5); 2d) 5x(5x+2)(x-1); 2e) y²(x+5)(4x-21); 2f) (4x-3t)(3x-4t); 2g) (-7x+2)(x+5); 2h) 3x²(6x-7)(x+1); 2i) x(2x²+5y²)(x²-3y²), 3a) (x+1)², 3b) (2x-3)², 3c) (5x+6y)² 3d) x(4x-y)², 3e) 5x(x-1)², 3f) 2a(1-6y)²*

Mini-Lecture 6.4
Factoring Trinomials of the Form $ax^2 + bx + c$ by Grouping

Learning Objectives

1. Use the grouping method to factor trinomials of the form $ax^2 + bx + c$.

Examples:

1. Factor the following trinomial by grouping. Complete the outlined steps.

   a) $12y^2 + 17y + 6$

   Find two numbers whose product is 72 $(12 \cdot 6)$ and whose sum is 17: _____
   Write $17y$ using the factors from previous step: _____
   Factor by grouping: _____

   b) $10x^2 + 9x - 9$

   Find two numbers whose product is $-90\left[10 \cdot (-9)\right]$ and whose sum is (-9): _____
   Write (-9x) using the factors from part (a): _____
   Factor by grouping: _____

   Factor by grouping.

   c) $8x^2 + 18x + 9$ d) $6x^2 + 7x - 3$ e) $7x^2 - 19x - 6$

   f) $4x^2 - 12x + 9$ g) $6x^2 - 17x + 5$ h) $20x^2 - 15x - 50$

   i) $45x^3 + 45x^2 - 50x$ j) $x - 15 + 6x^2$ k) $10z^2 - 12z - 1$

Teaching Notes:

- Most students appreciate seeing the grouping method. This method gives the student a step-by-step guide to factoring.
- Encourage students to use whatever method works for them (trial-and-error or grouping).
- Remind students to put the trinomial into standard form before attempting to factor.
- Encourage students to check their factoring answers by multiplication.
- Each section in the text has 3 worksheets in the Extra Practice featuring differentiated learning.

Answers: 1a) 9,8; 9y+8y; (4y+3)(3y+2); 1b) -6, 15; -6x+15x; (5x-3)(2x+3); 1c) (4x+3)(2x+3); 1d) (2x+3)(3x-1); 1e) (7x+2)(x-3); 1f0 (2x-3)²; 1g) (2x-5)(3x-1); 1h) 5(x-2)(4x+5); 1i) 5x(3x-2)(3x+5); 1j) (3x+5)(2x-3); 1k) prime

Mini-Lecture 6.5
Factoring Binomials

Learning Objectives:

1. Factor the difference of two squares.
2. Factor the sum or difference of two cubes.

Examples:

1. Factor each binomial completely.

   a) $x^2 - 9$ b) $x^2 - 25$ c) $y^2 - 64$

   d) $4a^2 - 9$ e) $49x^2 - 1$ f) $9a^2 + 16b^2$

   g) $36m^2 - 100n^2$ h) $\frac{1}{4}x^2 - 1$ i) $64 - \frac{9}{25}a^2$

2. Factor each sum or difference of two cubes completely.

   a) $8x^3 + 1$ b) $a^3 - 1$ c. $64x^3 + 27y^3$

   d) $54y^4 - 2y$ e) $125b^5 + b^2$ f) $a^6 - 1$

Teaching Notes:

- Some students will have a better understanding of a difference of two squares if they are first shown 3a) and 3b) with a middle term of $0x$.
- Encourage students to become proficient with special case factoring as it will be important for future algebra topics such as completing the square.
- Each section in the text has 3 worksheets in the Extra Practice featuring differentiated learning.

Answers: *1a) (x+3)(x-3); 1b) (x+5)(x-5); 1c) (y+8)(y-8); 1d) (2a+3)(2a-3); 1e) (7x+1)(7x-1); 1f) cannot be factored; 1g) (6m+10n)(6m-10n); 1h) (1/2x+1)(1/2x-1); 1i) (8+3/5a)(8-3/5a); 2a) (2x + 1)(4x² -2x+1); 2b) (a – 1)(a²+a+1); 2c) (4x + 3y)(16x²-12xy+9y²); 2d) 2y(3y-1)(9y²+3y+1); 2e) b²(5b+1)(25b²-5b+1); 2f) (a²-1)(a⁴+a²+1)*

Mini-Lecture 6.6
Solving Quadratic Equations by Factoring

Learning Objectives:

1. Solve quadratic equations by factoring.
2. Solve equations with degree greater than 2 by factoring.
3. Find the *x*-intercepts of the graph of a quadratic equation in two variables.

Examples:

1. Solve each equation.

   a) $(x-1)(x+4)=0$ b) $(x+5)(x+9)=0$ c) $(x-10)(x+8)=0$

   d) $5x(x-15)=0$ e) $(2x-5)(x+3)=0$ f) $\left(x-\dfrac{2}{7}\right)\left(x-\dfrac{1}{3}\right)=0$

   g) $x^2-x-30=0$ h) $x^2-9x+20=0$ i) $y^2-y-42=0$

   j) $x^2-7x=0$ k) $x^2=25$ l) $x^2+2x=15$

   m) $5x^2-30x+40=0$ n) $x(x-4)=21$ o) $x(x-6)=16$

2. Solve the following equations with degree greater than 2 by factoring.

   a) $y^3+14y^2+49y=0$ b) $24x^3-4x^2-20x=0$ c) $(x-4)(x^2-3x+2)=0$

   d) $16a^3-9a=0$ e) $49t^3-4t=0$ f) $(9x+5)(10x^2-3x-4)=0$

3. Find the *x*-intercepts of the graph.

   a) $y=(x-4)(x+5)$ b) $y=(x-1)(x+1)$ c) $y=x^3-x^2-4x-4$

Teaching Notes:

- Remind students to always put the equation into standard form.
- Some students try to use the zero factor property before the equation is in standard form. For example 1n) $x(x-4)=21 \rightarrow x=21, x-4=21, etc.$
- Students will find this section challenging.
- Remind students to always check their answers.
- Each section in the text has 3 worksheets in the Extra Practice featuring differentiated learning.

Answers: *1a)* 1, -4; *1b)* -5, -9; *1c)* 10, -8; *1d)* 0, 15; *1e)* 5/2, -3; *1f)* 2/7, 1/3; *1g)* 6, -5; *1h)* 4, 5; *1i)* 7, -6; *1j)* 0, 7; *1k)* 5, -5; *1l)* -5, 3; *1m)* 2, 4; *1n)* 7, -3; *1o)* -2, 8; *2a)* 0, -7; *2b)* 0, -5/6, 1; *2c)* 4, 2, 1; *2d)* 0, ¾, -3/4; *2e)* 0, 2/7, -2/7; *2f)* -5/9, -1/2, 4/5; *3a)* (4,0), (-5,0), *3b)* (1,0), (-1,0), *3c)* (2,0), (-2,0), (1,0)

Mini-Lecture 6.7
Quadratic Equations and Problem Solving

Learning Objectives:

1. Solve problems that can be modeled by quadratic equations.

Examples:

1. Represent each given condition using a single variable, *x*.

   a) The length and width of a rectangle whose width is half the measurement of the length.

   b) Two consecutive integers.

   c) The base and height of a triangle whose height is 3 less than 5 times its base.

2. Use the information given to solve the following problems.

   a) The area of a square is 144 ft^2. Find the length of its side.

   b) The area of the circle is 81π square inches. Find the radius.

   c) The sum of two numbers is 16. The sum of their squares is 130. Find the numbers.

   d) A roofer drops a hammer from the top of a 64-foot roof. The height of the hammer after *t* seconds is given by $h = -16t^2 + 64$. When will the hammer hit the ground?

   e) The hypotenuse of a right triangle is 6 inches more than the shorter leg. The longer leg is 3 inches more than the shorter leg. Find the lengths of all three sides.

Teaching Notes:

- Many students struggle with word problems.
- Most students have trouble with converting the words to mathematical expressions.
- Refer students to Chapter 2, Section 2.4, **General Strategy for Problem Solving**.
- Each section in the text has 3 worksheets in the Extra Practice featuring differentiated learning.

Answers: *1a) x=length, 1/2x = width; 1b) x, x+1; 1c) b=x, h=5x-3; 2a) 12 ft.; 2b) 9 in.; 2c) 7, 9; 2d) after 2 seconds; 2e) 9, 12, 15*

Mini-Lecture 7.1
Simplifying Rational Expressions

Learning Objectives:

1. Find the value of a rational expression given a replacement number.
2. Identify values for which a rational expression is undefined.
3. Simplify or write rational expressions in lowest terms.
4. Write equivalent rational expressions of the form $-\dfrac{a}{b} = \dfrac{-a}{b} = \dfrac{a}{-b}$.

Examples:

1. Find the value of the expression for the given value (s).

   a) $\dfrac{x+4}{x-2}$; $x = 4$

   b) $\dfrac{y^2}{y-3}$; $y = 5$

   c) $\dfrac{x^2+5x-2}{x^2-x-2}$; $x = -3$

2. Find any numbers for which each rational expression is undefined.

   a) $\dfrac{7}{4a}$

   b) $\dfrac{3y^3}{y^2-5y}$

   c) $\dfrac{x}{2x^2-7x-4}$

3. Simplify each expression.

   a) $\dfrac{(y+3)(y-1)}{(y-1)(y+5)}$

   b) $\dfrac{6-a}{a-6}$

   c) $\dfrac{-2x-2y}{x+y}$

   d) $\dfrac{6x-12}{3x^2-12}$

   e) $\dfrac{y^2+8y+15}{y^2+9y+18}$

   f) $\dfrac{x^2-xy+5x-5y}{x^2+5x}$

4. List four equivalent forms for each rational expression.

   a) $-\dfrac{x-2}{x+5}$

   b) $-\dfrac{y+3}{y-11}$

   c) $-\dfrac{5y+2}{3y-1}$

Teaching Notes:

- Some students need a review of simplifying numerical fractions before applying to rational expressions.
- Many students need to be reminded to factor completely before simplifying.
- Each section in the text has 3 worksheets in the Extra Practice featuring differentiated learning.

Answers: 1a) 4; 1b) 25/2; 1c) -4/5; 2a) 0; 2b) 0, 5; 2c) -1/2, 4; 3a) $\dfrac{y+3}{y+5}$; 3b) -1; 3c) -2; 3d) $\dfrac{2}{x+2}$;

3e) $\dfrac{y+5}{y+6}$; 3f) $\dfrac{x-y}{x}$; 4a) $\dfrac{-(x-2)}{x+5}, \dfrac{2-x}{x+5}, \dfrac{x-2}{-(x+5)}, \dfrac{x-2}{-x-5}$; 4b) $\dfrac{-(y+3)}{y-11}, \dfrac{-y-3}{y-11}, \dfrac{y+3}{-(y-11)}, \dfrac{y+3}{11-y}$;

4c) $\dfrac{-(5y+2)}{3y-1}, \dfrac{-5y-2}{3y-1}, \dfrac{5y+2}{-(3y-1)}, \dfrac{5y+2}{1-3y}$

Mini-Lecture 7.2
Multiplying and Dividing Rational Expressions

Learning Objectives:

1. Multiply rational expressions.
2. Divide rational expressions.
3. Multiply or divided rational expressions.

Examples:

1. Find each product and simplify if possible.

   a) $\dfrac{8p-8}{p} \cdot \dfrac{7p^2}{9p-9}$
   b) $\dfrac{x^2+5x+6}{x^2+11x+24} \cdot \dfrac{x^2+8x}{x^2-4x+3}$
   c) $\dfrac{x^3-x^2+x}{x^3+1} \cdot \dfrac{-45x-45}{5x}$

2. Find each quotient and simplify.

   a) $\dfrac{-4k^2}{4k^5} \div \dfrac{16k^4}{12k^6}$
   b) $\dfrac{2-2x}{x} \div \dfrac{5x-5}{3x^2}$
   c) $\dfrac{y^2-11y+30}{y^2-36} \div \dfrac{y^2-9}{y^2-3y-18}$

3. Multiply or divide. Simplify if possible.

   a) $\dfrac{x^2-11x+10}{x^2-11x+28} \cdot \dfrac{x^2-9x+20}{x^2-16x+60}$
   b) $\dfrac{2k^2+8k+6}{k^2-9} \div \dfrac{4k^2+18k+14}{2k-6}$

Teaching Notes:

- Many students need to review multiplying and dividing numerical fractions.
- When dividing, remind students to change division to multiplication by the reciprocal <u>first,</u> then begin factoring. Many students will begin factoring and forget that they are dividing.
- Some students will need additional practice using unit fractions.
- Each section in the text has 3 worksheets in the Extra Practice featuring differentiated learning.

<u>*Answers:*</u> *1a)* $\dfrac{56p}{9}$; *1b)* $\dfrac{x(x+2)}{(x-3)(x-1)}$; *1c)* -9; *2a)* $\dfrac{-3}{4k}$; *2b)* $\dfrac{-6x}{5}$; *2c)* $\dfrac{(y-5)(y-6)}{(y+6)(y-3)}$;

3a) $\dfrac{(x-5)(x-1)}{(x-6)(x-7)}$; *3b)* $\dfrac{2}{2k+7}$;

Mini-Lecture 7.3
Adding and Subtracting Rational Expressions with Common Denominators and Least Common Denominator

Learning Objectives:

1. Add and subtract rational expressions with the same denominator.
2. Find the least common denominator of a list of rational expressions.
3. Write a rational expression as an equivalent expression whose denominator is given.
4. Key Vocabulary: *least common denominator (LCD), equivalent expressions.*

Examples:

1. Add or subtract as indicated. Simplify the result if possible.

   a) $\dfrac{3}{12x} + \dfrac{4}{12x}$ b) $\dfrac{8a+2b}{2} - \dfrac{8a-2b}{2}$ c) $\dfrac{7y^2}{y-1} + \dfrac{-7y}{y-1}$

   d) $\dfrac{m^2 - 7m}{m-3} + \dfrac{12}{m-3}$ e) $\dfrac{3x+2}{x^2+4x-21} - \dfrac{2x-5}{x^2+4x-21}$

2. Find the LCD for each list of rational expressions.

   a) $\dfrac{1}{20x^5}, \dfrac{1}{36x^4}$ b) $\dfrac{2}{x+3}, \dfrac{3}{x-5}$ c) $\dfrac{4}{3a+27}, \dfrac{6}{a^2+9a}$

3. Rewrite each rational expression as an equivalent rational expression with the given denominator.

   a) $\dfrac{3}{8m} = \dfrac{?}{72m}$ b) $\dfrac{x}{x+4} = \dfrac{?}{5x+20}$

   c) $\dfrac{a}{a+3b} = \dfrac{?}{a^2-9b^2}$ d) $\dfrac{-25}{x^3+2x^2-3x} = \dfrac{?}{x(x-1)(x+3)(x+5)}$

Teaching Notes:

- Most students need a review of finding the LCD for numerical fractions.
- Many students have a difficult time finding the LCD. Refer them back to the process they use when finding the LCD for numerical fractions.
- Each section in the text has 3 worksheets in the Extra Practice featuring differentiated learning.

Answers: 1a) $\dfrac{7}{12x}$; 1b) 2b; 1c) 7y; 1d) m-4; 1e) $\dfrac{1}{x-3}$; 2a) $180x^5$; 2b) $x^2 - 2x - 15$; 2c) $3a^2 + 27a$; 3a) 27; 3b) 5x; 3c) $a^2 - 3ab$; 3d) $-25x - 125$

Mini-Lecture 7.4
Adding and Subtracting Rational Expressions
With Unlike Denominators

Learning Objectives:

1. Add and subtract rational expressions with unlike denominators.

Examples:

1. Perform each indicated operation. Simplify if possible.

a) $\dfrac{x}{9} + \dfrac{8}{7}$

b) $\dfrac{x}{5} - \dfrac{3}{11}$

c) $-\dfrac{9}{40} - \dfrac{2}{5x}$

d) $\dfrac{6}{z^2} - \dfrac{4}{z}$

e) $\dfrac{5}{r} + \dfrac{9}{r-3}$

f) $\dfrac{9-5y}{63} - \dfrac{8-7y}{18}$

g) $\dfrac{-8x+3}{x} + \dfrac{-8x+2}{5x}$

h) $\dfrac{6x}{x+6} + \dfrac{3}{x-6}$

i) $\dfrac{7}{6-m} + \dfrac{2}{m-6}$

j) $\dfrac{-5}{y-4} - \dfrac{7}{4-y}$

k) $\dfrac{m-5}{m^2+9m+20} + \dfrac{4m-1}{m^2+7m+10}$

l) $\dfrac{x}{x^2-16} - \dfrac{6}{x^2+5x+4}$

m) $\dfrac{3}{y^2-3y+2} + \dfrac{5}{y^2-1}$

Teaching Notes:

- Most students have difficulty with adding and subtracting rational expressions, mainly with finding the LCD.
- Remind students that with subtraction, they are subtracting the entire numerator (i.e. Distributive Property).
- Some students may find working in a vertical format easier to build equivalent expressions.
- Each section in the text has 3 worksheets in the Extra Practice featuring differentiated learning.

Answers: 1a) $\dfrac{7x+72}{63}$; 1b) $\dfrac{11x-15}{55}$; 1c) $\dfrac{-9x-16}{40x}$; 1d) $\dfrac{6-4z}{z^2}$; 1e) $\dfrac{14r-15}{r^2-3r}$; 1f) $\dfrac{39y-38}{126}$;

1g) $\dfrac{-48x+17}{5x}$; 1h) $\dfrac{6x^2-33x+18}{x^2-36}$; 1i) $\dfrac{6}{6-m}$; 1j) $\dfrac{2}{y-4}$; 1k) $\dfrac{5m^2+12m-14}{m^3+11m^2+38m+40}$;

1l) $\dfrac{x^2-5x+24}{x^3+x^2-16x-16}$; 1m) $\dfrac{8y-7}{y^3-2y^2-y+2}$

Mini-Lecture 7.5
Solving Equations Containing Rational Expressions

Learning Objectives:

1. Solve equations containing rational expressions.
2. Solve equations containing rational expressions for a specified variable.
3. Key Vocabulary: *rational expressions.*

Examples:

1. Solve each equation and check each solution.

   a) $\dfrac{x}{3} - \dfrac{x}{9} = 8$

   b) $\dfrac{4x}{5} - 8 = x$

   c) $\dfrac{x-3}{7} = \dfrac{x+4}{3}$

   d) $\dfrac{x+10}{x-5} = \dfrac{9}{5-x}$

   e) $\dfrac{4}{x-4} + \dfrac{4}{2x-8} = 6$

   f) $\dfrac{x}{x-7} + 6 = \dfrac{7}{x-7}$

   g) $\dfrac{-5x}{3x+3} = \dfrac{2x}{6x+6} + \dfrac{6x-4}{x+1}$

   h) $\dfrac{1}{x} + \dfrac{1}{x-8} = \dfrac{x-7}{x-8}$

   i) $\dfrac{-2}{m+5} - \dfrac{3}{m-5} = \dfrac{15}{m^2-25}$

   j) $\dfrac{x+4}{x^2+2x-15} - \dfrac{4}{x^2+10x+25} = \dfrac{x-4}{x^2+2x-15}$

2. Solve each equation for the indicated variable.

   a) $\dfrac{1}{a} + \dfrac{1}{b} = c$ for b

   b) $A = \dfrac{1}{2}h(B+b)$ for B

   c) $F = \dfrac{-GMm}{r^2}$ for m

Teaching Notes:

- Remind students to always determine the values for *x* that will make the denominators of the equation equal to zero.
- Some students prefer to create equivalent expressions using the LCD then set numerators equal.
- Most students have difficulty solving a formula for a specific variable.
- To help students focus on solving a formula for a specific variable, encourage them to write the variable with a different color pencil.

Answers: 1a) 36; 1b) -40; 1c) -37/4; 1d) -19; 1e) 5; 1f) no solution; 1g) ½; 1h) 1; 1i) -4; 1j) -13;
2a) $b = \dfrac{a}{ac-1}$; 2b) $B = \dfrac{2A}{h} - b$ or $\dfrac{2A-bh}{h}$; 2c) $m = -\dfrac{Fr^2}{GM}$

Mini-Lecture 7.6
Proportion and Problem Solving with Rational Equations

Learning Objectives:

1. Solve proportions.
2. Use proportions to solve problems.
3. Solve problems about numbers.
4. Solve problems about work.
5. Solve problems about distance.

Examples:

1. Solve each proportion.

   a) $\dfrac{x}{39} = \dfrac{6}{13}$
   b) $\dfrac{2}{7} = \dfrac{5}{x}$
   c) $\dfrac{8+x}{5} = \dfrac{5+x}{3}$
   d) $\dfrac{7}{2} = \dfrac{z-5}{z-3}$

2. Solve. Find the unknown length (x) in the pair of similar triangles.

   a) There are 170 calories in 3 peanut butter cookies. How many calories are in 7 cookies?

   b)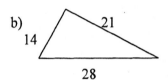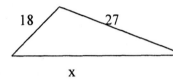

3. Solve the following: problems about numbers.

   a) Five divided by the difference of a number and one equals the quotient of ten and the sum of the number and twelve. Find the number.

   b) If three times a number added to five is divided by the number plus nine, the result is four thirds. Find the number.

4. Solve the following: problems about work.

   a) A painter can paint a sign in 4 hours. His assistant can paint the same sign in 6 hours. How long will it take them to paint the sign if they paint it together.

   b) A conveyer belt can move 1000 cans of soup to the loading area in 7 minutes. A smaller conveyer belt can move the same number of cans in 11 minutes. How long will it take to move 1000 cans of soup if both conveyer belts are used.

5. Solve the following: problems about distance.

   a) A cyclist bikes at a constant speed for 18 miles. His return trip is a different route of 23 miles long and will take 1 hour longer. Find the speed.

Teaching Notes:

- Most students will struggle with applications.
- Refer students to Chapter 2, Section 2.4, **General Strategy for Problem Solving**.
- Each section in the text has 3 worksheets in the Extra Practice featuring differentiated learning.

Answers: _1a) 18; 1b) 35/2; 1c) -1/2; 1d) 11/5; 2a) 396⅔; 2b) 36; 3a) 14; 3b) 21/5; 4a) 2.4 hours; 4b) 4 5/18 min.; 5a) 5 mph._

Mini-Lecture 7.7
Variation and Problem Solving

Learning Objectives:

1. Solve problems involving direct variation.
2. Solve problems involving inverse variation.
3. Other types of direct and inverse variation.
4. Variation and problem solving.

Examples:

1. Write a direct variation equation, $y=kx$, that satisfies the ordered pairs in each table.

   a)

x	0	2	5	7
y	0	10	25	35

   b)

x	0	5	-1	$-\frac{5}{8}$
y	0	2	$-\frac{2}{5}$	$-\frac{1}{4}$

   c) y varies directly as x. If $y = 24$ when $x = 3$, find y when x is 6.

2. Write an inverse variation equation, $y = \dfrac{k}{x}$, that satisfies the ordered pairs in each table.

   a)

x	1	2	4	8
y	4	2	1	0.5

   b)

x	-2	3	10	0.05
y	-0.15	0.1	0.03	6

   c) y varies inversely as x. If $y = 10$ when $x = 6$, find y when x is 12.

3. Solve.

   a) y varies directly as x^2. If $y = 72$ when $x = 3$, find y when x is $\dfrac{1}{4}$.

   b) z varies inversely as a^2. If $z = 25$ when $a = 2$, find z when a is 5.

4. Solve the following.

   a) Your paycheck (before deductions) varies directly as the number of hours you work. If your paycheck is $147.25 for 15.5 hours, find your pay for 24.5 hours.

   b) For a constant distance, the rate of travel varies inversely as the time traveled. If a truck driver travels 45 mph and arrives at a destination in 8 hours. How long will the return trip take traveling at 60 mph?

Teaching Notes:

- Most students understand direct variation but struggle with inverse variation.
- Most students struggle with the applications that involve both direct and inverse variation.
- Each section in the text has 3 worksheets in the Extra Practice featuring differentiated learning.

Answers: 1a) y=5x; 1b) $y = \dfrac{2}{5}x$; 1c) 48; 2a) $y = \dfrac{4}{x}$; 2b) $y = \dfrac{0.3}{x}$; 2c) 5; 3a) $\dfrac{1}{2}$; 3b) 4; 4a) $232.75;
4b) 6

Mini-Lecture 7.8
Simplifying Complex Fractions

Learning Objectives

1. Simplify complex fractions using method 1.
2. Simplify complex fractions using method 2.

Examples:

1. Simplify using Method 1.

   a) $\dfrac{\dfrac{1}{11}}{\dfrac{5}{6}}$

   b) $\dfrac{\dfrac{7m^6n^3}{5m}}{\dfrac{9m^2n^8}{4n^2}}$

   c) $\dfrac{\dfrac{8}{a}+8}{\dfrac{8}{a}-8}$

2. Simplify using Method 2.

   a) $\dfrac{\dfrac{x+7}{8}}{\dfrac{x+1}{x}}$

   b) $\dfrac{\dfrac{4}{y}}{\dfrac{7}{y+10}}$

   c) $\dfrac{\dfrac{9s^2-25t^2}{st}}{\dfrac{3}{t}-\dfrac{5}{s}}$

3. Simplify using either method.

   a) $\dfrac{\dfrac{1}{7}-\dfrac{1}{5}}{\dfrac{1}{5}+\dfrac{1}{2}}$

   b) $\dfrac{9+\dfrac{3}{x}}{\dfrac{x}{4}+\dfrac{1}{12}}$

   c) $\dfrac{\dfrac{3}{5x-1}-3}{\dfrac{3}{5x-1}+3}$

Teaching Notes:

- A brief review of division with fractions may be needed.
- Students with more mathematical confidence tend to use Method 2 – LCD.
- Each section in the text has 3 worksheets in the Extra Practice featuring differentiated learning.

Answers: *1a)* $6/55$; *1b)* $\dfrac{28m^3}{45n^3}$; *1c)* $\dfrac{1+a}{1-a}$; *2a)* $\dfrac{x^2+7x}{8x+8}$; *2b)* $\dfrac{4y+40}{7y}$; *2c)* $3s+5t$; *3a)* $-4/49$;

3b) $\dfrac{36}{x}$; *3c)* $\dfrac{2-5x}{5x}$

Mini-Lecture 8.1
Introduction to Radicals

Learning Objectives:

1. Find square roots.
2. Find cube roots.
3. Find nth roots.
4. Approximate square roots.
5. Simplify radicals containing variables.

Examples:

1. Find each square root.

   a) $\sqrt{49}$

   b) $\sqrt{\dfrac{1}{36}}$

   c) $-\sqrt{9}$

   d) $\sqrt{-100}$

   e) $\sqrt{\dfrac{25}{121}}$

   f) $\sqrt{0.64}$

2. Find each cube root.

   a) $\sqrt[3]{8}$

   b) $\sqrt[3]{-216}$

   c) $\sqrt[3]{-\dfrac{8}{27}}$

3. Find each root.

   a) $\sqrt[4]{16}$

   b) $\sqrt[3]{-27}$

   c) $-\sqrt[4]{\dfrac{81}{625}}$

4. Approximate each square root to three decimal places.

   a) $\sqrt{12}$

   b) $\sqrt{22}$

   c) $-\sqrt{120}$

5. Find each root. Assume that all variables represent positive numbers.

   a) $\sqrt{x^2}$

   b) $\sqrt{a^4}$

   c) $\sqrt{m^8}$

   d) $\sqrt{81x^4}$

   e) $\sqrt{x^{10}y^8z^2}$

   f) $\sqrt[3]{27a^6b^9c^3}$

Teaching Notes:

- Many students confuse 1c), 1d), and 2b).
- Students have a hard time understanding $\sqrt{x^2} = |x|$ even though we assume that all variable represent positive numbers.
- It is very important to stress that using a calculator gives an *approximation* and leaving an answer in radical form is an *exact* value.

Answers: 1a) 7; 1b) 1/6; 1c) -3; 1d) not a real number; 1e) 5/11; 1f) 0.8; 2a) 2; 2b) -6; 2c) -2/3; 3a) 2; 3b) -3; 3c) -3/5; 4a) 3.464; 4b) 4.69; 4c) -10.954; 5a) x; 5b) a^2; 5c) m^4; 5d) $9x^2$; 5e) x^5y^4z ; 5f) $3a^2b^3c$

Mini-Lecture 8.2
Simplifying Radicals

Learning Objectives:

1. Use the product rule to simplify square roots.
2. Use the quotient rule to simplify square roots.
3. Simplify radicals containing variables.
4. Simplify higher roots.
5. Key Vocabulary: *perfect squares.*

Examples:

1. Use the product rule to simplify each radical.

   a) $\sqrt{18}$ b) $\sqrt{12}$ c) $\sqrt{33}$

   d) $\sqrt{160}$ e) $5\sqrt{16}$ f) $-3\sqrt{50}$

2. Use the quotient rule and the product rule to simplify each radical.

   a) $\sqrt{\dfrac{25}{16}}$ b) $\sqrt{\dfrac{99}{4}}$ c) $\sqrt{\dfrac{125}{144}}$

3. Simplify each radical. Assume that all variables represent positive numbers.

   a) $\sqrt{x^5}$ b) $\sqrt{y^9}$ c) $\sqrt{a^{13}}$

   d) $\sqrt{\dfrac{18}{x^2}}$ e) $\sqrt{36y^3}$ f) $\sqrt{80y^{12}}$

   g) $\sqrt{\dfrac{98}{p^6}}$ h) $\sqrt{\dfrac{300}{x^{20}}}$ i) $\sqrt{\dfrac{16x}{z^{10}}}$

4. Simplify each radical.

   a) $\sqrt[3]{40}$ b) $\sqrt[3]{300}$ c) $\sqrt[3]{\dfrac{625}{216}}$

Teaching Notes:

- Many students have trouble with radicals.
- When simplifying, students get confused where to write the numbers – outside the radical symbol or in the radicand.
- A common error is to evaluate "$\sqrt{16} = \sqrt{4} = 2$". Many students do not know when to stop!
- Each section in the text has 3 worksheets in the Extra Practice featuring differentiated learning.

Answers: 1a) $3\sqrt{2}$; 1b) $2\sqrt{3}$; 1c) $\sqrt{33}$; 1d) $4\sqrt{10}$; 1e) 20; 1f) $-15\sqrt{2}$; 2a) 5/4; 2b) $\dfrac{3\sqrt{11}}{2}$;

2c) $\dfrac{5\sqrt{5}}{12}$; 3a) $x^2\sqrt{x}$; 3b) $y^4\sqrt{y}$; 3c) $a^6\sqrt{a}$; 3d) $\dfrac{3\sqrt{2}}{x}$; 3e) $6y\sqrt{y}$; 3f) $4y^6\sqrt{5}$; 3g) $\dfrac{7\sqrt{2}}{p^3}$;

3h) $\dfrac{10\sqrt{3}}{x^{10}}$; 3i) $\dfrac{4\sqrt{x}}{z^5}$; 4a) $2\sqrt[3]{5}$; 4b) $\sqrt[3]{300}$; 4c) $\dfrac{5\sqrt[3]{5}}{6}$

Mini-Lecture 8.3
Adding and Subtracting Radicals

Learning Objectives:

1. Add or subtract like radicals.
2. Simplify radical expressions, and then add or subtract any like radicals.

Examples:

1. Add or subtract as indicated.

   a) $20\sqrt{5} + 3\sqrt{5}$

   b) $11\sqrt{7} - 3\sqrt{7}$

   c) $-7\sqrt{11} - 5\sqrt{11}$

   d) $11\sqrt{3} - 12\sqrt{3} + 35 + 3\sqrt{3}$

   e) $3\sqrt{7} + 5\sqrt{21} - 8\sqrt{21} - 10\sqrt{7}$

2. Add or subtract by first simplifying each radical and then combining any like radicals. Assume that all variables represent positive numbers.

   a) $8\sqrt{5} + 9\sqrt{20}$

   b) $-7\sqrt{2} + 9\sqrt{50}$

   c) $-8\sqrt{3} - 3\sqrt{75}$

   d) $-10\sqrt{48} - 3\sqrt{75}$

   e) $-5\sqrt{8x} - 6\sqrt{18x}$

   f) $-5\sqrt{x^2} + 3x + 8\sqrt{x^2}$

3. Simplify each radical expression.

   a) $5\sqrt[3]{7} + 8\sqrt[3]{7}$

   b) $-3\sqrt[3]{12} + 8\sqrt[3]{12} - 10$

   c) $2\sqrt[3]{25} - 7\sqrt[3]{5} + 6\sqrt[3]{25}$

   d) $\sqrt[3]{40} + 6\sqrt[3]{135}$

   e) $\sqrt[3]{128} - 5\sqrt[3]{250}$

   f) $7\sqrt[3]{x} + \sqrt[3]{64x}$

Teaching Notes:

- Many students need extra practice in identifying like radicals.
- Some students combine the coefficients and multiply the like radicals.
- Many students confuse $\sqrt{}$ *and* $\sqrt[3]{}$. In fact, a common error is to evaluate $\sqrt[3]{4} = 2$ *or* $\sqrt[3]{36} = 6$. Encourage students to be cautious determining the index.
- Each section in the text has 3 worksheets in the Extra Practice featuring differentiated learning.

Answers: *1a)* $23\sqrt{5}$; *1b)* $8\sqrt{7}$; *1c)* $-12\sqrt{11}$; *1d)* $2\sqrt{3} + 35$; *1e)* $-3\sqrt{21} - 7\sqrt{7}$; *2a)* $26\sqrt{5}$; *2b)* $38\sqrt{2}$; *2c)* $-23\sqrt{3}$; *2d)* $-55\sqrt{3}$; *2e)* $-28\sqrt{2x}$; *2f)* $6x$; *3a)* $13\sqrt[3]{7}$; *3b)* $5\sqrt[3]{12} - 10$; *3c)* $8\sqrt[3]{25} - 7\sqrt[3]{5}$; *3d)* $20\sqrt[3]{5}$; *3e)* $-21\sqrt[3]{2}$; *3f)* $11\sqrt[3]{x}$

Mini-Lecture 8.4
Multiplying and Dividing Radicals

Learning Objectives:

1. Multiply radicals.
2. Divide radicals.
3. Rationalize denominators.
4. Rationalize using conjugates.
5. Key Vocabulary: *product rule for radicals, quotient rule for radicals, rationalizing, conjugates.*

Examples:

1. Multiply and simplify. Assume that all variables represent positive real numbers.

   a) $\sqrt{3}\cdot\sqrt{5}$ b) $\sqrt{5x}\cdot\sqrt{5x}$ c) $\sqrt{2}\cdot\sqrt{6}$

   d) $\left(3\sqrt{x}\right)^2$ e) $\sqrt{5x^3}\cdot\sqrt{15x}$ f) $\sqrt{6}\left(\sqrt{3}+\sqrt{2}\right)$

   g) $\left(\sqrt{7}+3\right)\left(\sqrt{7}-3\right)$ h) $\left(8\sqrt{5}+9\right)\left(9\sqrt{5}+3\right)$ i) $\left(4\sqrt{3}-8\right)^2$

2. Divide and simplify. Assume that all variables represent positive real numbers.

   a) $\dfrac{\sqrt{12}}{\sqrt{3}}$ b) $\dfrac{\sqrt{50}}{\sqrt{2}}$ c) $\dfrac{\sqrt{50y^3}}{\sqrt{2y}}$

3. Rationalize each denominator and simplify. Assume that all variables represent positive real numbers.

   a) $\dfrac{\sqrt{7}}{\sqrt{5}}$ b) $\sqrt{\dfrac{5}{12}}$ c) $\dfrac{3x}{\sqrt{2}}$

4. Rationalize each denominator and simplify. Assume that all variables represent positive real numbers.

   a) $\dfrac{2}{6-\sqrt{3}}$ b) $\dfrac{7}{\sqrt{5}+2}$ c) $\dfrac{15}{3+\sqrt{x}}$

Teaching Notes:
- Many students have trouble with problem 1i. They tend to square each term in the binomial rather than squaring the binomial.
- Most students are able to rationalize a denominator with one term.
- Many students have difficulty rationalizing a denominator with 2 terms.
- Each section in the text has 3 worksheets in the Extra Practice featuring differentiated learning.

Answers: 1a) $\sqrt{15}$; 1b) $5x$; 1c) $2\sqrt{3}$; 1d) $9x$; 1e) $5x^2\sqrt{3}$; 1f) $3\sqrt{2}+2\sqrt{3}$; 1g) -2;

1h) $387+105\sqrt{5}$; 1i) $112-64\sqrt{3}$; 2a) 2; 2b) 5; 2c) $5y$; 3a) $\dfrac{\sqrt{35}}{5}$; 3b) $\dfrac{\sqrt{15}}{6}$; 3c) $\dfrac{3x\sqrt{2}}{2}$;

4a) $\dfrac{12+2\sqrt{3}}{33}$; 4b) $7\sqrt{5}-14$; 4c) $\dfrac{45-15\sqrt{x}}{9-x}$

Mini-Lecture 8.5
Solving Equations Containing Radicals

Learning Objectives:

1. Solve radical equations by using the squaring property of equality once.
2. Solve radical equations by using the squaring property of equality twice.

Examples:

1. Solve each equation.

   a) $\sqrt{x} = 5$

   b) $\sqrt{x} - 3 = 13$

   c) $3\sqrt{x} - 15 = 60$

   d) $2\sqrt{x} + 11 = 9$

   e) $1 + \sqrt{y+4} = 11$

   f) $\sqrt{y+9} = y+3$

   g) $\sqrt{5x-2} = \sqrt{2x+1}$

   h) $\sqrt{x+8} - x = 2$

   i) $\sqrt{9x^2 + 5x - 20} = 3x$

2. Solve each equation.

   a) $\sqrt{x} + 3 = \sqrt{x+21}$

   b) $\sqrt{x-27} = \sqrt{x} - 3$

   c) $\sqrt{x} - 1 = \sqrt{x-9}$

   Mixed Practice. Solve each equation.

   d) $\sqrt{5x-1} = 3$

   e) $x + 3 = \sqrt{2x} + 7$

   f) $\sqrt{x+11} = \sqrt{6x-9}$

Teaching Notes:

- Many students have to be reminded to isolate the radical before squaring both sides.
- Refer students to the textbook for *To Solve a Radical Equation Containing Square Roots*.
- Many students find the concept of extraneous solutions confusing.
- Show students a simple example of an extraneous solution, such as:
  $x = 5 \rightarrow$ square both sides $\rightarrow x^2 = 25 \rightarrow x = \pm 5 \rightarrow x = -5$ is extraneous.
- Each section in the text has 3 worksheets in the Extra Practice featuring differentiated learning.

Answers: *1a) 25; 1b) 256; 1c) 625; 1d) not real; 1e) 96; 1f) 0; 1g) 1; 1h) 1; 1i) 4; 2a) 4; 2b) 36; 2c) 25; 2d) 2; 2e) 8; 2f) 4*

Mini-Lecture 8.6
Radical Equations and Problem Solving

Learning Objectives:

1. Use the Pythagorean formula to solve problems.
2. Use the distance formula.
3. Solve problems using formulas containing radical.

Examples:

1. Use the Pythagorean Theorem to find the length of the unknown side of each right triangle. Give an exact answer and a two-decimal-place approximation.

a)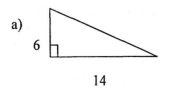

b)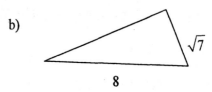

Find the length of the unknown side of each right triangle with sides a, b, and c, where c is the hypotenuse. Give an exact answer and a two-decimal-place approximation.

c) $a = 15, b = 20$ d) $b = 18, c = 82$ e) $a = 20, c = 28$

2. Use the distance formula to find the distance between the points given.
   a) (4,2), (5,8)   b) (-4,-6), (-1,5)   c) (-8,6), (8,-6)

3. Solve. Give a two decimal place approximation.

   a) A baseball diamond is a square measuring 90 feet on each side. What is the distance from first base to third base?

   b) A firefighter places a 37-foot ladder 9 feet from the base of the wall of a building. Will the top reach a window ledge that is 35 feet above the ground?

   c) Denise set up a volleyball net in her backyard. One of the poles, which forms a right angle with the ground, is 7 feet high. To secure the poles, he attached a rope from the top of the pole to a stake 3 feet from the bottom of the pole. Find the length of the rope.

   d) Cindy and Dan leave home at the same time. Dan drives eastward at 30 miles per hour, while Cindy drives south at 50 miles per hour. Find how far apart they are to the nearest mile after 3 hours.

Teaching Notes:

- Most students can use Pythagorean Theorem when the triangle is in the form of 1a).
- Many students get confused when the triangle is rotated as in 1b). Remind students to locate the right angle; the side directly across from the right angle is the hypotenuse.
- Remind students to draw a picture, label a diagram, etc. when solving applications. Again, always locate the right angle, which will lead to identifying the hypotenuse.

Answers: 1a) $2\sqrt{58}$, 15.23; 1b) $\sqrt{57}$, 7.55; 1c) 25; 1d) 80; 1e) $8\sqrt{6}$, 19.60; 2a) $\sqrt{37}$, 6.08; 2b) $\sqrt{130}$, 11.40; 2c) 2; 3a) 127.28 ft. 3b) yes; 3c) 7.62 ft.; 3d) 175 mi.

Mini-Lecture 8.7
Rational Exponents

Learning Objectives:

1. Evaluate exponential expressions of the form $a^{1/n}$.
2. Evaluate exponential expressions of the form $a^{m/n}$.
3. Evaluate exponential expressions of the form $a^{-m/n}$.
4. Use rules for exponents to simplify expressions containing fractional exponents.

Examples:

1. Evaluate exponential expressions of the form $a^{1/n}$ Write in radical form and then simplify.

   a) $36^{\frac{1}{2}}$ b) $1^{\frac{1}{3}}$ c) $\left(\dfrac{1}{1000}\right)^{\frac{1}{3}}$

2. Evaluate exponential expressions of the form $a^{m/n}$. Write first in radical form, then simplify.

   a) $9^{\frac{3}{2}}$ b) $64^{\frac{2}{3}}$ c) $-81^{\frac{3}{4}}$

3. Evaluate exponential expressions of the form. $a^{-m/n}$. Write first in radical form, then simplify.

   a) $4^{-\frac{1}{2}}$ b) $16^{-\frac{3}{4}}$ c) $125^{-\frac{2}{3}}$

4. Use rules for exponents to simplify expression containing fractional exponents.

   a) $27^{\frac{4}{3}} \cdot 27^{\frac{1}{3}}$ b) $\dfrac{64^{\frac{4}{3}}}{64^{\frac{5}{3}}}$ $-25^{\frac{3}{2}}$

Teaching Notes:

- Identify the power and the index of the exponent before students work the problem.
- Remind students a negative outside the parentheses is not affected by the exponent
- Review exponent rules before simplifying expressions.
- Each section in the text has 3 worksheets in the Extra Practice featuring differentiated learning.

Answers: 1a) $\sqrt{36}=6$; 1b) $\sqrt[3]{1}=1$; 1c) $\sqrt[3]{\dfrac{1}{1000}}=\dfrac{1}{10}$; 2a) $\left(\sqrt{9}\right)^{3}$, 27; 2b) $\left(\sqrt[3]{64}\right)^{2}$, 16; 2c) $-\left(\sqrt[4]{81}\right)^{3}$, -27;

3a) $\dfrac{1}{2}$, 3b) $\dfrac{1}{8}$; 3c) $\dfrac{1}{25}$; 4a) $\left(\sqrt[3]{27}\right)^{5}$, 3^{5}; 4b) $\dfrac{1}{\sqrt[3]{64}}$, $\dfrac{1}{4}$; 4c) $\left(-\sqrt{25}\right)^{3}$, -5^{3}

Mini-Lecture 9.1
Solving Quadratic Equations by the Square Root Property

Learning Objectives:

1. Use the square root property to solve quadratic equations.
2. Solve problems modeled by quadratic by quadratic equations.

Examples:

1. Solve each equation by factoring.

   a) $x^2 - 36 = 0$ b) $5x^2 - 125 = 0$ c) $x^2 - 4x = 21$ d) $2x^2 = x + 10$

   Use the square root property to solve each quadratic equation.

   e) $x^2 = 49$ f) $x^2 - 33 = 0$ g) $x^2 + 100 = 0$ h) $25x^2 = 8$

   i) $(x - 4)^2 = 25$ j) $\left(x - \dfrac{1}{5}\right)^2 = \dfrac{1}{25}$ k) $(2x - 1)^2 = 49$ l) $(a + 2)^2 = 15$

2. Solve the following applications. Round each answer to the nearest tenth of a second.

   a) Use the formula $h = 16t^2$ to solve the following: determine the time of a stuntman's fall if he jumped from a height of 450 feet.

   b) Use the formula for the area of a square $A = s^2$ where s is the length of a side. If the area of a square is 40 square inches, find the length of the side.

   c) Use the formula for the area of a square $A = s^2$ where s is the length of a side. If the area of the square base of a monument is 2200 square feet, find the length of the side.

Teaching Notes:

- Many students will need a review of factoring, especially factoring difference of two squares.
- Many students need extra practice working with the "$\pm$ " symbol.
- Some students need to always write their answers by separating the "$\pm$" symbol, and writing the positive solution and negative solution.
- Remind students with applications that the negative solution will be an *extraneous solution*.
- Each section in the text has 3 worksheets in the Extra Practice featuring differentiated learning.

Answers: 1a) ± 6; 1b) ± 5; 1c) -3, 7; 1d) -2, $\dfrac{5}{2}$; 1e) ± 7; 1f) $\pm\sqrt{33}$; 1g) *not real*; 1h) $\pm\dfrac{2\sqrt{2}}{5}$;

1i) -1, 9; 1j) 0, $\dfrac{2}{5}$; 1k) -3, 4; 1l) $-2 \pm \sqrt{15}$; 2a) 5.3 s; 2b) 6.3 in.; 2c) 46.9 ft.

Mini-Lecture 9.2
Solving Quadratic Equations by Completing the Square

Learning Objectives:

1. Write perfect square trinomials.
2. Solve quadratic equations of the form $x^2 + bx + c = 0$ by completing the square.
3. Solve quadratic equations of the form $ax^2 + bx + c = 0$ by completing the square.

Examples:

1. Solve each quadratic equation by completing the square.

   a) $x^2 + 12x = -35$

   b) $a^2 - 10a + 21 = 0$

   c) $z^2 + 10z + 3 = 0$

   d) $x^2 = 7 - 4x$

   e) $x^2 = 5 - 5x$

   f) $a(3a - 2) + 1 = 5$

2. Solve each quadratic equation by completing the square.

   a) $16x^2 + 24x + 5 = 0$

   b) $9y^2 + 18y + 8 = 0$

   c) $9x^2 - 35 = 6x$

   d) $2x^2 + 4x + 11 = 0$

   e) $2n^2 + 6n + 3 = 0$

   f) $2x(2x + 5) = -3$

   Mixed Practice. Solve each quadratic equation by completing the square.

   g) $k^2 + 8k + 7 = 0$

   h) $x(6x + 1) - 10 = -8$

   i) $2x^2 + 5x - 2 = 0$

Teaching Notes:

- Refer students to the textbook for steps used to solve by completing the square: *To Solve a Quadratic Equation in x by Completing the Square.*
- Many students will need a review of perfect square trinomials to understand the goal of completing the square.
- Most students need to see many examples done out for them to understand the process.
- Some students need to write out both solutions instead of using the "$\pm$" symbol.
- Each section in the text has 3 worksheets in the Extra Practice featuring differentiated learning.

Answers: 1a) -7, -5; 1b) 3, 7; 1c) $-5 \pm \sqrt{22}$; 1d) $-2 \pm \sqrt{11}$; 1e) $\dfrac{-5 \pm 3\sqrt{5}}{2}$; 1f) $\dfrac{1 \pm \sqrt{13}}{3}$;

2a) -1/4, -5/4; 2b) -2/3, -4/3; 2c) 7/3, -5/3; 2d) not real; 2e) $\dfrac{-3 \pm \sqrt{3}}{2}$ 2f) $\dfrac{-5 \pm \sqrt{13}}{4}$; 2g) -7, -1;

2h) ½, -2/3; 2i) $\dfrac{-5 \pm \sqrt{41}}{4}$

Mini-Lecture 9.3
Solving Quadratic Equations by the Quadratic Formula

Learning Objectives:

1. Use the quadratic formula to solve quadratic equations.
2. Approximate solutions to quadratic equations.
3. Determine the number of solutions of a quadratic equation by using the discriminant.

Examples:

1. Identify the value of a, b, and c in each quadratic equation.

   a) $2x^2 - 7x - 9 = 0$ b) $4x^2 - 3x - 7 = 0$ c) $x^2 - 15 = 0$

   Use the quadratic formula to solve each quadratic equation.

   d) $x^2 + 7x + 10 = 0$ e) $3p^2 - 23p + 14 = 0$ f) $2x^2 - 7x - 4 = 0$

   g) $x^2 + 5x - 8 = 0$ h) $x^2 - 7 = 0$ i) $x^2 - 3x + 4 = -5$

2. Use the quadratic formula to solve each quadratic equation. Find the exact solutions; then approximate these solutions to the nearest tenth.

   a) $4y^2 + 2y - 3 = 0$ b) $2x^2 + 4x = -1$ c) $\frac{1}{8}x^2 - \frac{1}{4}x = \frac{1}{2}$

3. Use the discriminant to determine the number of solutions of each quadratic equations.

   a) $x^2 - 5x + 4 = 0$ b) $2x^2 - 3x + 5 = 0$ c) $x^2 - 12x + 36 = 0$

Teaching Notes:

- Most students have difficulty learning the quadratic formula. Suggest that they put the formula to the tune of "Pop Goes The Weasel". "x equals negative b plus or minus square root, b squared minus 4ac all over 2a".
- Most students make careless errors upon evaluation.
- Encourage students to clearly write the values for a, b, and c before substitution.
- Remind students that the fraction bar is under the entire numerator $-b \pm \sqrt{b^2 - 4ac}$.
- Each section in the text has 3 worksheets in the Extra Practice featuring differentiated learning.

Answers: 1a) a=2, b=-7, c=-9; 1b) a=4, b=-3, c=-7; 1c) a=1, b=0, c=-15; 1d) -2, -5 ; 1e) 7, 2/3; 1f) 4, -1/2

1g) $\dfrac{-5 \pm \sqrt{57}}{2}$; 1h) $\pm\sqrt{7}$; 1i) not a real number; 2a) $\dfrac{-1 \pm \sqrt{13}}{4}$, 0.7, -1.2; 2b) $\dfrac{-2 \pm \sqrt{2}}{2}$, -0.3, -1.7;

2c) $1 \pm \sqrt{5}$, 3.2, -1.2; 3a) two distinct real solutions; 3b) no real solutions; 3c) one real solution

Mini-Lecture 9.4
Complex Solutions of Quadratic Equations

Learning Objectives:

1. Write complex numbers using i notation.
2. Add and subtract complex numbers.
3. Multiply complex numbers.
4. Divide complex numbers.
5. Solve quadratic equations that have complex solutions.

Examples:

1. Simplify each of the following using $\sqrt{-1} = i$.

   a) $\sqrt{-49}$ b) $\sqrt{-12}$ c) $\sqrt{-80}$

2. Add or subtract as indicated.

   a) $(3-i)+(5+4i)$ b) $(2+5i)-(3+2i)$ c) Subtract $(8-i)$ from $(3+4i)$

3. Multiply complex numbers.

   a) $2i(4-8i)$ b) $(5-2i)(3+i)$ c) $(1+2i)(1-2i)$

4. Divide complex numbers.

   a) $\dfrac{9-12i}{3}$ b) $\dfrac{20+5i}{5i}$ c) $\dfrac{6-i}{3-2i}$

5. Solve the following quadratic equations for complex solutions.

   a) $(x+2)^2 = -16$ b) $(3x-5)^2 = -12$ c) $x^2 + 8x + 20 = 0$

Teaching Notes:

- Remind students $i^2 = -1$ and $i = \sqrt{-1}$.
- Complex numbers can be written in the form $a + bi$.
- Complex numbers written in the form $0 + bi$ $b \neq 0$ is also called a pure imaginary number.
- Complex number written in the form $a + bi$ is in standard form.
- Each section in the text has 3 worksheets in the Extra Practice featuring differentiated learning.

Answers: 1a) $7i$; 1b) $2i\sqrt{3}$; 1c) $4i\sqrt{5}$; 2a) $8+3i$; 2b) $-9+3i$; 2c) $-5+5i$; 3a) $16+8i$; 3b) $17-i$; 3c) 5; 4a) $3-4i$; 4b) $\dfrac{20+9i}{14}$; 4c) $1-4i$; 5a) $2\pm4i$; 5b) $\dfrac{5\pm2\sqrt{3}}{3}$; 5c) $-4\pm2i$

M-61

Mini-Lecture 9.5
Graphing Quadratic Equations

Learning Objectives:

1. Graph quadratic equations of the form $y = ax^2$.
2. Graph quadratic equations of the form $y = ax^2 + bx + c$.
3. Use the vertex formula to determine the vertex of a parabola.

Examples:

1. Graph each quadratic equation by finding and plotting ordered pair solutions.

   a) $y = x^2$ b) $y = 4x^2$ c) $y = -2x^2$

2. Sketch the graph of each equation. Label the vertex and the intercepts.

   a) $y = x^2 - 4$ b) $y = x^2 + 16$ c) $y = -x^2 - 2$

   d) $y = x^2 + 7x + 10$ e) $y = -x^2 + x + 6$ f) $y = -x^2 + 6x - 9$

   g) $y = \frac{1}{5}x^2$ h) $y = x^2 + 5x$ i) $y = -2x^2 + 5x - 3$

Teaching Notes:

- Remind students that a parabola is a smooth curve; not a point.
- Encourage students to always find the x- and y-intercepts, if they exist.
- Most students prefer graphing by vertex and intercepts rather than by finding points.
- Each section in the text has 3 worksheets in the Extra Practice featuring differentiated learning.

Answers: 1a) – 2i) see mini-lecture graphing answers; 2a) $V=(0,-4)$, $(2, 0)$, $(-2, 0)$; *2b)* $V=(0, 16)$;
2c) $V = (0,-2)$; *2d)* $V=\left(-\frac{7}{2}, -\frac{9}{4}\right)$, $(-2, 0)$, $(-5, 0)$, $(0, 10)$; *2e)* $V=\left(\frac{1}{2}, \frac{25}{4}\right)$, $(0, 6)$, $(-2,0)$, $(3,0)$;
2f) $V = (3, 0)$, $(0, -9)$; *2g)* $V=(0, 0)$; *2h)* $V=\left(-\frac{5}{2}, -\frac{25}{4}\right)$, $(0, 0)$, $(-5, 0)$; *2i)* $V=\left(\frac{5}{4}, \frac{1}{8}\right)$, $(1, 0)$, $(3/2, 0)$, $(0, -3)$

M-62

Mini-Lecture
Graph Answers

Chapter 2

Mini-Lecture 2.9

1. **a.** [number line: bracket at −5, shaded right, −5 and 0 marked]

    b. [number line: shaded left from 7 with parenthesis at 7, 0 and 7 marked]

    c. [number line: bracket at $-\frac{3}{2}$, shaded left, $-\frac{3}{2}$ and 0 marked]

    d. [number line: parenthesis at $-\frac{2}{5}$, shaded right, $-\frac{2}{5}$ and 0 marked]

2. **a.** [number line: bracket at 5, shaded left, 0 and 5 marked]

    b. [number line: parenthesis at 7, shaded right, 0 and 7 marked]

    c. [number line: parenthesis at 3, shaded right, 0 and 3 marked]

    d. [number line: bracket at 6, shaded left, 0 and 6 marked]

    e. [number line: bracket at −24, shaded left, −48, −24, 0 marked]

    f. [number line: parenthesis at $\frac{73}{3}$, shaded left, 0, 12, $\frac{73}{3}$ marked]

    g. [number line: parenthesis at 0, shaded right]

    h. [number line: bracket at −15, shaded right, −15, 0, 15 marked]

    i. [number line: parenthesis, shaded right, −8, 0, 8 marked]

    j. [number line: bracket at −4, shaded right, −4, 0, 4 marked]

    k. [number line: parenthesis at $-\frac{7}{5}$, shaded right, $-\frac{7}{5}$ and 0 marked]

3. **a.** [number line: parenthesis and bracket, −5 and 0 marked]

    b. [number line: bracket at −6, parenthesis near −4, −6, −4, 0 marked]

    c. [number line: bracket at 3, bracket at 4, 0 1 2 3 4 5 marked]

Chapter 3

Mini-Lecture 3.2

1. **a.**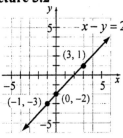

    b.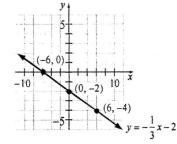

    c.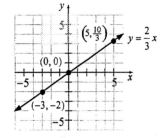

    d.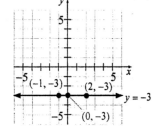

    e.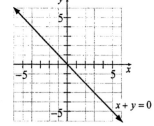

    f.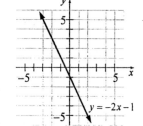

g.

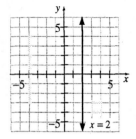

Mini-Lecture 3.3

2. **a.**

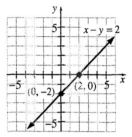

b.

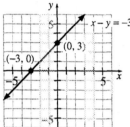

c.

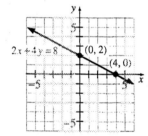

d.

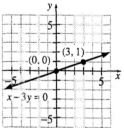

e.

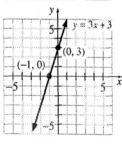

f.

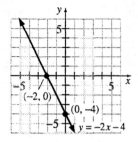

3. **a.**

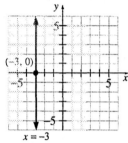

b.

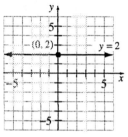

c.

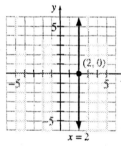

Mini-Lecture 3.5

2. **a.**

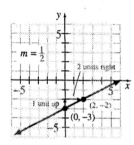

b.

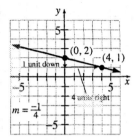

c.

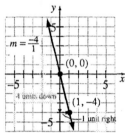

d.

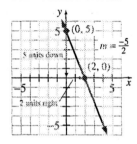

Chapter 4

Mini-Lecture 4.1

2. **a.**

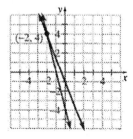

b.

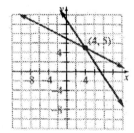

c.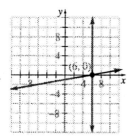

d.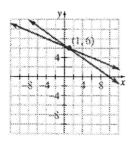

Mini-Lecture 4.5

1. e.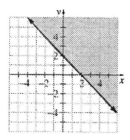

f.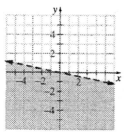

g.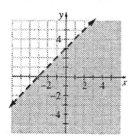

h.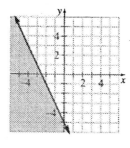

i.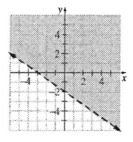

j.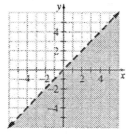

k.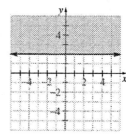

l.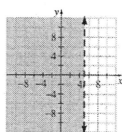

m.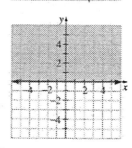

Mini-Lecture 4.6

1. a.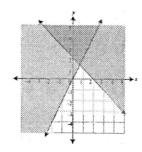

b.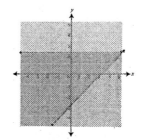

c.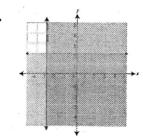

d.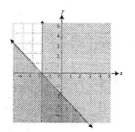

Additional Exercises 1.2
Form I

Insert <, >, or = to make a true statement.

1. 0 _____ 44

2. 3.05 _____ 3.5

3. $|-4|$ _____ $|-3|$

4. $|-1|$ _____ -1

5. The angles of a particular triangle are 90°, 60°, and 30°. Use an inequality symbol ($\leq$ or $\geq$) to represent the relationship between the angle of the triangle from smallest to largest.

Tell whether each statement is true or false.

6. $15 \leq 17$

7. $-2.4 \geq -8.1$

8. $\dfrac{3}{4} \leq -\dfrac{3}{4}$

9. $-\dfrac{5}{8} \geq -\dfrac{5}{8}$

10. $0 \geq -7$

Rewrite the following inequalities so that the inequality symbol points in the opposite direction and the resulting statement has the same meaning as the given one.

11. $\dfrac{1}{2} \geq -\dfrac{1}{2}$

12. $7 > 2$

Use integers to represent the values in each sentence.

13. Victoria wrote a check for $275. Then at the end of the week she deposited $700.

14. Garrett was at the quarry practicing his for his diving certification. During his dive, he descended 27 feet and later descending another 20 feet.

1. _____

2. _____

3. _____

4. _____

5. _____

6. _____

7. _____

8. _____

9. _____

10. _____

11. _____

12. _____

13. _____

14 _____

Additional Exercises 1.2 *(cont.)*

Name _____

Given the set $\left\{ \sqrt{15}, \dfrac{3}{4}, 24, -6.\overline{1}, 0, -25, 7.5, -\sqrt{3} \right\}$, list the numbers in this set that belong to the set of:

15. Natural numbers

15. _____

16. Whole numbers.

16. _____

17. Integers

17. _____

18. Rational numbers

18. _____

19. Irrational numbers

19. _____

20. Real numbers

20. _____

Additional Exercises 1.2
Form II

Name_____

Date_____

Graph the numbers on the number line.

1. $1, -1\frac{2}{3}, 0.5, 2\frac{1}{3}, -3$

2. $2, -3, 0.75, 0, -4$

Given the set $\left\{-2.2, |-5|, 3\frac{1}{3}, 14, 0, -0.5, \sqrt{14}\right\}$ list the numbers in this set that belong to the set of:

3. Natural numbers

4. Whole numbers

5. Integers

6. Rational numbers

7. Irrational numbers

8. Real numbers

Tell whether each statement is true or false.

9. $-19 \le -14$

10. $-44 > -50$

11. $0 \ge -7$

12. $|-4.5| \ge |4.5|$

Insert <, >, or = in the appropriate space to make each statement true.

13. $|0| \qquad -|-3|$

14. $\left|-\frac{4}{5}\right| \qquad |-0.8|$

15. $|-1| \qquad -1$

1. ⟵——————————⟶

2. ⟵——————————⟶

3. _____

4. _____

5. _____

6. _____

7. _____

8. _____

9. _____

10. _____

11. _____

12. _____

13. _____

14 _____

15 _____

Additional Exercises 1.2 *(cont.)*

Name _____

Write each sentence as a mathematical statement.

16. Negative five is greater than or equal to negative fourteen..

16. _____

17. Seven tenths is not greater than the absolute value of negative nine tenths.

17. _____

Rewrite each inequality so that the inequality symbol points in the opposite direction and the resulting statement has the same meaning as the given one.

18. $-2 \geq -5$

18. _____

19. $|15| \leq |-17|$

19. _____

20. $-6 > -14$

20. _____

Additional Exercises 1.2
Form III

Name_____

Date_____

Graph the numbers on the number line.

1. $-10, 5, -3.5, 14\frac{1}{2}, 9$

2. $0.1, -0.3, 0.4, 0, 0.25$

Given the set $\left\{ \sqrt{25}, \frac{6}{2}, |-0.1|, 0, \pi, -25, \frac{7}{11}, 0.5, 100 \right\}$, list the numbers in this set that belong to the set of:

3. Natural numbers

4. Whole numbers

5. Integers

6. Rational numbers

7. Irrational numbers

8. Real numbers

Tell whether each statement is true or false.

9. Every integer is also a rational number

10. Zero is a natural number.

11. Every natural number is a whole number.

12. All real numbers are also rational.

13. $\sqrt{3}$ is an irrational number.

Insert <, >, or = in the appropriate space to make each statement true.

14. $|-3.2|$ $|-3|$

15. $\left| \frac{3}{5} \right|$ $\left| -\frac{2}{3} \right|$

16. $|-15|$ $-\frac{45}{3}$

1. ⟵——————————⟶

2. ⟵——————————⟶

3. _____

4. _____

5. _____

6. _____

7. _____

8. _____

9. _____

10. _____

11. _____

12. _____

13. _____

14 _____

15 _____

16. _____

Additional Exercises 1.2 *(cont.)*

Write each sentence as a mathematical statement.

17. Fourteen is greater than or equal to five.

17. _____

18. Nine is not equal to negative nine

18. _____

Tell which set or sets each number belongs to: natural numbers, whole numbers, integers, rational numbers, irrational numbers, or real numbers.

Ocean	Size	Lowest Point	Depth of Lowest Point
Pacific	155,557,000 sq km	Mariana Trench	35,827 ft
Atlantic	76,762,000 sq km	Puerto Rico Trench	30,246 ft
Indian	68,556,000 sq km	Java Trench	24,460 ft
Artic	14,056,000 sq km	Arctic Basin	18,456 ft
Southern	20,327,000 sq km	In dispute	

19. Which ocean has the deepest known point?

19. _____

20. Use integers to represent the size of the Pacific Ocean and the depth of the Mariana Trench.

20. _____

Additional Exercises
Chapter 1.3 Form I

Name_____

Date_____

Write each fraction as an equivalent fraction with the given denominator.

1. Write the prime factorization for each number.

    a. 27   **d.** 375

    b. 24   **e.** 200

    c. 180   **f.** 910

1a._____ 1d._____

1b._____ 1e._____

1c._____ 1f._____

2. $\dfrac{2}{3}$ with a denominator of 48.

2. _____

3. $\dfrac{4}{5}$ with a denominator of 50.

3. _____

4. $\dfrac{5}{4}$ with a denominator of 24.

4. _____

Simplify each fraction.

5. $\dfrac{36}{9}$

5. _____

6. $\dfrac{150}{300}$

6. _____

7. $\dfrac{0}{28}$

7. _____

8. $\dfrac{66}{0}$

8. _____

9. $\dfrac{120}{510}$

9. _____

10. $\dfrac{76}{1}$

10. _____

Perform the indicated operations and simplify.

11. $\dfrac{2}{3} \cdot \dfrac{8}{9}$

11. _____

12. $\dfrac{2}{3} \cdot \dfrac{21}{66}$

12. _____

13. $1\dfrac{3}{7} \cdot 2\dfrac{4}{5}$

13. _____

Additional Exercises Ch 1.3 *(cont.)*

14. $6\dfrac{2}{5} \div 1\dfrac{1}{15}$

14. _____

15. $\dfrac{13}{15} + \dfrac{7}{15}$

15. _____

16. $\dfrac{4}{5} + \dfrac{3}{20}$

16. _____

17. $16\dfrac{3}{4} + 12\dfrac{1}{2}$

17. _____

18. $\dfrac{15}{16} - \dfrac{3}{16}$

18. _____

19. $\dfrac{7}{8} - \dfrac{2}{3}$

19. _____

20. $100 - 12\dfrac{3}{5}$

20. _____

Additional Exercises
Chapter 1.3 Form II

Name_____

Date_____

1. Find the prime factorization of each number.

    a. 112   **d.** 244
    b. 756   **e.** 288
    c. 336

1a. _____ 1d. _____

1b. _____ 1e. _____

1c. _____

Simplify each fraction.

2. $\dfrac{44}{77}$

2. _____

3. $\dfrac{18}{0}$

3. _____

4. $\dfrac{67}{1}$

4. _____

5. $\dfrac{0}{20}$

5. _____

6. $\dfrac{26}{39}$

6. _____

7. $\dfrac{34}{51}$

7. _____

8. $\dfrac{57}{45}$

8. _____

Perform the indicated operations and simplify.

9 $\dfrac{15}{16} \cdot \dfrac{2}{5} \div \dfrac{4}{5}$

9. _____

10. $\dfrac{5}{8} \cdot \dfrac{32}{45} \cdot 1\dfrac{1}{4}$

10. _____

11. $4\dfrac{2}{3} \cdot 1\dfrac{2}{7} \div 2\dfrac{1}{2}$

11. _____

12. $\dfrac{3}{4} \div \dfrac{9}{16} \cdot \dfrac{9}{10}$

12. _____

Name_____

13. $8\dfrac{1}{4} \div 22 \cdot \dfrac{1}{4}$

14. $\dfrac{15}{16} + \dfrac{3}{16}$

15. $\dfrac{3}{5} + \dfrac{9}{10} - \dfrac{2}{25}$

16. $10\dfrac{4}{5} + 12\dfrac{3}{4} - 5\dfrac{1}{10}$

17. $\dfrac{41}{50} - \dfrac{21}{50} + \dfrac{1}{200}$

18. $\dfrac{7}{9} - \dfrac{3}{4} + 3\dfrac{1}{12}$

19. $21\dfrac{1}{2} - 17\dfrac{3}{5} + 14\dfrac{3}{20}$

20. $14\dfrac{2}{3} \cdot 2\dfrac{2}{11} \div 3\dfrac{3}{8}$

13. _____

14. _____

15. _____

16. _____

17. _____

18. _____

19. _____

20. _____

Additional Exercises
Chapter 1.3 Form III

Mixed Practice. Perform the indicated operat6ions

1. $\dfrac{29}{135}+\dfrac{25}{9}+4\dfrac{7}{27}$

   1. _____

2. $\dfrac{12}{25}\div 18$

   2. _____

3. $4\dfrac{1}{6}\cdot 7\dfrac{2}{5}$

   3. _____

4. $21\div\dfrac{1}{3}$

   4. _____

5. $7\dfrac{2}{15}-5\dfrac{2}{3}$

   5. _____

6. $\dfrac{22}{55}\cdot\dfrac{11}{14}$

   6. _____

7. $6\dfrac{4}{7}+2\dfrac{1}{3}-5\dfrac{16}{21}$

   7. _____

8. $9\dfrac{1}{5}-3\dfrac{3}{5}-4\dfrac{5}{6}$

   8. _____

9. $6\dfrac{2}{3}\cdot\dfrac{9}{10}\cdot\dfrac{14}{15}$

   9. _____

10. $\dfrac{2}{5}\div 16\div\dfrac{5}{8}$

    10. _____

11. $45\dfrac{1}{2}+6\dfrac{4}{5}+19\dfrac{3}{4}$

    11. _____

12. $101-\dfrac{2}{3}-16\dfrac{1}{5}$

    12. _____

13. _____

13. Find the area of a triangle whose base is $14\frac{1}{2}$ feet and height $10\frac{3}{7}$ feet using the formula for the area of a triangle $A = \frac{1}{2}bh$.

14. _____

14. If the formula for the area of a triangle is $A = \frac{1}{2}bh$, find the area of a triangle that has a height of $1\frac{3}{4}$ cm. and the base is $1\frac{1}{4}$ cm.

15. _____

15. If the formula for finding the area of a parallelogram is $A = bh$, find the area of a parallelogram with a height of $11\frac{1}{5}$ inches, and base that is $12\frac{3}{4}$ inches.

In the 2006 Winter Olympics held in Turin, Italy, the top four countries winning gold, silver and bronze medal is summarized in the following pie chart.

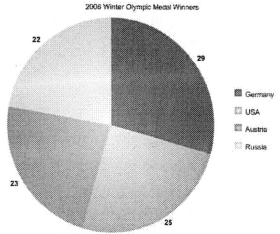

2006 Winter Olympic Medal Winners

- Germany
- USA
- Austria
- Russia

16. _____

16. Germany won 11 Gold Medals, 12 Silver Medals and 6 Bronze Medals. What fraction represents the total number Gold Medals won by Germany to the total number of medals awarded to the top four winners?

17. _____

17. The USA won 9 Gold, 9 Silver, and 7 Bronze.. What fraction represents the total number Gold Medals won by the USA to the total number of medals awards to the top four winners?

18. _____

18. Russia won 8 Gold, 6 Silver, and 8 Bronze. What fraction represents the total number of medals won by Russia to the total number of medals won by the top four?

Additional Exercises 1.4
Form I

Name_____

Date_____

Evaluate.

1. 5^4

2. $\left(\dfrac{1}{3}\right)^2$

3. $\left(\dfrac{4}{5}\right)^3$

4. 1^7

5. $(0.51)^3$

Simplify each expression.

6. $16 + 3 \cdot 12$

7. $4 + (7 - 2) + 2^3$

8. $\dfrac{1}{3} \cdot \dfrac{9}{4} - \dfrac{1}{3}$

9. $5 \cdot 3^2$

10. $\dfrac{13 - |10 - 2|}{5^2 - 4^2}$

11. $\dfrac{1}{5} - \dfrac{2}{5} \cdot \dfrac{5}{10}$

Evaluate each expression if $x = -5$ and $y = 3$.

12. $-6x$

13. $\dfrac{-5y}{3x}$

14. $|-2y - x|$

15. $-xy + y^2$

1. _____

2. _____

3. _____

4. _____

5. _____

6. _____

7. _____

8. _____

9. _____

10. _____

11. _____

12. _____

13. _____

14. _____

15. _____

Decide whether the given number is a solution of the given equation

    16. $5x - 1 = 9$; 2   **16.** _____

    17. $3x + 2 = x + 2$; 0   **17.** _____

    18. $x - 4 = 2x$; 3   **18.** _____

    19. $x + 3x = 12$; 4   **19.** _____

    20. $-x + 2x = 5$; 5   **20.** _____

Additional Exercises 1.4
Form II

Name _____

Date _____

Evaluate.

1. $\left(\dfrac{5}{4}\right)^3$

2. 5^3

3. $(0.1)^3$

Simplify each expression.

4. $3^2 + 4 \cdot 6$

5. $|7-3|^3 - 2 \cdot 2^3$

6. $5 + 2\{15 - 3(4-2) + 12\}$

7. $\dfrac{10 + |10-2| + 2^3}{5^2 - 12}$

Evaluate each expression if $x = 4$, $y = 3$, and $z = 1$.

8. $5z - y$

9. $\dfrac{x}{4y}$

10. $|5y - x|$

11. $xy + z^4$

Decide whether the given number is a solution to the equation.

12. $\dfrac{1}{5}x = 30;\ 6$

13. $x + 15 = x + 3;\ 0$

1. _____

2. _____

3. _____

4. _____

5. _____

6. _____

7. _____

8. _____

9. _____

10. _____

11. _____

12. _____

13. _____

Additional Exercises 1.4 *(cont.)*

Write each phrase as an algebraic expression. Let *x* represent the unknown number.

14. Four added to a number

15 Three less than twice a number

Write each sentence as an equation. Use *x* to represent any unknown number.

16. The difference of a number and 6 is 12.

17. The sum of 14 and two times a number is 56.

18. Sixteen subtracted from a number is 23.

19. The quotient of a number and 4 is equal to three squared.

20. Three times a number increased by 15 is negative forty-five.

14. _____

15. _____

16. _____

17. _____

18. _____

19. _____

20. _____

Additional Exercises 1.4
Form III

Name_____

Date_____

Match each expression in the first column with its value in the second column..

1.	$(7+4) \bullet (3+2)$	27
2.	$(7+4) \bullet 3+2$	55
3.	$7+4 \bullet 3+2$	35
4.	$7+4 \bullet (3+2)$	21

1. _____
2. _____
3. _____
4. _____

Complete the chart for the given lengths and widths. Be sure to include units

	Length l	Width w	Perimeter of Rectangle $2l + 2w$	Area of Rectangle lw
5.	14 cm	5 cm		
6.	7 in	3 in		
7.	10 in	10 in		
8.	15 yd	10 yd		

5. _____
6 _____
7. _____
8. _____

Insert one set of parentheses so that the following expression simplifies to 10.

9. $2 + 2 \cdot 40 \div 7 + 3$

9. _____

Write each algebraic expression or equation in words. Tell whether it is an expression or an equation.

10. $\dfrac{2x}{7y}$

10. _____

11. $5 - 2x = 15$

11. _____

12. $4(x-3) = 12$

12. _____

Decide whether the given number is a solution to the equation.

13. $2.2x - 1 = 3.4;\ 2$

13. _____

14. $\dfrac{3}{4}x - 3 = 6;\ 16$

14. _____

Additional Exercises 1.4 *(cont.)*

Simplify each expression.

15. $\left(\dfrac{5}{6}\right)^2 + \dfrac{1}{4} + \dfrac{1}{4} \cdot \dfrac{1}{9}$

15. _____

16. _____

16. $\dfrac{5 + |9 - 3|^2 - 1^7}{3 \cdot 2^3 - 4}$

Evaluate each expression if $x = 5$, $y = 2$, and $z = 4$.

17. $\dfrac{xy - xz}{z}$

17. _____

18. $x(2y - z)$

18. _____

19. $\dfrac{y}{z} + \dfrac{x}{3y}$

19. _____

20. $x^3 - 3yz$

20. _____

Additional Exercises 1.5
Form I

Name_____

Date_____

Add.

1. $-10+(-18)$

2. $5+(-13)$

3. $-14+(18)$

4. $10+(-10)$

5. $-20+(-20)$

6. $-9+15+(-4)$

7. $-7+(-14)+(-35)$

8. $[-15+(19)]+(-17)$

9. $\left|-3+(-17)\right|+\left|3+17\right|$

10. Find the sum of -42 and 14.

Find the additive inverse or the opposite.

11. $-\dfrac{13}{14}$

12. $\left|-22\right|$

13. $\left|0\right|$

Simplify the following.

14. $\left|-9\right|$

15. $-\left|-9\right|$

16. $-\left|9\right|$

1. _____

2. _____

3. _____

4. _____

5. _____

6. _____

7. _____

8. _____

9. _____

10. _____

11. _____

12. _____

13. _____

14. _____

15. _____

16. _____

Name _____

17. If you are standing on a bridge 68 feet above the water, how far are you above the lowest point in the river which is at −22 feet?

16. _____

18. A company had a net profit of −$3.4 million one year and a +$1.4 million the next year. What was the total net profit for the two years?

17. _____

Simplify the following expressions

19. Assume x is a positive number. $-(-6x)$

19. _____

20. Assume x is a positive number. $-|-6x|$

20. _____

Additional Exercises 1.5
Form II

Add:

1. $(-18) + 12 + (-4)$

2. $(-20) + (-8) + (-4)$

3. $-\dfrac{3}{7} + 1\dfrac{2}{7} + \left(-7\dfrac{4}{7}\right)$

4. $-\dfrac{5}{12} + \left(-\dfrac{1}{4}\right)$

5. $-\left|-5 + (-3)\right| + \left|-14\right| + (-2)$

6. $\dfrac{-50 + \left|-6 + (-14)\right| + \left|-3 + 8\right|}{5^5}$

7. $\left|6 + (-14)\right| + \left|-3 + (-8)\right|$

8. Find the sum of -40 and (-5.3).

9. Find the sum of -37 and 22.

Find the additive inverse or the opposite.

10. -0.45

11. $\left|-\dfrac{3}{4}\right|$

12. $\left(-\dfrac{3}{4}\right)$

13. 0

Simplify the following.

14. $\left|-\dfrac{9}{10}\right|$

15. $-\left|-4\right|$

1. _____

2. _____

3. _____

4. _____

5. _____

6. _____

7. _____

8. _____

9. _____

10. _____

11. _____

12. _____

13. _____

14. _____

15. _____

16. If p is a positive number and q is a negative number, then the sum of p and the opposite of q will be a positive or negative number?

16. _____

17. If p is a positive number and q is a negative number, then the sum of the opposite of p added to q will be a positive or negative number?

17. _____

18. In a weeks time, Ramadl's stock was erratic during the entire week. Find the value of the stock at the end of the week

18. _____

Prize Stock	Monday	Tuesday	Wednesday	Thursday	Friday	Saturday
$344	⬆	⬇	⬇	⬆	⬇	⬆
	$47	$70	$100	$33	$65	$150

19. If the drops are added, what will be the total in drops for the week?

19. _____

20. If the increases are added, what will be to total in increases for the week?

20. _____

Additional Exercises 1.5
Form III

Name_____

Date_____

Add.

1. $\dfrac{9}{33} + \left(-\dfrac{9}{33}\right)$

2. $-\left|\dfrac{4}{17}\right| + \left(-\dfrac{4}{17}\right)$

3. $\left|44 + (-55)\right| + \left|-15\right|$

Solve

4. Janis played four basketball games last week. On Monday, she scored 8 points in her game, 10 points on Wednesday, 15 points on Friday, and 11 points on Sunday. How many points did she score for the week?

5. At the beginning of the chemistry experiment, Yates measured the temperature of the liquid to be -19°. At the end of the experiment, the temperature had risen 27°. What was the liquid's temperature at the end of the experiment?

Change the following algebraic expressions or equations to words. Solve the problem where applicable.

6. $(-7) + \left|-7\right| = 0$

7. $\left|-3\right| + 15 + (-16) + (-9) = x$

8. $-\dfrac{12}{7} + \dfrac{9}{14} + \left(-\dfrac{1}{2}\right)$

9. $-\left|\dfrac{2}{3}\right| + \left|\dfrac{1}{2}\right| + \left(-\dfrac{5}{6} + \dfrac{1}{9}\right)$

10. $-4.44 + \left|15.8 + (-22.3)\right|$

Find the additive inverse or opposite of each number.

11. $\left|-\dfrac{1}{3}\right|$

12. $-\left|-\dfrac{1}{3}\right|$

1. _____

2. _____

3. _____

4. _____

5. _____

6. _____

7. _____

8. _____

9. _____

10. _____

11. _____

12. _____

E-23

Name _____

13. The elevator was on the top floor of four story building at the open of business. The basement is considered 1st floor and the top floor is considered 5th floor. During the day, the elevator made the following moves. Where is the elevator at the close of business?

13. _____

Movements	-4	+2	-1
	+3	-4	+1
	+3	-1	-1

14. A submarine was positioned 800 feet below sea level. It ascends 250 feet. What is its new position

14 _____

15. Roman Civilization began in 508 B.C. and ended 24 years before the beginning of the 6th century A.D. How long did the Roman Empire last?

15. _____

16. Mercury has a melting point of -39° C. Alcohol melts at -114° C. Which is the coldest, and how much colder it is at that melting point?

16. _____

Insert <, >, or = in the appropriate space to make each a true statement

17. $-|-14+12|$ $-(14+(-12))$

17. _____

18. $-\dfrac{1}{2}+\left(-\dfrac{3}{5}\right)$ $-\dfrac{1}{3}+\left(-\dfrac{3}{5}\right)$

18. _____

19. $0+(-16)$ $|0+(-16)|$

19.. _____

20. $|(-16)+14|$ $\dfrac{8+(-6)}{2}$

20. _____

Additional Exercises 1.6
Form I

Name_____

Date_____

Subtract.

1. $-10-15$

2. $15-30$

3. $-35-(-15)$

4. $-22-(-45)$

5. $-2-5-(-10)$

6. $12-(-12)-(-15)$

7. $44-(-14)-(-22)-8$

8. $-16-32-(-48)$

9. $-100+(-200)-(-500)+(-100)$

Write each phrase as an expression and then simplify.

10. Subtract negative 15 from negative 3

11. Decrease negative 44 by 18

Simplify each expression.

12. $- -44+(-17)-14$

13. $1.5+(-2.7)-8.8-(-2.1)$

14. $-\dfrac{1}{3}-\dfrac{4}{5}+\left(-\dfrac{1}{4}\right)$

15. $-7+|-12-14|-(-20)$

16. $4^3-15-|26-(-3)|+(-2)$

1. _____

2. _____

3. _____

4. _____

5. _____

6. _____

7. _____

8. _____

9. _____

10. _____

11. _____

12. _____

13. _____

14. _____

15. _____

16. _____

Additional Exercises 1.6 (*cont.*)

Name _____

Find the value of each expression when $x = 4, y = -3,$ and $z = -5$.

17. $\dfrac{x-y}{z-2}$

18. $y^2 - z^2 - x$

19. $\dfrac{3y}{4z} + \dfrac{1}{x}$

20. $x^2 + y^2 - z^2$

17. _____

18. _____

19. _____

20. _____

Additional Exercises 1.6
Form II

Name_____

Date_____

Write each phrase as an expression and simplify.

1. Subtract 15 from negative 14.

2. Subtract negative nine from negative 24.

3. Find the difference between negative four and negative 13.

4. Decrease 25 by negative 22.

Decide whether the given number is a solution of the given equation.

5. $9 - x = 5;\ -4$

6. $-x + 3 = -2x - 3;\ -6$

7. $-2x + 5 = -2x - 1;\ 0$

8. $-2x - 1 = -2x - 1;\ 0$

Find the measure of each unknown complementary and supplementary angle.

9.

10.

Simplify each expression. (Remember the order of operations.)

11.. $-|-6 - 5| - 13 + (-5 + 15)$

12. $|-3|^3 + 5^2 - 4^2$

13. $\dfrac{|-2| + (6 - 3)^2}{7 - (-4)}$

14. $4 - 8(4 - 9)$

1. _____

2. _____

3. _____

4. _____

5. _____

6. _____

7. _____

8. _____

9. _____

10. _____

11. _____

12. _____

13. _____

14. _____

15. In 1943, the temperature in Spearhead was $-4°$ at 7:30 am. Two minutes later the temperature was $45°$ above zero. What was this sudden rise in temperature that still holds a world record?

15. _____

16. The lowest temperature ever recorded in the contiguous 48 states was -69.7 degrees Fahrenheit on January 20, 1954. The highest temperature ever recorded in the contiguous 48 states was 134 degrees Fahrenheit recorded at Death Valley, California. What is the difference between the lowest and the highest recorded temperatures?

16. _____

If r is a positive number and s is a negative number, decide if each statement is true or false.

17. $|r| - |s|$ is always a negative number.

17. _____

18. $r - (-s)$ is always a positive number.

18. _____

19. $-r + (-s)$ is always a negative number.

19. _____

20. $|r - s|$ can possibly be zero.

20. _____

Additional Exercises 1.6
Form III

Name_____

Date_____

Simplify.

1. $-8-(-3)-6-(-14)$

2. $|-5-(-2)|-(-10)-|-14|$

3. $-1.5+|-4.1-(-1.5)-(-8.8)|+|-1.4|$

4. $\left(-\dfrac{5}{8}-\left(-\dfrac{2}{3}\right)\right)-\left(\dfrac{3}{4}\right)^2$

Evaluate each expression when $x=-2, y=12,$ and $z=-3$.

5. $\dfrac{x-y}{7z}$

6. $\dfrac{|y-12|}{x+z}$

7. $|x-y-z|$

8. $\dfrac{2y}{-1-x-z}$

Simplify.

9. If two negative numbers are added, what will be the sign of the sum?

10. If a positive number is subtracted from a negative number, what will be the sign of the answer?

11. Find the difference in -15 and -6.

12. Subtract $-\dfrac{3}{14}$ from the sum of $\dfrac{1}{7}$ and $-\dfrac{1}{2}$.

13. Add -1.7 to the difference of -3.3 and -5.2.

14. $\dfrac{-50-(-47)+(-32)-(-10)}{|-15+(-5)|+(-5+3)^2+(6-7)^2}$

1. _____

2. _____

3. _____

4. _____

5. _____

6. _____

7. _____

8. _____

9. _____

10. _____

11. _____

12. _____

13. _____

14. _____

15. The highest point in Argentina is Mt. Aconcagua at 6960 meters. The lowest point in Argentina is Salinas Chicas at 40 meters below sea level. What is the difference between the highest point and the lowest point?

15. _____

16. The mathematician Apollonius of Perga was born around 262 BC and died around 190 BC. Approximately how long did Apollonius live?

16. _____

The graph shows the temperature at different times during a spring day.

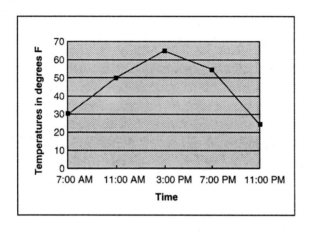

17.. What was the change in the temperature from 3 p.m. to 7 p.m.?

17. _____

18. What was the change in the temperature from 11 a.m. to 11 p.m.?

18. _____

Additional Exercises 1.7
Form I

Name_____

Date_____

1. The product of two numbers with the same sign is: <u>positive</u> or <u>negative?</u>

2. The product of two numbers with different signs is: <u>positive</u> or <u>negative?</u>

Multiply.

3. $-5(-3)$

4. $8(-4)$

5. $-16(2)$

6. $-14(0)$

7. $-\dfrac{1}{5}\left(-\dfrac{5}{7}\right)$

8. $4.1(-2.2)(-1)$

9. $(-4)^2$

10. -4^2

11. $\left(-\dfrac{4}{7}\right)^2$

12. Find the reciprocal of -3

13. Find the reciprocal of $\dfrac{5}{12}$

14. $-44 \div 11$

15. $\dfrac{25}{-15}$

16. $-\dfrac{5}{8} \div -\dfrac{3}{4}$

1. _____

2. _____

3. _____

4. _____

5. _____

6. _____

7. _____

8. _____

9. _____

10. _____

11. _____

12. _____

13. _____

14. _____

15. _____

16. _____

17. $\dfrac{-15}{0}$

17. _____

18. $\dfrac{0\cdot(-3)}{-5}$

18. _____

Use the order of operations to evaluate each expression.

19. $\dfrac{-14(-2)-(-23)(-1)}{\left|-10+(-3)^2\right|}$

19. _____

20. $(-4)^3 \div (-2)^3 - 3(-5)^2$

20. _____

Additional Exercises 1.7
Form II

Name_____

Date_____

Evaluate each expression when $x = -3, y = -5,$ and $z = 2$.

1. $-5x + 4y - 3z$

2. $\dfrac{x^2 - y^2}{z^3}$

Simplify:

3. $\dfrac{-15(3)}{-9}$

4. -1^4

5. $(-2)^5$

6. $(-0.1)^4$

7. $-\dfrac{8}{9}\left(-\dfrac{3}{4}\right) \div \left(-\dfrac{1}{3}\right)^2$

8. $\dfrac{\left|-9+5\right| - \left|-2(-3)(-4)\right|}{(-5)^2 - (-5)}$

Determine whether the given number is a solution of the given equation.

9. $-5x - 3 = 27;\ -6$

10. $24 - 3x = -x + 4;\ -10$

11. $\dfrac{x-5}{8} = -3;\ 19$

12. $-3x + 5 = 2x - 5;\ 2$

Write as an algebraic expression. Then simplify the expression.

13. The product of negative four and the sum of negative three and nine.

14. Three times the difference of fourteen and negative seven.

1. _____

2. _____

3. _____

4. _____

5. _____

6. _____

7. _____

8. _____

9. _____

10. _____

11. _____

12. _____

13. _____

14. _____

Simplify:

15. $-2(-3)(-4) - (-2)(-1)(-5)$ **15.** _____

16. $-\dfrac{1}{15} \div \dfrac{3}{5} - \left(-\dfrac{1}{2} \cdot \dfrac{5}{9}\right)$ **16.** _____

17. $6.2(-1.2) \div (-4 + 2^2)$ **17.** _____

Additional Exercises 1.7
Form III

Name_____

Date_____

Match the expression with the correct answer.

1. $(-4)(-5)-(-6)(-8)$ **a.** 5

2. $(-4)[(-5)-(-6)]-8$ **b.** -12

3. $(-4-5)-(-6-8)$ **c.** -212

4. $-4|-5-(-6)(-8)|$ **d.** -28

1. _____
2. _____
3. _____
4. _____

Simplify each expression..

5. $\left(-\dfrac{1}{2}\right)^2 \div \dfrac{5}{6} \cdot (-4)^2\left(-\dfrac{3}{4}\right)$

5. _____

6. $\left)\ \dfrac{-5^2 \div (-2-3)}{-3\left|-5^2\right|}\right.$

6. _____

7. $-1.3|-3.3+4(-5.1)|+(-0.2)^3$

7. _____

8. $-\dfrac{1}{16}\left(\dfrac{8}{3}\right)\left(-\dfrac{2}{9}\right)+\left(-\dfrac{2}{3}\right)^3$

8. _____

Write each as an algebraic expression. Then simplify the expression.

9. The quotient of -15 and three times -2, divided by the reciprocal of $-\dfrac{2}{3}$.

9. _____

10. The quotient if the numerator of the fraction is negative two minus four squared, and the denominator is the product of three and negative 6.

10. _____

11. The product of $-\dfrac{4}{5}$ and the reciprocal of $-\dfrac{5}{8}$.

11. _____

12. Three times the difference of -16 and -23.

12. _____

13. One-fourth of $-\dfrac{2}{5}$ divided by $-\dfrac{5}{6}$

13. _____

Simplify

14. $\left|4-2^2\right| \cdot 3\dfrac{1}{5} \div \left(-4\dfrac{1}{3}\right)$

14. _____

15. $\dfrac{5(-2)+(7)(-4)}{(-2)(-6)+(-3)(-5)}$ 15. _____

16. $\dfrac{-15^2+3(-5)(-1)}{-3(-5)^2+5}$ 16. _____

Additional Exercises 1.8
Form I

Name_____

Date_____

Use the commutative property to rewrite each statement.

1. $-4 \cdot a$

2. $4 + y$

Use the associative property to rewrite each statement.

3. $(xy) \cdot z$

4. $3x + (y + 4)$

Use the commutative and associative properties to simplify each expression.

5. $(12 + x) + 5$

6. $-\dfrac{7}{8}\left(\dfrac{8}{7}r\right)$

Use the distributive property to write each expression without parentheses. Then simplify the results.

7. $2(3x - 7)$

8. $-5(x - 4)$

9. $-\dfrac{1}{2}(10 - 16z)$

10. $-4(x + 3) - 14$

Use the distributive property to write the sum as a product.

11. $3x - 3y$

Find the additive inverse or opposite of each of the following numbers.

12. $\dfrac{2}{7}$

13. $-|-5|$

1. _____

2. _____

3. _____

4. _____

5. _____

6. _____

7. _____

8. _____

9. _____

10. _____

11. _____

12. _____

13. _____

Additional Exercises 1.8 *(cont.)*

Name the multiplicative inverse or reciprocal of each of the following numbers.

14. $\dfrac{3}{14}$

14. _____

15. $-1\dfrac{2}{3}$

15. _____

Name the property illustrated by each true statement.

16. $\dfrac{1}{5} \cdot 1 = \dfrac{1}{5}$

16. _____

17. $0 \cdot \dfrac{1}{7} = 0$

17. _____

18. $(ab)c = a(bc)$

18. _____

19. $(5+3)+10 = 5+(3+10)$

19. _____

20. $\dfrac{1}{3}(6x+1) = \dfrac{1}{3} \cdot 6x + \dfrac{1}{3} \cdot 1$

20. _____

Additional Exercises 1.8
Form II

Name the properties illustrated by each statement.

1. $\left(-\dfrac{2}{3}\right)\left(-\dfrac{3}{2}\right)=1$

2. $x+0=x$

3. $\left(-\dfrac{2}{3}\right)\left(\dfrac{3}{4}\right)=\left(\dfrac{3}{4}\right)\left(-\dfrac{2}{3}\right)$

4. $2(-3)+4=4+2(-3)$

5. $2(-3)+4=-3(2)+4$

Use the distributive property to write each expression without parentheses. Then simplify the result, if possible.

6. $-\dfrac{1}{2}(3x+2)$

7. $-4(x-3y)$

8. $-(x-y+z)-y$

9. $\dfrac{1}{3}(9x-12)+4$

10. $-12(x-4)-18$

11. $-(x-3y)+3(x+2y)$

12. $-5(3x-y+7)+42$

13. $-\dfrac{3}{4}(4x-16)-\left(-\dfrac{1}{2}\right)$

14. $1.7(-0.1x-0.3)+(-5.4)$

15. $-(-x-2)-5$

1. _____

2. _____

3. _____

4. _____

5. _____

6. _____

7. _____

8. _____

9. _____

10. _____

11. _____

12. _____

13. _____

14. _____

15. _____

Name the properties illustrated by each true statement.

16. $5 \cdot \dfrac{1}{5} = 1$

                                             16. _____

17. $-7.1(3 + 2y) = -7.1(2y + 3)$

                                             17. _____

18. $\dfrac{1}{5} \cdot 0 = 0$

                                             18. _____

19. $7 + 0 = 7$

                                             19. _____

20. $\dfrac{1}{2}(x + 6) = \dfrac{1}{2} \cdot x + \dfrac{1}{2} \cdot 6$

                                             20. _____

Additional Exercises 1.8
Form III

Name _____

Date _____

Name the property illustrated by each step.

1. a. $(\triangle + \blacktriangleleft) + \text{✱} = \text{✱} + (\triangle + \blacktriangleleft)$

    b. $= \text{✱} + (\blacktriangleleft + \triangle)$

    c. $= (\text{✱} + \blacktriangleleft) + \triangle$

2. a. $(\triangle \cdot \blacktriangleleft) \cdot \text{✱} = (\blacktriangleleft \cdot \triangle) \cdot \text{✱}$

    b. $= \blacktriangleleft \cdot (\triangle \cdot \text{✱})$

    c. $= \blacktriangleleft \cdot (\text{✱} \cdot \triangle)$

1a. _____

  b. _____

  c. _____

2a. _____

  b. _____

  c. _____

Decide whether each statement is true or false.

3. The reciprocal of $\dfrac{x}{y}$ is $-\dfrac{x}{y}$

4. The opposite of $\dfrac{3}{z}$ is $\dfrac{-3}{z}$

5. $-5(x - 2y) = -5x - 10y$

6. Two numbers are called multiplicative inverses if their sum is zero.

7. The identity for multiplication is one.

3. _____

4. _____

5. _____

6. _____

7. _____

Use the distributive property to rewrite each expression without parentheses. Then simplify, if possible.

8. $-5(x - 2y + 3) - (-15)$

9. $\dfrac{3}{5}\left(-\dfrac{1}{3}a + 1\right) + \left(-\dfrac{7}{5}\right)$

10. $-(x + 2y - 7) + 14$

11. $-4(-2x - 2y + 3) - (-9)$

12. $-4\triangle \cdot (3\blacktriangleleft - 2\text{✱})$

8. _____

9. _____

10. _____

11. _____

12. _____

13. $-\dfrac{2}{13}\left(-\dfrac{13}{2}x+\dfrac{13}{14}\right)-\dfrac{5}{7}$

14. $4\dfrac{1}{5}\left(-\dfrac{2}{7}x+\dfrac{1}{21}\right)$

15. $\dfrac{1}{5}+0(-14x+8)$

13. _____

14. _____

15. _____

Additional Exercises 2.1
Form I

1. Identify the numerical coefficient in the following term:
   $-x^2 y$

2. Indicate whether the terms in the following list are like or unlike: $30a^2b,\ -6a^2b$

Simplify each expression by combining any like terms.

3. $12k + 4k$

4. $9y - 16y + 2y$

5. $15x - 4 - 5x + 17$

6. $2.8w - 0.8 - 1.9w - 1.2$

Simplify each expression. Use the distributive property to remove any parentheses.

7. $10(y + 8)$

8. $-5(x + 7) - 5(x + 7)$

9. $-(4m^2 - n + 7)$

10. $-6(3x - 6y - 4)$

Remove the parentheses and simplify each expression.

11. $8(x - 5) + 12$

12. $-7(2y - 6) + 20y$

13. $4(3x - 2) - 3(x - 7))$

14. $0.8(m + 4) - 0.3m$

Write each of the following as an algebraic expression. Simplify if possible.

15. Add $5x - 12$ to $7x + 4$

16. Subtract $4m - 7$ from $16m - 3$

1. _____

2. _____

3. _____

4. _____

5. _____

6. _____

7. _____

8. _____

9. _____

10. _____

11. _____

12. _____

13. _____

14. _____

15. _____

16 _____

Write each of the following phrases as an algebraic expression and simplify if possible. Let x represent the unknown number.

17. Five times a number decreased by eleven

18. The sum of −6 and 8 times a number, subtracted from 7 times the number

19. Six times the sum of a number and 9, added to 4 times the number

20. Express the perimeter of a triangle if the three sides are represented by $(3x-8)$ cm, $(2x-9)$ cm, and 7cm.

17. _____

18. _____

19. _____

20. _____

Additional Exercises 2.1
Form II

Name_____

Date_____

Simplify each expression by combining any like terms.

1. $\quad 4x - 7 + 2x - 15$

2. $\quad -(6x + 2y - 3)$

3 $\quad (24y - 7) - (5y - 17)$

4 $5(3x - 2) - 2(x - 9)$

Simplify each expression. Use the distributive property to remove any parentheses and simplify each expression.

5 $\quad -3(y - 3) + 6(y - 8)$

6 $\quad -5(2x - 1) - 10(x + \frac{1}{2})$

7 $\quad -(4m^2 - n + 7) - (-2m^2 + 4n + 1)$

8 $\quad 3(-5x^2 + 2y^3 - 5x)$

Remove the parentheses and simplify each expression.

9. $\quad 8(x - 5) + 2(4x + 3)$

10. $-6(-2y - 6) + 2(4y - 16)$

11. $-2(x - 14) + 5(x + 30)$

12. $0.5(x - 3) - 0.3(x + 5)$

Write each of the following as an algebraic expression. Simplify if possible.

13. Subtract $x - 15$ from the sum of $2x - 8$ and $-3(-x + 2)$

14. Subtract $6b - 3$ from $3b - 15$

1. _____

2. _____

3. _____

4. _____

5. _____

6. _____

7. _____

8. _____

9. _____

10. _____

11. _____

12. _____

13. _____

14. _____

Additional Exercises 2.1 *(cont.)*

Find the perimeter of the following geometrid figures.

15.

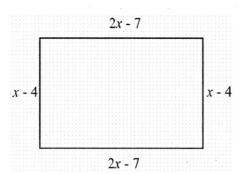

15. _____

16.

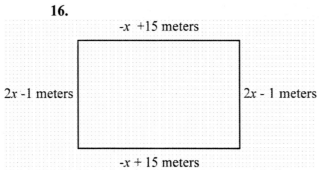

16. _____

17

3x meters $\diagup\diagdown$ (2x - 5) meters

(5x + 1) meters

17. _____

18.

$\frac{1}{5}x - \frac{3}{4}$

$\frac{3}{4}x + \frac{2}{3}$ $\frac{3}{4}x + \frac{2}{3}$

$\frac{1}{5}x - \frac{3}{4}$

18. _____

Additional Exercises 2.1
Form III

Name_____

Date_____

Simplify by removing parentheses when necessary using the distributive property, and then combine like terms.

1. $-x^2y - 3y + 3x^2y - 6 + 12y$

2. $30a^2b + 25ab^2 - 6a^2b - 19ab^2$

3. $-12(x - 2y) + 24(y - x)$

4. $\dfrac{1}{3}(9x^2 + 27x - 18) - \dfrac{1}{5}(15x^2 + 25x - 30)$

5. $\dfrac{1}{3}(4x^2 - 2x + 1) - \dfrac{1}{4}(5x^2 + 11x + 1)$

6. $5.1(w - 0.8) - 1.9(w - 1.2)$

7. $10(y + 8)$

8. $-5(x + 7) - 5(x + 7)$

9. $-(4m^2 - n + 7) + 3(m^2 - n + 7)$

10. $-6(3x - 6) + 5(x - 9) - 2(3x + 5)$

11. $-\dfrac{1}{4}(y - 6) + \dfrac{1}{3}(y + 2)$

12. $-0.5(y + 0.6) - 0.2(2y - 0.8)$

13. $4(3x^2 + 7x - 2) - 3(x^2 - 4x - 7))$

14. $0.3(m + 0.2) - 0.3m - 6$

Write each of the following as an algebraic expression. Then simplify, if possible.

15. Add $x^2 - 8x + 1$ to $x^2 - 2x - 6$

16. Subtract $2x^2 - 3x + 1$ from $5x^2 + x + 4$

1. _____

2. _____

3. _____

4. _____

5. _____

6. _____

7. _____

8. _____

9. _____

10. _____

11. _____

12. _____

13. _____

14. _____

15. _____

16 _____

Additional Exercises 2.1 *(cont.)*

Name_____

Write each of the following phrases as an algebraic expression and simplify if possible. Let x represent the unknown number.

17. Five times the sum of a number and 2 decreased by eleven times the difference of a number and 7

17. _____

18. The product of negative three times the difference of the number and 14, added to twice the product of 2 and the sum of the number and 1.

18. _____

19. _____

19. Negative two times the difference of a number and 1, added to 5 times the number

20. _____

20. The perimeter of a polygon if the five sides are represented by $(x+3)$ cm, $(x-14)$ cm, 7cm, and two sides that are both $(3x+2)$.

Additional Exercises 2.2
Form I

Name_____

Date_____

1.   Is 14 a solution to $9(x-4)=10(x-5)$?

1. _____

Solve each equation.

2. $x+8=12$

2. _____

3. $y-14=12$

3. _____

4. $-x+0.8=1.2$

4. _____

5. $\dfrac{5}{8}+k=\dfrac{1}{2}$

5. _____

6. $13x-11=14x$

6. _____

7. $3x+1=2x-8$

7. _____

8. $3x-2=2x+7$

8. _____

9. $14x-1=13x-8$

9. _____

10. $3x-5+4x=8x-8$

10. _____

11. $-x+1-2x=-4x-8$

11. _____

12. $9y-\dfrac{1}{5}=8y+\dfrac{2}{5}$

12. _____

13. $1-(3x-4)=-2x+5$

13. _____

14. $4(x-5)=3x+5$

14. _____

15. $-\dfrac{1}{2}(2x-10)=-2x+4$

15. _____

16. $-(x-5)=-2x-3$

16. _____

17. $7y-\dfrac{1}{4}=6y+\dfrac{2}{5}$

17. _____

18. Two angles have a sum of 150°. If one angle is x°, express the other angle in terms of x°.

18. _____

19. A 15-foot board is cut into two pieces. If one piece is x feet long, express the other length in terms of x.

19. _____

20. From Charlotte, it is 15 more miles to Lincolnton than it is to Gastonia. If it is m miles to Gastonia, express the distance to Lincolnton in terms of m.

20. _____

Additional Exercises 2.2
Form II

1. Is 0 a solution to $9(x+4) = -8(x-5)-4$?

1. _____

Solve each equation.

2. $x + \dfrac{5}{6} = 2x - \dfrac{1}{4}$

2. _____

3. $-(y-14) = 6$

3. _____

4. $4x - 0.5 = 3x - 0.2$

4. _____

5. $-3(\dfrac{1}{5}+k) = -2(k+1)$

5. _____

6. $-12x - 11 = 25 - 11(x+1)$

6. _____

7. $3x + 1 = 2x - 9$

7. _____

8. $3x - 2 = 2x + 13$

8. _____

9. $5x + 9 = 4x - 10$

9. _____

10. $x - 2 + 4x = 6x - 9$

10. _____

11. $-3x + 7 + x = -3x - 9$

11. _____

12. $0.7y - 0.25 = -0.3y + 0.25$

12. _____

13. $\dfrac{1}{3} - \dfrac{2}{3}(3x-4) = -3x + 5$

13. _____

14. $-2(-x+1) = x + 5$

14. _____

15. $-\dfrac{1}{5}(10x-15) = -x - 9$

15. _____

16. $-6(x-1) = -5x - 3$

16. _____

17. $-7y - \dfrac{1}{5} = -8y + \dfrac{2}{5}$

17. _____

Name_____

18. Two angles have a sum of 90°. If one angle is $(x-3)°$ express the other angle in terms of x°.

19. A 40-foot board is cut into three pieces. If two piece is are x feet long, express the other length in terms of x.

20. The walking trail splits after 2 miles. One trail goes through the woods and is twice as long as the other trail which goes along the waterfront. The trails meet again so a person can walk through the woods going out, and return by walking along the lake from on the way back to the beginning. If x is the number of miles through along the lakefront, how far will a person walk if this person walks along the lake front on the way out, and then through the woods on the way back to the beginning. How far has this person walked?

18. _____

19. _____

20. _____

Additional Exercises 2.2
Form III

Solve each equation.

1. $-x + \dfrac{2}{5} = -2x + \dfrac{3}{4}$

2. $-2(y - 0.5) = -3(y - 0.1)$

3. $-2x + 0.8 = -3x + 1.2$

4. $7(k + 1) = 6(k - 3)$

5. $-3(x - 1) = -4(x - 3)$

6. $3(x + 1) = 2(x - 8)$

7. $5x + 2 = 4(x + 7)$

8. $4(x - 1) - (x - 3) = 2(x - 5)$

9. $-(x - 5) + (x - 1) = x - 8$

10. $-5(x - 4) - x = -7x - 1$

11. $5\left(y - \dfrac{1}{5}\right) = 4\left(y + \dfrac{2}{5}\right)$

12. $3x - (x - 4) = x - 4$

13. $4(x - 5) - (x - 3) = 2(x - 1)$

14. $-(3x - 12) = -2x + 4$

15. $-(x - 5) + (x + 5) = -(x - 3)$

16. $9y - \dfrac{1}{4} = 8y + \dfrac{1}{10}$

17. $-3(x - 4) + 5(x - 12) = x - 15$

1. _____

2. _____

3. _____

4. _____

5. _____

6. _____

7. _____

8. _____

9. _____

10. _____

11. _____

12. _____

13. _____

14. _____

15. _____

16. _____

17. _____

18. The sum of the angles of a triangle is 180°. If one angle measures $y°$, and a second angle measures $(5y+3)°$ express the measure of the third angle in terms of y. Simplify the expression.

18. _____

19. A 15-foot board is cut into three pieces. If one piece is x feet long, the second piece is $(x + 3)$ feet long, express the third length in terms of x. Simplify the expression.

19. _____

20. Write the equation for the following word problem, and then solve the equation. If negative five times the sum of a number and one is added to four times the difference of twice times a number and three, the result is eight less than twice the sum of the number and two.

20. _____

Additional Exercises 2.3
Form I

Name_____

Date_____

1. If an equation contains fractions, multiply both sides by the _____ to clear the equation of fractions.

1. _____

Solve each equation.

2. $-8x = -24$

2. _____

3. _____

3. $-x = 0$

4. $\dfrac{3}{4}x = -12$

4. _____

5. $\dfrac{1}{5}x = \dfrac{1}{3}$

5. _____

6. $5x - 1 = 14$

6. _____

7. $-x + 3 = -23$

7. _____

8. $\dfrac{4}{5}y - \dfrac{1}{3} = \dfrac{2}{5}$

8. _____

9. $\dfrac{x}{5} - 2 = 4$

9. _____

10. $\dfrac{1}{3}(3x - 2) = \dfrac{4}{5}$

10. _____

11. $\dfrac{3}{8}y - \dfrac{1}{2} = \dfrac{3}{4}$

11. _____

12. _____

12. $2z - 5 = -2x - 15$

13. _____

13. $5a - 1 = -2a + 13$

14. $-\dfrac{5}{3}x = 25$

14. _____

15. $9y + 15 = 6y - 3$

15. _____

16. $10(y + 2) = 2y - 4$

16. _____

17. $\dfrac{7}{6}x - 4 = 10$

17. _____

18. $-2(x - 10) = -(1 + 5x)$

18. _____

Name_____

19. $2(y-3) = 6(6-4y)$

19. _____

20. The perimeter of a geometric figure is the sum of the lengths of its sides. If the perimeter of a trapezoid is 29 cm, and the sides are $2x, x, (2x+5),$ and $x \; cm$, find the length of each side.

20. _____

Additional Exercises 2.3
Form II

Name _____

Date _____

Solve each equation.

1. $12x - 7 = 8 + 15x$

2. $-3(4x - 7) = -10x$

3. $5(3n - 1) = (7n + 3) + 8$

4. $6(2x + 5) - 5(3x - 4) = -1$

5. $7(4 - 2x) + 3(8x) = 2$

6. $-4(x - 5) - 11 = 17$

7. $8x + 14 = 3x - 6$

8. $-(9a + 1) - a = 11 + 3a$

9. $\dfrac{4}{9}x - \dfrac{2}{3} = \dfrac{2}{9}$

10. $\dfrac{3}{8}y - 10 = y$

11. $\dfrac{x}{3} - 4 = \dfrac{x}{5} - 6$

12. $\dfrac{4(k - 3)}{6} = \dfrac{2(k - 5)}{4}$

13. $0.76x + 0.52(80) = 0.32(168)$

14. $0.44(y - 200) + 0.02y = 0.12y + 0.07(200)$

15. $\dfrac{10(y + 2)}{7} = 2y - 4$

16. $\dfrac{5}{6}x - \dfrac{2}{3} = \dfrac{1}{2}$

17. $8(5x - 10) = 2(5 + 10x)$

18. $-x - \dfrac{3}{4} = x + \dfrac{1}{3} + \dfrac{5}{8}$

1. _____

2. _____

3. _____

4. _____

5. _____

6. _____

7. _____

8. _____

9. _____

10. _____

11. _____

12. _____

13. _____

14. _____

15. _____

16. _____

17. _____

18. _____

19. $9(4y-3)=6(6y-4)-3$

20. The perimeter of a triangle is the sum of the lengths of its sides. If the perimeter of a triangle is 36 cm, and the sides are $3x$, x, and $(2x+6)$ cm, find the length of each side.

19. _____

20. _____

Additional Exercises 2.3
Form II

Solve each equation.

1. $2x - 7 - 3x + 1 = -6 + 5x$

2. $-\dfrac{1}{2}(4x - 7) = -8x$

3. $-15x - 13 = -11x - 9$

4. $-(-2x + 5) - 2(3x - 4) = -14$

5. $5 - (4 - 2x) + 3(8x) = 2$

6. $-3(x - 2) = 30$

7. $8(x + 1) - 4 = 3(x - 6)$

8. $-(a - 1) - a = 11 - a$

9. $\dfrac{4}{9}x - \dfrac{2}{3} = \dfrac{2}{9}$

10. $\dfrac{1}{4}(y - 8) = y$

11. $\dfrac{x}{2} - 4 = x - 6$

12. $4(k - 3) + (k - 3) = 2(k - 5)$

13. $0.22x + 0.11(80) = 0.32(x - 1)$

14. $0.04(y - 200) + 0.02y = -0.02y$

15. $\dfrac{5(y - 2)}{4} + 3y = \dfrac{2y - 4}{3}$

16. $\dfrac{5}{6}x - \dfrac{2}{3} = \dfrac{1}{2}x - \dfrac{3}{4}$

17. $3(x - 4) - 5x = -2(1 + x) + x$

1. _____

2. _____

3. _____

4. _____

5. _____

6. _____

7. _____

8. _____

9. _____

10. _____

11. _____

12. _____

13. _____

14. _____

15. _____

16. _____

17. _____

18. $-5x+3-2(x-4)=-4(x+3)-1$

18. _____

19. $t-3t=15+t-4t$

19. _____

20. Find the sum of five consecutive integers if the first is x.

20. _____

Additional Exercises 2.4
Form I

Name _____

Date _____

Solve each equation.

1. $-5y + 15 = -3(y - 10)$

2. $-3(4x - 2) = -10x$

3. $4 - 3(1 + x) = -4x - 9$

4. $-(-2x + 5) - 2(3x - 4) = -13$

5. $5 - (4 - 2x) + 3(8x) = 2$

6. $3(x + 5) = 3x - 15$

7. $4(x + 1) - 4 = 3(x - 6) + x + 18$

8. $-6(1 - x) = 6x - 6$

9. $3(x - 1) = -3$

10. $-5(y - 8) - 2(y - 1) - 1 = 3y - 9$

11. $\dfrac{x}{2} - 4 = \dfrac{1}{2}x - 6$

12. $k - 3 + 3(k - 2) = 2(2k - 5)$

13. $-3(x + \dfrac{2}{3}) + 5(x - \dfrac{1}{2}) = -2(x + \dfrac{3}{4})$

14. $2x - (x - 2) = 30 + x$

15. $-(a - 11) - a = 11 - a$

16. $\dfrac{x}{2} - 4 = \dfrac{x}{4} - 2$

17. $5(4x + 3) = 10(2x + 3) - 15$

1. _____

2. _____

3. _____

4. _____

5. _____

6. _____

7. _____

8. _____

9. _____

10. _____

11. _____

12. _____

13. _____

14. _____

15. _____

16. _____

17. _____

Answer True or False

18. Every linear equation has at least one solution.

18. _____

19. An equation whose solution is all real numbers is also called an identity.

19. _____

20. If an equation has no solution, there are several words or symbols we can use to indicate that result. Name some of these.

20. _____

Additional Exercises 2.4
Form II

Name_____

Date_____

Solve each equation.

1. $9 - \dfrac{3}{2}x = 15x - 24$

2. $x + \dfrac{3}{5} = \dfrac{5}{3}x$

3. $\dfrac{3-y}{2} = \dfrac{y+5}{3}$

4. $-2(x-1) + (x-4) = -x - 14$

5. $15 - 3x + 4(x - 20) = x + 12$

6. $-2(x-1) = -2x + 2$

7. $\dfrac{1}{7}x + \dfrac{1}{5} = \dfrac{1}{5}x - \dfrac{1}{7}$

8. $-\dfrac{1}{2}(3x + 2) = \dfrac{3(-x-6)}{2}$

9. $4a - 2(2a + 3) = -6$

10. $-z + 3(z - 4) = 4(z - 1)$

11. $0.5h - 2.2 = 0.25(h + 1.1)$

12. $\dfrac{x}{3} + 2 = x - \dfrac{2}{3}(x - 3)$

13. $3(3 + x) - 10 = 4x - (1 + x)$

14. $6(1 - x) + 2 = 8 - 5x$

15. $\dfrac{2}{3}x - \dfrac{1}{4} = x$

16. $\dfrac{3x}{2} + 1 = \dfrac{3x}{4} - 2$

17. $\dfrac{5(1 - z)}{3} = -z$

1. _____

2. _____

3. _____

4. _____

5. _____

6. _____

7. _____

8. _____

9. _____

10. _____

11. _____

12. _____

13. _____

14. _____

15. _____

16. _____

17. _____

Additional Exercises 2.4 *(cont.)*

Name_____

In the following equations, the answers are one of the following: all real numbers, no solution, or 0. In the answer blank, write the correct choice.

18. $-3(x-2)+6=2-3(x-4)$

19. $0.4(1-3x)=0.6(x+3)-1.2$.

20. $\dfrac{3}{4}(\dfrac{4}{3}x-8)=x+1$

18. _____

19. _____

20. _____

Additional Exercises 2.4
Form III

Solve each equation.

1. $\dfrac{2x-1}{6}+x=\dfrac{2x+1}{2}+3$

2. $0.05y+0.13(6000-6y)=0.07y$

3. $3(x-1)+x=4(x-(-1))-7$

4. $0.09y+0.14(300-y)=0.2y$

5. $\dfrac{x+4}{4}-\dfrac{3x-12}{10}=1$

6. $\dfrac{x+2}{2}-\dfrac{5x-12}{6}=1$

7. $\dfrac{x}{5}=\dfrac{x}{6}+\dfrac{3}{5}$

8. $x-13.9=-19.1+x$

9. $\dfrac{x+6}{3}+\dfrac{x-2}{6}=\dfrac{13}{6}$

10. $-5(x-1)+21=3x-8(x-4)$

11. $2x+8+7x+9=6x+3x+14$

12. $7(x+2)+5=7x+2$

13. $3(x-4)+x=4(x-2)-4$

14. $-7x+2(-3x-5)=-16-7x$

15. $-\dfrac{3}{4}x+\dfrac{1}{5}=\dfrac{x}{-8}+\dfrac{1}{10}$

16. $-4s+63+=-2(2s-20)$

17. $-4.9=y+7.9$

1. _____

2. _____

3. _____

4. _____

5. _____

6. _____

7. _____

8. _____

9. _____

10. _____

11. _____

12. _____

13. _____

14. _____

15. _____

16. _____

17. _____

18. $-10.3t + 1.2 = -74.4 - 1.9t$

19. $-\dfrac{1}{4}(x+8) - \dfrac{1}{8}(x-8) = x + 7$

20. $-\dfrac{1}{2}(x-6) + \dfrac{1}{3}(x+3) = x - 7$

18. _____

19. _____

20. _____

Additional Exercises 2.5
Form I

Name _____

Date _____

Write an equation for each example and then solve the equation. Make sure that you answer the question asked.

1. The sum of twice a number and 10 is equals 180. Find the number.

2. A 97-foot rope is cut into two pieces so that the longer piece is 5 feet more than three times the smaller piece. Find the lengths of both pieces.

3. The sum of five times a number and 4 is equal to four times the sum of a number and 2. Find the number.

4. If a number is divided by 4,, the result is 15. What is the number?

5. A number subtracted from 28 is equal to four more than three times a number. Find the number.

6. A 21-foot log must be cut into two pieces so that the larger piece is three feet longer than the shorter piece.

7. Sue makes twice as much money as Tom. If the total of their salaries is $78,000, find the salary of each.

8. Peggy Fleming won two more U.S. Figure Skating Championships than Dorothy Hamill. If the total championship wins for both are 8, find how many each won.

9. A 30-inch board is to be cut into two pieces so the second piece is twice as long as the first piece. Find the length of the two pieces.

10. A carpenter gave an estimate of $980 to build a cover over a patio. His hourly rate is $28 and he expects to need $560 in materials. How many hours does he expect the job to take?

11. A television repair technician charges $65 to make a in house visit, and $40 as an hourly rate. If the materials needed to repair the television total $89, and it takes him an hour to finish the repair, find the total cost.

1. _____

2. _____

3. _____

4. _____

5. _____

6. _____

7. _____

8. _____

9. _____

10. _____

11. _____

12. A mechanic charged $239 to repair a car, including $107 in parts and 6 hours of labor. How much does she charge per hour for labor?

12. _____

13. Two consecutive integers have a sum of 59. Find the integers.

13. _____

14. Two angles are supplementary if their sum is 180°. One angle measures four times the measure of an angle supplementary to it. Find the measure of the angle.

14. _____

15. Two angles are complementary. The second angle is six less than three times the first. Find the two angles.

15. _____

16. The measures of the angles of a triangle are 3 consecutive integers. Find the measures of the three angles.

16. _____

17. The measures of the angles of a trapezoid are 4 consecutive odd integers. Find the integers.

17. _____

18. Find three consecutive even integers whose sum is negative 84.

18. _____

19. Karl's license plate is four consecutive integers with a sum of 26. What is his license plate number?

19. _____

20. The sum of the angles of any four-sided polygon is 360°. If the measure of two of the angles is $x°$ and two of the angles are $5x°$ find the measure of each angle.

20. _____

Additional Exercises 2.5
Form II

Write an equation for each example and then solve the equation and answer the question.

1. Four times a number subtracted from 28 is seven less than the number. Find the number.

2. The sum of three consecutive even integers is 276. Find the integers.

3. The sum of one-fourth a number and 17 is equal to the sum of one-fifth the number and 18. Find the number.

4. The sum of the three times the smaller of two consecutive odd integers and four times the larger is 113. Find the integers.

5. Find three consecutive even integers such that one-fourth of the first plus one-seventh of the second plus one-half of the third is 13. Find the integers.

6. Find the measure of two supplementary angles such that one angle is four-fifths as large as the other.

7. A 67-inch piece of string is cut into three pieces such that the second piece is three as large as the first, and the third piece is four more than five times as large as the first. Find the lengths of the three pieces of string.

8 Billie-Jean King won three less single titles at Wimbledon than Martina Navratilova. If the sum of their single wins was fifteen, how many singles did each of these women win at Wimbledon?

9 Five sevenths of a number is one-tenth. Find the number.

10. The measures of the angles of a particular triangle are such that the second angle is 6 degrees less than the first, and the third angle is four times as large as the first. Find the measure of all three angles.

11. One-half of the integer is eight more than the integer. Find this integer.

1. _____

2. _____

3. _____

4. _____

5. _____

6. _____

7. _____

8. _____

9. _____

10. _____

11. _____

Name_____

12. If six is subtracted from eight times a number, the result is the sum of 10 times the number and twenty.

12. _____

13. If a number is subtracted from seven, the result is three times the difference of the number and 7.

13. _____

14. Find three consecutive integers such that the sum of five times the first, six times the second and seven times the third is 148.

14. _____

15. Find three consecutive even integers such that twice the first minus three times the second plus five times the third is 54.

15. _____

16. Find three consecutive even integers whose sum is zero.

16. _____

17. Find three consecutive odd integers such that if six times the first is subtracted from the sum of twice the second plus five times the third, the result is 53.

Find the perimeter of the following geometric figures.

17. _____

18. Rectangle has a perimeter of 98 inches. The width is two inches less that twice the width.

18. _____

19. Trapezoid has a perimeter of 63 meters. The two non-parallel sides have the same length; but the top base is twice as long as the side, and the bottom base is three times as long as the side. Find the length of each side.

19. _____

20. An isosceles triangle has two sides that have the same length. If a particular isosceles triangle has the two equal sides that are three more than twice the third side each, and the perimeter is 96 inches, find the length of each side.

20. _____

Additional Exercises 2.5
Form III

Name_____

Date_____

Write an equation for each example and then solve the equation
and answer the question.

1. The sum of $\frac{1}{5}$ of a number and $\frac{1}{7}$ of that number is equal

   to $\frac{1}{3}$ of the sum of that number and 1.

   1. _____

2. A 200-foot rope is cut into four pieces so that the four
   pieces are consecutive even integers. Find the lengths of
   all four pieces.

   2. _____

   3. _____

3. The sum of one-half of a certain number and one-fourth of
   the same number is equal to 180. Find the numbers

4. If a number is divided by 4 and then the result is added to
   five times the original number,, the result is 315. Find the
   original number?

   4. _____

5. Find a number such that when five less than three times
   the number is added to the number, the result is 59.

   5. _____

6. A 95-inch piece of framing is cut into five pieces such that
   the third piece is 1 inch less than the two identical pieces.
   A fourth piece is five less than twice the length of the first
   and second piece, and the fifth piece is five inches more
   than three times the length of the first and second pieces.
   Find the length of each piece.

   6. _____

7. The length of a rectangle is 10 centimeters greater than the
   width. Find the length and width of the rectangle if the
   perimeter is 168 centimeters.

   7. _____

8. During the last soccer game, the Pythons lost by one goal.
   If Katie scored twice as many goals as Austin for the
   Pythons, and the winning team scored 10 points, find the
   number of points scored by Austin and Katie.

   8. _____

9. Three consecutive odd integers exist such that one third of
   the smallest plus twice the second plus one fifth of the
   third is 134. Find the integers.

   9. _____

10. The total bill for the flooring and sub-flooring in the
    sunroom was $850. If Mr. Helms charged $50 an hour for
    four hours, much did the material cost for the job?

    10. _____

11. Garrett mows the grass and works in the garden for his grandparents to make enough money to put gas in his car. If he is paid by the hour, and works for 4 hours on both Friday and Saturday, uses $55 to fill up his truck, and has enough money left to buy two tickets to the concert at $12.50 each, how much was he paid per hour?

11. _____

12. The soccer field where Nicholas plays is a rectangular field with a perimeter of 78 yards. If the length of the field is 15 yards more than the width, find the dimensions of the field. Note: The dimensions are described by stating the length of the length and the width.

12. _____

13. Two angles are supplementary if their sum is 180°. One angle measures one-third the measure of an angle supplementary to it. Find the measure of the angle.

13. _____

14. Two angles are complementary. The second angle is fifteen more than twice the measure of the first. Find the two angles.

14. _____

15. Find three consecutive even integers such that one-tenth of the first, plus one half of the second, plus one-forth of the third is equal to 70..

15. _____

Additional Exercises 2.6
Form I

Name_____

Date_____

Substitute the given values into the formula and solve for the unknown variable.

1. $A = bh$ when $A = 450$ and $b = 25$

2. $d = rt$ when $d = 350$ and $t = 7$

3. $V = lwh$ when $V = 504$, $l = 7$, $h = 9$.

4. $A = \frac{1}{2}h(B + b)$ when $A = 280$, $B = 15$, and $b = 13$

5. $A = \frac{1}{2}h(B + b)$ when $A = 182$, $B = 15$, and $b = 11$

6. $m = \frac{y_2 - y_1}{x_2 - x_1}$ when $y_2 = 7$, $y_1 = -3$, $x_2 = 2$, and $x_1 = 5$

7. $m = \frac{y_2 - y_1}{x_2 - x_1}$ when $y_2 = -15$, $y_1 = 5$, $x_2 = 3$, and $x_1 = 8$

8. $m = \frac{y_2 - y_1}{x_2 - x_1}$ when $y_2 = 3$, $y_1 = 3$, $x_2 = 7$, and $x_1 = -2$

9. $m = \frac{y_2 - y_1}{x_2 - x_1}$ when $y_2 = 7$, $y_1 = -2$, $x_2 = 3$, and $x_1 = 3$

Solve.

10. The great room has a length of 26 feet and width of 20 feet. For the purpose of purchasing carpet and wallpaper border, what is the perimeter and area of the great room? Which purchase has to do with the perimeter of the room?

11. It is 120 miles from Jeannie's house just outside Meadville, Pennsylvania to the airport in Pittsburgh, Pennsylvania. How long should it take Jeannie to drive to the airport if she averages driving 50 miles per hour on the trip?

12. The formula $F = \frac{9}{5}C + 32$ can be used to convert temperatures in degrees Celsius to degree Fahrenheit. Convert London's 20° C average daily high in June to Fahrenheit.

1. _____

2. _____

3. _____

4. _____

5. _____

6. _____

7. _____

8. _____

9. _____

10. _____

11. _____

12. _____

Solve each formula of the specified variable

    13. $A = lw$ for w

    14. $V = lwh$ for w

    15. $.c = a + 2b$ for a

    16. $c = a + 2b$ for b

    17. $A = \dfrac{1}{2}bh$ for h

    18. $2x + y = 5$ for y

    19. $4x - 2y = 8$ for y

    20.. $3x - 2y = 6$ for y

13. _____

14. _____

15. _____

16. _____

17. _____

18. _____

19. _____

20. _____

Additional Exercises 2.6
Form II

Name_____

Date_____

Substitute the given values into the formula and solve for the unknown variable.

1. $m = \dfrac{y_2 - y_1}{x_2 - x_1}$ when $m = \dfrac{1}{3}$, $y_1 = 3$, $x_2 = 7$, and $x_1 = -2$

2. $V = \dfrac{1}{3}\pi r^2 h$ when $V = 47.1$ and $r = 3$ (Use 3.14 for π.)

3. $V = \dfrac{4}{3}\pi r^3$ when $r = 9$ (Use 3.14 for π.)

4. $A = \dfrac{1}{2}h(B + b)$ when $A = 45.5$, $B = 8$, and $h = 7$

5. $I = PRT$ when $I = 1200$, $R = 4\%$, and $P = 10,000$

6. $y = mx + b$ when $y = 4$, $x = 9$, and $b = 2$

7. $V = \dfrac{1}{3}\pi r^2 h$ when $r = 5.5$, $h = 4.1$. (Use 3.14 for π.) Round to nearest hundredths place.

8. $S = 2\pi rh + 2\pi r^2$ when $r = 6$, $h = 10$ (Use 3.14 for π.)

Solve.

9. Convert 77° Fahrenheit to Celsius. Use the formula $C = \dfrac{5}{9}(F - 32)$.

10. Convert 55° Celsius to Fahrenheit. Use the formula $F = \dfrac{9}{5}C + 32$

11. A lawn is in the shape of a rectangle with a length of 100 ft and a width of 45 feet. How many whole bags of fertilizer must be purchased to cover the lawn if each bag covers 2000 square feet?

12. A family is planning their vacation to Myrtle Beach from their home just outside Charlotte, North Carolina., a distance of 240 miles. They plan to average 60 mph. How long will the trip take?

1. _____

2. _____

3. _____

4. _____

5. _____

6. _____

7. _____

8. _____

9. _____

10. _____

11. _____

12. _____

Additional Exercises 2.6 *(cont.)*

Name_____

Solve the following applications.

13. The perimeter of a pentagon is 130 centimeters. The side are x centimeters, $0.5x$ centimeters, $2x$ centimeters, and two side that are $1.5x$ centimeters. Find the length of each of the five sides.

13. _____

14. It is approximately 266 miles from San Antonio, Texas to Fort Worth Texas. If Carlos and his family leave Fort Worth at 4:30 am, at approximately what time will they arrive in San Antonio if they travel 50 miles per hour?

14. _____

Solve each formula for the specified variable.

15. _____

15. $P = a + b + c + d$ for d

16. $x - 7y = 14$ for y

16. _____

17.. $V = \dfrac{1}{3}Ah$ for A

17. _____

18. $S = 4lw + 2hw$ for l.

18. _____

19. $Ax + By = C$ for y.

19. _____

20. $Ax + By = C$ for x.

20. _____

Additional Exercises 2.6
Form III

Name_____

Date_____

Substitute the given values into the formula and solve for the unknown variable.

1. $V = \frac{1}{3}\pi r^2 h$ when $V = 188.4$ and $r = 6$ (Use 3.14 for π.)

2. $V = \frac{4}{3}\pi r^3$ when r = 15 (Use 3.14 for π.)

3. $m = \frac{y_2 - y_1}{x_2 - x_1}$ when $m = \frac{1}{2}$, $y_1 = 4, x_2 = 6$, and $x_1 = -8$.

Solve.

4. The area of a rectangle is 77 square inches. If the width is seven, find the length.

5. The area of a triangle is 120 square miles. If the height of this triangle is 15, find the length of the base.

6. Garrett received $4500 in simple interest after he deposited part of his inheritance in a savings account. If he left the money in the account for 3 years and had a 5% rate, how much was the original amount he deposited?

7. The perimeter of the certain triangle is 64 feet. If one side is x feet, the second side is $(3x + 1)$ feet, and the third side is $(4x - 9)$ feet, find the length of each side.

8. The average temperature recorded on Mars is $-63°$ Celsius. Convert this to Fahrenheit.

9. The normal body temperature is approximately 98.6° Fahrenheit. Convert this to Celsius temperature.

10. It takes one pound of grass seed for every 500 square feet of ground. A lawn measures 100 feet by 150 feet. If the grass is sold in five-pound bags, how many bags must be purchased to cover the lawn.

11. Bethany and Nicholas walk each day with their parents. They first walk 0.7 mile on along the street to the entrance to the park. Then it is 0.4 miles to the walking path. If they walk around the 0.5 mile track three times each day, what is the total distance they have walked when they get home assuming they follow the same path home?

1. _____

2. _____

3. _____

4. _____

5. _____

6. _____

7. _____

8. _____

9. _____

10. _____

11. _____

Additional Exercises 2.6 *(cont.)*

Solve the following applications.

12. If the length of the lawn is 15 meters longer than three times the width and the perimeter is 270 meters. Find the dimensions of the lawn.

13. A certain sized goldfish needs 1700 cubic centimeters of water. Find the maximum number of these goldfish you could put in a rectangular tank measuring 32 cm by 27 cm by 50 cm.

14. Find how many piranhas you can put in a cylindrical tank whose diameter is 4 feet and whose height is 1.25 feet if each piranha needs 1.5 cubic feet of water.

15. Which has more pizza, one 20-inch pizza or two 15-inch pizzas, if the size indicates the diameter of a round pizza?

16. When the space shuttle orbits 200 miles from the surface of the Earth, it is 4200 miles from the Earth's center. How far does the shuttle travel each time it circles the Earth at the distance? (Use 3.14 for π.)

Solve each formula for the specified variable.

17. $A = \dfrac{1}{2}bh$ for b.

18. $z = \dfrac{3}{4}w + 15$ for w

19. $x - y = -10$ for y

20. $V = \dfrac{1}{3}Ah$ for A

12. _____

13. _____

14. _____

15. _____

16. _____

17. _____

18. _____

19. _____

20. _____

Additional Exercises 2.7
Form I

Name_____

Date_____

Substitute the given values into the formula and solve for the unknown variable.

1. What number is 24% of 186?

2. What number is 77% of 952?

3. The number 404.4 is what percent of 674?

4. The number 8.5 is what percent of 25?

5. The number 42.4 is 53% of what number?

6. The number 13.8 is 92% of what number?

7. What number is 29% of 175?

8. The number 274.5 is 45% of what number?

9. The number 2450 is 35% of what number?

10. The number 140 is what percent of 350?

11. The number 67.2 is what percent of 560?

12. What number is 53% of 882?

Solve.

13. A recent celebration at a local restaurant cost $147.50 including tax. Find the total cost if a 15% tip is added to the cost.

14. The number of students at a local community college rose from 6,300 in 2004 to 8,505 in 2005. Find the percent increase.

15 Find the original price of a television if the sale price is $171.50 after a 30% discount.

16. Find last year's salary if, after a 6% pay raise, this year's salary is $40,280.

1. _____

2. _____

3. _____

4. _____

5. _____

6. _____

7. _____

8. _____

9. _____

10. _____

11. _____

12. _____

13. _____

14. _____

15. _____

16. _____

Solve.

17. Dempsey Candy & Nut Mix Company wants to make a
new mixture. How many pounds of Dempsey Mystery
Nut Mix worth $8 per pound should be added to 20
pounds of chocolate drops worth $5 per pound to get a
mixture worth $6 per pound? Complete the table and
solve.

17._____

	Number of pounds	Price Per Pound	Value
Mystery Nut Mix	x	$8.00	
Chocolates Drops	20	$5.00	
New Mixture		$6.00	

18. Homemade fudge can be made for $1.20 per pound and
sold for $4 per pound. Find the percent increase.

18._____

19. A student at Quinsigamond Community College sells used
electronic game systems to earn money for school. If she
purchased a game system and sold it for $54, which was a
35% profit, how much did she pay for the gaming system?

19._____

20._____

20. Target Department Store advertised a "Back-To-School"
sale with 30% off all computers. A computer system
originally sold for $990. Find the decrease in price and
the sale price.

Additional Exercises 2.7
Form II

Name_____

Date_____

Substitute the given values into the formula and solve for the unknown variable.

1. What number is 88% of 340?

2. What number is 15% of 315?

3. The number 209 is what percent of 950?

4. The number 211.2 is what percent of 320?

5. The number 3412.5 is 75% of what number?

6. The number 770 is 5% of what number?

1. _____

2. _____

3. _____

4. _____

5. _____

6. _____

Solve the following applications.

The circle graphs show sales of recorded music and music video in 2005. Use it to answer the following questions.

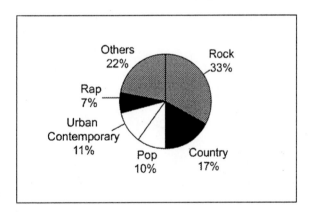

7. What percent of the recorded music sold was pop?

8. If $12 billion in recorded music was sold in 1995, what was the value of rock music sold?

9. If $12 billion in recorded music was sold in 1995, what was the value of rap music sold?

Solve.

7. _____

8. _____

9. _____

10. A popular clothing store advertised all coats reduced by 25%. If the price of a coat before the discount was $150, find the discount and new price.

11. The price for a pound of cheese rose from $1.70 per pound to $2.30 per pound. Find the percent of increase. Round to the nearest whole percent.

10. _____

11. _____

Name_____

Solve.

12. A recent dinner at a local restaurant cost $80.25 including tax. Find the total cost if a 15% tip is added to the cost.

13. Hosea's salary increased 8% this year. If his salary was $44,000, find his new salary.

14. Susanne received a 9% raise this year. Find her original salary if her new salary is $55590.

15. Find the raise and the old salary if, after a 6% pay raise, this year's salary is $53,000.

16. How many liters of a 20% salt solution must be added to 30 liters of a 15% solution to get a solution that is 18% salt?

17. Peanut Brittle can be made for $2.50 per pound and sold for $5.50 per pound. Find the percent increase.

18. The cost of a textbook rose from $110 to $150. Find the percent of increase rounded to the nearest percent.

19. Find the original price of a pair of jeans if the sale price is $56.25 after a 25% discount.

20. How much water should be added to 60 gallons of a solution that is 80% antifreeze in order to get a mixture that is 60% antifreeze?

12. _____

13. _____

14. _____

15. _____

16. _____

17. _____

18. _____

19. _____

20. _____

Additional Exercises 2.7
Form III

Substitute the given values into the formula and solve for the unknown variable.

1. What number is 120% of 86?

2. The number 650 is what percent of 130?

3. The number 600 is what percent of 400?

Solve the following applications.

4. A popular clothing store advertised all suits reduced by a certain percent. If the price of a suit before the discount was $400 and the price after the discount was $260, find the rate of discount and amount of discount.

5. The price for a gallon of gasoline rose from $1.80 to $3.10 per gallon. Find the rate of increase. Round to the nearest whole percent.

6. A recent wedding reception that included a sit-down meal at the club cost $55 per person with a invitation list of 200 people. If the club adds in a 20% gratuity and 7% tax (the gratuity is not taxed), find the total cost of the reception dinner.

7. The number of students at a local community college decreased from 5500 in 2005 to 4500 in 2006. Find the percent of decrease. Round to the nearest whole percent.

8. If Danielle had a really good review this year at the company where she is an accountant. This resulted in a $8250 raise. If her new salary is $74,250, find her original salary before the raise, and the percent of the raise she received.

9. After the Mooney's house had been on the market for 8 months, they decided that in order to sell the house, they would have to decrease the price of the house $13,650. This amount represented a 7% drop in price. What was the original asking price of their home, and what is the discounted price?

10. How many liters of a 3% saline solution must be added to an 8% saline solution to obtain 20 liters of a 6% saline solution?

1. _____

2. _____

3. _____

4. _____

5. _____

6. _____

7. _____

8. _____

9. _____

10. _____

Additional Exercises 2.7 *(cont.)*

Name_____

Solve.

11. Kohl's put their all of their bedding on a 30% sale. If Michelle's purchase of sheets, pillowcases, and comforter totals $360, find the amount after the 30% discount and 7% tax (figured after the discount).

11. _____

12. Walgreen's put all of their Halloween candy and decorations on sale November 1. Jennifer purchased many outdoor decorations which before the sale would have cost $170 before the sale for only $51. Find the rate of decrease.

12. _____

13. Explain in your own words how to find the rate of increase.

13. _____

14. Explain in your own words how to find the rate of decrease.

14. _____

15. How many cubic centimeters (cc) of a 30% antibiotic solution should be added 15 cc of a 70% antibiotic solution to get a 55% antibiotic solution?

15. _____

Additional Exercises 2.8
Form I

Complete the table.

		Number of Coins or Bills	Value of Coins or Bills (in dollars)
1.	Pennies	x	
2.	Dimes	y	
3.	Quarters	z	
4.	$5 bills	5x	
5.	$20 bills	(30 - x)	
6.	$100 bills	(25 – z)	

1. _____

2. _____

3. _____

4. _____

5. _____

6. _____

Substitute the given values into the formula and solve for the unknown variable.

7. A train traveling 120 mph east from Paris to passes the Midnight Special which was traveling the same direction at a speed of 80. The slower train had a 1 hour head start. How far were the two trains from their starting points?

7. _____

8. How long will it take a car traveling 65 mpg to pass a car traveling 50 mpg if their slower car had a 2 hour lead??

8. _____

9. A family drove from just south of Pittsburg to Meadville, Pennsylvania at 55 miles per hour and returned the same route traveling only 40 miles an hour due to the icy conditions. The total travel time was 4.75 hours. Find the distance one way.

9. _____

10. Victoria is counting all of quarters and dimes from the family piggy bank for the month. If there are 12 times as many dimes are there are quarters, and the total change is worth $21.75, how many quarters and how many dimes were in the piggy bank.

10. _____

11. Harrington received a $30,000 inheritance from his grandfather. For the first year, he invested part of the money in an account at 6% simple interest and the remainder of the money in an account at 9% simple interest. If he received $2100 in interest for the year, find the amount invested in each account.

11. _____

Additional Exercises 2.8 *(cont.)*

Name_____

Solve.

12. The Myers Center Auditorium in Gastonia contains 500 seats. Ticket prices for a recent play were $50 for adults and $25 for children. If the proceeds totaled $19,250, how many adults and how many children were there?

12. _____

13. Jeff and Adrianna were 9 miles apart on the hiking Jeff walked twice as fast as Adrianna, and it took 1.5 hours to meet. Find the rate of each hiker.

13. _____

14. Mark drove his new hybrid 60 mph for part of the trip and 70 miles per hour for the rest of the trip from home from Columbia, SC. If the entire trip was 310 miles, how many miles was he able to travel at each rate?

14. _____

15. Part of the proceeds from the children's play was $2000 in $10 bills and $20 bills. If there were twice as many $20 bills, find the number of each denomination.

15. _____

Additional Exercises 2.8
Form II

Solve.

1. Thomas has some money invested at 5% and $6000 more than that amount invested at 8%. His total annual investment was $2430. Find the amount invested at each amount.

    1. _____

2. Wes received a $10,000 advance when his book was published. He invested this in two different money markets, one at 12% simple interest and one at 15% simple interest. If he received $1320 in interest for the first year, how much did he have invested at each amount?

    2. _____

3. Grandma Mimi had a total of 340 bills hidden under her mattress. She had $100 bills and $20 bills and $10 bills which totaled $17,500. If there were 10 more $20 bills than there were $100 bills, and twenty less than half as many $10 bills as $100 bills, how many of each denominator did she have hidden under the mattress?

    3. _____

4. Antoine bought $340 worth of CD's and DVD's for his new collection in $20 bills and $5 bills. If he had 3 more $5 bills than $20 bills, how many of each denomination did he have?

    4. _____

5. Larry received a $500,000 bonus from the oil company from which he is retired. He invested part of this money in stocks and the remainder in bonds. The stocks had a simple interest rate of 12% and the bonds an interest rate of 8%. If his total earned yearly income from this investment was $53,600, how much was invested in stocks and how much in bonds?

    5. _____

6. A bank teller had to count the number of $20 bills and $50 bills received that day. She had four-fifths as many $50 bills as she had $20 bills. If the total was $30,000, how many of each denomination were there?

    6. _____

7. A stack of $20, $50, and $100 were retrieve as part of a fake CD investigation at one of the local flee markets. If they confiscated ten more $50 bills as $20 bills, and the $100 bills total ten more than twice as many $50 bills, then if the total amount confiscated was $5550, how many of each denomination were in the stack?

    7. _____

Additional Exercises 2.8 *(cont.)*

Solve.

8. Frederick invested $42,000 in two accounts, one with a simple interest of 8% and one at 10%. He made $3900 on the two accounts for the year, so how much was invested in each account?

9. Two bicyclists are 45 miles apart cycling towards one another. If they start at the same time and one travels fourteen miles per hour and the other travels 16 miles per hour, how long will it take them to meet?

10. Thomas rows upstream at 7 mph and down stream at 15 mph. If Thomas rowed for 5 hours, how far was his entire trip?

11. Two trains leave Austin, Texas – one traveling north and one traveling south. The northbound train is traveling at 80 mph and the southbound train is traveling 60 miles per hour. How long will it take them to be 420 miles apart?

8. _____

9. _____

10. _____

11. _____

Additional Exercises 2.8
Form III

Name_____

Date_____

Substitute the given values into the formula and solve for the unknown variable.

1. What number is 120% of 86?

1. _____

2. The number 650 is what percent of 130?

2. _____

3. The number 600 is what percent of 400?

3. _____

Solve the following applications.

4. A popular clothing store advertised all suits reduced by a certain percent. If the price of a suit before the discount was $400 and the price after the discount was $260, find the rate of discount and amount of discount.

4. _____

5. The price for a gallon of gasoline rose from $1.80 to $3.10 per gallon. Find the rate of increase. Round to the nearest whole percent.

5. _____

6. A recent wedding reception that included a sit-down meal at the club cost $55 per person with a invitation list of 200 people. If the club adds in a 20% gratuity and 7% tax (the gratuity is not taxed), find the total cost of the reception dinner.

6. _____

7. The number of students at a local community college decreased from 5500 in 2005 to 4500 in 2006. Find the percent of decrease. Round to the nearest whole percent.

7. _____

8. If Danielle had a really good review this year at the company where she is an accountant. This resulted in a $8250 raise. If her new salary is $74,250, find her original salary before the raise, and the percent of the raise she received.

8. _____

9. After the Mooney's house had been on the market for 8 months, they decided that in order to sell the house, they would have to decrease the price of the house $13,650. This amount represented a 7% drop in price. What was the original asking price of their home, and what is the discounted price?

9. _____

10. How many liters of a 3% saline solution must be added to an 8% saline solution to obtain 20 liters of a 6% saline solution?

10. _____

Additional Exercises 2.8 *(cont.)*

Solve.

11. Kohl's put their all of their bedding on a 30% sale. If Michelle's purchase of sheets, pillowcases, and comforter totals $360, find the amount after the 30% discount and 7% tax (figured after the discount).

    11. _____

12. Walgreen's put all of their Halloween candy and decorations on sale November 1. Jennifer purchased many outdoor decorations which before the sale would have cost $170 before the sale for only $51. Find the rate of decrease.

    12. _____

13. Explain in your own words how to find the rate of increase.

    13. _____

14. Explain in your own words how to find the rate of decrease.

    14. _____

15. How many cubic centimeters (cc) of a 30% antibiotic solution should be added 15 cc of a 70% antibiotic solution to get a 55% antibiotic solution?

    15. _____

Additional Exercises 2.9
Form I

Name_____

Date_____

Graph each on a number line.

   1. $x < 0$

   2. $x \geq 3.5$

   3. $-5 < x \geq -1$

   4. $y \leq \dfrac{3}{2}$

   5. $-3 \leq x < 1$

   6. $0 < x \leq 4$

Solve each inequality.

   7. $x + 8 \geq 15$

   8. $4x + 3 > 2x - 7$

   9. $4x - 3 > 5x - 4$

  10. $-5x \geq 15$

  11. $-0.7y > -2.1$

  12. $\qquad 8 - x \geq 5x - 2x$

  13. $-4x + 5 > 3(2x + 5)$

  14. $2(7x - 6) < 3(5x - 3)$

  15. $8(2x + 3) - 5x \geq 4(2x - 1) + 22$

  16. $7(3x - 5) - 11x \leq 3(4x - 12) + 3$

  17. $-3(x - 8) + x \geq -(4x - 5) + 12$

1. ⟵———————————→

2. ⟵———————————→

3. ⟵———————————→

4. ⟵———————————→

5. ⟵———————————→

6. ⟵———————————→

7. _____

8. _____

9. _____

10. _____

11. _____

12. _____

13. _____

14. _____

15. _____

16. _____

17. _____

Additional Exercises 2.9 *(cont.)*

Solve the following.

18. Seven more than three times a number is greater than negative fourteen. Find all numbers that make this statement true.

19. Tamara scored an 86 and a 92 on her last two math exams. What must she score on her third exam to have an average of at least a 90?

20. Alex has at most 90 yards of fencing available to enclose a rectangular garden. If the width of the garden is to be 15 yards, find the maximum length that the garden can be.

18. _____

19. _____

20. _____

Additional Exercises 2.9
Form II

Name_____

Date_____

Graph each on a number line.

1. $x \geq -7$

2. $x < 2$

3. $4 < x \leq 8$

Solve each inequality.

4. $2x - 8 < 14$

5. $-x - 1 > 2x + 8$

6. $-3x \leq 15$

7. $2x + 10 > 4x - 6$

8. $7 - x < 7 + 3x$

9. $4(x + 3) \geq 2x - 8$

10. $-3(2x - 3) - 8 > -x + 3(x + 1)$

11. $0.2(x + 1.3) > 0.1(1 + x)$

12. $(x + \frac{1}{3}) - 2x \geq \frac{1}{2}x + \frac{5}{6}$

13. $5(2x - 1) - 8x \leq -2(3x - 2) - 5$

14. $-0.2(x + 3) + 0.6 > -0.1(x + 0.3) + 1.6$

15. $-0.8(x - 0.6) \geq 0.2(x - 1)$

16. $\frac{1}{2}(x - \frac{1}{3}) < \frac{1}{3}(\frac{3}{4}x - \frac{1}{6})$

1.

2.

3.

4. _____

5. _____

6. _____

7. _____

8. _____

9. _____

10. _____

11. _____

12. _____

13. _____

14. _____

15. _____

16. _____

Additional Exercises 2.9 *(cont.)*

Solve the following.

17. One side of a triangle is three times as long as a second side, and the third side is 14 meters. If the perimeter can be no longer than 86 meters, find the maximum lengths of the other two sides.

17. _____

18. A 200-pound person uses 5.29 calories per minute when walking at work. If Julia walks 40 minutes each day, how many days will it take Julia to walk off at least 500 calories?

18. _____

19. James and Alexandra have $1000 to spend on their 10th anniversary celebration. If the club charges $150 cleanup fee and $15 per person, find the greatest number of people that they can invite and stay within their budget.

19. _____

20. _____

20. Sandra has test scores of 86, 82, 95, and 93 in her Introductory Algebra class. She wants to make an A average which at her college is 90 or above. What is the lowest score she can make on the final, if the final counts as two test grades?

Additional Exercises 2.9
Form III

Name_____

Date_____

Solve and graph each on a number line.

1. $-2(x-3) \geq -(3+x) - 4$

2. $-\dfrac{1}{2}x - 1 > \dfrac{2}{3}x + 6$

3. $\dfrac{2}{3}x \geq 5 + \dfrac{1}{3}x$

Solve

4. $0.2x - 2.4 \geq 0.3x + 7.4$

5. $\dfrac{1}{2}(2x-3) > \dfrac{3}{5}(x-1)$

6. $3(x-5) < -x - 2(x+8)$

7. $\dfrac{1}{3}x > -\dfrac{2}{3}x + \dfrac{4}{5}(x-5)$

8. $-7(x+2) > -6(1+x)$

9. $(x+3) - 5x \geq -(1-2x) + 4$

10. $5(2x-1) - 8x \leq -2(3x-2) + 3$

11. $-4(y+3) + 2y > -(y+2) + 12$

12. $\dfrac{1}{2}(x-5) \geq \dfrac{1}{3}(4x-2)$

13. $\dfrac{1}{6}(x-3) < \dfrac{1}{4}(2x-1)$

Solve the following

14. Five less than twice the sum of a number and four is less than or equal to twenty-seven. Find all numbers that make this statement true.

1. ⟵——————————→

2. ⟵——————————→

3. ⟵——————————→

4. _____

5. _____

6. _____

7. _____

8. _____

9. _____

10. _____

11. _____

12. _____

13. _____

14. _____

Additional Exercises 2.9 *(cont.)*

15. Hosea needs an average of 80 to get a B in the course. He has earned scores of 82, 87, and 77 on her tests. The final exam counts as two tests. What score does he need on the final to get a B?

15. _____

16 Rene scored an 83 and a 80 on her first two math tests. To pass the class, she must have at least a 70 average. What must she score on her third test and still pass the class?

16. _____

Additional Exercises 3.1
Form I

Name _____

Date _____

The following bar graph shows the rating of the top five television programs in October 2007 on Broadcast TV. Use the graph to answer questions 1 through 5. (Data was obtained from *Nielsen Media Research.*)

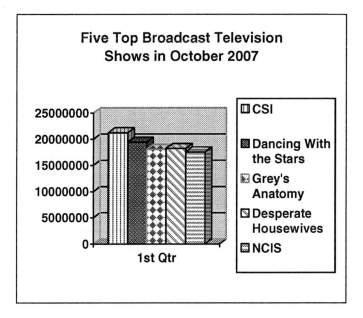

1. Which program has the highest viewer rating?

    1. _____

2. Which program had a higher rating, *NCIS* or *Dancing with the Stars?*

    2. _____

3. Approximate how many people watch CSI ?

    3. _____

4. Approximate how many people watch Grey's Anatomy?

    4. _____

5. About how many more people watch CSI than Grey's Anatomy?

    5. _____

Additional Exercises 3.1 *(cont.)*

Plot and label each order pair. State in which quadrant, if any, each point lies.

6. (2, 3)

6.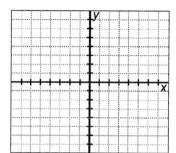

7. (− 4, 0)

7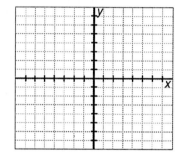

8. (0, 1)

8.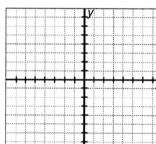

9. $\left(\dfrac{1}{2},\ -3\right)$

9.

Additional Exercises 3.1 *(cont.)*

Find the *x*- and *y*-coordinates of the following labeled points and state in which quadrant the point lies, if any. If the point is not in a quadrant, tell on which axis the point is located.

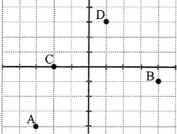

10. A

11. B

12. C

13. D

10. _____

11. _____

12. _____

13. _____

Complete each ordered pair so that it is a solution of the given linear equation.

14. $7x - y = 2$; $(2, \quad)$

15. $x = \dfrac{2}{3}$, $(\quad, 7)$

14. _____

15. _____

Complete the table of values for each given linear equation.

16 $4x - 2y = 8$

16.

x	y
0	
	0
	2

17. $3x + 4y = 6$

17.

x	y
	0
0	
	3

18. $x = -2$

18.

x	y
	0
	-4
	3

19. $x = -4y$

19..

x	y
0	
	1
4	

20. $y = 0.5x + 6$

20.

x	y
0	
2	
6	
8	

Additional Exercises 3.1
Form II

Name_____

Date_____

The following bar graph shows the some of the worst hurricanes in history of the United States and the number of people killed in that hurricane.

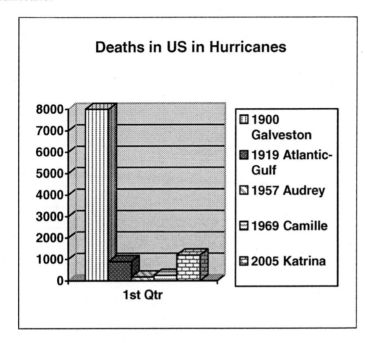

1. Which of these five hurricanes caused the most loss of life?

1. _____

2. Approximately how many more people were killed in the Galveston hurricane in 1900 than were killed in the 1919 Atlantic Gulf hurricane?

2. _____

Plot and label each order pair. State in which quadrant, if any, each point lies.

3. $(-5, 4)$

3.

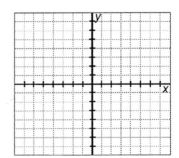

Additional Exercises 3.1 *(cont.)*

Name_____

Plot and label each order pair. State in which quadrant, if any,
each point lies.

4. $(0,0)$

4.

5. $(3,0)$

5.

6. $(0,-4)$

6.

7. $(2,6)$

7.

8. $(-5,-3)$

8..

Additional Exercises 3.1 *(cont.)*

Name _____

Find the *x*- and *y*-coordinates of the following labeled points and state in which quadrant the point lies, if any. If the point is not in a quadrant, tell on which axis the point is located.

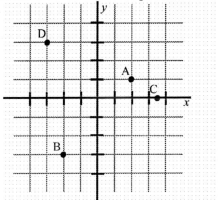

9. A

10. B

11. C

12. D

Complete the table of values for each given linear equation.

13. $7x - y = 2$

14. $y = -4$

15 $x - y = 8$

16. $2x - 3y = 12$

9. _____

10. _____

11. _____

12. _____

13.

x	y
0	
	0
	-1

14..

x	y
0	
-4	
5	

15.

x	y
0	
	0
	6

16.

x	y
	0
0	
	-3

Name_____

17. $-x = 2y$

x	y
0	
	0
4	
	4

18. $y = \dfrac{1}{3}x - 2$

18.

x	y
	0
0	
	6
	9

19. $x = 0$

19..

x	y
	-5
	0
	2

20. $y = 0$

20.

x	y
-4	
0	
2	

Additional Exercises 3.1
Form III

Name_____

Date_____

Complete the table of ordered pairs for each equation. Then plot the three points on the graph provided.

1. $y = -\dfrac{1}{2}x$

x	y
0	
	0
-6	
6	

1.

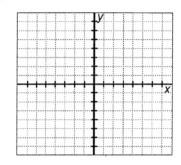

2. $2x + y = 4$

x	y
0	
	0
2	
	6

2.

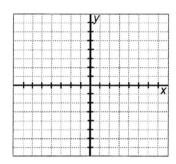

3. $x = -6$

x	y
	-5
	0
	1
	6

3.

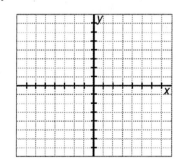

4. $2y + 4 = -6$

x	y
-6	
0	
1	
6	

4.

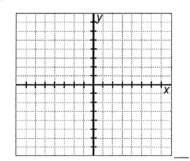

Additional Exercises 3.1 *(cont.)*

Name_____

Plot and label each order pair. State in which quadrant, if any, each point lies.

5. $-y = 2x + 1$

x	y
2	
	3
-4	
	0

6. $x - \dfrac{1}{2}y = 2$

x	y
0	
	0
	4
6	

7. $y - x = 5$

x	y
0	
	0
	2
2	

8. $\dfrac{1}{2}x - 2y = 4$

x	y
0	
	0
	2
2	

5.
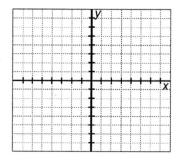

6
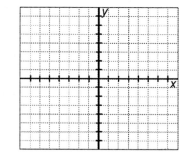

7.
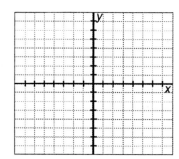

8.
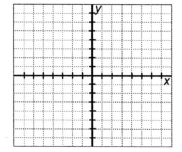

Additional Exercises 3.1 *(cont.)*

Name_____

Find the x- and y-coordinates of the following labeled points and state in which quadrant the point lies, if any. If the point is not in a quadrant, tell on which axis the point is located.

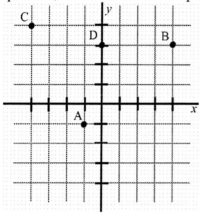

9. A

10. B

11. C

12. D

Complete each ordered pair so that it is a solution of the given linear equation.

13. $\frac{2}{3}x - \frac{1}{2}y = 2;\ (3,\ \ )$

14. $\frac{1}{3}y - \frac{1}{2}x = 2;\ (\ \ ,3\ )$

Write the ordered pair for each point described.

15 Point A is six units to the right of the y-axis, and two units above the x-axis.

16. Point B is five units beneath the origin.

17. Point C is on the x-axis five units to the left of the origin.

Three vertices of a rectangle are $(-5,-3)$, $(-5,4)$, and $(2,-3)$.

18. Find the coordinates of the fourth vertex.

19. Find the perimeter of the rectangle.

20. Find the area of the rectangle.

9. _____

10. _____

11. _____

12. _____

13. _____

14. _____

15. _____

16. _____

17. _____

18. _____

19. _____

20. _____

Additional Exercises 3.2
Form I

For each equation, find three ordered pair solutions by completing the table. Then, use the ordered pairs to graph the equation.

1. $x + y = 8$

x	y
0	
	2
	0

1.

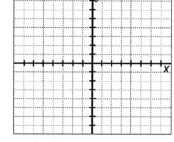

2. $x - y = 7$

x	y
0	
3	
	0

2.

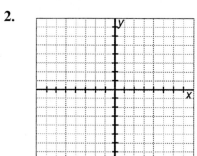

3. $y = -3x$

x	y
0	
2	
	3

3.

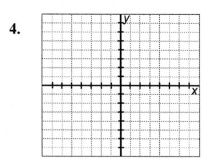

4. $y = \frac{1}{4}x$

x	y
0	
-4	
8	

4.

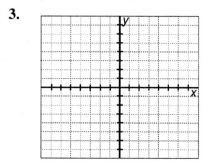

5. $y = -2x + 8$

5.

x	y
0	
1	
5	

6. $7x - y = 7$

6.

x	y
0	
	0
2	

Make your table of values for three points and then graph each linear equation.

7.

7. $x + y = -4$

x	y

8. $x - y = 8$

8.

x	y

9. $-x + 2y = 6$

x	y

9.

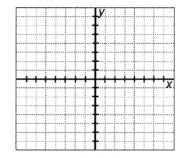

10. $y = -2x + 5$

x	y

10.

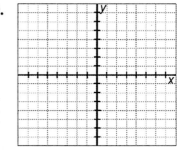

11. $y = 6x$

x	y

11.

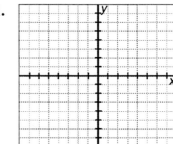

12. $y = -2x$

x	y

12.

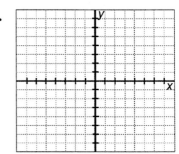

13. $x + 2y = 8$

x	y

13.

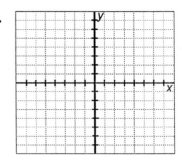

14. $y = \dfrac{2}{3}x - 4$

x	y

14.

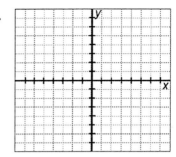

15. $5y = 3x + 15$

x	y

15.

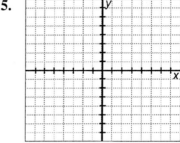

16. $x = 6y$

x	y

16.

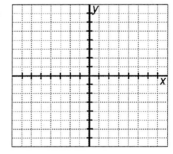

17. $2x - 5y = 10$

x	y

17.

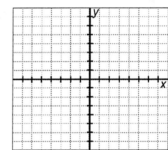

Name_____

Date_____

18. $x = -\dfrac{2}{3}y$

x	y

18.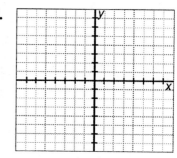

19. $y = x - 6$

x	y

19.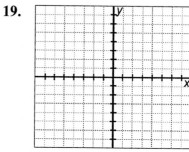

20. $x + y = 4$

x	y

20.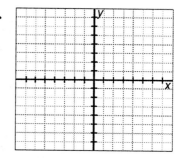

Additional Exercises 3.2
Form II

Name_____

Date_____

Graph each equation on the same set of axes. Discuss how the graphs are similar and how they are different

1. $y = -\frac{3}{4}x; y = -\frac{3}{4}x + 2$

2. $y = \frac{3}{4}x; y = \frac{3}{4}x - 4$

3. $y = -3x; y = -3x + 5$

4. $y = -\frac{1}{3}x; y = -\frac{1}{3}x + 3$

1.

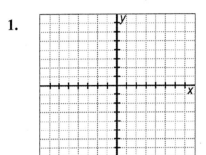

2.

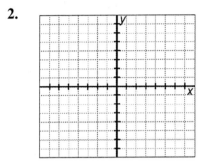

3.

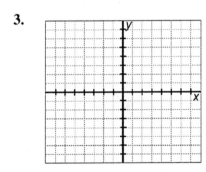

4.

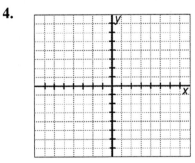

Additional Exercises 3.2 *(cont.)*

Graph each linear equation.

5. $y = 3$

5.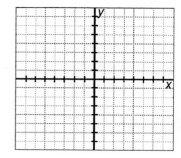

6. $x = -4$

6.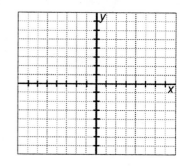

7. $x + y = -4$

7.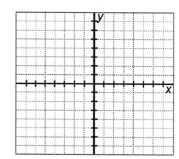

8. $x - y = 8$

8.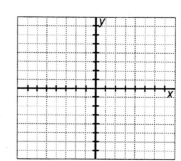

9. $-x + 2y = 6$

9.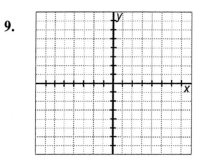

10. $y = -2x + 5$

10.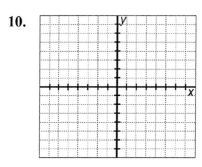

11. $y = 6x$

11.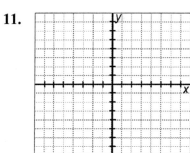

12. $y = -2x$

12.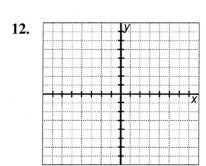

13. $x + 2y = 8$

13.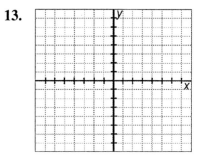

14. $y = \dfrac{2}{3}x - 2$

14.

15. $y = 3x - 2$

15.

16. $x = -\dfrac{1}{2}y$

16.

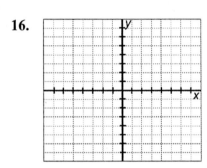

17. $2x - y = 4$

17.

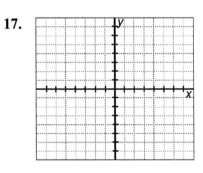

Additional Exercises 3.2 *(cont.)*

Name_____

Date_____

18. $x = -\dfrac{3}{4}y$

18.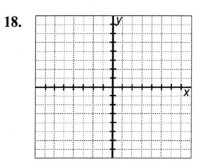

19. $y = x + 2$

19.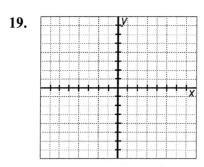

20. $x + y = 4$

20.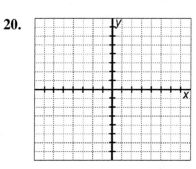

Additional Exercises 3.2
Form III

For each equation, find a table of values for three ordered pairs, then graph the equation

1. $2x + 3y = 6$

x	y
0	
	2
	0

1.

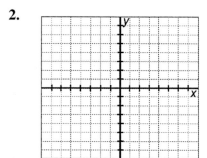

2. $\dfrac{1}{2}x - y = 4$

x	y
0	
4	
	0

2.

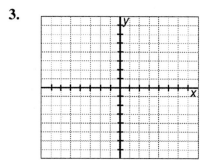

3. $y = -\dfrac{5}{4}x$

x	y
0	
4	
−4	

3.

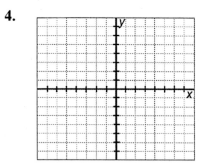

4. $y = -1.5x + 2$

x	y
0	
−4	
6	

4.

Additional Exercises 3.2 *(cont.)*

5. $y = -\dfrac{4}{3}x + 2$

x	y
0	
3	
-6	

5.

6. $2(x - 3) = y - 7$

x	y
0	
	0
2	

6.

Graph each linear equation.

7. $2x - (y + 2) = -4$

7.

8. $y = -y + 8$

8.

Additional Exercises 3.2 *(cont.)*

9. $x - 2(x + 3) = 6$

9.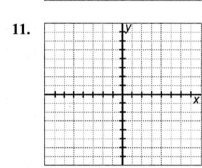

10. $-y = -x - 4$

10.

11. $y = \dfrac{5}{2}$

11.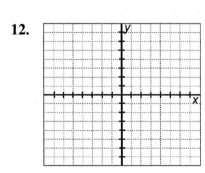

12. $x = 0$

12.

13. $y = 0$

13.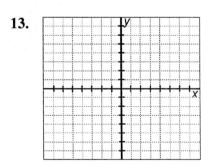

14. If the equation $y = 0.25x + 0.35$ can be used to determine the cost of making a phone call using a calling card where y is the cost of making the call x minutes long. Find the cost of a 25 minute call.

14._____

15. The total value y of a certain investment that has been left for x years can be determined by the equation $y = 551x + 3500$. How long has many years will it take for the investment to have the total value of $6255?

15._____

16. In 2006, the average teacher's salary in the US was $47,602. Use the linear equation $y = 775x + 47602$ where y = the salary and x is the number of years after 2006 to determine the salary of a teacher hired in 2006 after 5 in 2011.

16._____

Additional Exercises 3.3
FormI

Name_____

Date_____

The following graphs are windows from a TI-84 graphing calculator. Identify the intercept points if each tick is one unit.

1.

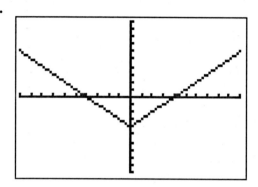

1. _____

2.

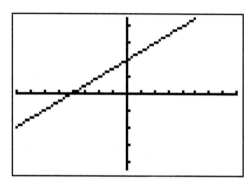

2. _____

3.

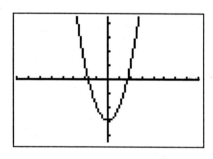

3. _____

4. Graph the line with *x*-intercept at −8 and *y*-intercept at 6.

4.

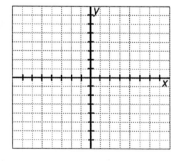

Additional Exercises 3.3 *(cont.)*

Name_____

Graph each linear equation by finding *x*- and *y*-intercepts. Check by finding a third point on the line.

5. $x - y = 5$

x	y
0	
	0

5.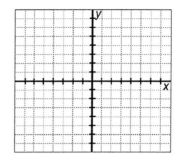

6. $x = 3y - 6$

x	y
0	
	0

6.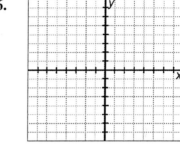

7. $x + 2y = 7$

x	y
0	
	0

7.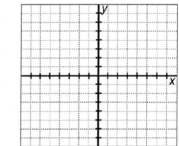

8. $3x - 6y = 18$

x	y
0	
	0

8.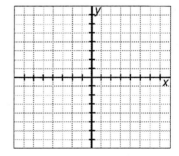

Additional Exercises 3.3 *(cont.)*

Name_____

Graph each linear equation.

9. $x = -6$

9.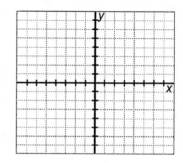

10. $y = 5$

10.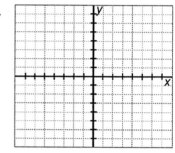

11. $x - 4 = 0$

11.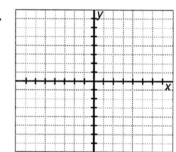

12. $y + 8 = 0$

12.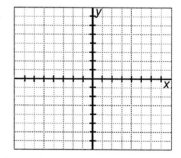

Additional Exercises 3.3 *(cont.)*

13 - 15, Match each equation to the graph A, B, or C.

A.

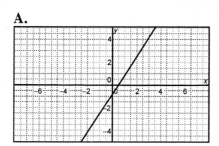

B.

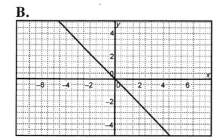

C.

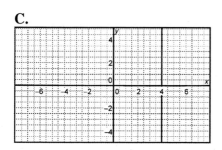

13. $y = -x$

14. $x = 4$

15. $y = 2x - 1$

16. Two lines in the same plane that do not intercept are called parallel lines. Graph the line $x = -2$. Then graph a line parallel to the line $x = -2$ that intersects the *x*-axis at 3. What is the equation of this line?

13. _____

14. _____

15. _____

16.

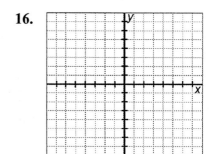

Additional Exercises 3.3 *(cont.)*

Name_____

At Toni's Furniture Production, it takes 5 hours to manufacture a certain bed and 8 hours to manufacture a matching chest. If a total of 400 hours is available to manufacture these beds and chests, then the linear equation that models this situation is $5x + 8y = 400$

17. Complete the ordered pair solution, $(0, \quad)$ of this equation. Describe the manufacturing situation that corresponds to this solution.\

18. Complete the ordered pair solution, $(\quad, 0)$ of this equation. Describe the manufacturing situation that corresponds to this solution.

19. Use the ordered pairs found in problems 18 and 19 to graph the equation $5x + 8y = 400$

20. If 25 chests are manufactured, find the greatest number of beds that they can make.

17. _____

18. _____

19.

20. _____

Additional Exercises 3.3
Form II

Name_____

Date_____

The following graphs are windows from a TI-84 graphing calculator. Identify the intercept points if each tick is one unit.

1. _____

1.

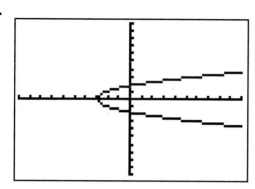

2. _____

2.

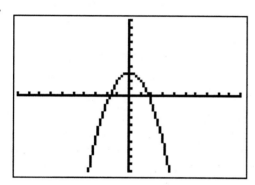

3. _____

3.

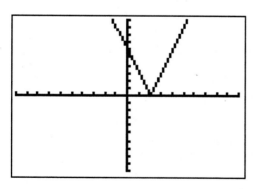

4. Graph the line with *x*-intercept at $(-4, 0)$ and *y*-intercept at $(0, 4)$.

4.

Additional Exercises 3.3 *(cont.)*

Graph each linear equation by finding *x*- and *y*-intercepts. Check by finding a third point on the line.

5. $4x + y = -1$

x	y
0	
	0

5.

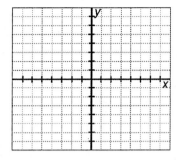

6. $3y = x - 6$

x	y
0	
	0

6.

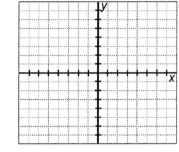

7. $-x - 2y = 6$

x	y
0	
	0

7.

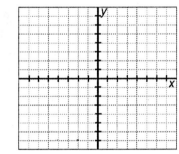

8. $2x + 4y = 10$

x	y
0	
	0

8.

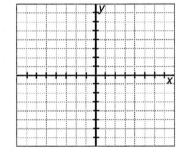

Additional Exercises 3.3 *(cont.)*

Graph each linear equation.

9. $2 - x = -3$

9.
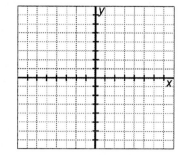

10. $-y - 4 = 2$

10.
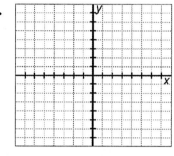

11. $3x + 6 = -6$

11.
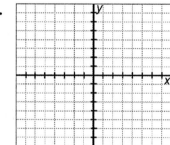

12. $2y + 8 = 12$

12.
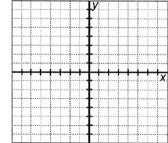

Additional Exercises 3.3 *(cont.)*

Name_____

Graph each pair of linear equation on the same set of axes. Discuss how they are alike and how they are different.

13. $y = -x; \ y = -x - 4$

13.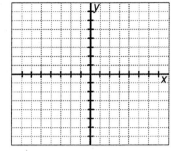

14. $3x = -6; \ -3x = -9$

14.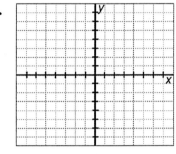

15. $-y + 2 = -1; \ -2y - 2 = 4$

15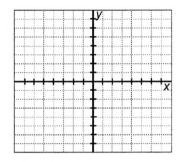

Additional Exercises 3.3
Form III

Name_____

Date_____

The following graphs are windows from a TI-84 graphing calculator. Identify the intercept points if each tick is one unit.

1.

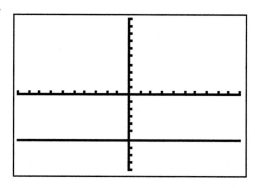

1. _____

2.

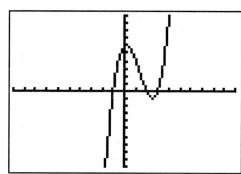

2. _____

3.

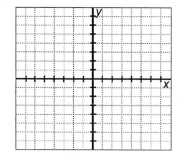

3. _____

4. Graph the line with x-and y-intercept at $(0,0)$ and passes through the point $(-4,5)$

4.

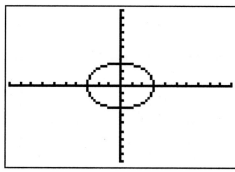

Additional Exercises 3.3 *(cont.)*

Name_____

Graph the first linear equation by finding *x*- and *y*-intercepts. Check by finding a third point on the line. The on the same set of axes, draw a line parallel to the first line that passes through the y-axis 2 units above the y-intercept of the first equation. Label the intercept of the second line in the second chart. Approximate where necessary

5. $2x + y = 5$

x	y
0	
	0

x	y
0	
	0

6. $y = -x - 3$

x	y
0	
	0

x	y
0	
	0

7. $-y + 3 = 7$

x	y
0	
	0

x	y
0	
	0

5.

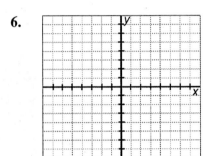

6.

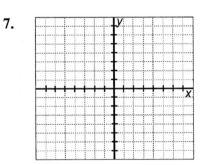

7.

Additional Exercises 3.3 *(cont.)*

Graph each linear equation.

8.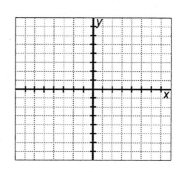

8. Draw a line parallel to the line $4x = -4$ that intersects the
x-axis at $(3,0)$. What is the equation of this line?

9.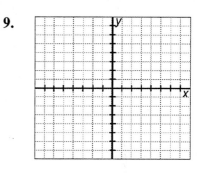

9. Draw a line parallel to the line $3y = -9$ that intersects the
y-axis at the point $(0,5)$. What is the equation of this line?

10.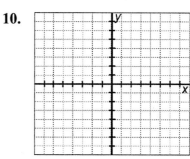

10. What is the *x*-intercept for the equation $4x = -4$? What is
the y-intercept for the equation? See problem 8.

11.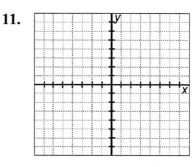

11. What is a *x*-intercept for the equation $3y = -9$? What is the
y-intercept? See problem 9.

Additional Exercises 3.3 *(cont.)*

Name_____

For the following equations, list the *x*-intercept, the *y*-intercept, and tell whether the line is horizontal, vertical, or neither.

12.. $-x + 4 = 4$

12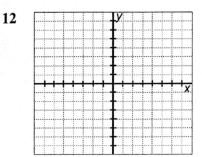

13. $3y - 3 = -12$

13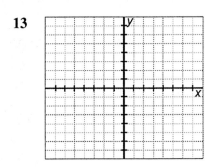

14. $-x - y = -3$

14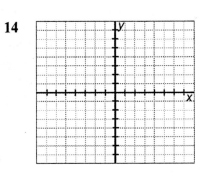

Additional Exercises 3.4
Form I

Name

Date _____

Tell whether the slope of the line is positive, negative or is undefined.

1.

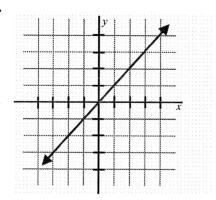

2.

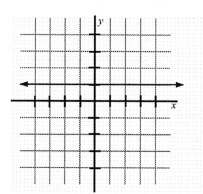

3.

Find the slope of the line that goes through the given points.

4. (2, 1) and (4, 5)

5. (3, 7) and (5, 4)

6. (-7, 3) and (-7, -6)

7. (8, −2) and (5, −3)

1.

2. _____

3. _____

4. _____

5. _____

6. _____

7. _____

Additional Exercises 3.4 *(cont.)*

8. Determine which line in the graph has the greater slope.

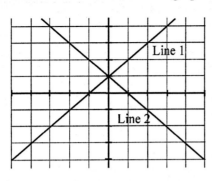

8. _____

Find the slope of each line.

9. $y = -12x + 5$

9. _____

10. $4x - 7y = 11$

10. _____

11. $y + 5 = 0$

11. _____

12. $x = -8y$

12. _____

13. $x = -8x + 18$

13. _____

Name the two points on the graph, and find the slope of the line.

14.

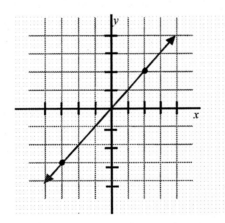

14. _____

15.

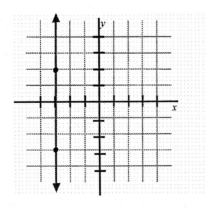

15. _____

E-136

Additional Exercises 3.4
Form II

State the two points on each graph, and find the slope of the line.

1. _____

1.

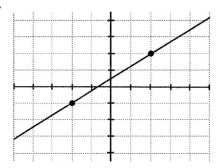

2.

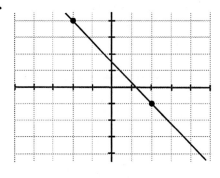

2. _____

3.

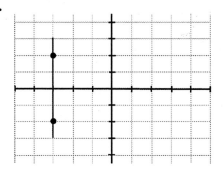

3. _____

Find the slope of the line that goes through the given points.

4. _____

4. (4, 2) and (4, 5)

5. _____

5. (3, −7) and (5, −7)

6. _____

6. (7, 3) and (5, − 2)

7. _____

7. (7, 12) and (8, 10)

8. _____

8. (−3, −5) and (−6, −4)

9. Determine which line in the graph has the greater slope.

9. _____

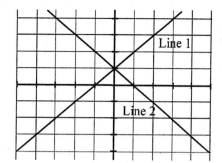

Find the slope of each line.

10. $y = -2x + 1$

10. _____

11. $2x - 6y = 8$

11. _____

12. $4 - y = 0$

12. _____

13. $-x = 2y$

13. _____

Determine whether the lines are parallel, perpendicular, or neither.

14. $3x + y = 6$
    $x - 3y = 12$

14. _____

15. $x - 4y = 8$
    $4y = x - 12$

15. _____

16. $x - 5y = 7$
    $x + 5y = 9$

16. _____

Use the points given, (a) find the slope of the line parallel and (b) find the slope of the line perpendicular to the line through each pair of points.

17. (8, 3) and (14, 6)

17. _____

18. (−5, −6) and (7, 9)

18. _____

19. Find the slope of a ski run that rises 100 feet over a run of 280 feet.

19. _____

20. The grade of a road is its slope written as a percent. Find the grade of a road that rises 7 feet over a run of 50 feet.

20. _____

Additional Exercises 3.4
Form III

Name

Date _____

Find the slope of each equation.

1. $x + 3 = -2x + 9$

2. $y + 2 = -2x + 4$

3. $4x - 2y = 8$

4. $y - 1 = -3y + 10$

Find the slope of the line that goes through the given points.

5. $(2, 2)$ and $(5, 7)$

6. $(7, 3)$ and $(4, 5)$

7. $(7, 3)$ and $(0, 0)$
8. $(8, -2)$ and $(5, -3)$

9. $(0.4, 1.5)$ and $(3.2, -1.3)$

Find the slope of each line.

10. $y = -12x + 5$

11. $4x - 7y = 11$

12. $y + 5 = 0$

13. $x = -8y$

Find the slope of each line. Then determine if the two lines are parallel, perpendicular, or neither.

14. $2x + y = 4$
    $x - 2y = 14$

15. $3x - 4y = 8$
    $4y = 3x - 12$

16. $x + 5y = 7$
    $x + 5y = 9$

1. _____

2. _____

3. _____

4. _____

5. _____

6. _____

7. _____

8. _____

9. _____

10. _____

11. _____

12. _____

13. _____

14. _____

15. _____

16. _____

Additional Exercises 3.4 *(cont.)*

The pitch of a roof is its slope written as a percent. Find the pitch of each roof described.

17.

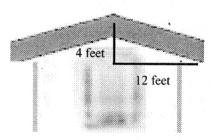

17. _____

18.

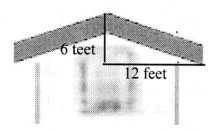

18. _____

Solve.

19. According to federal regulations, a wheelchair ramp should rise no more than 1 foot for horizontal distance of 12 feet. If a ramp rises 2 feet for a distance of 28 feet, does this stay within federal regulations?

19. _____

20. Find the slope of the line containing the points $(5, -2)$ and $(3, -4)$ that is (a) parallel to the given line, and (b) perpendicular to the given line.

20. _____

Additional Exercises 3.5
Form I

Write the equation of each line in the form $y = mx + b$ and standard form if possible.

1. $m = \dfrac{2}{3}, b = -4$

2. $m = \dfrac{7}{12}, b = 0$

3. $m = -\dfrac{1}{8}, b = 4$

4. $m = 0, b = -9$

1. _____

2. _____

3. _____

4. _____

Use the slope-intercept form to graph each equation.

5. $y = -2x + 3$

5.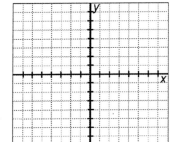

6. $y = \dfrac{3}{5}x - 2$

6.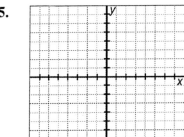

7. $3x + y = 4$

7.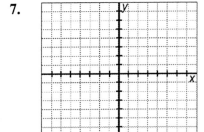

8. $3x - 2y = 8$

8.

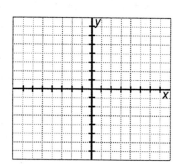

Find the equation of the line with given slope and passing through the given point. Write the equation in the form $Ax + By = C$.

9. $m = 9$, through $(3, 1)$

9. _____

10. $m = -5$, through $(2, 7)$

10. _____

11. $m = -7$, through $(-1, -6)$

11. _____

12. $m = \dfrac{4}{5}$, through $(10, -12)$

12. _____

13. $m = -\dfrac{1}{8}$, through $(-16, 5)$

13. _____

Find the equation of the line passing through each pair of points. Write the equation in the form $Ax + By = C$. and $y = mx + b$.

14. $(4, 7)$ and $(5, 12)$

14. _____

15. $(3, -7)$ and $(-3, -11)$

15. _____

16. $(-9, 2)$ and $(0, 0)$

16. _____

17. $(-3, 2)$ and $(-5, -6)$

17. _____

18. $(10, 8)$ and $(-6, -6)$

18. _____

19. Through the origin and $(4,2)$.

19. _____

20. Through the y-intercept -6 and the x-intercept -2.

20. _____

Additional Exercises 3.5
Form II

Name_____

Date_____

Write the equation of each line in slope intercept form and standard form if possible.

1. Vertical line through the point (5,2).

2. Horizontal line through the point (5,2).

3. Line parallel to x = 4 through the point (0, 0)

4. Line perpendicular to x = 5 through the point (2,-6).

5. Through (0, 5) and (3, 4)

6. Through $(\frac{1}{2}, 3)$ and $(2, -\frac{1}{2})$

7. With slope $-\frac{3}{5}$ through (1, 5)

8. Through (2, 3) perpendicular to the y-axis

9. Through (2, 3) and parallel to the y-axis.

10. Through (-5, -2) perpendicular to the x-axis.

Write the equation for the line and write your answer in $y = mx + b$ form and in standard form where possible.

11. Through (5, -3) parallel to the x-axis.

12. $m = -\frac{1}{5}$ through the point $(5,3)$.

13. $m = 2$ through the point $(\frac{1}{2}, \frac{1}{3})$.

14. $m = -1$ through the point $(0,4)$

15. Through $(-1, -4)$ and $(0, 5)$

1. _____

2. _____

3. _____

4. _____

5. _____

6. _____

7. _____

8. _____

9. _____

10. _____

11. _____

12. _____

13. _____

14. _____

15. _____

Additional Exercises 3.5
Form III

Name_____

Date_____

Write the equation of each line in the form $y = mx + b$ and standard form when possible.

1. $m = 0; b = 0$

2. $m = \dfrac{5}{3}; b = -\dfrac{1}{4}$

3. $m = -\dfrac{2}{3}$, y-intercept $(0,-5)$

4. Parallel to $y = 0$, through $(-4,5)$

5. Through the point $(-3,6)$ with $m = \dfrac{1}{4}$

6. Intercepts $(0,3)$ and $(-2,0)$

7. $m = -\dfrac{2}{3}$; x-intercept $(\dfrac{7}{2}, 0)$

8. Through points $\left(\dfrac{1}{2}, -\dfrac{2}{3}\right)$ and $\left(\dfrac{1}{2}, -4\right)$

9, Through points $\left(3, -\dfrac{2}{3}\right)$ and $\left(5, -\dfrac{2}{3}\right)$

10. Vertical line through $(-6,5)$

11. Horizontal line through $(3, -4)$

12. Slope = 0 through point $(4,-7)$

13. Slope undefined, through the point $(5,1)$

14. Through $(0,4)$ perpendicular to the y-axis

15. Through $(4,7)$ perpendicular to the x-axis

1. _____

2. _____

3. _____

4. _____

5. _____

6. _____

7. _____

8. _____

9. _____

10. _____

11. _____

12. _____

13. _____

14. _____

15. _____

Additional Exercises 3.6
Form I

Name_____

Date_____

Find the domain and range of each relation.

1. $\{(-9, 12), (0, 8), (12, -15), (3, 15)\}$

2. $\{(7, -7), (4, -7), (-5, 17)\}$

3. $\{(-9, 12), (0, 8), (12, -15), (3, 15)\}$

4. $\{(-2, 4), (12, 14), (-2, -4)\}$

Determine if the set of points represents a function.

5. $\{(-9, 12), (0, 8), (12, -15), (3, 15)\}$

6. $\{(7, -7), (4, -7), (-5, 17)\}$

7. $\{(-9, 12), (0, 8), (12, -15), (3, 15)\}$

8. $\{(-2, 4), (12, 14), (-2, -4)\}$

Use vertical line test to determine whether each graph is the graph of a function.

9.

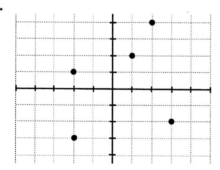

10.

1. _____

2. _____

3. _____

4. _____

5. _____

6. _____

7. _____

8. _____

9. _____

10. _____

Name_____

11.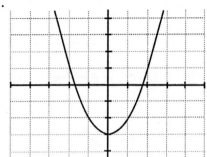

11. _____

Given the function $f(x) = 4 - 9x$, find the indicated function values.

12. $f(-1)$

12. _____

13. $f(2)$

13. _____

14. $f(0)$

14. _____

Given the function $f(x) = x^2 - 7$, find the indicated function values.

15. $f(0)$

15. _____

16. $f(-5)$

16. _____

17. $f(2)$

17. _____

Given the function $f(x) = |8 - x|$, find the indicated function values.

18. $f(0)$

18. _____

19. $f(11)$

19. _____

20. $f(9)$

20. _____

Additional Exercises 3.6
Form II

Name _____

Date _____

Find the domain and range of each relation.

1. $\{(-1,-4),(-1,-2),(-1,0),(-1,2)\}$

2. $\{(7,-1),(5,-1),(3,-1),(1,-1)\}$

Determine if the set of points represents a function.

3. $\{(-1,-4),(-1,-2),(-1,0),(-1,2)\}$

4. $\{(7,-1),(5,-1),(3,-1),(1,-1)\}$

Use vertical line test to determine whether each graph is the graph of a function.

5.

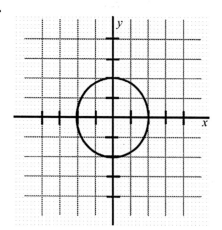

6.

1. _____

2. _____

3. _____

4. _____

5. _____

6. _____

7.

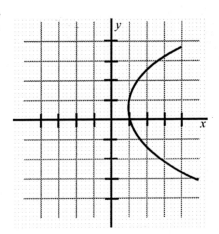

8.

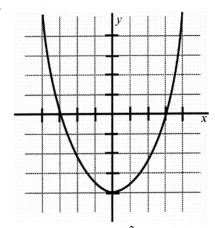

8. _____

Given the function $f(x) = x^2 - 4x$, find the indicated function values.

    9. $f(-2)$

9. _____

    10. $f(0)$

10. _____

    11. $f(2)$

11. _____

Given the function $f(x) = -x^2 + 1$, find the indicated function values.

    12. $f(0)$

12. _____

    13. $f(-5)$

13. _____

    14. $f(3)$

14. _____

Additional Exercises 3.6 *(cont.)*

The graph below shows the estimated cost of raising a child born in 1955. Estimates are for the younger child in a two-parent, two child, middle income family.

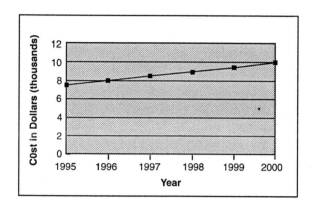

15. Approximate the cost in the year 1998.

15. _____

16. Approximate the cost in the year 2000.

16. _____

17. Is this the graph of the function? Why or why not?

17. _____

18. The profit a company makes when producing x units of a product is given by the equation $P(x) = 45x - 10,000$. Find the amount of profit the company makes by producing 500 units.

18. _____

Find the domain and the range of each relation graphed.

19.

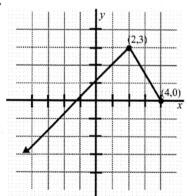

19. _____

Additional Exercises 3.6
Form III

Name_____

Date_____

Find the domain of each function

    1. $f(x) = 5x - 1$

    2. $g(x) = \dfrac{3}{x-7}$

    3. $h(x) = |x - 5|$

    4. $f(x) = \dfrac{1}{x}$

    5. $g(x) = x^2 - x - 2$

Find the domain and the range of each relation graphed.

1. _____

2. _____

3. _____

4. _____

5. _____

6. _____

6.

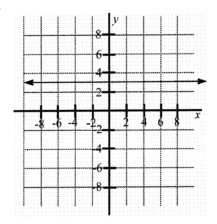

7. _____

7.

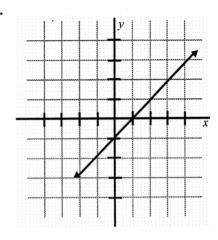

8.

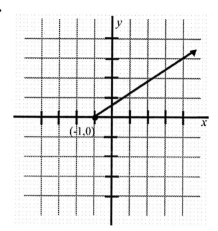

(-1,0)

9.

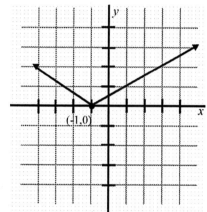

(-1,0)

Find $f(-2), f(0), f(2)$ for each function

10. $f(x) = -3x + 2$

11. $g(x) = \left| x^2 - 5 \right|$

12. $h(x) = 4$

Find $f(-2), f(0), f(2)$ for each function

13. $f(x) = x^2 - x - 1$

14. $g(x) = \left| -3x \right|$

15. $h(x) = 4 - x^2$

10. _____

11. _____

12. _____

13. _____

14. _____

15. _____

Name_____

Solve.

16. If a certain linear function *f(x)*.is evaluate at 0, the answer is 4. In other words, $f(0) = 4$. If the same function *f(x)* is evaluated at 3, the answer is 5. In other words, $f(3) = 5$. Use this information to find the equation of the function in $f(x) = mx + b$ form.

16. _____

17. Forensic scientists use the function
$$H(x) = 2.59x + 47.24$$
to estimate the height of a woman in centimeters given the length of the femur bone.

a. Estimate the height of a woman whose femur measures 42 centimeters.

b. Estimate the height of a woman whose femur measures 50 centimeters.

17a._____

. b._____

Additional Exercises 4.1
Form I

Determine whether the ordered pair satisfies the system of linear equations.

1. $5x + y = 9$ (1, 4)
$3x - 2y = 4$

2. $x - 3y = 17$ (2, –5)
$2x + 5y = -21$

3. $2x + 7y = -5$ (1, -1)
$4x - y = 6$

4. $y = 3x - 1$ (3, 8)
$5x - 2y = -1$

1. _____

2. _____

3. _____

4. _____

Solve each system of equations by graphing.

5. $x + y = 1$
$x - y = 3$

5.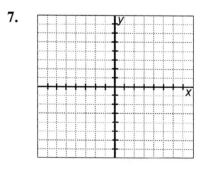

6. $x + 2y = 4$
$2x - y = 3$

6.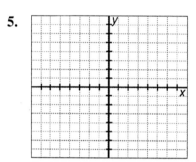

7. $y = -2x + 4$
$y = -3x + 7$

7.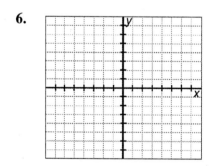

8. $y = 2x + 5$

$y = -\dfrac{1}{3}x - 2$

8.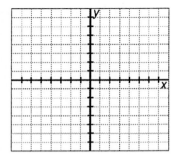

9. $y = 3x + 4$
$y = 5x + 8$

9.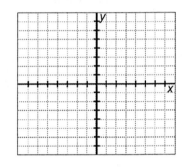

10. $4x - 3y = 12$
$3x + 4y = -16$

10.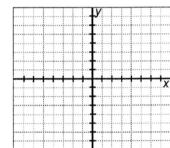

11. $y = 2x + 5$
$y = -x + 2$

11.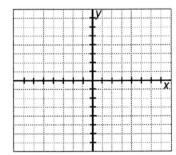

12. $3x + 2y = 6$
$y = -3$

12.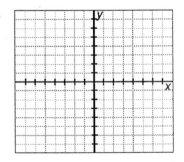

Name_____

13. $y = 2x - 4$
$\quad\;\, y = 2x + 1$

13.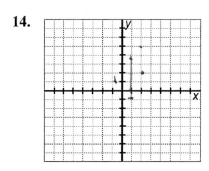

14. $3x - 4 = 2y$
$\quad\;\; 6x = 4y - 8$

14.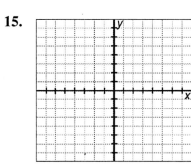

15. $x + y = 4$
$\quad\;\; y = 2x - 5$

15.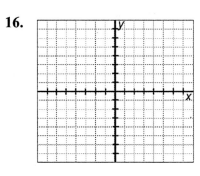

16. $y = 2x - 3$
$\quad\;\; x = 3$

16.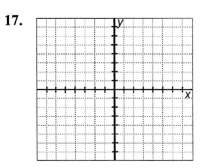

17. $y = 5x - 4$
$\quad\;\; y = -2x + 3$

17.

18. $2x = 4$
$\quad\quad y = 2$

The following graph shows the number of home runs hit by Hank Aaron and Babe Ruth during their first 8 years in the major leagues.

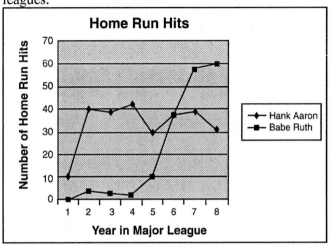

19. What was the difference between Babe Ruth and Hank Aaron homerun record in the fifth year?

20. In which year did Babe Ruth hit the most home runs?

18.

19. _____

20. _____

Additional Exercises 4.1
Form II

Name_____

Date_____

Determine whether the ordered pair satisfies the system of linear equations.

1. $2x = y - 5$ $(-2, 1)$
$x + y = -1$

2. $2x - 3y = 6$ $(0, -2)$
$2x + y = 10$

3. $-x + 3y = -11$ $(5, 2)$
$3x - y = 17$

4. $\dfrac{3}{4}x + \dfrac{2}{3}y = \dfrac{-19}{6}$ $(-6, 2)$

$y = -\dfrac{1}{3}x$

1. _____

2. _____

3. _____

4. _____

Solve each system of equations by graphing.

5. $y = \dfrac{2}{3}x - 1$

$y = -x + 4$

5.

6. $y = -2x + 1$
$y = x - 5$

6.

7. $y = \dfrac{1}{2}x - 3$

$y = \dfrac{3}{2}x - 1$

7.

Additional Exercises 4.1 *(cont.)*

Name _____

8. $2x - y = 3$
    $x = -1$

8.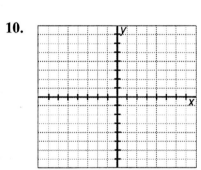

9. $2x + 3y = 6$
    $x = 3$

9.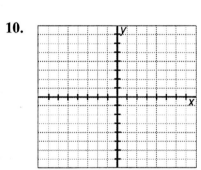

10. $3x - y = 1$
    $y = -4$

10.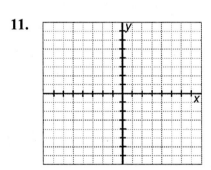

11. $4x + 6y = -2$
    $y = 1$

11.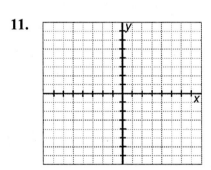

12. $3x + 2y = -4$
    $3x - 2y = -8$

12.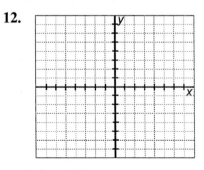

Name_____

13. $3x - y = 1$
    $4x + 3y = -3$

13.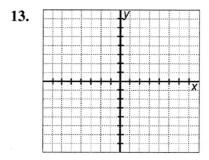

14. $x - y = 4$
    $x + 2y = -2$

14.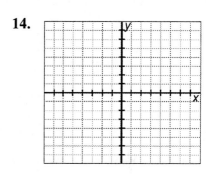

15. $x - 2y = 2$
    $y = \dfrac{1}{2}x - 1$

15.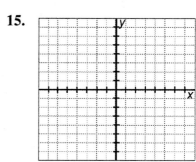

16. $3x - 2y = 7$
    $4y + 14 = 6x$

16.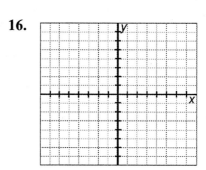

17. $y = 3x - 1$
    $3x - y = 5$

17.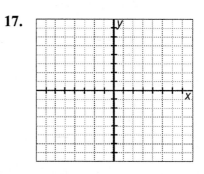

Additional Exercises 4.1 *(cont.)*

18. $\dfrac{2}{5}x = y + \dfrac{7}{5}$

$2x - 5y = 2$

18.

The following graph shows the number of home runs hit by Hank Aaron and Babe Ruth during their first 8 years in the major leagues.

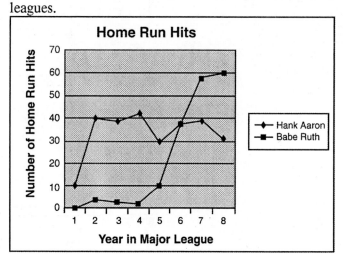

19. In what year did Babe Ruth and Hank Aaron hit close to the same number of home runs?

19. _____

20. In which year did Hank Aaron hit the most home runs?

20. _____

Additional Exercises 4.1
Form III

Name_____

Date_____

Determine whether the ordered pair satisfies the system of linear equations.

1. $x + y = 4$ $(3, 1)$
    $-2x + y = -5$

2. $y = 4x$ $(2, 4)$
    $y = 4$

3. $3x - y = 7$ $(2, -1)$
    $x - 2y = 4$

4. $\dfrac{1}{3}x + \dfrac{4}{5} = \dfrac{2}{5}y$ $(0, 2)$

    $-\dfrac{3}{4}x + 2 = \dfrac{1}{2}y$

1. _____

2. _____

3. _____

4. _____

Solve each system of equations by graphing.

5. $x - y = -3$
    $4x - y = 0$

6. $4x + y = -5$
    $x + y = 1$

7. $5x - y = 4$
    $3x + 2y = 18$

5.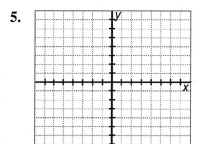

6.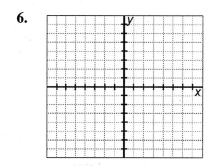

7.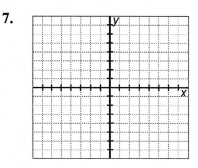

Additional Exercises 4.1 *(cont.)*

Name_____

8. $4x + 3y = -13$
   $7x - 5y = -33$

8.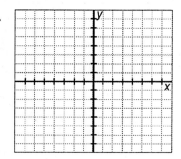

9. $y + 2 = \dfrac{1}{2}x$
   $3x - y = 12$

9.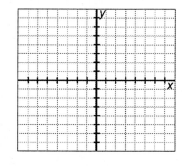

10. $3y + 16 = x$
   $x - 25 = 6y$

10.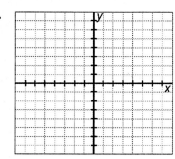

11. $3x + 2y = -2$
   $x - y = -4$

11.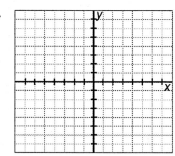

12. $x - 3y = 13$
   $4x + y = -26$

12.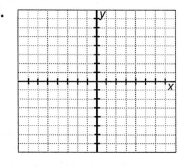

Additional Exercises 4.1 *(cont.)*

13. $3x = y - 6$
$6x - 2y = -12$

13.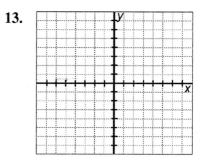

14. $3y = 9$
$2x = 8$

14.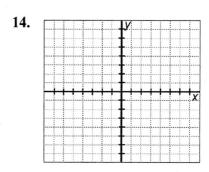

15. $y - 2 = \dfrac{1}{2}x$

$y + 2 = \dfrac{5}{2}x$

15.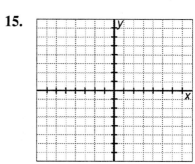

16. $3y - x = -15$
$3y + 2x = -6$

16.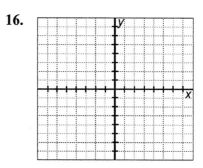

17. $x = 3y - 9$

$y = \dfrac{1}{3}x - 2$

17.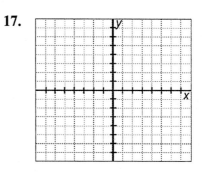

18. $y = -3x + 4$

   $-4y = 2x - 6$

18.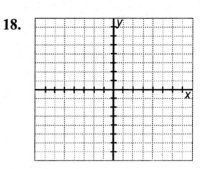

19. Draw a graph of two linear equations whose associated system has the solution (1, 5).

19.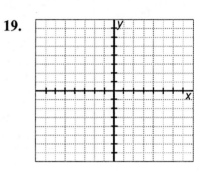

20. Draw a graph of two linear equations whose associated system has no solution.

20.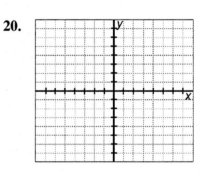

Additional Exercises 4.2
Form I

Solve each system of equations by substitution.

1. $x + y = -8$
   $y = -2x$

2. $2x + y = -10$
   $x = -3y$

3. $x - 4y = 18$
   $y = -2x$

4. $4x - 3y = 36$
   $x = 3y$

5. $3y = x - 5$
   $x = -7y$

6. $3x - 2y = -6$
   $4x + y = 3$

7. $x + y = 2$
   $x - y = 4$

8. $x - 3y = 5$
   $-y = 4$

9. $7x + 6y = 4$
   $3x = 5y - 21$

10. $3x - 4y = -5$
    $2x + y = -7$

11. $y = -\dfrac{1}{2}x - 4$
    $y = 4x - 13$

12. $2x - 6y = -2$
    $10x - 30y = -10$

1. _____

2. _____

3. _____

4. _____

5. _____

6. _____

7. _____

8. _____

9. _____

10. _____

11. _____

12. _____

Additional Exercises 4.2 *(cont.)*

Name_____

13. $2x + y = 13$
$4x - 3y = -19$

13. _____

14. $\dfrac{1}{2}x + y = 3$
$2x + 4y = 5$

14. _____

15. $2x + 8y = 22$
$2x - 5y = -4$

15. _____

16. $8x + 12y = -8$
$-2x + 2y = 2$

16. _____

17. $2x + 4y = -4$
$5x + y = 2$

17. _____

18. $2x + 3y = 5$
$x - y = 5$

18. _____

Additional Exercises 4.2
Form II

Name_____

Date_____

Solve each system of equations by substitution.

1. $2x + y = 16$
    $y = 2x$

    1. _____

2. $3x + y = 7$
    $y = 4x$

    2. _____

3. $x = 3y - 1$
    $x + 2y = 14$

    3. _____

4. $4x - y = 7$
    $y = 2x - 3$

    4. _____

5. $2x - 3y = 16$
    $x = 4y + 3$

    5. _____

6. $x + 6y = 6$
    $3x - 4y = -4$

    6. _____

7. $2x + 3y = 14$
    $x + 2y = 7$

    7. _____

8. $\frac{1}{2}x + \frac{1}{2}y = 5$
    $x - y = 8$

    8. _____

9. $5x - 3y = -11$
    $x - 2y = 2$

    9. _____

10. $5x - y = 4$
    $10x - 2y = 10$

    10. _____

11. $5x + 2y = 4$
    $3x + y = 9$

    11. _____

12. $4x + 3y = 9$
    $3x + 4y = 12$

    12. _____

13. $3x - 5y = 15$

$y = \dfrac{3}{5}x - 3$

13. _____

14. $2x - y = -7$

$4x - y = -27$

14. _____

15. $2x + 3y = 7$

$y = -\dfrac{2}{3}x + 3$

15. _____

16. $x - y = 3$

$6x + 4y = 13$

16. _____

17. $3x + 3y = 7$

$4x - y = 6$

17. _____

18. $3y + 1 = 7x$

$14x - 2 = 6y$

18. _____

Suppose that the demand and supply equations for coal in a certain marketing area are $y = -2x + 150$ and $y = 3x$, respectively, where x is the price per ton in dollars and y is the quantity of coal in thousands of tons. In economics, *market equilibrium* is said to occur when these equations are solved simultaneously. Solve the system using substitution to answer the following.

19. At what price per ton will the market reach equilibrium?

19. _____

20. How much coal needs to be sold to reach market equilibrium?

20. _____

Additional Exercises 4.2
Form III

Solve each system of equations by substitution.

1. $2x - 2y = 12$
   $x = -5$

   1. _____

2. $x - 2y = 5$
   $3x - 6y = 15$

   2. _____

3. $y = \dfrac{1}{2}x + 8$
   $y - 4 = -2(x + 3)$

   3. _____

4. $3x + 2y = 4$
   $2x - 3y = -6$

   4. _____

5. $x + 4y = \dfrac{11}{2}$
   $8x + 5y = -10$

   5. _____

6. $2x + 5y = 7$
   $4x - 3y = 1$

   6. _____

7. $\dfrac{x}{10} - \dfrac{y}{5} = 1$
   $\dfrac{x}{6} - y = 5$

   7. _____

8. $\dfrac{x}{4} + y = \dfrac{5}{4}$
   $-2x - 3y = 12$

   8. _____

9. $2x + 5y = -5$
   $3x + 2y = \dfrac{7}{2}$

   9. _____

10. $2x + \dfrac{1}{3}y = -\dfrac{1}{3}$
    $12x + 2y = -2$

    10. _____

11. $4x + 2y = -17$
    $x + 2y = -2$

    11. _____

12. $3x + 2y = -1$
    $\dfrac{3}{2}x + y = 4$

    12. _____

13. $3x + y = 10$
$2(x - y) = 4$

13. _____

14. $5x + 5y = 5$
$2x - y = -2$

14. _____

15. $\dfrac{x}{2} - \dfrac{y}{3} = 2$

$\dfrac{x}{4} + \dfrac{y}{3} = \dfrac{5}{2}$

15. _____

16. $2x - 8y = 12$
$3x - 12y = -9$

16. _____

17. $3x - 9y = 39$
$4x + y = -26$

17. _____

18. $5x + 2y = -24$
$4x - 3y = -10$

18. _____

Suppose that the demand and supply equations for coal in a certain marketing area are $y = 3x + 150$ and $y = 5x$, respectively, where x is the price per ton in dollars and y is the quantity of coal in thousands of tons. In economics, *market equilibrium* is said to occur when these equations are solved simultaneously. Solve the system using substitution to answer the following.

19. At what price per ton will the market reach equilibrium?

19. _____

20. How much coal needs to be sold to reach market equilibrium?

20. _____

Additional Exercises 4.3
Form I

Name_____

Date_____

Solve each system of equations by addition.

1. $2x + 5y = 10$
   $x - 5y = 5$

2. $2x - 4y = 10$
   $-4x + 4y = -14$

3. $x + y = 2$
   $x - y = -6$

4. $3x - y = 7$
   $x + y = 5$

5. $5x - 2y = 4$
   $3x + y = 9$

6. $2x - 7y = 3$
   $-2x + y = -9$

7. $2x - 5 = y$
   $x - 7 = -y$

8. $3y + 4x = 5$
   $y + 4x = 7$

9. $3a - 4b = 0$
   $a - b = 1$

10. $3x + 6y = 6$
    $2x + y = 1$

11. $8x + 3y = -21$
    $4x + 5y = -7$

12. $x + y = -1$
    $2x - y = -5$

1. _____

2. _____

3. _____

4. _____

5. _____

6. _____

7. _____

8. _____

9. _____

10. _____

11. _____

12. _____

13. $3x + 5y = 16$
$2x - y = 2$

14. $x + 5y = -7$
$2x + 7y = -8$

15. $2x + 8y = 22$
$x + 2y = 5$

16. $2x - 3y = 13$
$x + 5y = 13$

17. $3x + 12y = 3$
$x + 4y = 8$

18. $5x - 2y = 15$
$2y = -3x - 7$

If the supermarket price of a certain cut of beef is p dollars per pound, then q million pounds will be sold according to the demand equation $p + q = 4$. When the price is p dollars per pound, the packing company will supply q million pounds of meat according to the supply equation $p - 4q = -2$. Use the addition method to find the point of market equilibrium to answer the following.

19. At market equilibrium, what is the price per pound?

20. At market equilibrium, how many pounds of meat will be supplied?

Additional Exercises 4.3
Form II

Name_____

Date_____

Solve each system of equations by addition.

1. $2x + y = 3$
    $-2x + 5y = -9$

2. $3x + 5y = 0$
    $2x - 5y = -25$

3. $-4x - y = -6$
    $4x - 3y = 18$

4. $12 = x + 4y$
    $-36 = -5x + 4y$

5. $5x + y = 2$
    $5x - 3y = 14$

6. $3x - y = 5$
    $x - 2y = -5$

7. $5x - 2y = 4$
    $3x + y = 9$

8. $x + 2y = 6$
    $5x + 3y = 2$

9. $3a - 6b = 18$
    $4a + 8b = 24$

10. $3x + 4y = 11$
    $4x - 3y = 23$

11. $-7x + 8y = -16$
    $2x - 5y = 10$

12. $x - y = 5$
    $x = y + 3$

1. _____

2. _____

3. _____

4. _____

5. _____

6. _____

7. _____

8. _____

9. _____

10. _____

11. _____

12. _____

13. $2x + y = 5$

$\dfrac{1}{2y} = -x + \dfrac{5}{2}$

13. _____

14. $\dfrac{1}{3}x + \dfrac{1}{2}y = -4$

$\dfrac{1}{6}x - \dfrac{1}{2}y = 1$

14. _____

15. $2x - 3y = 6$
$3x + 4y = -2$

15. _____

16. $3x - 5y = 7$
$5x - 2y = -1$

16. _____

17. $5x + 2y = 7$
$10x + 4y = 13$

17. _____

18. $x + 2y = 8$

$y = -\dfrac{1}{2}x + 4$

18. _____

If the supermarket price of a certain cut of beef is p dollars per pound, then q million pounds will be sold according to the demand equation $p + q = 4$. When the price is p dollars per pound, the packing company will supply q million pounds of meat according to the supply equation $p - 4q = -6$. Use the addition method to find the point of market equilibrium to answer the following.

19. At market equilibrium, what is the price per pound?

19. _____

20. At market equilibrium, how many pounds of meat will be supplied?

20. _____

Additional Exercises 4.3
Form III

Solve each system of equations by addition.

1. $y = 2x - 3$
   $-y = x$

2. $-2x + y = -6$
   $6x - 13y = -12$

3. $-4y = x$
   $2y = x - 6$

4. $10x - 10y = 20$
   $5x - 2y = 10$

5. $6x - 9y = -15$
   $5x - 2y = -40$

6. $3x + 2y = 12$
   $4x + 3y = 7$

7. $1.8x + 0.8y = 1.4$
   $1.2x + 0.6y = 1.2$

8. $4x + 6y = 6$
   $6x + 4y = -11$

9. $y = -\dfrac{2}{5}x + \dfrac{9}{5}$

   $y = \dfrac{4}{7}x + \dfrac{16}{7}$

10. $4x - 5y = 0$
    $8(x - 1) = 10y$

11. $-3(x - 2) + 7y = 5$
    $5y = 2x$

12. $5x + y = -5$
    $6x - 3 = -3y$

1. _____

2. _____

3. _____

4. _____

5. _____

6. _____

7. _____

8. _____

9. _____

10. _____

11. _____

12. _____

13. $\dfrac{a}{4} - \dfrac{3b}{2} = \dfrac{15}{2}$

$\dfrac{1}{5}(a + 2b) = -2$

14. $-3x - 5y = -21$
$-9x + 2y = -63$

15. $-3x + 3y = 12$
$-6x - y = -39$

16. $3x + 5y = 3$
$x + 2y = 13$

17. $x + 2y = 4$
$x = -\dfrac{8}{3}y + 8$

18. $4(x + y) = 6$
$2(x - y) = 9$

19. $2(2y + 3) - 2x = 1 - x$
$x + y = \dfrac{1}{5}(7 + y)$

20. $6x - 2y = 5$
$5x + 3y = -2$

21. If the supermarket price of a certain cut of beef is p dollars per pound, then q million pounds will be sold according to the demand equation $p + q = 4$. When the price is p dollars per pound, the packing company will supply q million pounds of meat according to the supply equation $p - 4q = -2$. Use the addition method to find the point of market equilibrium to answer the following.

    a. At market equilibrium, what is the price per pound?

    b. At market equilibrium, how many pounds of meat will be supplied?

13._____

14._____

15._____

16._____

17._____

18._____

19._____

20._____

21a._____

b._____

Additional Exercises 4.4
Form I

Name

Date _____

Solve each problem using systems of equations.

1. The sum of two numbers is 45. Their difference is 25. Find the two numbers.

2. The sum of two numbers is 52. The larger number is 2 more than four times the smaller number. Find the numbers.

3. The difference between two numbers is 7. If three times the smaller is subtracted from twice the larger, the result is 6. Find the numbers.

4. One record and four tapes cost $35. Two records and three tapes cost $40. Find the cost of each record and tape.

5. At school, two photography packages are available. Package A contains 2 class picture and 25 wallet-size pictures for $62. Package B contains 1 class pictures and 15 wallet-size pictures for $36. Find the cost of a class picture and the cost of a wallet-size picture.

6. Jennifer invested a total of $500, part of it at 9% interest and the rest at 10%. If $48 was earned from the investment, how much money was invested in each?

7. The price of admission for a concert was $10 for adults and $3 for children. Altogether, 520 tickets were sold, and the resulting revenue was $3,450. How many adults and how many children attended the concert?

8. Two cyclist start at the same pint and travel in opposite directions. One travels 4mph faster than the other. In 3 hours they are 492 miles apart. How fast is each traveling?

9. If a plane can travel 460 miles per hour with the wind and 400 miles per hour against the wind, find the speed of the plane in still air.

10. A hot air balloon travels 40 miles against the wind in the same amount of time that it travels 200 miles with the wind. If the speed of the wind is 20 mph, how fast does the hot air balloon travel against the wind?

1. _____

2. _____

3. _____

4. _____

5. _____

6. _____

7. _____

8. _____

9. _____

10. _____

Name _____

11. A druggist has one solution that is 40% iodine and another solution that is 70% iodine. How much of each solution should the druggist use to get 30 ml of a mixture that is 50% iodine.

11. _____

12. A chemist has one solution that is 20% alcohol and another that is 60% alcohol. How much of each solution should the chemist use to get 40 ml of a solution that is 35% alcohol?

12. _____

13. The perimeter of a rectangle is 74 cm. The length is 3 meters less than four times the width. Find the length and the width of the rectangle.

13. _____

14. The perimeter of a rectangle is 58 inches. The length is 5 inches more than the width. Find the length and width of the rectangle.

14. _____

15. In a right triangle, one acute angle is 15° greater than two times the other acute angle. Find the difference between the measures of the angles.

15. _____

16. Jennifer has a number of dimes and quarters totaling $12.05. The number of quarters is 5 more than twice the number of dimes. How many of each coin does she have?

16. _____

17. Two angles are complementary. One angle is 6° less than twice the other angle. Find the measure of each angle.

17. _____

18 Two acute angles of a right triangle are complementary. The larger angle is $2\frac{1}{3}$ times greater than the smaller angle. Find the measure of each angle.

18. _____

19. Two angles are supplementary. The larger angle is 20° less than three times the smaller angle. Find the measure of each angle.

19. _____

Additional Exercises 4.4
Form II

Name_____

Date_____

Solve each problem using systems of equations.

1. The sum of two numbers is 56. Their difference is 4. Find the two numbers.

1. _____

2. The sum of two numbers is 44. The second number is 5 more than twice the first. Find the numbers.

2. _____

3. The difference between two numbers is 16. Five times the smaller is the same as 8 less than twice the larger. Find the numbers.

3. _____

4. Two records and three tapes cost $31. Three records and two tapes cost $29. Find the cost of each record and tape.

4. _____

5. At school, two photography packages are available. Package A contains 1 class picture and 10 wallet-size pictures for $19. Package B contains 2 class pictures and 15 wallet-size pictures for $31. Find the cost of a class picture and the cost of a wallet-size picture.

5. _____

6. A broker invested a total of $4500 in two different stocks. One stock earned 9% per year. The other earned 6% per year. If $360 was earned from the investment, how much money was invested in each?

6. _____

7. The price of admission for a concert was $9 for adults and $4 for children. Altogether, 1770 tickets were sold, and the resulting revenue was $14,680. How many adults and how many children attended the concert?

7. _____

8. Mike made a trip in 40 hours. Joe made the same trip in 30 hours because Joe was traveling 6 km per hour faster. How many km was the trip?

8. _____

9. The hiking club hiked to a state park at 4 mph. They got a ride back to town in a truck that went 20 mph. If the round trip took 18 hours, how far was it from town to the park?

9. _____

10. When Lucy swims with the current, she swims 18 km in 6 hours. Against the current, she can swim only 14 km in the same time. How fast can Lucy swim in still water? What is the rate of the current?

10. _____

Additional Exercises 4.4 *(cont.)*

11. A druggist has one solution that is 10% iodine and another solution that is 50% iodine. How much of each solution should the druggist use to get 100 ml of a mixture that is 20% iodine.

11. _____

12. A chemist has one solution that is 20% alcohol and another that is 60% alcohol. How much of each solution should the chemist use to get 100 ml of a solution that is 52% alcohol?

12. _____

13. The perimeter of a rectangle is 54 cm. Two times the height is 3 cm more than the base. Find the length of the height and length of the base.

13. _____

14. The perimeter of a rectangle is 58 inches. The base is 5 more than three times the height. Find the length of the height and the length of the base.

14. _____

15. The sum of the legs of a right triangle is 17 inches. The longer leg is 2 more than twice the shorter. The hypotenuse is 13 in. Find the length of each leg.

15. _____

16. Todd has 27 total coins in his bank, all dimes and quarters. The coins have a total value of $4.95. How many of each coin does he have?

16. _____

17. Two angles are complementary. The larger angle is 6 less than 5 times the smaller angle.. Find the measure of each angle.

17. _____

18. The two acute angles of a right triangle are complementary. The larger angle is $1\frac{1}{2}$ times larger than the smaller angle. Find the measure of each angle.

18. _____

19. Two angles are supplementary. The larger angle is 15° less than twice the smaller angle. Find the measure of each angle.

19. _____

Additional Exercises 4.4
Form III

Name _____

Date _____

Solve each problem using systems of equations.

1. The sum of two numbers is 46. Their difference is 22. Find the two numbers.

2. The sum of two numbers is 88. The second number is 5 more than four times the first. Find the numbers.

3. The sum of two numbers 113. The larger number is 1 less than twice the smaller number. Find the numbers.

4. Five records and three tapes cost $47. Three records and five tapes cost $41. Find the cost of each record and tape.

5. At school, two photography packages are available. Package A contains 3 class picture and 6 wallet-size pictures for $24. Package B contains 2 class pictures and 10 wallet-size pictures for $19. Find the cost of a class picture and the cost of a wallet-size picture.

6. A broker invested a total of $1300 in two different stocks. One stock earned 10% per year. The other earned 12% per year. If $146 was earned from the investment, how much money was invested in each?

7. The price of admission for a concert was $5 for adults and $3 for children. Altogether, 5000 tickets were sold, and the resulting revenue was $21,000. How many adults and how many children attended the concert?

8. Brady spent $8.35 on four pretzels and five cokes. Two cokes cost $0.35 more than one pretzel. Find the cost of a pretzel and the cost of a coke.

9. Jerrod rides a motorcycle 165 miles in the same amount of time Jaycie rides her bicycle 45 miles. Jerrod can ride his motorcycle 40 mph faster than Jaycie can ride her bicycle. How fast does Jerrod ride his motorcycle?

10. Jeremy traveled 85 miles downstream on a canoe in the same amount of time he traveled 15 miles upstream on his raft. If the speed of the current was 7 mph, how fast did he travel upstream?

1. _____

2. _____

3. _____

4. _____

5. _____

6. _____

7. _____

8. _____

9. _____

10. _____

Name_____

11. A druggist has one solution that is 30% iodine and another solution that is 70% iodine. How much of each solution should the druggist use to get 10 ml of a mixture that is 40% iodine.

11. _____

12. A chemist has one solution that is 50% alcohol and another that is 90% alcohol. How much of each solution should the chemist use to get 32 ml of a solution that is 75% alcohol?

12. _____

13. The perimeter of a rectangle is 50 cm. The length is 1 cm more than three times the width. Find the length and the width.

13. _____

14. The perimeter of a rectangle is 38 inches. The width is 5 cm less than the length. Find the length and the width.

14. _____

15. The sum of the legs of a right triangle is 7. The longer leg is one more than the shorter leg. The hypotenuse is 5. Find the length of each leg.

15. _____

16. Cindy has three times as many nickels as pennies in her purse. Together her pennies and nickels have a value of $4.80. How many of each coin does he have?

16. _____

17. Two angles are complementary. The larger angle is 6 more than 3 times the smaller angle.. Find the measure of each angle.

17. _____

18. Two acute angles of a triangle are complementary. The larger angle is twice the smaller angle. Find the measure of each angle.

18. _____

19. Two angles are supplementary. The larger angle is 5 times greater than the smaller angle. Find the measure of each angle.

19. _____

Additional Exercises
4.5
Form I

Determine which ordered pairs given are solutions of the linear inequality $x - 3y > 9$

    1.   (1, -4)

    2.   (-3, -4)

    3.   (5, 2)

Determine which ordered pairs are solutions of the linear inequality $4x - 5y \geq 2$.

    4. $(-3, -2)$

    5.   (5, -1)

    6.   (-2, -2)

Determine which ordered pairs given are solutions of the linear inequality $y < 4x$.

    7. $(-5, 0)$

    8. $(3, -2)$

Graph each inequality

    9. $x + y \leq 5$

    10. $x - 4y > 8$

1. _____

2. _____

3. _____

4. _____

5. _____

6. _____

7. _____

8. _____

9.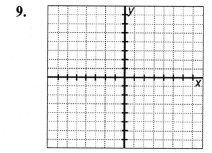

10.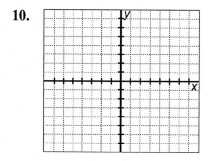

11. $y < x$

11.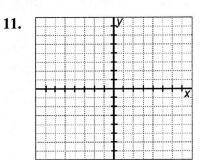

12. $x \leq -3y$

12.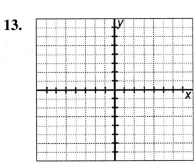

13. $x + 2 > 0$

13.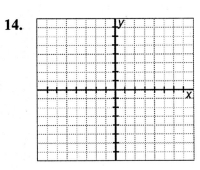

14. $x < -3$

14.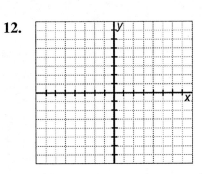

15. $y \geq 4$

15.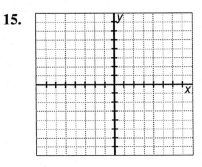

Additional Exercises 4.5

Form II

Determine which ordered pairs given are solutions of the linear inequality $x - 2y > 8$

    1.   (2, -5)

    2.   (-2, 4)

    3.   (4, -2)

Determine which ordered pairs are solutions of the linear inequality $3x - 4y \geq 2$.

    4.   (−1, −2)

    5.   (2, 1)

    6.   (3, 2)

Determine which ordered pairs given are solutions of the linear inequality $x > 2y$.

    7.   (−4, -3)

    8.   (-10, −5)

Graph each inequality

    9. $x + y \leq 6$

    10. $x - 4y > 4$

Name _____

Date _____

1. _____

2. _____

3. _____

4. _____

5. _____

6. _____

7. _____

8. _____

9.

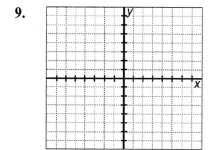

10.

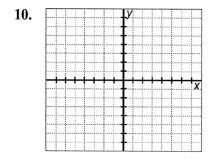

11. $y < 5x$

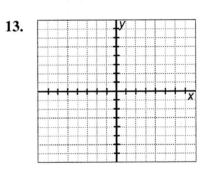

11.

12. $x \leq -4y$

12.

13. $y > x - 8$

13.

14. $y < 6$

14.

15. $x \geq -7$

15.

Additional Exercises 4.5

Form III

Determine which ordered pairs given are solutions of the linear inequality $x - y > 5$

    1.   (1, -4)

    2.   (-4, -3)

    3.   (7, -1)

Determine which ordered pairs are solutions of the linear inequality $2x - 5y \geq 7$.

    4.   (5, 3)

    5.   (4, -8)

    6.   (-2, 1)

Determine which ordered pairs given are solutions of the linear inequality $y < -3x$.

    7.   (3, 0)

    8.   (-4, 5)

Graph each inequality

    9. $x + y \leq -4$

    10. $x - 3y > 8$

1. _____

2. _____

3. _____

4. _____

5. _____

6. _____

7. _____

8. _____

9.
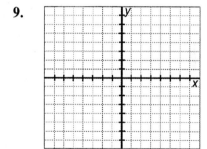

10.
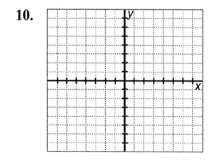

Name _____

11. $y < -x$

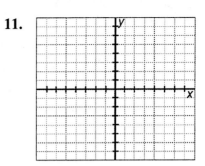

12. $x \le 7y$

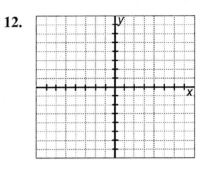

13. $x + 4 > 0$

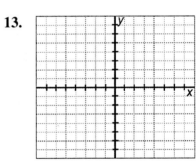

14. $x < 1$

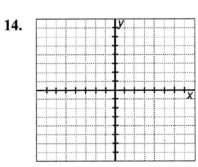

15. $y \ge -3$

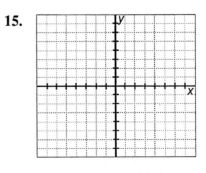

Additional Exercises
4.6
Form I

Name _____

Date _____

Graph each inequality

1. $\begin{cases} y < 4x - 3 \\ y \le x + 5 \end{cases}$

2. $\begin{cases} y < 3x - 2 \\ y \le x + 2 \end{cases}$

3. $\begin{cases} y < 5x - 3 \\ y \le x + 1 \end{cases}$

4. $\begin{cases} y < 3x - 5 \\ y \le x + 3 \end{cases}$

5. $\begin{cases} x \ge 3y \\ x + 3y \le -8 \end{cases}$

1.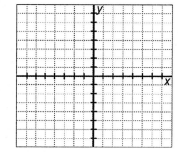

2.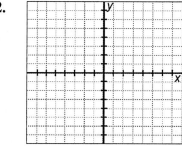

3.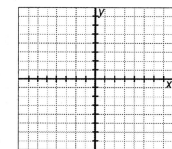

4.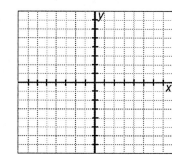

5.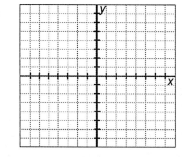

Additional Exercises 4.6 *(cont.)*

6. $\begin{cases} x \geq 4y \\ x + 4y \leq 5 \end{cases}$

6.

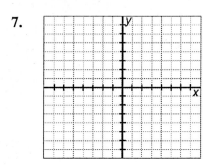

7. $\begin{cases} x \geq 2y \\ x + 2y \leq -5 \end{cases}$

7.

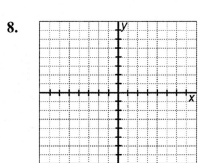

8. $\begin{cases} x \geq 4y \\ x + 4y \leq -6 \end{cases}$

8.

9. $\begin{cases} -5x < y \\ x + 5y < 3 \end{cases}$

9.

10. $\begin{cases} -3x < y \\ x + 2y < 3 \end{cases}$

10.

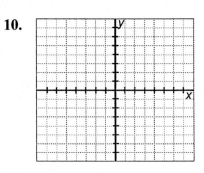

Additional Exercises 4.6
Form II

Name _____

Date _____

Graph each inequality

1. $\begin{cases} -4x < y \\ x + 2y < 3 \end{cases}$

2. $\begin{cases} -3x < y \\ x + 3y < 4 \end{cases}$

3. $\begin{cases} 4x - 4y \geq -12 \\ 2x + y \leq 5 \end{cases}$

4. $\begin{cases} 3x - 4y \geq -9 \\ 2x + y \leq 4 \end{cases}$

5. $\begin{cases} 5x - 2y \geq -15 \\ 2x + y \leq 4 \end{cases}$

1.

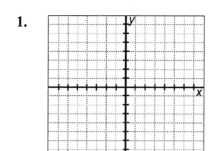

2.

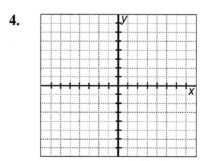

3.

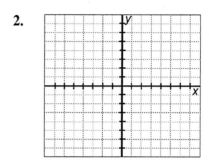

4.

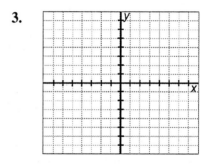

5.

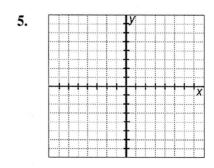

Additional Exercises 4.6 *(cont.)*

6. $\begin{cases} 2x - 5y \geq -4 \\ 3x + y \leq 5 \end{cases}$

6.

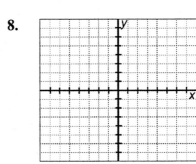

7. $\begin{cases} y \geq 3 \\ x < -4 \end{cases}$

7.

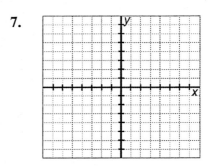

8. $\begin{cases} y \geq -5 \\ x < -5 \end{cases}$

8.

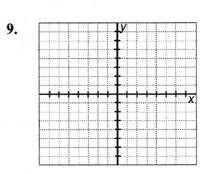

9. $\begin{cases} y \leq 3 \\ x > -4 \end{cases}$

9.

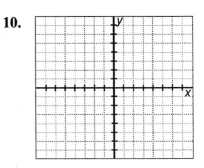

10. $\begin{cases} y \leq -4 \\ x > 4 \end{cases}$

10.

Additional Exercises 4.6
Form III

Graph each inequality

1. $\begin{cases} 2x + 4y \leq 8 \\ x < 3 \end{cases}$

2. $\begin{cases} 3x + 2y \leq 6 \\ x < 3 \end{cases}$

3. $\begin{cases} 2x + 4y \leq 8 \\ x < 4 \end{cases}$

4. $\begin{cases} 2x + 2y \leq 4 \\ x < -2 \end{cases}$

5. $\begin{cases} 3x - 3y \leq 9 \\ y \leq -2 \end{cases}$

1.

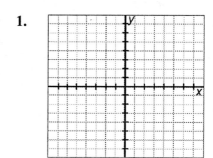

2.

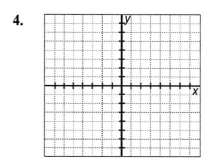

3.

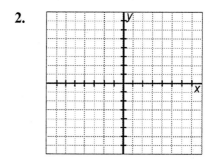

4.

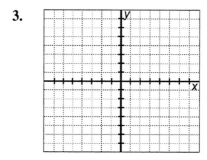

5.

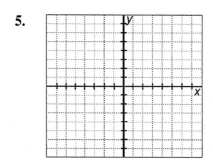

Additional Exercises 4.6 *(cont.)*

6. $\begin{cases} 4x - 2y \le 8 \\ y \le 2 \end{cases}$

6.

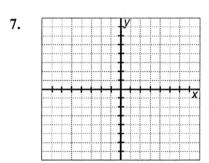

7. $\begin{cases} 2x - y > 4 \\ y < 3 \end{cases}$

7.

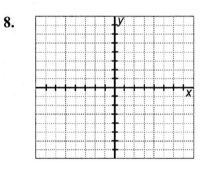

8. $\begin{cases} 3x - 3y \le 9 \\ y \le 5 \end{cases}$

8.

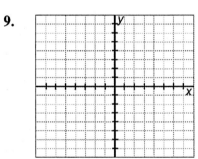

9. $\begin{cases} y \ge \dfrac{1}{2}x + 6 \\ y \le \dfrac{1}{2}x - 4 \end{cases}$

9.

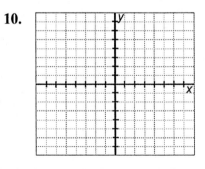

10. $\begin{cases} y \ge \dfrac{1}{4}x + 1 \\ y \le \dfrac{1}{4}x - 7 \end{cases}$

10.

Additional Exercises 5.1
Form I

Name _____

Date _____

Simplify each expression. Write results with positive exponents.

1. Complete the table for the polynomial $6x^3 - 3x^2 - x - 8$

Term	Coefficient
$6x^3$	
	-3
x	
-8	

1. _____

Find the degree of each of the following polynomials and determine whether it is a monomial, binomial, trinomial, or none of these.

2. $6x - 14$

3. $8 - 2x + 5x^2$

2. _____

3. _____

Find the value of each polynomial when **(a)** $x = 3$ and **(b)** $x = -2$.

4. $2x - 4$

5. $x^2 - 4x + 3$

4(a). _____

4(b). _____

5(a). _____

5(b). _____

Simplify each of the following by combining like terms.

6. $11x^3 + 8x^3$

7. $6x^2 - 17x^2 + x$

8. $12xy - 10xy + 3y - y$

9. Identify the degree of each term and the degree of the polynomial: $a^3b^4 - 3 + 2a^3b^3 + 5a^5$

6. _____

7. _____

8. _____

9. _____

Add or subtract as indicated.

10. $(13y + 8) - (-5y - 6)$

11. $(3a^2 - 6a - 5) + (2a - 2a^2 - 8)$

12. $(-x^2 + 5) - (x^2 - 3) + (4x^2 - 5x - 8)$

10. _____

11. _____

12. _____

13. $(12a^2 - 3a + 5) + (a^2 - 5a - 3) - (4a^2 - 8)$

13. _____

14. _____

14. $(6x - 8y + 4) - (-5x - y - 10)$

15. $\left(3x^2 + \dfrac{3}{5}y^2 - 8\right) - \left(2x^2 + \dfrac{1}{5}y^2 - 2\right)$

15. _____

16. $(2x^2y - 7xy + x^2y^2 - 8) - (10x^2y^2 - 3 + 4yx^2)$

16. _____

Evaluate the following expressions by combining like terms.
Write the results in standard form.

17. Add $(7x^2 - 17x + 4)$ and $(-x^2 + 3x - 9)$

17. _____

18. Subtract $(3y - 11)$ from $(3y^2 - 6y - 9)$

18. _____

19. Find the perimeter of a triangle with sides $(5x - 2x^2)$ in, $(6x^2 + 8)$ in, and $(7 - 12x)$ in.

19. _____

20. A piece of gutter is $(5y^2 - 3y + 2)$ meters. A piece $(y^2 - 10)$ meters is cut off. Express the remaining length as a polynomial

20. _____

Additional Exercises 5.1
Form II

Name _____

Date _____

Simplify each expression. Write results with positive exponents.

1. Complete the table for the polynomial $5x^3 - 4x^2 - x - 7$

Term	Coefficient
$5x^3$	
	-4
x	
-7	

Find the degree of each of the following polynomials and determine whether it is a monomial, binomial, trinomial, or none of these.

2. $7x - 12$

3. $5 - 3x + 4x^2$

Find the value of each polynomial when **(a)** $x = 0$ and **(b)** $x = -1$.

4. $3x - 4$

5. $x^2 - 6x + 2$

Simplify each of the following by combining like terms.

6. $12x^3 + 9x^3$

7. $7x^2 - 17x^2 + 6x$

8. $10xy - 12xy + 2y - y$

9. Identify the degree of each term and the degree of the polynomial: $a^2b^4 - 7 + 3a^3b^3 + 5a^4$

Add or subtract as indicated.

10. $(15y + 7) - (-4y - 5)$

11. $(3a^2 - 7a - 4) + (2a - 5a^2 - 7)$

12. $(-x^2 + 3) - (x^2 - 4) + (3x^2 - 4x - 9)$

1. _____

2. _____

3. _____

4(a). _____

4(b). _____

5(a). _____

5(b). _____

6. _____

7. _____

8. _____

9. _____

10. _____

11. _____

12. _____

Name _____

13. $(15a^2 - 4a + 7) + (a^2 - 6a - 4) - (3a^2 - 8)$

13. _____

14. _____

14. $(5x - 7y + 4) - (-3x - y - 9)$

15. $\left(\dfrac{1}{3}x^2 + \dfrac{3}{4}y^2 - 8\right) - \left(\dfrac{4}{9}x^2 + \dfrac{5}{6}y^2 - 2\right)$

15. _____

16. $(2x^2y - 7xy + x^2y^2 - 7) - (17x^2y^2 - 1 + 5yx^2)$

16. _____

Evaluate the following expressions by combining like terms. Write the results in standard form.

17. Add $(7x^2 - 19x + 4)$ and $(-x^2 + 4x - 9)$

17. _____

18. Subtract $(2y - 15)$ from $(3y^2 - 4y - 8)$

18. _____

19. Find the perimeter of a triangle with sides $(4x - 3x^2)$ in, $(5x^2 + 7)$ in, and $(9 - 10x)$ in.

19. _____

20. A piece of gutter is $(6y^2 - 4y + 3)$ meters. A piece $(y^2 - 12)$ meters is cut off. Express the remaining length as a polynomial

20. _____

Additional Exercises 5.1
Form III

Name _____

Date _____

Simplify each expression. Write results with positive exponents.

1. Complete the table for the polynomial $8x^3 - 6x^2 - x - 6$

Term	Coefficient
$8x^3$	
	-6
x	
-6	

Find the degree of each of the following polynomials and determine whether it is a monomial, binomial, trinomial, or none of these.

2. $5x - 9$

3. $3x^4yz^2$

Find the value of each polynomial when **(a)** $x = 3$ and **(b)** $x = -1$.

4. $4x - 6$

5. $x^2 - 5x + 4$

Simplify each of the following by combining like terms.

6. $10x^3 + 7x^3$

7. $15x^2 - 12x^2 + 5x$

8. $16xy - 14xy + 5y - y$

9. Identify the degree of each term and the degree of the polynomial: $a^5b^4 - 9 + 3a^2b^3 + 6a^3$

Add or subtract as indicated.

10. $(10y + 6) - (-3y - 7)$

11. $(5a^2 - 4a - 3) + (8a - 5a^2 - 7)$

12. $(-x^2 + 4) - (x^2 - 7) + (5x^2 - 4x - 10)$

1. _____

2. _____

3. _____

4(a). _____

4(b). _____

5(a). _____

5(b). _____

6. _____

7. _____

8. _____

9. _____

10. _____

11. _____

12. _____

13. $(13a^2 - 5a + 8) + (a^2 - 4a - 2) - (3a^2 - 6)$

13. _____

14. _____

14. $(7x - 9y + 2) - (-2x - y - 10)$

15. $\left(\frac{4}{9}x^2 + \frac{1}{2}y^2 - 10\right) - \left(\frac{1}{3}x^2 + \frac{5}{6}y^2 - 12\right)$

15. _____

16. $(4x^2y - 6xy + 17x^2y^2 - 7) - (10x^2y^2 - 1 + 3yx^2)$

16. _____

Evaluate the following expressions by combining like terms.
Write the results in standard form.

17. Add $(9x^2 - 12x + 4)$ and $(-x^2 + 2x - 10)$

17. _____

18. Subtract $(y - 13)$ from $(5y^2 - 4y - 10)$

18. _____

19. Find the perimeter of a triangle with sides $(7x - x^2)$ in, $(8x^2 + 6)$ in, and $(10x)$ in.

19. _____

20. A piece of gutter is $(5y^2 - 2y + 1)$ meters. A piece $(y^2 - 8)$ meters is cut off. Express the remaining length as a polynomial

20. _____

Additional Exercises 5.2
Form I

Name _____

Date _____

Multiply.

1. $12x^2 \cdot 6x$

2. $(-3.2x^3)(5x^4)$

3. $\left(-\dfrac{5}{6}y^4\right)\left(-\dfrac{2}{20}y^4\right)$

4. $(3x)(-4x^2)(2x^7)$

5. $7y(2y^2 - 6y - 4)$

6. $-4a^2(4ab - 5b + 8a)$

7. $ab^2(2a^2 - 6a^4b^2 - 7b^5)$

8. $(y - 11)(y + 4)$

9. $\left(x + \dfrac{3}{5}\right)\left(x - \dfrac{3}{5}\right)$

10. $(6x - 2)(x + 6)$

11. $(3x^2 - 4)(5x^2 + 9)$

12. $(5y - 3)^2$

13. $(y - 5)(y^2 - 3y + 2)$

14. $\begin{array}{r} 4x^2 + 6x + 4 \\ \underline{x - 2} \end{array}$

15. Write the expression for the area of a rectangle with sides $(4x + 7)$ and $(x + 8)$.

16. Find the area of a triangle with height $5x$ in. and base $(8x - 2)$ in.

17. Find the area of a rectangle with sides $(x + 10)$ ft. and $(5x - 11)$ ft.

18. Find the area of a square with sides $(8x - 7)$ m.

1. _____

2. _____

3. _____

4. _____

5. _____

6. _____

7. _____

8. _____

9. _____

10. _____

11. _____

12. _____

13. _____

14. _____

15. _____

16. _____

17. _____

18. _____

Additional Exercises 5.2
Form II

Name _____

Date _____

Multiply.

1. $15x^2 \cdot 2x$

2. $(-5.2x^3)(2x^4)$

3. $\left(-\dfrac{5}{7}y^4\right)\left(-\dfrac{2}{35}y^2\right)$

4. $(7x)(-5x^2)(x^7)$

5. $5y(2y^2 - 7y - 3)$

6. $-5a^2(ab - 7b + 6a)$

7. $4ab^2(3a^3 - 9a^2b^2 - 10b^3)$

8. $(y - 15)(y + 3)$

9. $\left(x + \dfrac{1}{5}\right)\left(x - \dfrac{2}{9}\right)$

10. $(5x - 3)(4x + 7)$

11. $(2x^2 - 7)(5x^2 + 10)$

12. $(6y - 11)^2$

13. $(y - 8)(y^2 - 5y + 8)$

14. $2x^2 + 7x + 3$
    $\underline{x - 5}$

15. Write the expression for the area of a rectangle with sides $(3x + 5)$ and $(2x + 3)$.

16. Find the area of a triangle with height $8x$ in. and base $(3x + 8)$ in.

17. Find the area of a rectangle with sides $(4x + 3)$ ft. and $(2x - 7)$ ft.

18. Find the area of a square with sides $(3x - 5)$ m.

1. _____

2. _____

3. _____

4. _____

5. _____

6. _____

7. _____

8. _____

9. _____

10. _____

11. _____

12. _____

13. _____

14. _____

15. _____

16. _____

17. _____

18. _____

Additional Exercises 5.2
Form III

Name _____

Date _____

Multiply.

1. $10x^2 \cdot 4x$

2. $(-4.2x^3)(3x^4)$

3. $\left(-\dfrac{5}{9}y^6\right)\left(-\dfrac{3}{10}y^5\right)$

4. $(5x)(-4x^2)(2x^7)$

5. $8y(3y^2 - 6y - 5)$

6. $-3a^2(5ab - 3b + 7a)$

7. $5ab^2(4a^3 - 7a^2b^2 - 9b^3)$

8. $(y - 12)(y + 3)$

9. $\left(x + \dfrac{3}{4}\right)\left(x - \dfrac{1}{4}\right)$

10. $(7x - 4)(2x + 5)$

11. $(4x^2 - 3)(3x^2 + 8)$

12. $(7y - 2)^2$

13. $(y - 7)(y^2 - 4y + 3)$

14. $3x^2 + 5x + 1$
        $\underline{x - 4}$

15. Write the expression for the area of a rectangle with sides $(x + 6)$ and $(4x + 9)$.

16. Find the area of a triangle with height $6x$ in. and base $(9x - 1)$ in.

17. Find the area of a rectangle with sides $(2x + 5)$ ft. and $(x - 9)$ ft.

18. Find the area of a square with sides $(x - 5)$ m.

1. _____

2. _____

3. _____

4. _____

5. _____

6. _____

7. _____

8. _____

9. _____

10. _____

11. _____

12. _____

13. _____

14. _____

15. _____

16. _____

17. _____

18. _____

Additional Exercises 5.3
Form I

Name _____

Date _____

Multiply using the FOIL method.

1. $(x + 9)(x + 2)$

2. $(4x - 11)(x + 6)$

3. $(3x - 13)(x - 2)$

4. $(y^2 + 7)(2y^2 - 9)$

5. $\left(x - \dfrac{3}{10}\right)\left(x + \dfrac{1}{5}\right)$

6. $(4 - 6a)(2 - 3a)$

7. $(x + 8y)(3x - 4y)$

Multiply.

8. $(x + 12)^2$

9. $(10a - 3)^2$

10. $\left(y - \dfrac{3}{5}\right)^2$

11. $(2y - 13)^2$

12. $(x - 11)(x + 11)$

13. $(4x - 10)(4x + 10)$

14. $(3y^2 - 5)(3y^2 + 5)$

15. $\left(3x - \dfrac{1}{6}\right)\left(3x + \dfrac{1}{6}\right)$

Express the following as a product of polynomials in x. Then, multiply and simplify.

16. Find the area of a rectangular rug if its length is $(7x - 6)$ ft and its width is $(x + 4)$ ft.

17. Find the area of a square that has sides $(3x - 1)$ m.

18. Find the area of a rectangle with length $(2x + 7)$ in. and width $(x - 8)$ in.

1. _____

2. _____

3. _____

4. _____

5. _____

6. _____

7. _____

8. _____

9. _____

10. _____

11. _____

12. _____

13. _____

14. _____

15. _____

16. _____

17. _____

18. _____

Additional Exercises 5.3
Form II

Name _____

Date _____

Multiply using the FOIL method.

1. $(x + 8)(x + 1)$

2. $(3x - 10)(x + 4)$

3. $(5x - 12)(x - 1)$

4. $(y^2 + 9)(3y - 8)$

5. $\left(x - \dfrac{5}{12}\right)\left(x + \dfrac{1}{12}\right)$

6. $(5 - 7a)(3 - 4a)$

7. $(x + 9y)(4x - 5y)$

Multiply.

8. $(x + 10)^2$

9. $(11a - 2)^2$

10. $\left(y - \dfrac{5}{7}\right)^2$

11. $(3y - 12)^2$

12. $(x - 10)(x + 10)$

13. $(5x - 12)(5x + 12)$

14. $(7y^2 - 4)(7y^2 + 4)$

15. $\left(4x - \dfrac{2}{5}\right)\left(4x + \dfrac{2}{5}\right)$

Express the following as a product of polynomials in x. Then, multiply and simplify.

16. Find the area of a rectangular rug if its length is $(9x - 7)$ ft and its width is $(x + 5)$ ft.

17. Find the area of a square that has sides $(7x - 1)$ m.

18. Find the area of a rectangle with length $(4x + 5)$ in. and width $(4x - 5)$ in.

1. _____

2. _____

3. _____

4. _____

5. _____

6. _____

7. _____

8. _____

9. _____

10. _____

11. _____

12. _____

13. _____

14. _____

15. _____

16. _____

17. _____

18. _____

Additional Exercises 5.3
Form III

Name _____

Date _____

Multiply using the FOIL method.

1. $(x + 7)(x + 3)$

2. $(5x - 11)(x + 3)$

3. $(4x - 9)(x - 3)$

4. $(y^3 + 6)(4y^2 - 7)$

5. $\left(x - \dfrac{2}{9}\right)\left(x + \dfrac{3}{8}\right)$

6. $(3 - 4a)(1 - 5a)$

7. $(x + 7y)(5x - 6y)$

Multiply.

8. $(x + 14)^2$

9. $(12a - 5)^2$

10. $\left(y - \dfrac{4}{9}\right)^2$

11. $(4y - 13)^2$

12. $(x - 9)(x + 9)$

13. $(3x - 11)(3x + 11)$

14. $(4y^2 - 7)(4y^2 + 7)$

15. $\left(2x - \dfrac{3}{7}\right)\left(2x + \dfrac{3}{7}\right)$

Express the following as a product of polynomials in x. Then, multiply and simplify.

16. Find the area of a rectangular rug if its length is $(8x - 9)$ ft and its width is $(x + 3)$ ft.

17. Find the area of a square that has sides $(8x - 3)$ m.

18. Find the area of a rectangle with length $(5x + 6)$ in. and width $(4x - 3)$ in.

1. _____

2. _____

3. _____

4. _____

5. _____

6. _____

7. _____

8. _____

9. _____

10. _____

11. _____

12. _____

13. _____

14. _____

15. _____

16. _____

17. _____

18. _____

Additional Exercises 5.4
Form I

Name _____

Date _____

Multiply using the FOIL method.

1. $(x + 8)(x + 2)$

2. $(2x - 9)(x + 5)$

3. $(4x - 12)(x - 5)$

4. $(y^2 + 8)(3y - 7)$

5. $\left(x - \dfrac{5}{11} \right)\left(x + \dfrac{1}{11} \right)$

6. $(4 - 7a)(3 - a)$

7. $(x + 10y)(4x - 3y)$

Multiply.

8. $(x + 13)^2$

9. $(14a - 3)^2$

10. $\left(y - \dfrac{3}{7} \right)^2$

11. $(2y - 11)^2$

12. $(x - 8)(x + 8)$

13. $(3x - 13)(3x + 13)$

14. $(9y^2 - 4)(9y^2 + 4)$

15. $\left(2x - \dfrac{1}{5} \right)\left(2x + \dfrac{1}{5} \right)$

Express the following as a product of polynomials in x. Then, multiply and simplify.

16. Find the area of a rectangular rug if its length is $(5x - 7)$ ft and its width is $(x + 4)$ ft.

17. Find the area of a square that has sides $(5x - 3)$ m.

1. _____

2. _____

3. _____

4. _____

5. _____

6. _____

7. _____

8. _____

9. _____

10. _____

11. _____

12. _____

13. _____

14. _____

15. _____

16. _____

17. _____

Additional Exercises 5.4
Form II

Multiply using the FOIL method.

1. $(x + 4)(x + 1)$

2. $(3x - 11)(x + 2)$

3. $(4x - 13)(x - 5)$

4. $(y^2 + 7)(y - 8)$

5. $\left(x - \dfrac{7}{12}\right)\left(x + \dfrac{1}{12}\right)$

6. $(5 - 8a)(2 - 5a)$

7. $(x + 7y)(3x - 5y)$

Multiply.

8. $(x + 100)^2$

9. $(15a - 2)^2$

10. $\left(y - \dfrac{5}{9}\right)^2$

11. $(5y - 12)^2$

12. $(x - 20)(x + 20)$

13. $(6x - 1)(6x + 1)$

14. $(8y^2 - 5)(8y^2 + 5)$

15. $\left(7x - \dfrac{2}{7}\right)\left(7x + \dfrac{2}{7}\right)$

Express the following as a product of polynomials in x. Then, multiply and simplify.

16. Find the area of a rectangular rug if its length is $(7x - 5)$ ft and its width is $(x + 3)$ ft.

17. Find the area of a square that has sides $(8x - 1)$ m.

1. _____

2. _____

3. _____

4. _____

5. _____

6. _____

7. _____

8. _____

9. _____

10. _____

11. _____

12. _____

13. _____

14. _____

15. _____

16. _____

17. _____

Additional Exercises 5.4
Form III

Name _____

Date _____

Multiply using the FOIL method.

1. $(x + 8)(x + 7)$

2. $(5x - 11)(x + 4)$

3. $(6x - 11)(x - 1)$

4. $(a^2 + b^2)(a + b)$

5. $\left(x - \dfrac{7}{13}\right)\left(x + \dfrac{1}{13}\right)$

6. $(3 - 8a)(3 - 4a)$

7. $(x + 10y)(3x - 5y)$

Multiply.

8. $(x + 10.5)^2$

9. $(12a - 7)^2$

10. $\left(y - \dfrac{3}{14}\right)^2$

11. $(5y - 8)^2$

12. $(x - 7)(x + 7)$

13. $(3x - 15)(3x + 15)$

14. $(9y^2 - 2)(9y^2 + 2)$

15. $\left(5x - \dfrac{3}{8}\right)\left(5x + \dfrac{3}{8}\right)$

Express the following as a product of polynomials in x. Then, multiply and simplify.

16. Find the area of a rectangular rug if its length is $(4x - 9)$ ft and its width is $(x + 7)$ ft.

17. Find the area of a square that has sides $(5x - 2)$ m.

1. _____

2. _____

3. _____

4. _____

5. _____

6. _____

7. _____

8. _____

9. _____

10. _____

11. _____

12. _____

13. _____

14. _____

15. _____

16. _____

17. _____

Additional Exercises 5.5
Form I

Name _____

Date _____

Simplify each expression. Write results with positive exponents.

1. 4^{-2}

2. $\left(-\dfrac{1}{2}\right)^{-4}$

3. $5^{-1} + 3^{-1}$

4. $\dfrac{1}{p^{-6}}$

5. $(3x)^{-4}$

6. $\left(\dfrac{x^{-6}y^3}{x^3 y^{-7}}\right)^3$

7. $(3)^2 (2)(7)^0$

8. $\dfrac{(x^3)^5}{(x^4)^3}$

9. $\dfrac{(a^3 b^4 c)^3}{(2a^{-1}b)^{-4}}$

10. $\dfrac{(-4x^2 y^{-4})^{-3}}{(xy^{-3})^{-2}}$

Write each number in scientific notation.
11. 15,000,000

12. 0.00042

Write each number in standard form.
13. 7.53×10^{-6}

14. 3.051×10^8

Evaluate the following expressions using exponential rules. Write the results in standard form.
15. $(5.1 \times 10^7)(5 \times 10^3)$

16. $\dfrac{5.6 \times 10^{-2}}{8 \times 10^{-7}}$

1. _____

2. _____

3. _____

4. _____

5. _____

6. _____

7. _____

8. _____

9. _____

10. _____

11. _____

12. _____

13. _____

14. _____

15. _____

16. _____

Additional Exercises 5.5
Form II

Name _____

Date _____

Simplify each expression. Write results with positive exponents.

1. 5^{-2}

2. $\left(-\dfrac{1}{3}\right)^{-4}$

3. $4^{-1} + 5^{-1}$

4. $\dfrac{1}{p^{-7}}$

5. $(4x)^{-3}$

6. $\left(\dfrac{x^{-5}y^3}{x^2y^9}\right)^2$

7. $(4)^2(3)(5)^0$

8. $\dfrac{(x^2)^4}{(x^5)^3}$

9. $\dfrac{(a^2b^3c)^4}{(3a^{-1}b)^{-2}}$

10. $\dfrac{(-5xy^{-4})^{-3}}{(xy^{-2})^{-1}}$

Write each number in scientific notation.

11. 12,000,000,000

12. 0.00031

Write each number in standard form.

13. 784×10^{-7}

14. 6.052×10^6

Evaluate the following expressions using exponential rules. Write the results in standard form.

15. $(6.1 \times 10^3)(7 \times 10^4)$

16. $\dfrac{2.7 \times 10^{-3}}{9 \times 10^{-7}}$

1. _____

2. _____

3. _____

4. _____

5. _____

6. _____

7. _____

8. _____

9. _____

10. _____

11. _____

12. _____

13. _____

14. _____

15. _____

16. _____

Additional Exercises 5.5
Form III

Name _____

Date _____

Simplify each expression. Write results with positive exponents.

1. 3^{-3}

2. $\left(-\dfrac{2}{5}\right)^{-3}$

3. $7^{-1} + 3^{-1}$

4. $\dfrac{1}{p^{-9}}$

5. $\dfrac{1}{(5x)^{-4}}$

6. $\left(\dfrac{x^{-8} y^2}{x^2 y^{-7}}\right)^5$

7. $(4)^2 (2)(10)^0$

8. $\dfrac{(x^4)^7}{(x^5)^3}$

9. $\dfrac{\left(a^{-5} b^3 c\right)^5}{\left(4a^{-4} b\right)^{-3}}$

10. $\dfrac{(-7x^2 y^{-7})^{-2}}{(x^{-5} y^{-8})^{-3}}$

Write each number in scientific notation.

11. 13,500,000,000

12. 0.00000871

Write each number in standard form.

13. 843×10^{-4}

14. 8.072×10^5

Evaluate the following expressions using exponential rules. Write the results in standard form.

15. $(7.1 \times 10^5)(7 \times 10^4)$

16. $\dfrac{3.7 \times 10^{-5}}{5 \times 10^{-7}}$

1. _____

2. _____

3. _____

4. _____

5. _____

6. _____

7. _____

8. _____

9. _____

10. _____

11. _____

12. _____

13. _____

14. _____

15. _____

16. _____

Additional Exercises 5.6
Form I

Divide.

1. $\dfrac{12x^2 - 36x - 66}{6}$

2. $\dfrac{a^4b - a^3b^5}{ab}$

3. $\dfrac{56p^5 - 14p^2}{7p}$

4. $\dfrac{4a^3 - 16a^2 + 12a}{4a}$

5. $\dfrac{10x^8 - 15x^7 + 5x^5}{-5x^5}$

6. $\dfrac{21x^3y^4 - 36xy^5 - 3x^2y}{3xy}$

7. $\dfrac{x^2 + 9x + 8}{x + 8}$

8. $\dfrac{x^2 + 2x - 35}{x + 7}$

9. $\dfrac{21x^2 + 22x - 8}{3x + 4}$

10. $\dfrac{21a^3 + 23a^2 - 9a - 10}{3a + 2}$

Perform each division. Write the polynomials in descending order and fill in any missing terms.

11. $\dfrac{x^3 - 8}{x - 2}$

12. $\dfrac{-2b + 3b^2 + 1}{b + 2}$

Solve.

13. The area of the top of a pool table is $(7x^2 - 3x - 4)$ square inches. If its length is $(x - 2)$ inches, find its width.

1. _____

2. _____

3. _____

4. _____

5. _____

6. _____

7. _____

8. _____

9. _____

10. _____

11. _____

12. _____

13. _____

Additional Exercises 5.6
Form II

Divide.

1. $\dfrac{36x^2 - 24x - 18}{6}$

2. $\dfrac{a^3b - a^2b^4}{ab}$

3. $\dfrac{42p^3 - 21p^2}{7p}$

4. $\dfrac{16a^3 - 12a^2 + 8a}{4a}$

5. $\dfrac{5x^7 - 10x^6 + 20x^5}{5x^5}$

6. $\dfrac{27x^2y^3 - 33xy^4 - 42x^2y}{3xy}$

7. $\dfrac{5x^3 - 37x - 24}{x - 8}$

8. $\dfrac{x^2 + 10x + 21}{x + 7}$

9. $\dfrac{12x^2 - 5x - 2}{3x - 2}$

10. $\dfrac{3a^3 + 20a^2 + 21a - 20}{a + 5}$

Perform each division. Write the polynomials in descending order and fill in any missing terms.

11. $\dfrac{x^3 + 125}{x + 5}$

12. $\dfrac{-5b + 6b^2 + 4}{3b - 1}$

Solve.

13. The area of the top of a pool table is $(24x^2 + 34x + 5)$ square inches. If its length is $(6x + 1)$ inches, find its width

1. _____

2. _____

3. _____

4. _____

5. _____

6. _____

7. _____

8. _____

9. _____

10. _____

11. _____

12. _____

13. _____

Additional Exercises 5.6
Form III

Name_____

Date_____

Divide.

1. $\dfrac{10x^2 - 15x - 55}{5}$

2. $\dfrac{a^7b^3 - a^4b^5}{ab}$

3. $\dfrac{49p^6 - 21p^3}{7p}$

4. $\dfrac{4a^2 - 20a + 8}{4a}$

5. $\dfrac{10x^6 - 4x^4 + 10}{-5x^5}$

6. $\dfrac{12x^5y^3 - 33xy^7 - 42x^2y}{3xy}$

7. $\dfrac{x^2 + 7x + 10}{x + 2}$

8. $\dfrac{x^2 - 3x - 40}{x + 5}$

9. $\dfrac{4x^2 - 11x - 3}{4x + 1}$

10. $\dfrac{4a^3 + 23a^2 - 30a + 32}{a + 7}$

Perform each division. Write the polynomials in descending order and fill in any missing terms.

11. $\dfrac{27x^3 - 64}{3x - 4}$

12. $\dfrac{-5b + b^2 - 14}{b - 7}$

Solve.

13. The area of the top of a pool table is $(12x^2 + x - 6)$ square inches. If its length is $(3x - 2)$ inches, find its width

1. _____

2. _____

3. _____

4. _____

5. _____

6. _____

7. _____

8. _____

9. _____

10. _____

11. _____

12. _____

13. _____

Additional Exercises 6.1
Form I

Name_____

Date_____

Find the GCF for each list.

   1. $35, 45$

   2. a^8, a^4, a^7

   3. $-14x^4y, \; 7x^2y^3, \; 28x^2y^2$

Factor out the GCF from each polynomial.

   4. $4a - 12$

   5. $5x^2y + 5xy^2 + 5x$

   6. $3x^3y + 6x^2y^2 + 27xy$

   7. $3y^4 + 6y^3 + 15y^2 - 3y + 21$

   8. $3a^4b^2 - 2a^3b^3 + 5a^3b^2$

   9. $3x^2y + 6x + 3$

   10. $12y^5 + 6y^3 - 18y^2$

   11. $7x^5y^5 - 14x^3y - 21x^2y^2$

   12. $4a^4 + 12a^2 - 8a + 8$

   13. $y(x + 3) + 2(x + 3)$

   14. $a(b^2 + 2) - 3(b^2 + 2)$

   15. $x(y + 1) - 5(y + 1)$

Factor the following four-term polynomials by grouping.

   16. $3x + 15 + xy + 5y$

   17. $3y - 9 + xy - 3x$

   18. $4x^2 - 12xy - 7x + 21y$

   19. $3x^2 - 6xy - 5x + 10y$

   20. $12x^3 + 21x^2 - 20x - 35$

1. _____

2. _____

3. _____

4. _____

5. _____

6. _____

7. _____

8. _____

9. _____

10. _____

11. _____

12. _____

13. _____

14. _____

15. _____

16. _____

17. _____

18. _____

19. _____

20. _____

Additional Exercises 6.1
Form II

Name_____

Date_____

Find the GCF for each list.

1. 18, 36, 96

2. $x^3 y^4, x^2 y^2, xy$

3. $-12x^3, 36x^2, 42$

Factor out the GCF from each polynomial.

4. $3a^2 + 12a$

5. $5x^2 y + 10xy^2 + 25x$

6. $3x^4 y^2 + 9x^3 y^2 + 30xy$

7. $4y^4 + 8y^3 + 12y^2 - 4y + 24$

8. $4a^5 b^3 - 2a^4 b^2 + 5a^3 b^2$

9. $4x^2 y + 8x + 4$

10. $12y^5 + 4y^3 - 16y^2$

11. $6x^5 y^5 - 12x^3 y - 18x^2 y^2$

12. $4a^4 + 16a^2 - 12a + 12$

13. $x(y + 4) + 2(y + 4)$

14. $c(a^2 + 5) - 3(a^2 + 5)$

15. $x(y + 2) - 4(y + 2)$

Factor the following four-term polynomials by grouping.

16. $3x + 12 + xy + 4y$

17. $3y - 6 + xy - 2x$

18. $4x^2 - 16xy - 3x + 12y$

19. $3x^2 - 6xy - 5x + 10y$

20. $20x^3 + 45x^2 - 12x - 27$

1.	_____
2.	_____
3.	_____
4.	_____
5.	_____
6.	_____
7.	_____
8.	_____
9.	_____
10.	_____
11.	_____
12.	_____
13.	_____
14.	_____
15.	_____
16.	_____
17.	_____
18.	_____
19.	_____
20.	_____

Additional Exercises 6.1
Form III

Name_____

Date_____

Find the GCF for each list.

1. 46, 115

2. $a^5b^3c^2, a^3b^2, a^3bc$

3. $-36x^2y^3, 117xy^2, 9y$

Factor out the GCF from each polynomial.

6. $3a^2b + 15ab$

7. $7x^2y + 21xy^2 + 7x$

6. $9x^3y + 63x^2y^2 + 18xy$

7. $6y^4 + 12y^3 + 15y^2 - 3y + 24$

8. $4a^4b^2 - 5a^3b^3 + 7a^3b^2$

9. $7x^2y + 42x + 7$

10. $11y^5 + 22y^3 - 55y^2$

11. $8x^5y^5 - 16x^3yz^2 - 64x^2y^2z$

12. $a^4b^3c^2 + a^3b^2c - a^2bc + abc$

13. $y(x + 5) + 7(x + 5)$

14. $a(b^2 + 9) - 4(b^2 + 9)$

15. $x(y + 8) - 5(y + 8)$

Factor the following four-term polynomials by grouping.

16. $5x + 20 + 4xy + 16y$

17. $7y - 63 + y - 9$

18. $9x^2 + 40y - 36xy - 10x$

19. $12a^3 - 9a^2b - 8ab^2 + 6b^3$

20. $8x^4 - 6x^2 - 20x^2 + 15$

1. _____

2. _____

3. _____

4. _____

5. _____

6. _____

7. _____

8. _____

9. _____

10. _____

11. _____

12. _____

13. _____

14. _____

15. _____

16. _____

17. _____

18. _____

19. _____

20. _____

Additional Exercises 6.2
Form I

Name_____

Date_____

Factor the following trinomials completely. Write "prime" if they do not factor.

1. $x^2 + 13x + 36$

2. $x^2 - 15x + 56$

3. $x^2 - 6x - 27$

4. $x^2 + 3x - 108$

5. $x^2 + 7x + 3$

6. $x^2 - 3x - 10$

7. $x^2 + 16x + 55$

8. $x^2 - 10x + 21$

9. $x^2 - 5x - 24$

10. $x^2 + 2x - 63$

11. $x^2 - 7x - 11$

12. $x^2 + 5x - 12$

13. $5x^2 + 35x + 60$

14. $32 - 20x + 2x^2$

15. $2x^2 + 14x - 16$

16. $x^3 - 4x^2 - 5x$

17. $-4y^2 - 21y + y^3$

18. $3x^3 - 36x^2 + 105x$

19. $2y^4 - 20y^3 + 32y^2$

20. $-9y^4 - 54y^3 + 3y^5$

1. _____

2. _____

3. _____

4. _____

5. _____

6. _____

7. _____

8. _____

9. _____

10. _____

11. _____

12. _____

13. _____

14. _____

15. _____

16. _____

17. _____

18. _____

19. _____

20. _____

Additional Exercises 6.2
Form II

Name_____

Date_____

Factor the following trinomials completely. Write "prime" if they do not factor.

1. $x^2 + 11x - 42$

2. $x^2 - x + 56$

3. $x^2 - x - 30$

4. $x^2 + x - 20$

5. $x^2 + 8x + 9$

6. $x^2 - 7x - 10$

7. $x^2 + 2x - 24$

8. $x^2 - 3x - 28$

9. $x^2 + 7x - 18$

10. $x^2 - 2x - 63$

11. $x^2 + 15x + 16$

12. $x^2 + 14xy + 45y^2$

13. $5x^2 - 5x - 30$

14. $105 - 36x + 3x^2$

15. $2x^2 + 14x - 12$

16. $x^3 - 5x^2 - 6x$

17. $x^3 - 7x^2 - 44x$

18. $4x^5 + 28x^4 + 40x^3$

19. $x^3y - 6x^2y^2 + 5xy^3$

20. $-24y^3 + 10y^4 + 2y^5$

1. _____

2. _____

3. _____

4. _____

5. _____

6. _____

7. _____

8. _____

9. _____

10. _____

11. _____

12. _____

13. _____

14. _____

15. _____

16. _____

17. _____

18. _____

19. _____

20. _____

Additional Exercises 6.2
Form III

Name_____

Date_____

Factor the following trinomials completely. Write "prime" if they do not factor.

1. $x^2 + 5x - 36$

2. $x^2 - 16x + 63$

3. $x^2 - 17x + 42$

4. $x^2 + 30x + 225$

5. $x^2 + 2x + 3$

6. $x^2 - 6x - 9$

7. $x^2 + 12x - 325$

8. $x^2 - 26x - 56$

9. $x^2 - 2x - 15$

10. $x^2 + 20x + 64$

11. $x^2 + 20x + 51$

12. $x^2 + 26xy + 48y^2$

13. $4x^2 + 8x - 96$

14. $-168 - 3x + 3x^2$

15. $2x^2 - 6x - 56$

16. $x^3 - 9x^2 - 10x$

17. $x^3 + 29x^2 - 62x$

18. $x^4 + 15x^3 + 21x^2$

19. $4y^4 + 48y^3 + 140y^2$

20. $-4y^4 - 24y^3 + 4y^5$

1. _____

2. _____

3. _____

4. _____

5. _____

6. _____

7. _____

8. _____

9. _____

10. _____

11. _____

12. _____

13. _____

14. _____

15. _____

16. _____

17. _____

18. _____

19. _____

20. _____

Additional Exercises 6.3
Form I

Name_____

Date_____

Complete the following.

1. $2y^2 + 5y - 3 = (2y - 1)(\qquad)$

2. $3y^2 - 7y + 4 = (3y - 4)(\qquad)$

3. $6y^2 + 17y + 5 = (3y + 1)(\qquad)$

4. $4y^2 - 3y - 10 = (4y + 5)(\qquad)$

Factor the following trinomials completely. Write "prime" if they do not factor.

5. $2x^2 + 7x + 3$

6. $3x^2 + 14x + 8$

7. $6x^2 - 5x - 6$

8. $5x^2 - 22x + 8$

9. $8x^2 - 30x + 7$

10. $2a^2 + 9a + 4$

11. $6x^2 + 19x + 10$

12. $2a^2 + a + 7$

13. $3a^2 - 2a - 8$

14. $-3x^2 + 3x - 90$

15. $8x^2 + 16x - 10$

16. $18x^2 - 30x - 28$

17. $x^2 + 18x + 81$

18. $a^2 - 24a + 144$

19. $9n^2 + 12n + 4$

20. $a^2 - 10a + 25$

1. _____
2. _____
3. _____
4. _____
5. _____
6. _____
7. _____
8. _____
9. _____
10. _____
11. _____
12. _____
13. _____
14. _____
15. _____
16. _____
17. _____
18. _____
19. _____
20. _____

Additional Exercises 6.3
Form II

Name_____

Date_____

Complete the following.

1. $6y^2 - y - 1 = (3y + 1)(\qquad)$

2. $4y^2 - 8y - 5 = (2y - 5)(\qquad)$

3. $3y^2 - 13y - 10 = (3y + 2)(\qquad)$

4. $15y^2 + y - 2 = (5y + 2)(\qquad)$

Factor the following trinomials completely. Write "prime" if they do not factor.

5. $15x^2 + 7x - 2$

6. $8x^2 - 10x + 3$

7. $6x^2 - 11x - 10$

8. $9x^2 + 18x + 8$

9. $21x^2 - 17x + 2$

10. $18a^2 - 3a - 10$

11. $12x^2 - 11x - 15$

12. $15a^2 - 4a - 4$

13. $14a^2 - 45a - 14$

14. $-4x^2 + 4x + 24$

15. $42x^2 + 91x + 35$

16. $50x^2 + 65xy - 15y^2$

17. $x^2 + 8x + 16$

18. $25n^2 + 30n + 9$

19. $2x^2 - 24x + 72$

20. $64x^2 + 16xy + y^2$

1. _____

2. _____

3. _____

4. _____

5. _____

6. _____

7. _____

8. _____

9. _____

10. _____

11. _____

12. _____

13. _____

14. _____

15. _____

16. _____

17. _____

18. _____

19. _____

20. _____

Additional Exercises 6.3
Form III

Name_____

Date_____

Complete the following.

1. $4x^2 + 7x - 2 = (4x - 1)(\quad)$

2. $5y^2 + 7y + 2 = (5y + 2)(\quad)$

3. $8y^2 + 10y + 3 = (2y + 1)(\quad)$

4. $15x^2 + 14x - 8 = (5x - 2)(\quad)$

Factor the following trinomials completely. Write "prime" if they do not factor.

5. $6x^2 - 11x + 3$

6. $9x^2 + 43x - 10$

7. $8x^2 - 10x + 3$

8. $3x^2 + 13x - 10$

9. $2x^2 + 9x - 18$

10. $9a^2 + 50a - 24$

11. $15x^2 - 19x + 6$

12. $6a^2 + 2a - 5$

13. $-2a^2 - 3a + 20$

14. $-10x^3 - 15x^2 - 10x$

15. $6x^2 + 9x - 60$

16. $5x^2 + 20x - 105$

17. $x^2 - 6x + 9$

18. $4 + 36x + 81x^2$

19. $36x^2 - 84x + 49$

20. $64a^2 + 16ab + b^2$

1. _____

2. _____

3. _____

4. _____

5. _____

6. _____

7. _____

8. _____

9. _____

10. _____

11. _____

12. _____

13. _____

14. _____

15. _____

16. _____

17. _____

18. _____

19. _____

20. _____

Additional Exercises 6.4
Form I

Name_____

Date_____

Factor by grouping.

1. $x^2 + 3x + 7x + 21$

2. $x^2 - 4x - 9x + 36$

3. $2x^2 + x - 10x - 5$

4. $6x^2 - 3x - 8x + 4$

5. $7x^2 - 30x + 8$

6. $4x^2 - 25x + 6$

7. $2n^2 + 13n - 24$

8. $3x^2 + x - 4$

9. $4n^2 + 4n - 3$

10. $3m^2 + 21m + 30$

11. $6m^3 + 18m^2 + 12m$

12. $3m^2 - 14m + 11$

13. $4m^2 + 12m + 9$

14. $2x^2 + 23x + 56$

15. $9x^3 - 6x^2 - 8x$

16. $8m^2 - 3m - 4$

17. $6x^2 - 5xy + y^2$

18. $6x^2 + 19x + 10$

19. $2x^2 + 25x + 72$

20. $7x^2 + 19x + 10$

1. _____

2. _____

3. _____

4. _____

5. _____

6. _____

7. _____

8. _____

9. _____

10. _____

11. _____

12. _____

13. _____

14. _____

15. _____

16. _____

17. _____

18. _____

19. _____

20. _____

Additional Exercises 6.4
Form II

Name_____

Date_____

Factor by grouping.

1. $21x^2 + 14x + 3x + 2$

2. $3x^2 - 15x - x + 5$

3. $5n^2 - 5n + n - 1$

4. $6x^2 + 18x + x + 3$

5. $3x^2 + 7x + 2$

6. $7x^2 - 9x + 2$

7. $10n^2 + 17n + 3$

8. $5x^2 - 9x - 2$

9. $9n^2 + 15n + 4$

10. $4m^2 - 17m + 18$

11. $3m^2 - m - 30$

12. $10m^2 - 3m - 27$

13. $14m^2 - 39m + 10$

14. $63m^2 + 130m + 63$

15. $12x^3 + 22x^2 + 6x$

16. $15m^3 + 24m^2 + 9m$

17. $60m^3 - 42m^2 + 6m$

18. $18x^3 + 112x^2 - 98x$

19. $10x^3 + 65x^2 - 35x$

20. $6x^2y + 13xy - 5y$

1. _____

2. _____

3. _____

4. _____

5. _____

6. _____

7. _____

8. _____

9. _____

10. _____

11. _____

12. _____

13. _____

14. _____

15. _____

16. _____

17. _____

18. _____

19. _____

20. _____

Additional Exercises 6.4
Form III

Factor by grouping.

1. $x^2 + 5x + 12x + 60$

2. $x^2 - 2x - 8x + 16$

3. $7n^3 - 21n^2 - 10n + 30$

4. $24x^3 - 6x^2 - 20x + 5$

5. $3x^2 + 14x + 8$

6. $4x^2 + 6x + 9$

7. $10n^2 + 17n - 6$

8. $6m^2 - 19m + 3$

9. $4n^2 - 4n - 15$

10. $7m^2 + 61m + 40$

11. $6x^2 + 17xy + 10y^2$

12. $14m^2 + 5m - 24$

13. $10m^2 + m - 5$

14. $8m^2 + 28m - 120$

15. $24x^2 + 26xy + 6y^2$

16. $10m^3 + 8m^2 - 2m$

17. $20m^2 + 39m + 18$

18. $36x^2 + 65x - 36$

19. $20x^2 + 41x + 20$

20. $24x^2 - 79x + 40$

1. _____

2. _____

3. _____

4. _____

5. _____

6. _____

7. _____

8. _____

9. _____

10. _____

11. _____

12. _____

13. _____

14. _____

15. _____

16. _____

17. _____

18. _____

19. _____

20. _____

Additional Exercises 6.5
Form I

Name_____

Date_____

Factor completely.

1. $a^2 - 25$

2. $x^2 - 49$

3. $x^2 - 64$

4. $4x^2 - 81$

5. $9x^2 - 16$

6. $4x^2 + 25$

7. $a^2 - 100b^2$

8. $1 - 25x^2$

9. $18x^3 - 2x$

10. $5x^2 - 125$

11. $x^2 - \dfrac{4}{9}$

12. $x^4 - y^6$

13. $y^3 - 8$

14. $x^3 + 27$

15. $a^3 + 64$

16. $x^3 + 1$

17. $8y^3 - 27$

18. $1 + 125x^3$

19. $x^6 - 8y^3$

20. $x^3 - \dfrac{1}{8}$

1. _____

2. _____

3. _____

4. _____

5. _____

6. _____

7. _____

8. _____

9. _____

10. _____

11. _____

12. _____

13. _____

14. _____

15. _____

16. _____

17. _____

18. _____

19. _____

20. _____

Additional Exercises 6.5
Form II

Name_____

Date_____

Factor completely.

1. $1 - 9x^2$

2. $4x^2 - y^2$

3. $121 - a^2 b^2$

4. $x^2 y^2 - 100$

5. $a^4 b^2 - 9$

6. $a^6 - 144$

7. $16x^2 - 121$

8. $x^8 - 169$

9. $225x^2 - 841y^2$

10. $9x^3 - 36x$

11. $y^2 - \dfrac{16}{81}$

12. $16a^3 b^3 - 49ab$

13. $\dfrac{4}{49} x^2 - \dfrac{1}{25}$

14. $-36x^2 + 1$

15. $x^3 + y^3$

16. $27x^3 - 8y^3$

17. $x^3 y^3 + 216$

18. $a^3 - 343b^3$

19. $8a^3 + 512b^3$

20. $n^3 - \dfrac{8}{27}$

1. _____

2. _____

3. _____

4. _____

5. _____

6. _____

7. _____

8. _____

9. _____

10. _____

11. _____

12. _____

13. _____

14. _____

15. _____

16. _____

17. _____

18. _____

19. _____

20. _____

Additional Exercises 6.5
Form III

Name

Date _____

Factor completely.

1. $a^2 - 625$

2. $a^2 b^2 - c^2 d^2$

3. $a^{10} - 25$

4. $49a^2 - 100b^2$

5. $a^2 b^2 - 196$

6. $y^2 + 36$

7. $-64a^2 + 9$

8. $a^2 - \dfrac{81}{100}$

9. $\dfrac{4}{25} a^2 - \dfrac{9}{16}$

10. $3x^3 - 108x$

11. $x^5 y^3 - 64x^3 y$

12. $3x^2 - 300$

13. $4x^3 - 324x$

14. $4x^2 - 10$

15. $a^3 - 729$

16. $x^3 y^3 - 1000$

17. $a^3 - \dfrac{125}{216}$

18. $a^3 + 6$

19. $1331a^3 - b^3$

20. $y^7 - 8y$

1. _____

2. _____

3. _____

4. _____

5. _____

6. _____

7. _____

8. _____

9. _____

10. _____

11. _____

12. _____

13. _____

14. _____

15. _____

16. _____

17. _____

18. _____

19. _____

20. _____

Additional Exercises 6.6
Form I

Solve each equation.

1. $(x + 10)(x - 3) = 0$

2. $(4x - 2)(3x + 1) = 0$

3. $(2x - 3)(2x + 2) = 0$

4. $5x(x - 5)(x + 5)$

5. $3(x - 3)(x - 1) = 0$

6. $6x(3x - 5)(x + 7) = 0$

7. $(x - 4)(x + 5) = 0$

8. $x^2 - 4x - 45 = 0$

9. $2x^2 - 11x - 21 = 0$

10. $9y^2 - 16 = 0$

11. $6x^2 + 25x + 25 = 0$

12. $6b^2 + b - 7 = 0$

13. $n^2 - 8n = 48$

14. $m^2 = 9m$

15. $x^2 = 18 - 3x$

16. $4y^2 = 25$

17. $2p^2 + 7p = 30$

18. $n^3 + 8n^2 + 15n = 0$

19. $48y^3 = 3y$

20. $15w^3 = -35w^2 - 10w$

Name_____

Date_____

1. _____

2. _____

3. _____

4. _____

5. _____

6. _____

7. _____

8. _____

9. _____

10. _____

11. _____

12. _____

13. _____

14. _____

15. _____

16. _____

17. _____

18. _____

19. _____

20. _____

Additional Exercises 6.6
Form II

Name _____

Date _____

Solve each equation.

1. $(x + 11)(x - 2) = 0$

2. $(5x - 2)(3x + 1) = 0$

3. $(3x - 2)(3x + 2) = 0$

4. $2x(5x - 1)(x + 2)$

5. $5(x - 7)(2x - 5) = 0$

6. $6x^2(x - 5)(3x + 7) = 0$

7. $(x - 0.3)(x + 0.5) = 0$

8. $x^2 + 5x - 6 = 0$

9. $2x^2 - 3x - 5 = 0$

10. $4y^2 - 25 = 0$

11. $4x^2 + 20x + 25 = 0$

12. $3b^2 + b - 10 = 0$

13. $n^2 - 10n = -21$

14. $m^2 = 11m$

15. $x^2 = 32 - 4x$

16. $9y^2 = 16$

17. $5p^2 - 23p = -24$

18. $n^3 + 8n^2 + 12n = 0$

19. $8y^3 = 2y$

20. $5w^3 = 40w^2 - 80w$

1. _____

2. _____

3. _____

4. _____

5. _____

6. _____

7. _____

8. _____

9. _____

10. _____

11. _____

12. _____

13. _____

14. _____

15. _____

16. _____

17. _____

18. _____

19. _____

20. _____

Additional Exercises 6.6
Form III

Solve each equation.

1. $(x + 7)(x - 5) = 0$

2. $(5x - 4)(2x + 3) = 0$

3. $(4x - 5)(4x + 5) = 0$

4. $4x(x - 5)(x + 2)$

5. $6(x - 3)(2x - 7) = 0$

6. $3x(x - 4)(3x + 7) = 0$

7. $(x - 0.8)(x + 0.9) = 0$

8. $x^2 - 6x + 40 = 0$

9. $2x^2 + 13x + 6 = 0$

10. $16y^2 - 49 = 0$

11. $4x^2 - 16x + 15 = 0$

12. $21b^2 + b - 2 = 0$

13. $n^2 + 5n = 6$

14. $m^2 = 8m$

15. $x^2 = -28 + 16x$

16. $25y^2 = 144$

17. $16p^2 - 18p = 9$

18. $n^3 - 4n^2 - 45n = 0$

19. $5x(5x + 2) = 8$

20. $12w^2 + 17w = -6$

1. _____

2. _____

3. _____

4. _____

5. _____

6. _____

7. _____

8. _____

9. _____

10. _____

11. _____

12. _____

13. _____

14. _____

15. _____

16. _____

17. _____

18. _____

19. _____

20. _____

Additional Exercises 6.7
Form I

Name_____

Date_____

Solve.

1. A rectangle has an area of 40 square inches. The width is represented by $x + 1$ and the length is $x + 4$. Find the dimensions.

2. The length of a rectangle is 1 cm more than the twice its width. The area is 55 cm^2. Find the dimensions of the rectangle.

3. The length of a proposed rectangular flower garden is 1 ft more four times its width. The area of the proposed garden is 95 ft^2. Find the length of the proposed flower garden.

4. The perimeter of a rectangle is 80 inches, and the area is 375 square inches. Find the dimensions of the rectangle.

5. A student dropped a ball from the top of a 81-foot building. The height of the ball after t seconds is given by the quadratic equation $h = -9t^2 + 81$. How long will it take the ball to hit the ground?

6. One leg of a right triangle measures 5 m while the length of the other leg measures x meters. The hypotenuse measures $(x + 1)$ m. Find the length of all 3 sides.

7. The longer leg of a right triangle measures two feet more than twice the length of the shorter leg. The hypotenuse measures 3 feet more than twice the shorter leg. Find the length of all three sides.

8. Find the length of a ladder leaning against a building if the top of the ladder touches the building at a height of 24 feet. Also, the length of the ladder is 18 feet more than its distance from the base of the building.

9. The hypotenuse of a right triangle is 4 cm more than than the longer leg. The shorter leg is 4 cm less than the longer leg. . Find the length of each leg.

10. Nine more than the cube of a number is the same as 81 times the number. Find the numbers.

11. Seventy-two than the square of a number is the same as eighteen times the number. Find the numbers.

1. _____

2. _____

3. _____

4. _____

5. _____

6. _____

7. _____

8. _____

9. _____

10. _____

11. _____

Name_____

12. Find two consecutive positive even integers whose product is 48.

12._____

13. . The sum of the squares of two consecutive integers is 41. Find the integers.

13._____

14. .Each of the three consecutive positive integers is squared. The three results are added and the sum is 245. Find the three positive integers.

14._____

15._____

15. .The difference between the square of a positive integer and the square of one-half the number is 243. Find the number.

Additional Exercises 6.7
Form II

Solve.

1. A rectangle has an area of 24 square inches. The width is represented by $x - 3$ and the length is $x + 2$. Find the dimensions.

2. The length of a rectangle is 3 cm more than the width. The area is 70 cm^2. Find the dimensions of the rectangle.

3. The length of a proposed rectangular flower garden is 6 m more that its width. The area of the proposed garden is 72m^2. Find the dimensions of the proposed flower garden.

4. The perimeter of a rectangle is 132 feet and its area is 1080 square feet. Find the dimensions of the rectangle.

5. A student dropped a ball from the top of a 64-foot building. The height of the ball after t seconds is given by the quadratic equation $h = -16t^2 + 64$. How long will it take the ball to hit the ground?

6. One leg of a right triangle measures 6 m while the length of the other leg measures x meters. The hypotenuse measures $(2x - 6)$ m. Find the length of all 3 sides.

7. The longer leg of a right triangle measures two feet more than twice the length of the shorter leg. The hypotenuse measures 3 feet more than twice the shorter leg. Find the length of all three sides.

8. Find the length of a ladder leaning against a building if the top of the ladder touches the building at a height of 12 feet. Also, the length of the ladder is 4 feet more than its distance from the base of the building.

9. One leg of a right triangle is 14 meters longer than the other leg. The hypotenuse is 26 meters long. Find the length of each leg.

10. Eight more than the square of a number is the same as six times the number. Find the number.

11. Fifteen less than the square of a number is the same as twice the number. Find the numbers.

1. _____

2. _____

3. _____

4. _____

5. _____

6. _____

7. _____

8. _____

9. _____

10. _____

11. _____

Name_____

12. Find two consecutive positive odd integers whose product is 35

12. _____

13. Find three consecutive integers is the sum of twice the first and 4 times the second is equal to 20 more than twice the third.

13. _____

14. _____

14. Find two consecutive odd integers such that the square of the first added to 3 times the second is 24.

15. The altitude of a triangle is 2 cm shorter than its base. The area is 17.5 cm². Find the base of the triangle.

15. _____

Additional Exercises 6.7
Form III

Name _____

Date _____

Solve.

1. A rectangle has an area of 65 square inches. The width is represented by x and the length is $2x + 3$. Find the dimensions.

2. The length of a rectangle is 5 cm more than the width. The area is 66 cm^2. Find the dimensions of the rectangle.

3. The length of a proposed rectangular flower garden is 4 feet less than five times the width. The area of the proposed garden is 57 ft^2. Find the length of the proposed flower garden

4. A square field had 5 m added to its length and 2 m added to its width. The field then had an area of 130 m^2. Find the length of a side of the original field.

5. A student dropped a ball from the top of a 100-foot building. The height of the ball after t seconds is given by the quadratic equation $h = -10t^2 + 100$. How long will it take the ball to hit the ground?

6. One leg of a right triangle measures 15 m while the length of the other leg measures x meters. The hypotenuse measures $(2x + 1)$ m. Find the length of all 3 sides.

7. The shorter leg of a right triangle measures 2 feet less than the longer leg. The hypotenuse measures 10 feet. Find the length of all three sides.

8. A 10 foot ladder is leaning against the side of a building. The distance from the bottom of the building to the top of the ladder is 2 feet more than the distance from the bottom of the ladder to the base of the building. At what height is the top of the ladder touching the building?

9. The sum of the lengths of the two legs of a right triangle is 14 cm. If the length of the hypotenuse is 10 cm, find the length of each leg.

10. Ten more than the square of a number is the same as 40. Find the numbers.

11. Ten more than the square of a number is the same as seven times the number. Find the numbers.

1. _____

2. _____

3. _____

4. _____

5. _____

6. _____

7. _____

8. _____

9. _____

10. _____

11. _____

12. Find two consecutive positive odd integers whose product is 63.

12. _____

13. Find three consecutive integers if the third is equal to 15 less than the sum of the first and second.

13. _____

14. . The base of a triangle is 3 cm longer than its altitude. The area of the triangle is 35 cm^2. Find the altitude.

14. _____

15. A 4 m by 6 m rug covers half the floor area of a room and leaves a uniform strip of base floor around the edges. What are the dimensions of the room?

15. _____

Additional Exercises 7.1
Form I

Name_____

Date_____

Find the value of the following rational expressions when $x = -4$ and $a = 5$

1. $\dfrac{x+5}{2x+6}$

2. $\dfrac{y^2}{1-y^2}$

3. $\dfrac{x^2-10x+5}{x^2+2x-1}$

Find any real number for which each rational expression is undefined.

4. $\dfrac{4}{a-4}$

5. $\dfrac{z-5}{4}$

6. $\dfrac{x-2}{x}$

Simplify each rational expression.

7. $\dfrac{15k^3}{5k}$

8. $\dfrac{-9x-9y}{x+y}$

9. $\dfrac{4x+3}{20x^2+23x+6}$

10. $\dfrac{5k-10}{6-3k}$

11. $\dfrac{4x^2-43x+63}{x-9}$

12. $\dfrac{11x^2+33x^3}{6x+18x^2}$

1. _____

2. _____

3. _____

4. _____

5. _____

6. _____

7. _____

8. _____

9. _____

10. _____

11. _____

12. _____

Additional Exercises 7.1 *(cont.)*

Name_____

13. $\dfrac{y^3 - 64}{y - 4}$

13. _____

14. $\dfrac{x^2 + 10x + 16}{x + 8}$

14. _____

15. $\dfrac{3x^2 - 12}{4x - 8}$

15. _____

16. Simplify, factor by grouping: $\dfrac{x^3 - x^2 - 2x + 2}{x - 1}$

16. _____

17. List four equivalent forms for the following rational expression: $-\dfrac{y - 12}{y + 17}$

17. _____

The cost C per machine of producing x computer printers is given by the equation:

$$C = \dfrac{250x + 10,000}{x}$$

18. Find the cost per machine when 200 printers are produced.

18. _____

19. Find the cost per machine when 2000 printers are produced.

19. _____

20. The formula for body-mass index B is $B = \dfrac{750w}{h^2}$ where w is weight in pounds and h is height in inches. Find the body-mass index for a person who is 5 feet 11 inches (71 inches) tall and weighs 180 pounds. If necessary, round to the nearest hundredth.

20. _____

Additional Exercises 7.1
Form II

Name_____

Date_____

Find the value of the following rational expressions when $x = 3$ and $y = -2$

1. $\dfrac{x+4}{2x-7}$

1. _____

2. $\dfrac{y^2}{y^3-1}$

2. _____

3. $\dfrac{y^2+7y+3}{y^2-y-8}$

3. _____

Find any real number for which each rational expression is undefined.

4. $\dfrac{x+5}{7x}$

4. _____

5. $\dfrac{5x^3+17}{3x-30}$

5. _____

6. $\dfrac{x^2-7x+2}{19}$

6. _____

Simplify each rational expression.

7. $\dfrac{6}{12x-18}$

7. _____

8. $\dfrac{3x-12}{5x-20}$

8. _____

9. $\dfrac{x+19}{19+x}$

9. _____

10. $\dfrac{x-12}{12-x}$

10. _____

11. $\dfrac{-8a-8b}{a+b}$

11. _____

12. $\dfrac{x+3}{x^2-5x-24}$

12. _____

13. $\dfrac{4x^2 + 19x - 5}{4x - 1}$

13. _____

14. $\dfrac{x^2 - x - 72}{x^2 - 18x + 81}$

14. _____

15. $\dfrac{2x^2 - 72}{6x - 36}$

15. _____

16. Simplify, factor by grouping: $\dfrac{4x - 28 + xy - 7y}{x - 7}$

16. _____

17. List four equivalent forms for the following rational expression: $-\dfrac{y - 2}{y + 7}$

17. _____

The cost C per machine of producing x computer printers is given by the equation:

$$C = \dfrac{210x + 12{,}000}{x}$$

18. Find the cost per machine when 200 printers are produced.

18. _____

19. Find the cost per machine when 2000 printers are produced.

19. _____

20. The formula for body-mass index B is $B = \dfrac{750w}{h^2}$ where w is weight in pounds and h is height in inches. Find the body-mass index for a person who is 5 feet 4 inches (64 inches) tall and weighs 104 pounds. If necessary, round to the nearest hundredth.

20. _____

Additional Exercises 7.1
Form III

Name_____

Date_____

Find the value of the following rational expressions when $x = -2$ and $y = 9$

1. $\dfrac{x+3}{-3x+2}$

2. $\dfrac{y^2}{1-y^2}$

3. $\dfrac{x^2-10x+5}{x^2+2x-1}$

Find any real number for which each rational expression is undefined.

4. $\dfrac{5}{z-2}$

5. $\dfrac{r-4}{8}$

6. $\dfrac{x^2+6x+5}{x}$

Simplify each rational expression.

7. $\dfrac{30k^3}{6k}$

8. $\dfrac{9x+9y}{x+y}$

9. $\dfrac{2x+3}{10x^2+19x+6}$

10. $\dfrac{x+12}{12+x}$

11. $\dfrac{7k-42}{18-3k}$

12. $\dfrac{9x^2-79x+56}{x-8}$

1. _____

2. _____

3. _____

4. _____

5. _____

6. _____

7. _____

8. _____

9. _____

10. _____

11. _____

12. _____

Name_____

13. $\dfrac{11x^2 + 33x^3}{4x + 12x^2}$

13. _____

14. $\dfrac{y^3 - 125}{y - 5}$

14. _____

15. $\dfrac{5x^2 - 125}{6x - 30}$

15. _____

16. Simplify, factor by grouping: $\dfrac{mn - 3m - 5n + 15}{n - 3}$

16. _____

17. List four equivalent forms for the following rational expression: $-\dfrac{x - 13}{x + 27}$

17. _____

The cost C per machine of producing x computer printers is given by the equation:

$$C = \dfrac{100x + 5,000}{x}$$

18. _____

18. Find the cost per machine when 200 printers are produced.

19. Find the cost per machine when 2000 printers are produced.

19. _____

20. The formula for body-mass index B is $B = \dfrac{750w}{h^2}$ where w is weight in pounds and h is height in inches. Find the body-mass index for a person who is 6 feet 1 inches (73 inches) tall and weighs 280 pounds. If necessary, round to the nearest hundredth.

20. _____

Additional Exercises 7.2
Form I

Name_____

Date_____

1. _____

1. The reciprocal of $-\dfrac{x+8}{4}$

Find each product and simplify if possible.

2. $\dfrac{4x^2}{5} \cdot \dfrac{10}{x^3}$

2. _____

3. $\dfrac{2z^3}{3} \cdot \dfrac{21}{z^2}$

3. _____

4. $\dfrac{6x^4 y^6}{12xy^{11}} \cdot y^5$

4. _____

5. $\dfrac{7y}{14y+7} \cdot \dfrac{10y+5}{6}$

5. _____

6. $\dfrac{3p-3}{p} \cdot \dfrac{3p^2}{4p-4}$

6. _____

7. $\dfrac{x^2 +14x+49}{x^2 +15x+56} \cdot \dfrac{x^2 +8x}{x^2 +5x-14}$

7. _____

8. Find the area of a rectangle whose width is $\dfrac{8x}{x^2 -121}$ m and length is $\dfrac{x+11}{9x^3}$ m.

8. _____

9. Find the area of a square with sides of $\dfrac{x}{x^2 -9}$ ft.

9. _____

Find each quotient and simplify.

10. $\dfrac{9x^{13}}{4x^6} \div \dfrac{81x}{36x^5}$

10. _____

11. $\dfrac{5m^2 c}{7mc^2} \div \dfrac{35m^2 c^2}{20mc}$

11. _____

Additional Exercises 7.2 *(cont.)*

Name_____

12. $\dfrac{(x+7)(x+3)}{5x} \div \dfrac{2x+14}{10x^8}$

12. _____

13. $\dfrac{(x+2)}{(x+2)(x-8)} \div \dfrac{6}{x-8}$

13. _____

14. $\dfrac{x^2-y^2}{x+y} \div \dfrac{2x}{x^2-xy}$

14. _____

15. $\dfrac{x+4}{2-x} \div \dfrac{x^2+5x+4}{x^2+2x-8}$

15. _____

Multiply or divide as indicated.

16. $\dfrac{x-8}{7} \div \dfrac{x-5}{14}$

16. _____

17. $\dfrac{x^2-y^2}{x} \cdot \dfrac{x+y}{x^2+xy}$

17. _____

18. $\dfrac{p^2-2p+pq-2q}{11p^2-11q^2} \div \dfrac{p-2}{4p-4q}$

18. _____

19. $\left(\dfrac{6x^2+23x-35}{4x-20} \cdot \dfrac{x^2-5x}{36x^2-49} \right) \div \dfrac{4x+20}{5x^3}$

19. _____

20. _____

20. A bullet leaves the barrel of a rifle traveling 1,000 feet/second. Convert 1,000 feet/second to miles/hour. (1 mile = 5,280 feet). Round to the nearest whole number.

E-247

Additional Exercises 7.2
Form II

1. _____

1. The reciprocal of $-\dfrac{3x+7}{5}$

Find each product and simplify if possible.

2. _____

2. $\dfrac{5x^2}{y} \bullet \dfrac{3y}{7x}$

3. _____

3. $\dfrac{8x^3}{14x} \bullet \dfrac{7}{4x}$

4. _____

4. $-\dfrac{9a^3b}{54a^2b^4} \bullet b^3$

5. _____

5. $\dfrac{x}{7x-21} \bullet \dfrac{x^2-3x}{5}$

6. _____

6. $\dfrac{x^2+8x}{11} \bullet \dfrac{44}{x+8}$

7. _____

7. $\dfrac{y^2-11y+18}{y^2-5y-36} \bullet \dfrac{y+4}{y}$

8. _____

8. Find the area of a rectangle whose width is $\dfrac{x+7}{7x}$ m and length is $\dfrac{2x}{x^2-49}$ m.

9. _____

9. Find the area of a square with sides of $\dfrac{3x}{4x^2-9x}$ ft.

Find each quotient and simplify.

10. _____

10. $\dfrac{12x^6}{11x^2} \div \dfrac{8x}{22x^4}$

11. _____

11. $\dfrac{12x^3}{y^4} \div \dfrac{3x^2y}{2y^2}$

Name_____

12. $\dfrac{(x-9)(x+12)}{3x} \div \dfrac{2x-18}{9x^2}$

13. $\dfrac{(x+4)}{(x+4)(3x-8)} \div \dfrac{26}{3x-8}$

14. $\dfrac{a^2-b^2}{a+b} \div \dfrac{2a}{a^2-ab}$

15. $\dfrac{x+2}{6-x} \div \dfrac{x^2-5x-14}{x^2-4x-12}$

Multiply or divide as indicated.

16. $\dfrac{2x-24}{30} \div \dfrac{3x-36}{25}$

17. $\dfrac{x^2-4y^2}{5x+20} \bullet \dfrac{x^2+4x}{5x^2-9xy-2y^2}$

18. $\dfrac{x^2-10x+25}{8y} \div \dfrac{5-x}{12xy}$

19. $\left(\dfrac{x^2-16}{x^2-36} \bullet \dfrac{x^2+2x-24}{3x^2+13x+4}\right) \div \dfrac{3x+1}{6-x}$

20. A bullet leaves the barrel of a rifle traveling 1,500 feet/second. Convert 1,500 feet/second to miles/hour. (1 mile = 5,280 feet). Round to the nearest whole number.

12. _____

13. _____

14. _____

15. _____

16. _____

17. _____

18. _____

19. _____

20. _____

Additional Exercises 7.2
Form III

1. _____

1. The reciprocal of $-\dfrac{2x-7}{6}$

Find each product and simplify if possible.

2. _____

2. $\dfrac{3x^2}{4} \cdot \dfrac{32}{x^3}$

3. _____

3. $\dfrac{4z^3}{5} \cdot \dfrac{10}{z^2}$

4. _____

4. $\dfrac{5x^5y^3}{30xy^{11}} \cdot y^8$

5. _____

5. $\dfrac{4y}{8y+4} \cdot \dfrac{6y+3}{4}$

6. _____

6. $\dfrac{4p-4}{p} \cdot \dfrac{5p^2}{7p-7}$

7. _____

7. $\dfrac{x^2+11x+24}{x^2+15x+56} \cdot \dfrac{x^2+7x}{x^2-6x-27}$

8. _____

8. Find the area of a rectangle whose width is $\dfrac{10x}{x^2-49}$ m and length is $\dfrac{x+7}{9x^3}$ m.

9. _____

9. Find the area of a square with sides of $\dfrac{3x}{16x^2-25x}$ ft.

Find each quotient and simplify.

10. _____

10. $\dfrac{4x^{13}}{7x^6} \div \dfrac{32x}{56x^5}$

11. _____

11. $\dfrac{7m^2n}{4mn^2} \div \dfrac{28m^2n^2}{35mn}$

Additional Exercises 7.2 *(cont.)*

12. $\dfrac{(x+5)(x-9)}{2x} \div \dfrac{3x+15}{6x^7}$

13. $\dfrac{(x+6)}{(x+6)(2x-5)} \div \dfrac{36}{2x-5}$

14. $\dfrac{z^2-b^2}{z+b} \div \dfrac{z}{z^2+zb}$

15. $\dfrac{x-2}{6+x} \div \dfrac{x^2+5x-14}{x^2+4x-12}$

Multiply or divide as indicated.

16. $\dfrac{5x-10}{12} \div \dfrac{8}{4x-8}$

17. $\dfrac{x^2-16y^2}{3x+18} \bullet \dfrac{x^2+6x}{3x^2-13xy+4y^2}$

18. $\dfrac{x^2-10x+21}{7-x} \div (x+3)$

19. $\left(\dfrac{6x^2+47x-63}{5x-25} \bullet \dfrac{x^2-5x}{36x^2-49} \right) \div \dfrac{5x+45}{8x^3}$

21. A bullet leaves the barrel of a rifle traveling 2,000 feet/second. Convert 2,000 feet/second to miles/hour. (1 mile = 5,280 feet). Round to the nearest whole number.

12. _____

13. _____

14. _____

15. _____

16. _____

17. _____

18. _____

19. _____

20. _____

Additional Exercises 7.3
Form I

Add or subtract as indicated. Simplify the result if possible.

1. $\dfrac{5m}{8n} + \dfrac{5m}{8n}$

2. $\dfrac{7m}{3n} + \dfrac{8m}{3n}$

3. $\dfrac{5x}{x-7} - \dfrac{35}{x-7}$

4. $\dfrac{2}{13+x} + \dfrac{x+3}{13+x}$

5. $\dfrac{5x}{x+2} - \dfrac{3x-4}{x+2}$

6. $\dfrac{x}{x^2+7x-60} - \dfrac{5}{x^2+7x-60}$

7. $\dfrac{10x-4}{x^2+6x+8} - \dfrac{9x-6}{x^2+6x+8}$

Find the LCD for the following lists of rational expressions.

8. $\dfrac{6}{9xy}, \dfrac{8}{12x^2}$

9. $\dfrac{7}{8x}, \dfrac{1}{2x+4}$

10. $\dfrac{1}{x^2+3x}, \dfrac{1}{x^2+6x+9}$

11. $\dfrac{13x}{x-2}, \dfrac{6x}{2-x}$

12. $\dfrac{2}{x^2+9x+18}, \dfrac{5}{x^2+8x+15}$

1. _____

2. _____

3. _____

4. _____

5. _____

6. _____

7. _____

8. _____

9. _____

10. _____

11. _____

12. _____

Name_____

Rewrite each rational expression as an equivalent rational expression whose denominator is the given polynomial.

13. $\dfrac{5}{4x} = \dfrac{}{16x^2}$

13. _____

14. $\dfrac{4x+1}{3x+6} = \dfrac{}{3y(x+2)}$

14. _____

15. $\dfrac{9y-1}{15x^2-30} = \dfrac{}{30x^2-60}$

15. _____

16. $\dfrac{x+4}{16x^2+324x+80} = \dfrac{}{x(16x+4)(x+12)(x+20)}$

16. _____

17. $\dfrac{21}{x^2+8x} = \dfrac{}{x(x+8)(x-4)}$

17. _____

18. A square has a side of length $\dfrac{7}{x+5}$ feet. Express its perimeter as a rational expression.

18. _____

19. The trapezoid has sides $\dfrac{4}{x+5}$ m, $\dfrac{x+1}{x+5}$ m, $\dfrac{x+4}{x+5}$ m, and $\dfrac{4}{x+5}$ m. Find its perimeter.

19. _____

Additional Exercises 7.3
Form II

Name_____

Date_____

Add or subtract as indicated. Simplify the result if possible.

1. $\dfrac{a}{17} + \dfrac{11}{17}$

2. $\dfrac{13m}{4n} + \dfrac{11m}{4n}$

3. $\dfrac{5y}{y-8} - \dfrac{40}{y-8}$

4. $\dfrac{7}{15+x} + \dfrac{x+3}{15+x}$

5. $\dfrac{12x+7}{x-6} - \dfrac{10x+19}{x-6}$

6. $\dfrac{x}{x^2-2x-48} - \dfrac{8}{x^2-2x-48}$

7. $\dfrac{7x-2}{x^2+3x-28} - \dfrac{6x-9}{x^2+3x-28}$

Find the LCD for the following lists of rational expressions.

8. $\dfrac{15}{5y^7}, \dfrac{7x}{15y}$

9. $\dfrac{1}{3y}, \dfrac{2x}{9y-15}$

10. $\dfrac{23x-14}{9x-18}, \dfrac{7}{3x^2-12x+12}$

11. $\dfrac{24}{x-y}, \dfrac{31}{y-x}$

12. $\dfrac{9}{x^2+12x+35}, \dfrac{11x-12}{x^2+9x+20}$

1. _____

2. _____

3. _____

4. _____

5. _____

6. _____

7. _____

8. _____

9. _____

10. _____

11. _____

12. _____

Additional Exercises 7.3 *(cont.)*

Name_____

Rewrite each rational expression as an equivalent rational expression whose denominator is the given polynomial.

13. $\dfrac{3}{6y^2} = \dfrac{}{48y^5}$

13. _____

14. $\dfrac{7a+3}{9a+3} = \dfrac{}{3b(3a+1)}$

14. _____

15. $\dfrac{11y-4}{12x^2-15} = \dfrac{}{36x^2-45}$

15. _____

16. $\dfrac{10}{x^2+4x-32} = \dfrac{}{(x+8)(x-4)(x+4)}$

16. _____

17. $\dfrac{x-7}{x^3-3x^2-18x} = \dfrac{}{x(x+4)(x-6)(x+3)}$

17. _____

18. A square has a side of length $\dfrac{9}{x-15}$ feet. Express its perimeter as a rational expression.

18. _____

19. The pentagon has sides $\dfrac{4}{x+6}$ m, $\dfrac{x+1}{x+6}$ m, $\dfrac{x+1}{x+6}$ m, $\dfrac{x+1}{x+6}$ m, and $\dfrac{4}{x+6}$ m. Find its perimeter.

19. _____

Additional Exercises 7.3
Form III

Name_____

Date_____

Add or subtract as indicated. Simplify the result if possible.

1. $\dfrac{5m}{8n} + \dfrac{5m}{8n}$

2. $\dfrac{15m}{2n} - \dfrac{m}{2n}$

3. $\dfrac{4x}{x-7} - \dfrac{28}{x-7}$

4. $\dfrac{2}{11+x} + \dfrac{x+8}{11+x}$

5. $\dfrac{7x^2 - 9}{2x+5} - \dfrac{16+3x^2}{2x+5}$

6. $\dfrac{x}{x^2+3x-108} - \dfrac{9}{x^2+3x-108}$

7. $\dfrac{4x+7}{x^2+11x+28} - \dfrac{3x+3}{x^2+11x+28}$

Find the LCD for the following lists of rational expressions.

8. $\dfrac{8}{10xy}, \dfrac{6}{15x^2}$

9. $\dfrac{8}{y}, \dfrac{x}{y-2}$

10. $\dfrac{x+3}{2x+4}, \dfrac{3}{x^2+11x+18}$

11. $\dfrac{13x}{x-17}, \dfrac{4x}{17-x}$

12. $\dfrac{5}{x^2-3x-10}, \dfrac{12}{x^2-11x+30}$

1. _____

2. _____

3. _____

4. _____

5. _____

6. _____

7. _____

8. _____

9. _____

10. _____

11. _____

12. _____

Additional Exercises 7.3 *(cont.)*

Name_____

Rewrite each rational expression as an equivalent rational
expression whose denominator is the given polynomial.

13. $\dfrac{3}{5x^2} = \dfrac{}{20x^2}$

13. _____

14. $\dfrac{9a+2}{5a+10} = \dfrac{}{5b(a+2)}$

14. _____

15. $\dfrac{8x+3}{7y^2-21} = \dfrac{}{21y^2-63}$

15. _____

16. $\dfrac{-11}{x^2-6x} = \dfrac{}{x(x-6)(x-3)}$

16. _____

17. $\dfrac{x+3}{10x^2+52x+10} = \dfrac{}{x(10x+2)(x+20)(x+5)}$

17. _____

18. A square has a side of length $\dfrac{11}{x+5}$ feet. Express its
    perimeter as a rational expression.

18. _____

19. The trapezoid has sides $\dfrac{4}{x+3}$ m, $\dfrac{x+2}{x+3}$ m, $\dfrac{x+5}{x+3}$ m, and

    $\dfrac{4}{x+3}$ m. Find its perimeter.

19. _____

Additional Exercises 7.4
Form I

Add or subtract as indicated. Simplify the result if possible.

1. $\dfrac{5}{2x} + \dfrac{4}{5x}$

2. $\dfrac{18}{2x} + \dfrac{54}{9x}$

3. $\dfrac{15}{a} + \dfrac{3a}{5}$

4. $\dfrac{9}{x^2} - \dfrac{3}{x}$

5. $\dfrac{2}{x+4} + \dfrac{9}{5x+20}$

6. $\dfrac{7}{x^2} - \dfrac{x}{8x+1}$

7. $\dfrac{4}{x} - 9$

8. $\dfrac{x}{x^2-16} - \dfrac{5}{x^2+5x+4}$

9. $\dfrac{-6x-5}{x} + \dfrac{-8x-6}{9x}$

10. $\dfrac{3}{x-8} + \dfrac{22}{8-x}$

11. $\dfrac{x}{x^2-25} + \dfrac{5}{x+5} - \dfrac{6}{x}$

12. $\dfrac{4a}{5a+10} - \dfrac{a-3}{a+2}$

1. _____

2. _____

3. _____

4. _____

5. _____

6. _____

7. _____

8. _____

9. _____

10. _____

11. _____

12. _____

13. The length of the rectangle is $\dfrac{9}{x-4}$ feet, while its width

Is $\dfrac{6}{x}$ feet. Find the perimeter.

13. _____

14. A board of length $\dfrac{5}{x+6}$ inches was cut into two pieces.

If one piece is $\dfrac{2}{x-6}$ inches, express the length of the

other board as a rational expression.

14. _____

15. A piece of gutter was $\dfrac{5}{x+8}$ inches long before Allison

used a piece $\dfrac{1}{x-8}$ inches long over her porch. How long is

the piece that is left?

15. _____

Additional Exercises 7.4
Form II

Name_____

Date_____

Add or subtract as indicated. Simplify the result if possible.

1. $\dfrac{7}{4x} + \dfrac{3}{5x}$

2. $\dfrac{4n}{m} + \dfrac{3m}{8}$

3. $\dfrac{4}{x} + \dfrac{2}{3x^2}$

4. $\dfrac{5}{x-2} - \dfrac{3}{3x-6}$

5. $\dfrac{9}{7x-28} + \dfrac{x}{x^2-16}$

6. $\dfrac{2}{y^2} - \dfrac{y}{3y+1}$

7. $\dfrac{11}{x-9} + \dfrac{3}{9-x}$

8. $\dfrac{4}{x} + 5$

9. $\dfrac{10}{x-7} + 3$

10. $\dfrac{5x^4}{x} - \dfrac{2x^2}{x^3}$

11. $\dfrac{1}{x+6} - \dfrac{1}{(x+6)^2}$

12. $\dfrac{9}{(x-4)^2} + \dfrac{11}{(x-4)(x+10)}$

13. $\dfrac{4}{x^2-8x-20} - \dfrac{2}{x^2+12x+20} + \dfrac{3}{x^2-100}$

1. _____

2. _____

3. _____

4. _____

5. _____

6. _____

7. _____

8. _____

9. _____

10. _____

11. _____

12. _____

13. _____

Name_____

14. A company earns \$8 on each hammer it sells. The cost to produce each hammer is $\dfrac{5x + 100}{x}$, where x is the number of hammers produced. Find the profit the company makes on each hammer by subtracting the cost to produce from the amount it earns. Then find the profit it makes on each hammer when it produces 2000 hammers.

14. _____

15. A piece of gutter was $\dfrac{5}{x + 6}$ inches long before Allison used a piece $\dfrac{1}{x - 6}$ inches long over her porch. How long is the piece that is left?

15. _____

Additional Exercises 7.4
Form III

Name_____

Date_____

Add or subtract as indicated. Simplify the result if possible.

1. $\dfrac{10}{11x} + \dfrac{6}{13x}$

2. $\dfrac{15}{5x} + \dfrac{49}{7x}$

3. $\dfrac{11y}{x} + \dfrac{3x}{7}$

4. $\dfrac{2}{x^2} - \dfrac{6}{x}$

5. $\dfrac{3}{x+8} + \dfrac{5}{6x+48}$

6. $\dfrac{7}{x^2} - \dfrac{x}{3x+1}$

7. $\dfrac{2}{x} - 5$

8. $\dfrac{x}{x^2-16} - \dfrac{8}{x^2+5x+4}$

9. $\dfrac{-8x+4}{x} + \dfrac{5x-6}{9x}$

10. $\dfrac{11}{x-7} + \dfrac{14}{7-x}$

11. $\dfrac{1}{x+3} - \dfrac{1}{(x+3)^2}$

12. $\dfrac{17}{x^2+x-56} - \dfrac{6}{x-7}$

1. _____

2. _____

3. _____

4. _____

5. _____

6. _____

7. _____

8. _____

9. _____

10. _____

11. _____

12. _____

Name_____

13. The length of the rectangle is $\dfrac{8}{x-4}$ feet, while its width

Is $\dfrac{5}{x}$ feet. Find the perimeter.

13. _____

14. A board of length $\dfrac{2}{x+5}$ inches was cut into two pieces.

If one piece is $\dfrac{4}{x-5}$ inches, express the length of the

other board as a rational expression.

14. _____

15. A piece of gutter was $\dfrac{10}{x+8}$ inches long before Allison

used a piece $\dfrac{-4}{x-8}$ inches long over her porch. How long is

the piece that is left?

15. _____

Additional Exercises 7.5
Form I

Solve each equation.

1. $\dfrac{x}{7} - 3 = 1$

2. $\dfrac{x}{6} + \dfrac{5x}{7} = \dfrac{x}{42}$

3. $\dfrac{x}{5} - \dfrac{x}{8} = 2$

4. $\dfrac{6x}{7} - 3 = x$

5. $\dfrac{x+3}{8} + 4 = \dfrac{5}{8}$

6. $\dfrac{x-3}{9} = \dfrac{x+9}{3}$

7. $\dfrac{x}{2} - 7 = -4$

8. $\dfrac{11}{x} = 4 - \dfrac{1}{x}$

9. $\dfrac{x+6}{7} = \dfrac{x+7}{8}$

10. $\dfrac{5-a}{a} + \dfrac{3}{4} = \dfrac{7}{a}$

11. $\dfrac{x}{2x+2} = \dfrac{-2x}{4x+4} + \dfrac{2x-3}{x+1}$

12. $\dfrac{1}{x+7} + \dfrac{5}{x+6} = \dfrac{-1}{x^2+13x+42}$

1. _____

2. _____

3. _____

4. _____

5. _____

6. _____

7. _____

8. _____

9. _____

10. _____

11. _____

12. _____

Name_____

Solve the equation for the specified variable.

13. $\dfrac{1}{a}+\dfrac{1}{b}=\dfrac{1}{c}$, for c

13. _____

14. $P=\dfrac{A}{1+rt}$; for r

14. _____

Two angles are supplementary if the sum of their measures is 180°. Find the measures of the following supplementary angles.

15. $\left(\dfrac{31x}{20}\right)^{\circ}$, $\left(\dfrac{7x}{10}\right)^{\circ}$

15 _____

Two angles are complementary if the sum of their measures is 90°. Find the measures of the following complementary angles.

16. $\left(\dfrac{180}{y}\right)^{\circ}$, $\left(\dfrac{630}{y}\right)^{\circ}$

16. _____

Additional Exercises 7.5
Form II

Solve each equation.

Name_____

Date_____

1. $\dfrac{x}{7} + 2 = 4$

    1. _____

2. $\dfrac{x}{9} + \dfrac{4x}{3} = \dfrac{26}{9}$

    2. _____

3. $\dfrac{5}{y} + \dfrac{1}{6} = \dfrac{23}{6y}$

    3. _____

4. $\dfrac{8}{x} + \dfrac{1}{4} = \dfrac{9}{2x}$

    4. _____

5. $3 + \dfrac{2}{a-4} = \dfrac{a}{a-4}$

    5. _____

6. $\dfrac{x}{x-1} = \dfrac{6}{x+1}$

    6. _____

7. $\dfrac{3y}{y-5} + 2 = \dfrac{4y}{y-5}$

    7. _____

8. $\dfrac{2x}{x+3} - 2 = \dfrac{x+2}{x-3}$

    8. _____

9. $\dfrac{t}{t-6} = \dfrac{t+6}{9}$

    9. _____

10. $\dfrac{t+2}{4} - \dfrac{t-2}{8} = \dfrac{1}{8}$

    10. _____

11. $\dfrac{1}{3y+1} = \dfrac{2}{9y^2-1} - \dfrac{1}{3y-1}$

    11. _____

12. $\dfrac{5}{x+2} = \dfrac{11x+1}{x^2+7x+10} - \dfrac{12}{x+5}$

    12. _____

Name_____

Solve each equation for the indicated variable.

13. $\dfrac{A}{h} = \dfrac{b}{2}$ for h

13. _____

14. $\dfrac{A}{B+b} = \dfrac{h}{2}$ for B

14. _____

Two angles are supplementary if the sum of their measures is 180°. Find the measures of the following supplementary angles.

15. $\left(\dfrac{21x}{6}\right)^{\circ}$, $\left(\dfrac{29x}{2}\right)^{\circ}$

15. _____

16. $\left(\dfrac{11x}{4}\right)^{\circ}$, $\left(\dfrac{7x}{4}\right)^{\circ}$

16. _____

Additional Exercises 7.5
Form III

Solve each equation.

1. $\dfrac{x}{7} - 5 = 1$

    1. _____

2. $\dfrac{x}{5} + \dfrac{3x}{7} = \dfrac{x}{35}$

    2. _____

3. $\dfrac{x}{8} - \dfrac{x}{9} = 6$

    3. _____

4. $\dfrac{2x}{5} - 7 = x$

    4. _____

5. $\dfrac{y+2}{5} + 1 = \dfrac{3}{5}$

    5. _____

    6. _____

6. $\dfrac{x-3}{5} = \dfrac{x+6}{3}$

7. $\dfrac{x}{11} - 9 = -5$

    7. _____

8. $\dfrac{47}{x} = 8 - \dfrac{1}{x}$

    8. _____

9. $\dfrac{x+3}{4} = \dfrac{x+4}{5}$

    9. _____

10. $\dfrac{5-a}{a} + \dfrac{3}{4} = \dfrac{7}{a}$

    10. _____

11. $\dfrac{x}{2x+2} = \dfrac{-2x}{4x+4} + \dfrac{2x-3}{x+1}$

    11. _____

12. $\dfrac{1}{x+7} + \dfrac{2}{x+3} = \dfrac{-4}{x^2+10x+21}$

    12. _____

Name_____

Solve each equation for the indicated variable.

13. $N = R + \dfrac{V}{G}$ for V

13. _____

14. $P = \dfrac{A}{1 + rt}$; for t

14. _____

Two angles are supplementary if the sum of their measures is 180°. Find the measures of the following supplementary angles.

15. $\left(\dfrac{7x}{6}\right)^{\circ}$, $\left(\dfrac{31x}{12}\right)^{\circ}$

15. _____

Two angles are complementary if the sum of their measures is 90°. Find the measures of the following complementary angles.

16. $\left(\dfrac{990}{y}\right)^{\circ}$, $\left(\dfrac{900}{y}\right)^{\circ}$

16. _____

Additional Exercises 7.6
Form I

Solve each proportion.

1. $\dfrac{x}{38} = \dfrac{1}{19}$

2. $\dfrac{2y+3}{y} = \dfrac{3}{2}$

3. $\dfrac{5}{11} = \dfrac{z-7}{z-12}$

Solve the following problems.

4. Two times the reciprocal of a number equals 16 times the reciprocal of 20. . Find the number.

5. If three times number added to 7 is divided by the number plus 2, the result is four thirds. Find the number.

6. Five divided by the sum of a number and 3, minus the quotient of 3 and the difference of the number and 3 is equal to 6 times the reciprocal of the difference of the number squared and 9. Find the number.

7. Cindy can finish painting a house in 4 hours. Jenny takes 6 hours to finish the same job. How long would it take if they worked together?

8. One conveyor belt can move 1000 boxes in 12 minutes. Another can move 1000 boxes in 10 minutes. If another conveyor belt is added and all three are used, the boxes are moved in 3 minutes. If the third conveyor belt worked alone, how long would it take to do the same job?

9. Jenny can decorate the day's cookie supply four times as fast as Shauna. If they decorate all the cookies working together in 20 minutes, how long would it take for each of them to decorate the cookies individually?

10. Jerrod bikes at a constant speed for 24 miles. He then returns home at the same speed but takes a different route. His return trip takes one hour longer and is 29 miles. Find his speed.

1. _____

2. _____

3. _____

4. _____

5. _____

6. _____

7. _____

8. _____

9. _____

10. _____

Additional Exercises 7.6 *(cont.)*

Name_____

11. A car travels 400 miles on level terrain in the same amount of time it travels 160 miles on mountainous terrain. If the rate of the car is 30 miles per hour less in mountains than on level ground, find its rate in the mountains.

11. _____

12. Cameron can run 5 miles per hour on level ground on a still day. One windy day, he runs 15 miles with the wind, and in the same amount of time runs 7 miles against the wind. What is the rate of the wind?

12. _____

13. In a race, Carl starts 1 mile behind Dave. Carl is traveling at 45 miles per hour, while Dave is traveling at 40 miles per hour. How long will it take for Carl to overtake Dave?

13. _____

14. For two similar triangles, two sides of the smaller triangle are 4 and 5. The corresponding sides of the larger triangle are x and 15, respectively. Find the length of side x.

14. _____

15. For two similar triangles, the three sides of the smaller triangle are 9, x, and 6. The corresponding sides of the larger triangle are 18, 11, and 12, respectively. Find the length of side x.

15. _____

Additional Exercises 7.6
Form II

Solve each proportion.

1. $\dfrac{x}{39} = \dfrac{4}{13}$

2. $\dfrac{y+4}{y} = \dfrac{9}{2}$

3. $\dfrac{5}{9} = \dfrac{z-8}{z-4}$

Solve the following problems.

4. Twelve times the reciprocal of a number is equal to 8 times the reciprocal of 6. Find the number.

5. If one more than 3 times a number is divided by the number, the result is four thirds. Find the number.

6. If fifteen less than two times a number is divided by six more than the number, the result is four less than 9 times the reciprocal of the number. Find the number.

7. George can install new wiring for a computer in 3 hours. It takes Pete 4 hours. How long would it take if they worked together?

8. Marcus assembles crafts in his home. It takes him 2 hours to complete a package of napkin holders. His daughter takes 8 hours to do a package. How long would it take them if they work together?

9. One housekeeper can clean a hotel room twice as fast as another one. Working together, they can clean a room in 8 minutes. How long does it take for each housekeeper to clean a room?

10. A boat can travel 22 miles upstream in the same amount of time it can travel 42 miles downstream. The speed of the current is 5 miles per hour. Find the speed of the boat in still water.

1. _____

2. _____

3. _____

4. _____

5. _____

6. _____

7. _____

8. _____

9. _____

10. _____

11. Olga walks 2 miles at one rate for half of her workout. In the same amount of time, she walks an additional 3 miles at a rate that is 2 miles per hour faster. Find both of Olga's rates.

11. _____

12. Karl walks 3 miles at one rate for half his workout. In the same amount of time, he walks an additional 4 miles at a rate that is 1 miles per hour faster. Find both of Karl's rates.

12. _____

13. Cameron and Whitney have a cabin in the mountains. To get there from home, they drive 36 miles on level ground and 20 miles on mountain roads. They can drive 28 miles per hour faster on the level roads than on the mountain ones. Each part of the trip takes the same amount of time. Find both their level and mountain road rates.

13. _____

14. For two similar triangles, two sides of the smaller triangle are x and 4. The corresponding sides of the larger triangle are 10 and 16, respectively. Find the length of side x.

14. _____

15. Maurice if building a city to go with his model train set. He wants to make a yield sign that is similar to an actual yield sign. An actual yield sign is a triangle that has a top that is 15 in. and two sides that are 12 in. each. If the top of his model yield sign is to have a top that is 1.75 in. How long should the two sides be?

15. _____

Additional Exercises 7.6
Form III

Solve each proportion.

1. $\dfrac{x}{36} = \dfrac{5}{18}$

2. $\dfrac{2y+3}{y} = \dfrac{3}{2}$

3. $\dfrac{2}{5} = \dfrac{z-3}{z-8}$

Solve the following problems.

4. Two times the reciprocal of a number equals 24 times the reciprocal of 30. Find the number.

5. If three times a number added to 4 is divided by the number plus 9, the result is four thirds. Find the number.

6. Five divided by the sum of a number and 4, minus the quotient of 3 and the difference of the number and 4 is equal to 6 times the reciprocal of the difference of the number squared and 16. Find the number.

7. Sue can finish painting a house in 8 hours. Jan takes 10 hours to finish the same job. How long would it take if they worked together?

8. One conveyor belt can move 1000 boxes in 6 minutes. Another can move 1000 boxes in 11 minutes. If another conveyor belt is added and all three are used, the boxes are moved in 3 minutes. If the third conveyor belt worked alone, how long would it take to do the same job?

9. Mary can decorate the day's cookie supply four times as fast as Kate. If they decorate all the cookies working together in 28 minutes, how long would it take for each of them to decorate the cookies individually?

10. Jerrod bikes at a constant speed for 21 miles. He then returns home at the same speed but takes a different route. His return trip takes one hour longer and is 26 miles. Find his speed.

1. _____

2. _____

3. _____

4. _____

5. _____

6. _____

7. _____

8. _____

9. _____

10. _____

Additional Exercises 7.6 (*cont.*)

Name_____

11. A car travels 400 miles on level terrain in the same amount of time it travels 160 miles on mountainous terrain. If the rate of the car is 30 miles per hour less in mountains than on level ground, find its rate in the mountains.

11. _____

12. Cameron can run 5 miles per hour on level ground on a still day. One windy day, he runs 13 miles with the wind, and in the same amount of time runs 7 miles against the wind. What is the rate of the wind?

12. _____

13. In a race, Carl starts 1 mile behind Dave. Carl is traveling at 65 miles per hour, while Dave is traveling at 50 miles per hour. How long will it take for Carl to overtake Dave?

13. _____

14. For two similar triangles, the three sides of the smaller triangle are 7, 6, and 4. The corresponding sides of the larger triangle are x, 9 and 6 respectively. Find the length of side x.

14. _____

15. In Maurice's model city, he wants to build a triangular shaped garden that is similar to his garden. His garden has sides that are 30 ft., 50 ft., and 40 ft. The garden in his model has sides 1.5 in, x in. and y in. Find x and y.

15. _____

Additional Exercises 7.7
Form I

State whether each equation is (a) direct or (b) inverse variation.

1. $y = 4x$

2. $y = \dfrac{30}{x}$

3. $y = 5.5x^4$

Write a direct variation equation, $y = kx$, that satisfies the ordered pairs in each table.

4.

x	0	-4	-18
y	0	2	9

5.

x	-5	2	7	13
y	$\dfrac{5}{4}$	$-\dfrac{1}{2}$	$-\dfrac{7}{4}$	$-\dfrac{13}{4}$

Write a direct variation equation, $y = kx$, that describes each graph.

6.

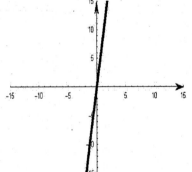

Write an inverse variation equation, $y = \dfrac{k}{x}$, that satisfies the ordered pairs in each table.

7.

x	1	-9	$\dfrac{9}{2}$	-2
y	9	-1	2	$-\dfrac{9}{2}$

1. _____

2. _____

3. _____

4. _____

5. _____

6. _____

7. _____

Additional Exercises 7.7 *(cont.)*

Write an inverse variation equation, $y = \dfrac{k}{x}$, that satisfies the
ordered pairs in each table.

8.

x	2	-13	$\dfrac{13}{2}$	-4
y	13	-2	4	$-\dfrac{13}{2}$

8. _____

Write an equation to describe each variation. Use k for the
constant of proportionality.

9. w varies directly as s

9. _____

10. a varies inversely as b

10. _____

11. a varies inversely as s

11. _____

Solve.

12. y varies directly as x. When y is 270, x is 15. Find y when x is 19.

12. _____

13. x varies inversely as v. When x is 36, v is 7. Find x when v is 28.

13. _____

14. y varies directly as x^2. If $y = 81$ when $x = 3$, find y when x is 4.

14. _____

15. x varies inversely as y^2. If $x = 4$ when $y = 10$, find x when y is 2.

15. _____

Solve.

16. _____

16. The amount of gas that a helicopter uses varies directly as the number of hours spent flying. The helicopter flies for 2 hours and uses 14 gallons of fuel. Find the number of gallons of fuel that the helicopter uses to fly for 4 hours.

17. The distance that an object falls when it is dropped varies directly as the square of the amount of time that has passed since it was dropped. An object falls 39.2 meters in 2 seconds. Find the distance the object falls in 4 seconds.

17. _____

Additional Exercises 7.7
Form II

State whether each equation is (a) direct or (b) inverse variation.

1. $y = 6x$

2. $y = \dfrac{15}{x}$

3. $y = 3x^3$

Write a direct variation equation, $y = kx$, that satisfies the ordered pairs in each table.

4.

x	0	8	16
y	0	2	4

5.

x	0	3	-5	7
y	0	24	-40	56

Write a direct variation equation, $y = kx$, that describes each graph.

6.

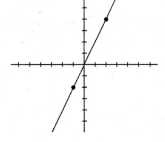

Write an inverse variation equation, $y = \dfrac{k}{x}$, that satisfies the ordered pairs in each table.

7.

x	1	3	-6	12
y	12	4	-2	1

1. _____

2. _____

3. _____

4. _____

5. _____

6. _____

7. _____

Name _____

Write an inverse variation equation, $y = \dfrac{k}{x}$, that satisfies the ordered pairs in each table.

8.

x	3	-10	0.5	0.01
y	0.1	-0.3	0.6	30

8. _____

Write an equation to describe each variation. Use k for the constant of proportionality.

9. s varies directly as t

9. _____

10. t varies directly as $\sqrt{x}$

10. _____

11. p varies inversely as x^3

11. _____

Solve.

12. y varies directly as x. When y is 12, x is 4. Find y when x is 9.

12. _____

13. a varies directly as b^2. When a is 4, b is 32. Find a when b is 50.

13. _____

14. a varies inversely as x. If $a = 4$ when $x = 3$, find a when x is 6.

14. _____

15. p varies inversely as x^2. If $p = 5$ when $x = 2$, find p when x is 6.

15. _____

Solve.

16. Ray's paycheck varies directly as the number of hours he works. If he earns \$21.75 for 3 hours, how much will he earn for 23 hours of work?

16. _____

17. The current, for a fixed voltage, in an electrical circuit varies inversely with the resistance in the circuit. If a particular circuit has a current of 2.5 amp when the resistance is 150 ohms, find the current in the circuit when the resistance is 300 ohms.

17. _____

Additional Exercises 7.7
Form III

Name_____

Date_____

State whether each equation is (a) direct or (b) inverse variation.

1. $y = 6x$

2. $y = \dfrac{11}{x}$

4. $y = 10x^2$

Write a direct variation equation, $y = kx$, that satisfies the ordered pairs in each table.

4.

x	0	-6	-14
y	0	3	7

5.

x	-5	5	6	12
y	$-\dfrac{5}{2}$	$\dfrac{5}{2}$	3	6

Write a direct variation equation, $y = kx$, that describes each graph.

6.

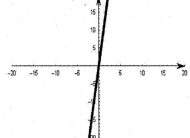

Write an inverse variation equation, $y = \dfrac{k}{x}$, that satisfies the ordered pairs in each table.

7.

x	1	-7	$\dfrac{7}{2}$	-2
y	7	-1	2	$-\dfrac{7}{2}$

1. _____

2. _____

3. _____

4. _____

5. _____

6. _____

7. _____

Additional Exercises 7.7 *(cont.)*

Write an inverse variation equation, $y = \dfrac{k}{x}$, that satisfies the ordered pairs in each table.

8. _____

8.

x	2	-10	5	-4
y	10	-2	4	-5

Write an equation to describe each variation. Use k for the constant of proportionality.

9. _____

9. y varies directly as t

10. _____

10. a varies directly as b

11. _____

11. b varies inversely as y

Solve.

12. y varies directly as x. When y is 170, x is 17. Find y when x is 11.

12. _____

13. x varies inversely as v. When x is 28, v is 9. Find x when v is 63.

13. _____

14. y varies directly as x^2. If $y = 576$ when $x = 8$, find y when x is 3.

14. _____

15. x varies inversely as y^2. If $x = 6$ when $y = 8$, find x when y is 2.

15. _____

Solve.

16. The amount of gas that a helicopter uses varies directly as the number of hours spent flying. The helicopter flies for 3 hours and uses 30 gallons of fuel. Find the number of gallons of fuel that the helicopter uses to fly for 5 hours.

16. _____

17. The distance that an object falls when it is dropped varies directly as the square of the amount of time that has passed since it was dropped. An object falls 88.2 meters in 3 seconds. Find the distance the object falls in 4 seconds.

17. _____

Additional Exercises 7.8
Form I

Simplify each complex fraction.

Name_____

Date_____

1. $\dfrac{\frac{4}{13}}{\frac{3}{5}}$

2. $\dfrac{\frac{1}{4}}{\frac{5}{6}}$

3. $\dfrac{\frac{x}{7}}{\frac{9}{x+3}}$

4. $\dfrac{1+\frac{1}{x}}{1-\frac{1}{x}}$

5. $\dfrac{\frac{1}{x+6}}{\frac{5}{x^2-36}}$

6. $\dfrac{\frac{1}{2}-\frac{1}{4}}{\frac{1}{6}+\frac{1}{4}}$

7. $\dfrac{\frac{4}{7y-1}-4}{\frac{4}{7y-1}+4}$

8. $\dfrac{\frac{x}{2}+\frac{1}{2}}{\frac{x^2}{3}+\frac{x}{3}}$

9. $\dfrac{4+\frac{2}{x}}{\frac{x}{4}+\frac{1}{8}}$

1. _____

2. _____

3. _____

4. _____

5. _____

6. _____

7. _____

8. _____

9. _____

10. $\dfrac{\dfrac{9}{a}+9}{\dfrac{9}{a}-9}$

10. _____

11. $\dfrac{\dfrac{8}{3y-1}-8}{\dfrac{8}{3y-1}+8}$

11. _____

12. $\dfrac{\dfrac{5}{a}+5}{\dfrac{5}{a}-5}$

12. _____

To find the average of two numbers, we find their sum and divide by 2.

13. Find the average of $\dfrac{1}{3}$ and $\dfrac{3}{4}$.

13. _____

14. Write the average of $\dfrac{3}{n}$ and $\dfrac{5}{n^2}$ as a simplified rational expression.

14. _____

15. In optics, a single lens can be equivalent to two thin lines with focal lengths of f_1 and f_2. If the two thin lenses are touching, the focal length of the single lens is given by the complex fraction $\dfrac{3}{\dfrac{3}{f_1}+\dfrac{3}{f_2}}$.   Simplify this expression.

15. _____

Additional Exercises 7.8
Form II

Name_____

Date_____

Simplify each complex fraction.

1. $\dfrac{\dfrac{1}{9}}{-\dfrac{4}{15}}$

2. $\dfrac{\dfrac{7y}{20}}{\dfrac{3y}{4}}$

3. $\dfrac{\dfrac{3}{8}}{\dfrac{1}{8}-\dfrac{3}{4}}$

4. $\dfrac{1-\dfrac{8}{9}}{2-\dfrac{3}{4}}$

5. $\dfrac{\dfrac{2x+8}{2}}{\dfrac{4x+16}{4}}$

6. $\dfrac{\dfrac{1}{6}-\dfrac{1}{x}}{\dfrac{2}{3}+\dfrac{1}{x^2}}$

7. $\dfrac{2+\dfrac{2}{y-3}}{y+\dfrac{2}{y-3}}$

8. $\dfrac{\dfrac{2x+2y}{x^2-y^2}}{\dfrac{x+y}{x-y}}$

1. _____

2. _____

3. _____

4. _____

5. _____

6. _____

7. _____

8. _____

9. $\dfrac{a-\dfrac{4}{a}}{\dfrac{1}{a^2}+\dfrac{1}{2a}}$

9. _____

10. $\dfrac{5+\dfrac{1}{x^2}}{5-\dfrac{1}{x}}$

10. _____

11. $\dfrac{\dfrac{5}{x+1}+6}{\dfrac{10}{x+1}-6}$

11. _____

12. $\dfrac{\dfrac{x}{2}+\dfrac{1}{2}}{\dfrac{x^2}{3}+\dfrac{x}{3}}$

12. _____

To find the average of two numbers, we find their sum and divide by 2.

13. _____

13. Find the average of $\dfrac{3}{5}$ and $\dfrac{1}{4}$.

14. _____

14. Write the average of $\dfrac{7}{n}$ and $\dfrac{4}{n^2}$ as a simplified rational expression.

15. _____

15. In optics, a single lens can be equivalent to two thin lines with focal lengths of f_1 and f_2. If the two thin lenses are touching, the focal length of the single lens is given by the complex fraction $\dfrac{1}{\dfrac{1}{f_1}+\dfrac{1}{f_2}}$. Simplify this expression.

Additional Exercises 7.8
Form III

Simplify each complex fraction.

Name_____

Date_____

1. $\dfrac{\frac{5}{9}}{\frac{2}{11}}$

2. $\dfrac{\frac{6}{19}}{\frac{1}{4}}$

3. $\dfrac{\frac{x}{3}}{\frac{2}{x+5}}$

4. $\dfrac{\frac{5}{2y}+7}{\frac{5}{2y}-7}$

5. $\dfrac{\frac{1}{y+2}}{\frac{5}{y^2-4}}$

6. $\dfrac{\frac{1}{3}-\frac{1}{9}}{\frac{1}{5}+\frac{1}{7}}$

7. $\dfrac{\frac{7}{7y-1}-7}{\frac{7}{7y}+7}$

8. $\dfrac{\frac{3x-21}{12}}{\frac{2x-14}{4}}$

1. _____

2. _____

3. _____

4. _____

5. _____

6. _____

7. _____

8. _____

9. $\dfrac{9+\dfrac{3}{x}}{\dfrac{x}{4}+\dfrac{1}{12}}$

9. ._____

10. $\dfrac{\dfrac{5}{a}+5}{\dfrac{5}{a}-5}$

10. _____

11. $\dfrac{\dfrac{10}{5y-1}-10}{\dfrac{10}{5y-1}+10}$

11. _____

12. $\dfrac{\dfrac{3}{a}+3}{\dfrac{3}{a}-3}$

12. _____

To find the average of two numbers, we find their sum and divide by 2.

13. Find the average of $\dfrac{2}{3}$ and $\dfrac{5}{8}$.

13. _____

14. Write the average of $\dfrac{12}{n}$ and $\dfrac{8}{n^2}$ as a simplified rational expression.

14. _____

15. In optics, a single lens can be equivalent to two thin lines with focal lengths of f_1 and f_2. If the two thin lenses are touching, the focal length of the single lens is given by the complex fraction $\dfrac{5}{\dfrac{5}{f_1}+\dfrac{5}{f_2}}$.   Simplify this expression.

15. _____

Additional Exercises 8.1
Form I

Name_____

Date_____

Find each square root. Indicate if the number is not real.

1. $\sqrt{4}$

2. $\sqrt{\dfrac{1}{81}}$

3. $-\sqrt{9}$

4. $\sqrt{-16}$

5. $\sqrt{\dfrac{100}{49}}$

Find the cube root.

6. $\sqrt[3]{343}$

7. $\sqrt[3]{-729}$

Find each root. Indicate if the number is not real.

8. $\sqrt[6]{64}$

9. $\sqrt[4]{1296}$

10. $\sqrt[4]{-625}$

11. $-\sqrt[5]{32}$

Approximate each square root to three decimal places.

12. $\sqrt{5}$

13. $\sqrt{94}$

14. The total area of a roof is exactly $12\sqrt{5}$ square feet. Approximate this area to the nearest whole number.

1. _____

2. _____

3. _____

4. _____

5. _____

6. _____

7. _____

8. _____

9. _____

10. _____

11. _____

12. _____

13. _____

14. _____

Name_____

Find each root. Assume that each variable represents a nonnegative real number.

15. $\sqrt{w^{14}}$

16. $\sqrt{4x^{14}}$

17. $\sqrt{\dfrac{49z^{28}}{9}}$

18. $\sqrt[3]{-8x^6 y^{12}}$

19. Complete the table, plot the points, and draw a smooth curve to graph $y = \sqrt{x-5}$.

x	y
5	
6	
9	
12	
14	

15. _____

16. _____

17. _____

18. _____

19.

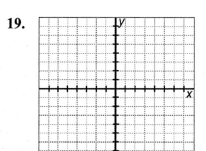

Additional Exercises 8.1
Form II

Name_____

Date_____

Find each square root. Indicate if the number is not real.

1. $\sqrt{81}$

2. $\sqrt{\dfrac{1}{49}}$

3. $-\sqrt{144}$

4. $\sqrt{-9}$

5. $\sqrt{\dfrac{121}{4}}$

Find the cube root.

6. $\sqrt[3]{8000}$

7. $\sqrt[3]{-64}$

Find each root. Indicate if the number is not real.

8. $\sqrt[5]{-1024}$

9. $\sqrt[5]{243}$

10. $\sqrt[4]{-81}$

11. $-\sqrt[4]{16}$

Approximate each square root to three decimal places.

12. $\sqrt{46}$

13. $\sqrt{178}$

14. The total area of a roof is exactly $160\sqrt{29}$ square feet. Approximate this area to the nearest whole number.

1. _____

2. _____

3. _____

4. _____

5. _____

6. _____

7. _____

8. _____

9. _____

10. _____

11. _____

12. _____

13. _____

14. _____

Find each root. Assume that each variable represents a nonnegative real number.

15. $\sqrt{n^4}$

16. $\sqrt{16y^6}$

17. $\sqrt{81z^{20}}$

18. $\sqrt[3]{-125x^3y^{15}}$

19. Complete the table, plot the points, and draw a smooth curve to graph $y = \sqrt{x-1}$.

x	y
1	
2	
5	
7	
10	

15. _____

16. _____

17. _____

18. _____

19.

Additional Exercises 8.1
Form III

Name_____

Date_____

Find each square root. Indicate if the number is not real.

1. $\sqrt{25}$

2. $\sqrt{\dfrac{1}{121}}$

3. $-\sqrt{36}$

4. $\sqrt{-49}$

5. $\sqrt{\dfrac{81}{16}}$

Find the cube root.

6. $\sqrt[3]{216}$

7. $\sqrt[3]{-8}$

Find each root. Indicate if the number is not real.

8. $\sqrt[4]{256}$

9. $\sqrt[4]{2401}$

10. $\sqrt[4]{-6561}$

11. $-\sqrt[5]{1024}$

Approximate each square root to three decimal places.

12. $\sqrt{3}$

13. $\sqrt{71}$

14. The total area of a roof is exactly $5\sqrt{20}$ square feet. Approximate this area to the nearest whole number.

1. _____

2. _____

3. _____

4. _____

5. _____

6. _____

7. _____

8. _____

9. _____

10. _____

11. _____

12. _____

13. _____

14. _____

Additional Exercises 8.1 *(cont.)*

Name_____

Find each root. Assume that each variable represents a nonnegative real number.

15. $\sqrt{n^{26}}$

16. $\sqrt{64x^6}$

17. $\sqrt{\dfrac{121z^{18}}{49}}$

18. $\sqrt[3]{-512x^9 y^{18}}$

15. _____

16. _____

17. _____

18. _____

19. Complete the table, plot the points, and draw a smooth curve to graph $y = \sqrt{x-3}$.

x	y
3	
4	
5	
7	
9	

19.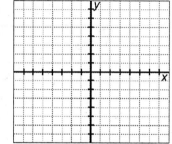

Additional Exercises 8.2
Form I

Name _____

Date _____

Use the product rule to simplify each expression.

1. $\sqrt{18}$

2. $\sqrt{28}$

3. $\sqrt{132}$

Use the product rule and the quotient rule to simplify each expression.

4. $\sqrt{\dfrac{49}{36}}$

5. $\sqrt{\dfrac{325}{49}}$

6. $-\sqrt{\dfrac{68}{81}}$

7. $\sqrt{\dfrac{17}{81}}$

Simplify each expression. Assume all variables represent real numbers.

8. $\sqrt{y^7}$

9. $\sqrt{486x^2}$

10. $\sqrt{12x^7y^8}$

11. $\sqrt{\dfrac{15}{x^4}}$

12. $\sqrt{\dfrac{245}{x^2}}$

13. $\sqrt{\dfrac{x^9}{49}}$

1. _____

2. _____

3. _____

4. _____

5. _____

6. _____

7. _____

8. _____

9. _____

10. _____

11. _____

12. _____

13. _____

Additional Exercises 8.2 *(cont.)*

Name_____

Simplify each radical.

14. $\sqrt[3]{16}$

15. $\sqrt[3]{128}$

16. $\sqrt[3]{\dfrac{48}{x^6}}$

17. $\sqrt[3]{729x^4y^5}$

18. The length of each side of a cube with a volume of 250 cubic inches is $\sqrt[3]{250}$. Simplify this radical.

19. The length of a path across a garden is $\sqrt{1500}$ feet. Simplify this radical.

14. _____

15. _____

16. _____

17. _____

18. _____

19. _____

Additional Exercises 8.2
Form II

Name_____

Date_____

Use the product rule to simplify each expression.

1. $\sqrt{75}$

2. $\sqrt{99}$

3. $\sqrt{72}$

Use the product rule and the quotient rule to simplify each expression.

4. $\sqrt{\dfrac{45}{64}}$

5. $-\sqrt{\dfrac{84}{25}}$

6. $\sqrt{\dfrac{75}{81}}$

7. $\sqrt{\dfrac{48}{225}}$

Simplify each expression. Assume all variables represent real numbers.

8. $\sqrt{x^{11}}$

9. $\sqrt{25y^3}$

10. $\sqrt{45x^6y^8}$

11. $\sqrt{\dfrac{56}{y^4}}$

12. $\sqrt{\dfrac{98y^2}{x^{10}}}$

13. $\sqrt{\dfrac{x^9}{y^{20}}}$

1. _____

2. _____

3. _____

4. _____

5. _____

6. _____

7. _____

8. _____

9. _____

10. _____

11. _____

12. _____

13. _____

Name_____

Simplify each radical.

14. $6\sqrt{25}$

15. $\sqrt[3]{56}$

16. $\sqrt[3]{\dfrac{14}{125}}$

Simplify each expression. Assume all variables represent positive real numbers.

17. $\sqrt{117x^7 y^6}$

18. The length of each side of a cube with a volume of 270 cubic inches is $\sqrt[3]{270}$. Simplify this radical.

19. The length of a path across a garden is $\sqrt{1300}$ feet. Simplify this radical.

14. _____

15. _____

16. _____

17. _____

18. _____

19. _____

Additional Exercises 8.2
Form III

Use the product rule to simplify each expression.

1. $\sqrt{150}$

2. $\sqrt{175}$

3. $\sqrt{140}$

Use the product rule and the quotient rule to simplify each expression.

4. $\sqrt{\dfrac{25}{64}}$

5. $\sqrt{\dfrac{867}{121}}$

6. $-\sqrt{\dfrac{575}{64}}$

7. $\sqrt{\dfrac{3}{49}}$

Simplify each expression. Assume all variables represent real numbers.

8. $\sqrt{y^{17}}$

9. $\sqrt{448x^2}$

10. $\sqrt{50x^7y^4}$

11. $\sqrt{\dfrac{46}{x^{10}}}$

12. $\sqrt{\dfrac{605y^2}{x^8}}$

13. $\sqrt{\dfrac{x^7}{25y^{30}}}$

1. _____

2. _____

3. _____

4. _____

5. _____

6. _____

7. _____

8. _____

9. _____

10. _____

11. _____

12. _____

13. _____

Additional Exercises 8.2 *(cont.)*

Simplify each radical.

14. $\sqrt{8192}$

15. $\sqrt[3]{250}$

16. $\sqrt[4]{\dfrac{810}{x^{24}}}$

Simplify each expression. Assume all variables represent positive real numbers.

17. $\sqrt[3]{125x^4y^5}$

18. The length of each side of a cube with a volume of 88 cubic inches is $\sqrt[3]{88}$. Simplify this radical.

19. The length of a path across a garden is $\sqrt{2700}$ feet. Simplify this radical.

14. _____

15. _____

16. _____

17. _____

18. _____

19. _____

Additional Exercises 8.3
Form I

Add or subtract.

1. $2\sqrt{6} + 5\sqrt{6}$

2. $21\sqrt{2} - 5\sqrt{2}$

3. $10\sqrt{5} + 9\sqrt{5} + 7\sqrt{5} + 26\sqrt{5}$

Add or subtract first simplifying each radical and then combining any like radical terms. Assume that all variables represent positive real numbers.

4. $-9\sqrt{3} - 5\sqrt{12}$

5. $\sqrt{\dfrac{2}{36}} + \sqrt{\dfrac{98}{25}}$

6. $4\sqrt{72} + 7\sqrt{200}$

7. $y - \sqrt{9y^2} + 4\sqrt{y}$

8. $\sqrt{100x} - \sqrt{36x} - 3\sqrt{x}$

9. $6\sqrt{x^4} - x^2\sqrt{16}$

10. $\sqrt{\dfrac{5}{49}} + \sqrt{\dfrac{5}{81}}$

11. $\sqrt{3x} + 5\sqrt{108x} + 7\sqrt{75x}$

12. $x\sqrt{3x} + 7\sqrt{75x^3} - 2x\sqrt{75x}$

13. $\sqrt{4x^{11}} - x^2\sqrt{25x^7} + \sqrt{x^3}$

14. $\sqrt{90x^2} + \sqrt{27x^2} + x\sqrt{75}$

15. $\sqrt[3]{8y} - \sqrt[3]{54y}$

16. $3\sqrt[3]{8x} + 3\sqrt[3]{125x}$

17. $\sqrt{5x^2} - \sqrt[3]{54} + \sqrt{720x^2}$

1. _____

2. _____

3. _____

4. _____

5. _____

6. _____

7. _____

8. _____

9. _____

10. _____

11. _____

12. _____

13. _____

14. _____

15. _____

16. _____

17. _____

Additional Exercises 8.3 *(cont.)*

18. Find the perimeter of a rectangular door if the width is $2\sqrt{6}$ ft and the length is 10 ft.

18. _____

19. Find the perimeter of a triangle whose sides are $3\sqrt{5}$ m, $2\sqrt{5}$ m, and $\sqrt{5}$ m.

19. _____

20. Find the perimeter of a four sided piece of land with sides of $\sqrt{6}$ ft, $\sqrt{16}$ ft, $\sqrt{24}$ ft, and $\sqrt{49}$ ft.

20. _____

Additional Exercises 8.3
Form II

Add or subtract.

1. $6\sqrt{7} - 9\sqrt{7}$

2. $\sqrt{10} + 6\sqrt{10} - 5\sqrt{10}$

3. $8\sqrt{19} - 5\sqrt{19} - 10\sqrt{19}$

Add or subtract first simplifying each radical and then combining any like radical terms. Assume that all variables represent positive real numbers.

4. $\sqrt{98} + \sqrt{8}$

5. $\sqrt{80} - \sqrt{180}$

6. $3\sqrt{96} + 2\sqrt{50} - \sqrt{600} - \sqrt{242}$

7. $y - 7\sqrt{y^2} + 3\sqrt{y}$

8. $\sqrt{144x} - \sqrt{64x} - 4\sqrt{x}$

9. $5\sqrt{x^3} - x\sqrt{9}$

10. $\sqrt{\dfrac{13}{25}} + \sqrt{\dfrac{13}{100}}$

11. $\sqrt{121x} - 8\sqrt{x} - \sqrt{16x}$

12. $6\sqrt{10yz^2} + z\sqrt{810y}$

13. $\sqrt{48x^2} - x\sqrt{245x} - x\sqrt{300} + \sqrt{500x^3}$

14. $\sqrt{32x^3} + \sqrt{49x} + x\sqrt{72x}$

15. $2\sqrt[3]{25} + 4\sqrt[3]{25} - \sqrt[3]{4}$

16. $\sqrt[3]{16y} + \sqrt[3]{128y}$

17. $2\sqrt[3]{64x} + 2\sqrt[3]{8x}$

1. _____
2. _____
3. _____
4. _____
5. _____
6. _____
7. _____
8. _____
9. _____
10. _____
11. _____
12. _____
13. _____
14. _____
15. _____
16. _____
17. _____

18. Find the perimeter of a rectangular door if the width is $2\sqrt{5}$ ft and the length is 8 ft.

18. _____

19. Find the perimeter of a triangle whose sides are $3\sqrt{7}$ m, $5\sqrt{7}$ m, and $4\sqrt{7}$ m.

19. _____

20. Find the perimeter of a four sided piece of land with sides of $3\sqrt{75}$ ft, $4\sqrt{108}$ ft, $6\sqrt{27}$ ft, and $2\sqrt{147}$ ft.

20. _____

Additional Exercises 8.3
Form III

Name _____

Date _____

Add or subtract.

1. $12\sqrt{3} - 15\sqrt{3}$

2. $21\sqrt{11} - 7\sqrt{11}$

3. $3\sqrt{10} + 12\sqrt{10} + 4\sqrt{10} + 19\sqrt{10}$

Add or subtract first simplifying each radical and then combining any like radical terms. Assume that all variables represent positive real numbers.

4. $-7\sqrt{5} - 4\sqrt{45}$

5. $\sqrt{\dfrac{5}{25}} + \sqrt{\dfrac{125}{9}}$

6. $3\sqrt{162} + 4\sqrt{50}$

7. $-3\sqrt{3} - 3\sqrt{108} + \sqrt{75}$

8. $\sqrt{169x} - \sqrt{121x} - 5\sqrt{x}$

9. $3\sqrt{28x^3} - 4x\sqrt{63x}$

10. $\sqrt{\dfrac{13}{4}} + \sqrt{\dfrac{13}{36}}$

11. $\sqrt{2x} - 5\sqrt{72x} - 4\sqrt{8x}$

12. $x\sqrt{3x} + 7\sqrt{27x^3} + 4x\sqrt{27x}$

13. $\sqrt{40x^4} + x^2\sqrt{180x^3} + x\sqrt{90x^2} - \sqrt{125x^7}$

14. $\sqrt{96x^7} - \sqrt{5y} + x\sqrt{150x^5}$

15. $\sqrt[3]{8y} - \sqrt[3]{128y}$

16. $4\sqrt[3]{8x} + 4\sqrt[3]{125x}$

17. $\sqrt{5x^2} - \sqrt[3]{24} + \sqrt{320x^2}$

1. _____

2. _____

3. _____

4. _____

5. _____

6. _____

7. _____

8. _____

9. _____

10. _____

11. _____

12. _____

13. _____

14. _____

15. _____

16. _____

17. _____

Additional Exercises 8.3 *(cont.)*

Name_____

18. Find the perimeter of a rectangular door if the width is $3\sqrt{3}$ ft and the length is 7 ft.

18. _____

19. Find the perimeter of a triangle whose sides are $2\sqrt{17}$ m, $6\sqrt{17}$ m, and $3\sqrt{17}$ m.

19. _____

20. Find the perimeter of a four sided piece of land with sides of $\sqrt{5}$ ft, $2\sqrt{100}$ ft, $3\sqrt{125}$ ft, and $\sqrt{16}$ ft.

20. _____

Additional Exercises 8.4
Form I

Name_____

Date_____

Multiply and simplify.

1. $\sqrt{2} \cdot \sqrt{5}$

2. $\sqrt{7} \cdot \sqrt{4}$

3. $\sqrt{72} \cdot \sqrt{50}$

4. $\sqrt{3y} \cdot \sqrt{3y}$

5. $\left(6\sqrt{y}\right)^2$

6. $\sqrt{3y} \cdot \sqrt{8x}$

7. $\sqrt{4x} \cdot \sqrt{5x^2 y}$

8. $\sqrt{7}\left(\sqrt{63} + \sqrt{21}\right)$

9. $\left(\sqrt{13} + \sqrt{3}\right)\left(\sqrt{5} - \sqrt{3}\right)$

10. $\left(7\sqrt{11} + 5\right)\left(8\sqrt{11} + 2\right)$

11. $\left(4\sqrt{11} + 2\right)^2$

12. $\left(2\sqrt{x} - 8\right)^2$

Divide and simplify

13. $\dfrac{\sqrt{100}}{\sqrt{4}}$

14. $\dfrac{\sqrt{140}}{\sqrt{5}}$

15. $\dfrac{\sqrt{189x^5 y^6}}{\sqrt{3y^4}}$

1. _____

2. _____

3. _____

4. _____

5. _____

6. _____

7. _____

8. _____

9. _____

10. _____

11. _____

12. _____

13. _____

14. _____

15. _____

Additional Exercises 8.4 *(cont.)*

Name_____

Rationalize each denominator and simplify.

16. $\sqrt{\dfrac{11}{13}}$

16. _____

17. $\sqrt{\dfrac{3}{20}}$

17. _____

18. $\dfrac{2}{\sqrt{17}-4}$

18. _____

19. $\dfrac{\sqrt{3}+1}{\sqrt{3}-\sqrt{2}}$

19. _____

20. A television is a rectangle with a length of $2\sqrt{24}$ in and a width of $2\sqrt{36}$ in. Find the area of the screen.

20. _____

Additional Exercises 8.4
Form II

Name_____

Date_____

Multiply and simplify.

1. $\sqrt{5} \cdot \sqrt{20}$

2. $\sqrt{14} \cdot \sqrt{14}$

3. $\sqrt{33} \cdot \sqrt{3}$

4. $\sqrt{17x} \cdot \sqrt{17x}$

5. $\left(7\sqrt{x}\right)^2$

6. $\sqrt{5y} \cdot \sqrt{10x}$

7. $\sqrt{2xy^2} \sqrt{6xy}$

8. $\sqrt{5}\left(\sqrt{7} + 1\right)$

9. $\left(\sqrt{11} + 4\right)\left(\sqrt{11} - 4\right)$

10. $\left(\sqrt{7} + \sqrt{6}\right)\left(\sqrt{5} - \sqrt{6}\right)$

11. $\left(\sqrt{x} - 4\right)^2$

12. $\left(\sqrt{3y} + 2\right)^2$

Divide and simplify

13. $\dfrac{\sqrt{44}}{\sqrt{11}}$

14. $\dfrac{\sqrt{90}}{\sqrt{5}}$

15. $\dfrac{\sqrt{84x^5 y^3}}{\sqrt{7x^2 y}}$

1. _____

2. _____

3. _____

4. _____

5. _____

6. _____

7. _____

8. _____

9. _____

10. _____

11. _____

12. _____

13. _____

14. _____

15. _____

Additional Exercises 8.4 *(cont.)*

Name_____

Rationalize each denominator and simplify.

16. $\dfrac{\sqrt{10}}{\sqrt{7}}$

16. _____

17. $\dfrac{\sqrt{2}}{\sqrt{12y}}$

17. _____

18. $\dfrac{9}{\sqrt{x}-6}$

18. _____

19. $\dfrac{\sqrt{6}+1}{\sqrt{3}+\sqrt{2}}$

19. _____

20. A television is a rectangle with a length of $3\sqrt{65}$ in and a width of $3\sqrt{35}$ in. Find the area of the screen.

20. _____

Additional Exercises 8.4
Form III

Name_____

Date_____

Multiply and simplify.

1. $\sqrt{3} \cdot \sqrt{2}$

2. $\sqrt{2} \cdot \sqrt{25}$

3. $\sqrt{98} \cdot \sqrt{18}$

4. $\sqrt{21y} \cdot \sqrt{21y}$

5. $\left(11\sqrt{y}\right)^2$

6. $\sqrt{2y} \cdot \sqrt{10x}$

7. $\sqrt{6x^3 y} \cdot \sqrt{7y^3}$

8. $\sqrt{5}\left(\sqrt{20} + \sqrt{10}\right)$

9. $\left(\sqrt{7} + \sqrt{13}\right)\left(\sqrt{5} - \sqrt{13}\right)$

10. $\left(4\sqrt{17} + 4\right)\left(4\sqrt{17} + 9\right)$

11. $\left(6\sqrt{11} + 8\right)^2$

12. $\left(6\sqrt{x} - 2\right)^2$

Divide and simplify

13. $\dfrac{\sqrt{96}}{\sqrt{6}}$

14. $\dfrac{\sqrt{100}}{\sqrt{5}}$

15. $\dfrac{\sqrt{56x^5 y^6}}{\sqrt{2y^4}}$

1. _____

2. _____

3. _____

4. _____

5. _____

6. _____

7. _____

8. _____

9. _____

10. _____

11. _____

12. _____

13. _____

14. _____

15. _____

Rationalize each denominator and simplify.

16. $\sqrt{\dfrac{5}{3}}$

16. _____

17. $\sqrt{\dfrac{2}{175}}$

17. _____

18. $\dfrac{6}{\sqrt{26}-5}$

18. _____

19. $\dfrac{\sqrt{6}+1}{\sqrt{6}-\sqrt{5}}$

19. _____

20. A television is a rectangle with a length of $3\sqrt{10}$ in and a width of $5\sqrt{5}$ in. Find the area of the screen.

20. _____

Additional Exercises 8.5
Form I

Name_____

Date_____

Solve each equation. Be sure to check for extraneous solutions.

1. $\sqrt{x} = 25$

2. $\sqrt{x+2} = 6$

3. $\sqrt{10x-9} = 9$

4. $\sqrt{x} - 9 = 8$

5. $\sqrt{3x+4} + 6 = 11$

6. $\sqrt{4x+8} + 4 = 10$

7. $\sqrt{10x-24} = \sqrt{x}$

8. $\sqrt{7x-44} = \sqrt{x}$

9. $\sqrt{8x-2} = \sqrt{x+4}$

10. $\sqrt{3x-8} = \sqrt{x+10}$

11. $\sqrt{4x^2 + 11x - 44} = 2x$

12. $\sqrt{16x^2 + 12x - 24} = 4x$

13. $\sqrt{4x^2 + 20x + 25} = 5$

14. $\sqrt{x} + 1 = \sqrt{x+7}$

15. $\sqrt{x} - 2 = \sqrt{x-28}$

16. $7\sqrt{x} + 11 = 4$

17. $7\sqrt{x} + 4 = 25$

18. $\sqrt{2x+2} + 5 = 12$

1. _____

2. _____

3. _____

4. _____

5. _____

6. _____

7. _____

8. _____

9. _____

10. _____

11. _____

12. _____

13. _____

14. _____

15. _____

16. _____

17. _____

18. _____

Additional Exercises 8.5
Form II

Solve each equation. Be sure to check for extraneous solutions.

1. $\sqrt{x} = 7$

2. $\sqrt{x+2} = 9$

3. $\sqrt{3x-2} = 5$

4. $\sqrt{x} - 1 = 3$

5. $2\sqrt{x} + 5 = 15$

6. $\sqrt{3x+1} + 16 = 7$

7. $\sqrt{5x+1} - 7 = -1$

8. $\sqrt{x} = \sqrt{3x-18}$

9. $\sqrt{3x} = \sqrt{2x+3}$

10. $\sqrt{5x-1} = \sqrt{4x+1}$

11. $\sqrt{2x+8} = \sqrt{5x-4}$

12. $\sqrt{25x^2 - 2x + 10} = 5x$

13. $\sqrt{9x^2 - 3x + 21} = 3x$

14. $\sqrt{3x^2 + 12x + 16} = 4$

15. $\sqrt{x} = x - 12$

16. $\sqrt{x} = x - 2$

17. $\sqrt{4x+13} = x + 2$

18. $\sqrt{x-5} = \sqrt{x} - 1$

1. _____

2. _____

3. _____

4. _____

5. _____

6. _____

7. _____

8. _____

9. _____

10. _____

11. _____

12. _____

13. _____

14. _____

15. _____

16. _____

17. _____

18. _____

Additional Exercises 8.5
Form III

Name_____

Date_____

Solve each equation. Be sure to check for extraneous solutions.

1. $\sqrt{x} = 36$

2. $\sqrt{x+2} = 2$

3. $\sqrt{3x-2} = 2$

4. $\sqrt{x} - 4 = 3$

5. $\sqrt{3x+5} + 5 = 12$

6. $\sqrt{5x+8} + 3 = 12$

7. $\sqrt{3x-8} = \sqrt{x}$

8. $\sqrt{7x-18} = \sqrt{x}$

9. $\sqrt{6x-5} = \sqrt{x+12}$

10. $\sqrt{7x-5} = \sqrt{x+9}$

11. $\sqrt{25x^2 + 24x - 8} = 5x$

12. $\sqrt{9x^2 + 7x - 14} = 3x$

13. $\sqrt{6x^2 + 24x + 16} = 4$

14. $\sqrt{x} + 1 = \sqrt{x+5}$

15. $\sqrt{x} - 3 = \sqrt{x-27}$

16. $7\sqrt{x} + 12 = 5$

17. $5\sqrt{x} + 7 = 42$

18. $\sqrt{5x+2} + 9 = 11$

1. _____

2. _____

3. _____

4. _____

5. _____

6. _____

7. _____

8. _____

9. _____

10. _____

11. _____

12. _____

13. _____

14. _____

15. _____

16. _____

17. _____

18. _____

Additional Exercises 8.6
Form I

Name_____

Date_____

Use the Pythagorean Theorem to find the unknown side of each triangle. Give an exact answer and a two decimal place approximation.

1.

15

20

1. _____

2.

$2\sqrt{46}$

3

2. _____

3.

2

3

3. _____

4.

25

15

4. _____

5.

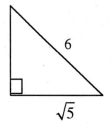

6

$\sqrt{5}$

5. _____

Additional Exercises 8.6 *(cont.)*

Find the length of the unknown side of each right triangle with sides a, b, and c where c is the hypotenuse. Give an exact answer and a two decimal place approximation.

6. $a = 4$, $b = 18$

7. $a = 10$, $c = 2\sqrt{106}$

8. $b = \sqrt{3}$, $c = 5$

6. _____

7. _____

8. _____

Solve the following.

9. The diagram shows the framing for a wall of a house. Find how long the brace needs to be to the nearest hundredth of a foot.

3ft

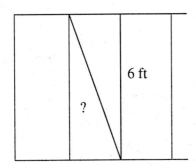

6 ft

?

9. _____

10. The diagram shows the framing for a wall of a house. Find how long the brace needs to be to the nearest hundredth of a foot.

10 ft

?

26 ft

10. _____

11. You want to stake a small tree. The cord will be attached to the tree 3 feet off the ground and each of the two stakes will be 5 feet from the base of the tree. How much cord do you need to buy, in whole feet, so you have enough?

11. _____

Additional Exercises 8.6 *(cont.)*

12. You need to brace a flagpole until it can be reset in the ground. There are rings you can use to attach twine to the pole. The rings are 23 feet off the ground. You plan to drive 2 stakes in the ground, each 17 feet from the base of the pole. How much cord do you need to buy, in whole feet, so you have enough?

12. _____

13. A 15-inch diagonal computer monitor screen is 9 inches high. Find its width to the nearest tenth of an inch.

13. _____

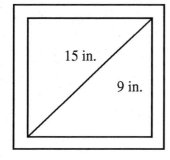

15 in.

9 in.

Police use the formula $s = \sqrt{30\,fd}$ to estimate the speed s of a car in miles per hour, given the distance d the car skidded and the type of road surface f. For wet concrete, f is 0.21.

14. Find how fast a car is going if it skidded 310 feet on wet concrete.

14. _____

Use the distance formula to find the distance between the points.

15. (7, -3), (1, -7)

15. _____

16. (-5, -4), (6, -6)

16. _____

17. (4, -1), (6, -7)

17. _____

Additional Exercises 8.6
Form II

Name_____

Date_____

Use the Pythagorean Theorem to find the unknown side of each triangle. Give an exact answer and a two decimal place approximation.

1.

2.

3.

4.

5.

1. _____

2. _____

3. _____

4. _____

5. _____

Additional Exercises 8.6 *(cont.)*

Name_____

Find the length of the unknown side of each right triangle with sides a, b, and c where c is the hypotenuse. Give an exact answer and a two decimal place approximation.

6. $a = 3, b = 6$

7. $a = \sqrt{20}, c = 10$

8. $b = \sqrt{22}, c = \sqrt{76}$

6. _____

7. _____

8. _____

Solve the following.

9. The diagram shows the framing for a wall of a house. Find how long the brace needs to be to the nearest hundredth of a foot.

3ft

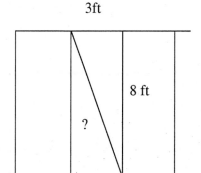

8 ft

?

9. _____

10. The diagram shows the framing for a wall of a house. Find how long the brace needs to be to the nearest hundredth of a foot.

5 ft

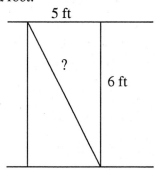

?

6 ft

10. _____

11. You want to stake a small tree. The cord will be attached to the tree 2.5 feet off the ground and each of the two stakes will be 3 feet from the base of the tree. How much cord do you need to buy, in whole feet, so you have enough?

11. _____

Additional Exercises 8.6 *(cont.)*

12. You need to brace a flagpole until it can be reset in the ground. There are rings you can use to attach twine to the pole. The rings are 8 feet off the ground. You plan to drive 2 stakes in the ground, each 5 feet from the base of the pole. How much cord do you need to buy, in whole feet, so you have enough?

12. _____

13. A 18-inch diagonal computer monitor screen is 12 inches high. Find its width to the nearest tenth of an inch.

13. _____

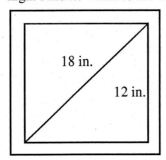

18 in.

12 in.

Police use the formula $s = \sqrt{30\,fd}$ to estimate the speed s of a car in miles per hour, given the distance d the car skidded and the type of road surface f. For wet concrete, f is 0.35.

14. Find how fast a car is going if it skidded 193 feet on wet concrete.

14. _____

Use the distance formula to find the distance between the points.

15. (1, 6), (-3, -7)

15. _____

16. (-2, -5), (5, -4)

16. _____

17. (-4, -6), (-2, 4)

17. _____

Additional Exercises 8.6
Form III

Name_____

Date_____

Use the Pythagorean Theorem to find the unknown side of each triangle. Give an exact answer and a two decimal place approximation.

1.

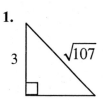

1. _____

2.

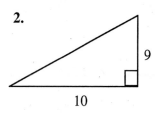

2. _____

3.

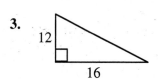

3. _____

4.

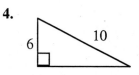

4. _____

5.

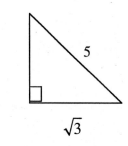

5. _____

Find the length of the unknown side of each right triangle with sides *a*, *b*, and *c* where *c* is the hypotenuse. Give an exact answer and a two decimal place approximation.

    6. $a = 11, b = 14$ **6.**

    7. $a = 10, c = \sqrt{389}$ **7.** _____

    8. $a = \sqrt{5}, \; c = 6$ **8.** _____

Solve the following.

    9.   The diagram shows the framing for a wall of a house. Find how long the brace needs to be to the nearest hundredth of a foot.   **9.** _____

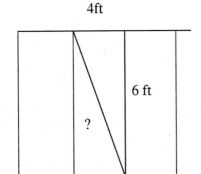

    10. The diagram shows the framing for a wall of a house. Find how long the brace needs to be to the nearest hundredth of a foot.   **10.**

    11. You want to stake a tree. The cord will be attached to the tree 9 feet off the ground and each of the two stakes will be 12 feet from the base of the tree. How much cord do you need to buy, in whole feet, so you have enough?   **11.** _____

12. You need to brace a flagpole until it can be reset in the ground. There are rings you can use to attach twine to the pole. The rings are 19 feet off the ground. You plan to drive 2 stakes in the ground, each 15 feet from the base of the pole. How much cord do you need to buy, in whole feet, so you have enough?

12. _____

13. A 26-inch diagonal TV screen is 20 inches wide. Find its height to the nearest tenth of an inch.

13. _____

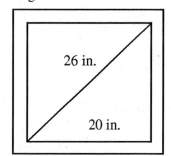

26 in.

20 in.

Police use the formula $s = \sqrt{30\,fd}$ to estimate the speed s of a car in miles per hour, given the distance d the car skidded and the type of road surface f. For wet concrete, f is 0.24.

14. Find how fast a car is going if it skidded 330 feet on wet concrete.

14. _____

Use the distance formula to find the distance between the points.

15. (-7, 3), (-2, -7)

15. _____

16. (-1, -4), (2, 2)

16. _____

17. (6, -4), (2, -6)

17. _____

Additional Exercises 8.7
Form I

Solve each equation. Be sure to check for extraneous solutions.

1. $81^{1/2}$

2. $125^{1/3}$

3. $-243^{1/5}$

4. $(-32)^{1/5}$

5. $\left(\dfrac{9}{16}\right)^{1/2}$

6. $-\left(\dfrac{81}{256}\right)^{1/4}$

7. $27^{4/3}$

8. $16^{5/4}$

9. $\left(\dfrac{1}{27}\right)^{2/3}$

10. $36^{-3/2}$

11. $\left(\dfrac{729}{1331}\right)^{-2/3}$

12. $16^{-1/2}$

13. $5^{1/4} \cdot 5^{3/4}$

14. $\left(2^{1/2}\right)^{2/3}$

15. $\dfrac{2^{1/5}}{2^{6/5}}$

16. $\left(c^{3/2}\right)^{1/3}$

17. $\left(\dfrac{x^{1/4}}{y^{1/6}}\right)^{3}$

1. _____
2. _____
3. _____
4. _____
5. _____
6. _____
7. _____
8. _____
9. _____
10. _____
11. _____
12. _____
13. _____
14. _____
15. _____
16. _____
17. _____

Additional Exercises 8.7
Form II

Name_____

Date_____

Solve each equation. Be sure to check for extraneous solutions.

1. $144^{1/2}$

2. $256^{1/4}$

3. $-32^{1/5}$

4. $(-243)^{1/5}$

5. $\left(\dfrac{4}{9}\right)^{1/2}$

6. $-\left(\dfrac{16}{81}\right)^{1/4}$

7. $64^{4/3}$

8. $81^{5/4}$

9. $\left(\dfrac{8}{64}\right)^{2/3}$

10. $64^{-3/2}$

11. $\left(\dfrac{8}{1000}\right)^{-2/3}$

12. $9^{-1/2}$

13. $2^{2/5} \cdot 2^{3/5}$

14. $\left(4^{1/3}\right)^{9/4}$

15. $\dfrac{5^{-3/4}}{5}$

16. $\left(y^{-1/3}\right)^{3/2}$

17. $\left(\dfrac{3m^{1/6}n^{1/3}}{4n^{-2/3}}\right)^{2}$

1. _____

2. _____

3. _____

4. _____

5. _____

6. _____

7. _____

8. _____

9. _____

10. _____

11. _____

12. _____

13. _____

14. _____

15. _____

16. _____

17. _____

Additional Exercises 8.7
Form III

Name_____

Date_____

Solve each equation. Be sure to check for extraneous solutions.

1. $64^{1/2}$

2. $216^{1/3}$

3. $-8^{2/3}$

4. $(-8)^{1/3}$

5. $\left(\dfrac{8}{27}\right)^{-1/3}$

6. $\left(\dfrac{1}{32}\right)^{3/5}$

7. $4^{-1/2}$

8. $625^{-3/4}$

9. $\left(\dfrac{9}{25}\right)^{3/2}$

10. $25^{-3/2}$

11. $\left(\dfrac{16}{36}\right)^{-3/2}$

12. $144^{-1/2}$

13. $7^{1/3} \cdot 7^{2/3}$

14. $\left(25x^2 y^4 z^6\right)^{1/2}$

15. $\dfrac{y^{5/3}}{y^{1/3}}$

16. $\left(\dfrac{16w^{-2}z}{2wz^{-8}}\right)^{1/3}$

17. $\left(\dfrac{x^{-2/3}}{y^{-3/4}}\right)^{12}$

1. _____

2. _____

3. _____

4. _____

5. _____

6. _____

7. _____

8. _____

9. _____

10. _____

11. _____

12. _____

13. _____

14. _____

15. _____

16. _____

17. _____

Additional Exercises 9.1
Form I

Solve each equation by factoring.

1. $h^2 - 49 = 0$

2. $6a^2 - 216 = 0$

Use the square root property to solve each quadratic equation.

3. $x^2 = 144$

4. $x^2 = 15$

5. $x^2 = \dfrac{1}{36}$

6. $x^2 = -64$

7. $10x^2 = 17$

8. $x^2 - 17 = 0$

9. $x^2 - 13 = 0$

10. $x^2 = 100$

11. $(x + 3)^2 = 81$

12. $(x + 1)^2 = 64$

13. $(x - 5)^2 = 71$

14. $\left(m - \dfrac{1}{8}\right)^2 = \dfrac{1}{64}$

15. $(3y + 4)^2 = 64$

16. $(5x + 4)^2 = 36$

17. $(3x - 2)^2 = 16$

18. Solve the quadratic equation by first factoring the perfect square trinomial on the left side of the equation. Then apply the square root property. $x^2 - 12x + 36 = 15$

1. _____

2. _____

3. _____

4. _____

5. _____

6. _____

7. _____

8. _____

9. _____

10. _____

11. _____

12. _____

13. _____

14. _____

15. _____

16. _____

17. _____

18. _____

Additional Exercises 9.1
Form II

Solve each equation by factoring.

    1. $h^2 - 121 = 0$

    2. $7a^2 - 112 = 0$

Use the square root property to solve each quadratic equation.

    3. $x^2 = 25$

    4. $x^2 = 98$

    5. $x^2 = \dfrac{1}{64}$

    6. $x^2 = -49$

    7. $10x^2 = 3$

    8. $6x^2 = 25$

    9. $x^2 - 11 = 0$

    10. $\dfrac{1}{7}x^2 = 4$

    11. $(x - 4)^2 = 36$

    12. $(x + 8)^2 = 9$

    13. $(x - 12)^2 = 3$

    14. $\left(m - \dfrac{1}{4}\right)^2 = \dfrac{1}{16}$

    15. $(2y - 11)^2 = 25$

    16. $(5x - 6)^2 = 54$

    17. $(4x - 7)^2 = 80$

18. The area of a circle is found by the equation $A = \pi r^2$. If the area of a certain circle is 20π square meters, find its radius to the nearest hundredth of a meter.

1. _____

2. _____

3. _____

4. _____

5. _____

6. _____

7. _____

8. _____

9. _____

10. _____

11. _____

12. _____

13. _____

14. _____

15. _____

16. _____

17. _____

18. _____

Additional Exercises 9.1
Form III

Solve each equation by factoring.

1. $h^2 - 169 = 0$

2. $5a^2 - 125 = 0$

Use the square root property to solve each quadratic equation.

3. $x^2 = 196$

4. $x^2 = 13$

5. $x^2 = \dfrac{1}{16}$

6. $x^2 = -4$

7. $2x^2 = 11$

8. $14x^2 = 29$

9. $x^2 - 14 = 0$

10. $5x^2 = 29$

11. $(x + 2)^2 = 4$

12. $(x + 8)^2 = 36$

13. $(x + 2)^2 = 89$

14. $\left(m + \dfrac{1}{7}\right)^2 = \dfrac{1}{49}$

15. $(y - 4)^2 = -100$

16. $(5x + 2)^2 = 45$

17. $(5x - 4)^2 = 36$

18. A square gymnastics mat has a diagonal of 35 feet. Find the length of each side to the nearest hundredth of a foot.

1. _____

2. _____

3. _____

4. _____

5. _____

6. _____

7. _____

8. _____

9. _____

10. _____

11. _____

12. _____

13. _____

14. _____

15. _____

16. _____

17. _____

18. _____

Additional Exercises 9.2
Form I

Name _____

Date _____

Solve each quadratic equation by completing the square.

1. $x^2 - 8x = -7$

2. $x^2 - 2x - 4 = 0$

3. $x^2 - 6x - 4 = 0$

4. $x^2 + 9x = 5$

5. $x^2 - 20x = 0$

6. $z^2 + 3z - 4 = 0$

7. $6x^2 + 16 = 5$

8. $x^2 - 5x + 6 = 0$

9. $x(x+1) = 6$

10. $y^2 - 2y - 4 = 0$

11. $x(x + 3) = 4$

12. $x(x - 1) = 12$

13. $3x^2 - 5x + 6 = 0$

14. $2x^2 - x - 10 = 0$

15. $2x^2 = 5x + 8$

16. $3x^2 = 4x + 3$

17. $4x^2 - 3x + 3 = 10$

18. $2y^2 - 3y + 2 = 0$

1. _____

2. _____

3. _____

4. _____

5. _____

6. _____

7. _____

8. _____

9. _____

10. _____

11. _____

12. _____

13. _____

14. _____

15. _____

16. _____

17. _____

18. _____

Additional Exercises 9.2
Form II

Solve each quadratic equation by completing the square.

1. $x^2 + 12x = -27$

2. $x^2 - 6x = 16$

3. $x^2 + 4x - 7 = 0$

4. $x^2 + 8x - 12 = 0$

5. $x^2 - 10x = 0$

6. $z^2 + 3z = 6$

7. $x^2 - 9x = 4$

8. $x^2 - 7x + 3 = 0$

9. $y^2 + 11y + 18 = 0$

10. $y^2 + 9y + 30 = 0$

11. $x(x + 5) = 6$

12. $x(x - 7) = 30$

13. $3x^2 - 12x = 36$

14. $7x^2 + 14x + 3 = 0$

15. $2x^2 = 10x + 7$

16. $4x^2 = 12x + 5$

17. $2x^2 + 4x + 17 = 8$

18. Find the value of h that will make $x^2 - hx + 49$ a perfect square trinomial.

1. _____
2. _____
3. _____
4. _____
5. _____
6. _____
7. _____
8. _____
9. _____
10. _____
11. _____
12. _____
13. _____
14. _____
15. _____
16. _____
17. _____
18. _____

Additional Exercises 9.2
Form III

Name_____

Date_____

Solve each quadratic equation by completing the square.

1. $x^2 - 6x = -5$

2. $x^2 + 9x = 2$

3. $3x^2 + 4x - 3 = 0$

4. $x^2 - 5x = 0$

5. $x^2 - 6x = -5$

6. $z^2 - 10z - 4 = 0$

7. $x^2 + 9x = -9$

8. $x^2 - 8x = -12$

9. $y^2 + 3y = 7$

10. $y^2 + 9y = -3$

11. $x(x + 2) = 15$

12. $x(x + 8) = -15$

13. $x(x - 9) = -18$

14. $3x^2 - 6x + 6 = 0$

15. $2x^2 = 6x + 4$

16. $2x^2 - 5x - 7 = 0$

17. $36x^2 + 36x = 7$

18. Find the value of h that will make x + hx + 144 a perfect square trinomial.

1. _____

2. _____

3. _____

4. _____

5. _____

6. _____

7. _____

8. _____

9. _____

10. _____

11. _____

12. _____

13. _____

14. _____

15. _____

16. _____

17. _____

18. _____

Additional Exercises 9.3
Form I

Name_____

Date_____

Use the quadratic formula to solve each quadratic equation.

1. $x^2 + 7x - 8 = 0$

2. $3x^2 - x - 4 = 0$

3. $4h^2 - 2h - 5 = 0$

4. $2h^2 - 3h + 4 = 0$

5. $25x^2 - 14 = 0$

6. $4x^2 = 28$

7. $a^2 - 14a + 30 = 0$

8. $a^2 - 6a + 7 = 0$

9. $x^2 - 11x - 26 = 0$

10. $2x^2 + 6x + 3 = 0$

11. $4x^2 - 1 = 0$

12. $3 - x^2 = 3x$

13. $6 - x^2 = 6x$

14. $\dfrac{x^2}{6} - \dfrac{x}{3} = 1$

15. $2z^2 - \dfrac{7}{2} = 6z$

1. _____

2. _____

3. _____

4. _____

5. _____

6. _____

7. _____

8. _____

9. _____

10. _____

11. _____

12. _____

13. _____

14. _____

15. _____

Additional Exercises 9.3
Form II

Use the quadratic formula to solve each quadratic equation.

1. $x^2 - 6x - 7 = 0$

2. $x^2 - x - 6 = 0$

3. $5h^2 + 7h + 2 = 0$

4. $2h^2 + 10h + 3 = 0$

5. $36x^2 - 1 = 0$

6. $m^2 - 56 = m$

7. $a^2 - 9a + 1 = 0$

8. $a^2 - 8a + 11 = 0$

9. $x^2 - 5x + 8 = 0$

10. $2x^2 = 8 - x$

11. $7x^2 = 14$

12. $3x^2 = 2x - 2$

13. $4x^2 = 1 - x$

14. $\frac{15}{7}p^2 - p = \frac{2}{7}$

15. $4z^2 - 3z = \frac{1}{4}$

1. _____

2. _____

3. _____

4. _____

5. _____

6. _____

7. _____

8. _____

9. _____

10. _____

11. _____

12. _____

13. _____

14. _____

15. _____

Additional Exercises 9.3
Form III

Name_____

Date_____

Use the quadratic formula to solve each quadratic equation.

1. $x^2 + 6x + 8 = 0$

2. $2x^2 - 3x + 4 = 0$

3. $5h^2 + 6h + 1 = 0$

4. $5h^2 - 6h + 10 = 0$

5. $100x^2 - 1 = 0$

6. $m^2 + 6 = 6m$

7. $4a^2 + 9a + 5 = 0$

8. $3 - a^2 = -5a$

9. $x^2 - 9x - 52 = 0$

10. $3x^2 + 8x - 8 = 0$

11. $2x^2 = 16$

12. $15x^2 = 6 + 13x$

13. $5 - x^2 = 2x$

14. $\dfrac{x^2}{18} - \dfrac{x}{9} = 1$

15. $4z^2 + \dfrac{1}{2} = -3z$

1. _____

2. _____

3. _____

4. _____

5. _____

6. _____

7. _____

8. _____

9. _____

10. _____

11. _____

12. _____

13. _____

14. _____

15. _____

Additional Exercises 9.4
Form I

Name_____

Date_____

Write each expression in i notation.

1. $\sqrt{-9}$

2. $\sqrt{-4}$

3. $\sqrt{-96}$

Add or subtract as indicated.

4. $(2+7i)+(9-6i)$

5. $(-6-2i)-(12+14i)$

6. $(-12-13i)-(-12+4i)$

7. Subtract $8+3i$ from $-15+8i$

Multiply.

8. $3i(-8+5i)$

9. $(5+9i)(8-4i)$

10. $(3+9i)(3-9i)$

11. $(2+9i)^2$

Divide.

12. $\dfrac{26-8i}{2}$

13. $\dfrac{5+8i}{9+7i}$

14. $(x+9)^2=-64$

15. $(9k-1)^2=-8$

16. $x^2+2x+26=0$

17. $3x^2=-192$

18. $2x^2-x+10=0$

1. _____

2. _____

3. _____

4. _____

5. _____

6. _____

7. _____

8. _____

9. _____

10. _____

11. _____

12. _____

13. _____

14. _____

15. _____

16. _____

17. _____

18. _____

Additional Exercises 9.4
Form II

Name_____

Date_____

Write each expression in *i* notation.

1. $\sqrt{-81}$

2. $\sqrt{-144}$

3. $\sqrt{-112}$

Add or subtract as indicated.

4. $(4+5i)+(2-4i)$

5. $(-6+12i)-(3+11i)$

6. $(-14-7i)-(-5-7i)$

7. Subtract $-8-6i$ from $-8-9i$

Multiply.

8. $4i(-7+7i)$

9. $(3+7i)(9-6i)$

10. $(5+8i)(5-8i)$

11. $(8+9i)^2$

Divide.

12. $\dfrac{15-15i}{5}$

13. $\dfrac{1+3i}{6+8i}$

14. $(x+6)^2 = -16$

15. $(3k-1)^2 = -27$

16. $x^2 + 4x + 13 = 0$

17. $4x^2 = -16$

18. $2x^2 - x + 3 = 0$

1. _____

2. _____

3. _____

4. _____

5. _____

6. _____

7. _____

8. _____

9. _____

10. _____

11. _____

12. _____

13. _____

14. _____

15. _____

16. _____

17. _____

18. _____

Additional Exercises 9.4
Form III

Name_____

Date_____

Write each expression in *i* notation.

1. $\sqrt{-121}$

2. $\sqrt{-25}$

3. $\sqrt{-180}$

Add or subtract as indicated.

4. $(4+4i)+(3-3i)$

5. $(5+2i)-(12-5i)$

6. $(2+6i)-(-7-i)$

7. Subtract $12+11i$ from $-2-6i$

Multiply.

8. $3i(-3+3i)$

9. $(5+3i)(9-6i)$

10. $(9+8i)(9-8i)$

11. $(7+8i)^2$

Divide.

12. $\dfrac{-10+10i}{5}$

13. $\dfrac{3+5i}{4+3i}$

14. $(x+7)^2 = -64$

15. $(2k-1)^2 = -8$

16. $x^2+4x+20=0$

17. $2x^2 = -200$

18. $2x^2-3x+6=0$

1. _____

2. _____

3. _____

4. _____

5. _____

6. _____

7. _____

8. _____

9. _____

10. _____

11. _____

12. _____

13. _____

14. _____

15. _____

16. _____

17. _____

18. _____

Additional Exercises 9.5
Form I

Name_____

Date_____

Graph each quadratic equation by finding and plotting ordered pair solutions.

1. $y = x^2$

x	y
-1	
0	
1	

2. $y = -5x^2$

x	y
-2	
-1	
0	
1	
2	

3. $y = \dfrac{1}{4}x^2$

x	y
-4	
0	
4	

Sketch the graph of each equation. Identify the vertex and the intercepts.

4. $y = x^2 - 9$

1.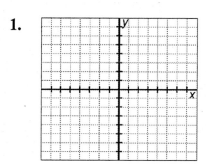

2.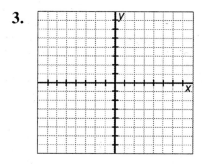

3.

4.

Additional Exercises 9.5 *(cont.)*

Name_____

5. $y = x^2 + 7$

5.

6. $y = x^2 + 4x$

6.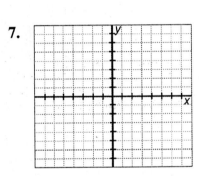

7. $y = x^2 + 8x - 9$

7.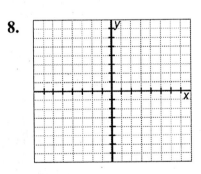

8. $y = x^2 + 2x - 3$

8.

9. $y = -x^2 - 6x - 5$

9.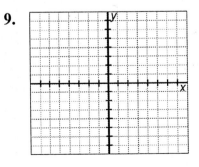

10. $y = x^2 + 4x - 9$

10.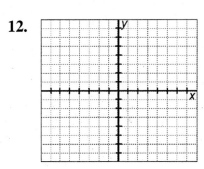

11. $y = -x^2 + 5x - 4$

11.

12. $y = x^2 + 6x + 12$

12.

13. $y = x^2 + 8x + 4$

13.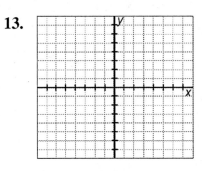

Additional Exercises 9.5
Form II

Graph each quadratic equation by finding and plotting ordered pair solutions.

1. $y = 4x^2$

x	y
-1	
0	
1	

1.

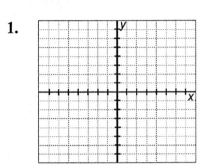

2. $y = -2x^2$

x	y
-2	
-1	
0	
1	
2	

2.

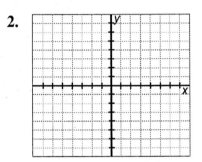

3. $y = \dfrac{2}{3}x^2$

x	y
-3	
0	
3	

3.

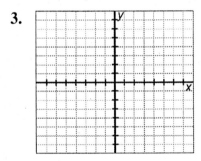

Sketch the graph of each equation. Identify the vertex and the intercepts.

4. $y = 9 - x^2$

4.

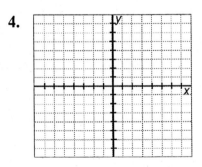

5. $y = x^2 + 3$

6. $y = x^2 - 6x$

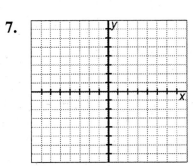

7. $y = x^2 + 8x + 7$

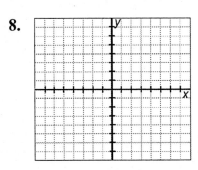

8. $y = x^2 - 2x - 3$

9. $y = -x^2 + 6x - 8$

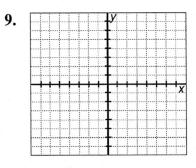

Name_____

10. $y = x^2 - 4x - 5$

10.

11. $y = -x^2 + 4x - 4$

11.

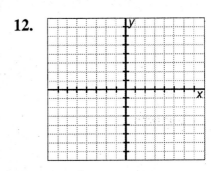

12. $y = x^2 + 5x + 6$

12.

13. $y = x^2 - 3x - 4$

13.

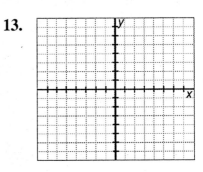

Additional Exercises 9.5
Form III

Graph each quadratic equation by finding and plotting ordered pair solutions.

1. $y = -6x^2$

x	y
-1	
0	
1	

1.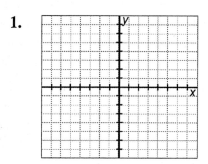

2. $y = -x^2$

x	y
-2	
-1	
0	
1	
2	

2.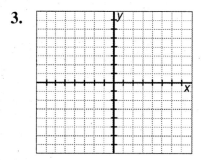

3. $y = -\dfrac{2}{5}x^2$

x	y
-5	
0	
5	

3.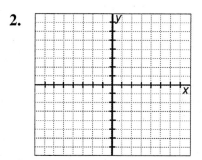

Sketch the graph of each equation. Identify the vertex and the intercepts.

4. $y = x^2 - 4$

4.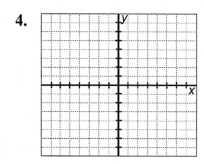

5. $y = x^2 + 16$

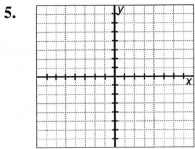

5.

6. $y = x^2 - 8x$

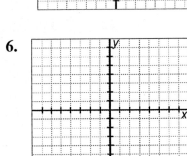

6.

7. $y = x^2 + 4x + 3$

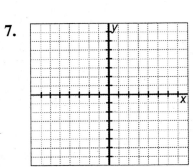

7.

8. $y = x^2 - 6x - 6$

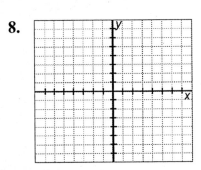

8.

9. $y = -x^2 + 2x + 8$

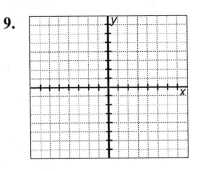

9.

Name_____

10. $y = x^2 + 4x + 1$

10.
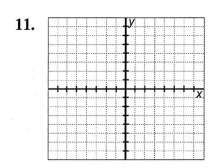

11. $y = -x^2 + 2x - 7$

11.
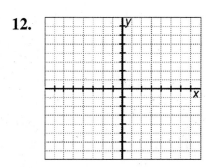

12. $y = x^2 + 4x + 6$

12.
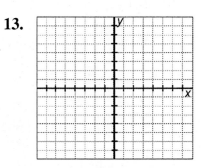

13. $y = x^2 + 2x - 4$

13.

Additional Exercises
Answers

Chapter 1 Answers
Additional Exercises, 1.2
Form I

1. <

2. <

3. >

4. >

5. $30^{\circ} \leq 60^{\circ} \leq 90^{\circ}$

6. True

7. True

8. False

9. True

10. True.

11. $-\dfrac{1}{2} \leq \dfrac{1}{2}$

12. $2 < 7$

13. $-275,700$

14. $-27,-20$

15. $\{24\}$

16. $\{24,0\}$

17. $\{24,0,-25\}$

18. $\left\{\dfrac{3}{4},24,6.\bar{1},0,-25,7.5\right\}$

19. $\left\{\sqrt{15},-\sqrt{3}\right\}$

20. $\{\sqrt{15},\dfrac{3}{4},24,6.\bar{1},$
    $0,-25,7.5-\sqrt{3}\}$

Additional Exercises, 1.2
Form II

1.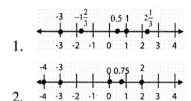

2.

3. $\{|-5|,14\}$

4. $\{|-5|,14,0\}$

5. $\{|-5|,14,0\}$

6. $\left\{-2.2,|-5|,3\dfrac{1}{3},14,0,-0.5\right\}$

7. $\left\{\sqrt{14}\right\}$

8. $\left\{-2.2,|-5|,3\dfrac{1}{3},14,0,-0.5,\sqrt{14}\right\}$

9. True

10. True

11 True

12. True

13. >

14. =

15. >

16. $-5 \geq -14$

17. $\dfrac{7}{10} \not> \left|\dfrac{9}{10}\right|$

18. $-5 \leq -2$

19. $|-17| \geq |15|$

20. $-14 < -6$

Additional Exercises, 1.2
Form III

1.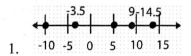

2.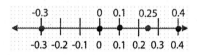

3. $\left\{\sqrt{25},\dfrac{6}{2},100\right\}$

4. $\left\{\sqrt{25},\dfrac{6}{2},0,100\right\}$

5. $\left\{\sqrt{25},\dfrac{6}{2},0,-25,100\right\}$

6. $\left\{\sqrt{25},\dfrac{6}{2},0,|-0.1|,-25,\dfrac{7}{11},100\right\}$

7. $\{\pi\}$

8. $\left\{\sqrt{25},\dfrac{6}{2},|-0.1|,0,\pi,-25,\dfrac{7}{11},100\right\}$

9. True

10. False.

11 True

12. False

13. True

14. >

15. <

16. >

17. $14 \geq 5$

18. $9 \neq -9$

19. Pacific

20. $155,557,000, \ -35,827$

Additional Exercises, 1.3

Form I

1. a. $3 \cdot 3 \cdot 3$
   b. $2 \cdot 2 \cdot 2 \cdot 3$
   c. $2 \cdot 2 \cdot 3 \cdot 3 \cdot 5$
   d. $3 \cdot 5 \cdot 5 \cdot 5$
   e. $2 \cdot 2 \cdot 2 \cdot 5 \cdot 5$
   f. $2 \cdot 5 \cdot 7 \cdot 13$
2. $\dfrac{2}{3} = \dfrac{32}{48}$
3. $\dfrac{4}{5} = \dfrac{40}{50}$
4. $\dfrac{5}{4} = \dfrac{30}{24}$
5. 4
6. $\dfrac{1}{2}$
7. 0
8. Undefined
9. $\dfrac{4}{17}$
10. 76
11. $\dfrac{16}{27}$
12. $\dfrac{7}{33}$
13. 4
14. 6
15. $\dfrac{4}{3} = 1\dfrac{1}{3}$
16. $\dfrac{19}{20}$
17. $29\dfrac{1}{4}$
18. $\dfrac{3}{4}$
19. $\dfrac{5}{24}$
20. $87\dfrac{2}{5}$

Additional Exercises, 1.3
Form II

1. a. $2^4 \cdot 7$
   b. $2^2 \cdot 3^3 \cdot 7$
   c. $2^4 \cdot 3 \cdot 7$
   d. $2^2 \cdot 61$
   e. $2^5 \cdot 3^2$
2. $\dfrac{4}{7}$
3. Undefined
4. 67
5. 0
6. $\dfrac{2}{3}$
7. $\dfrac{2}{3}$
8. $\dfrac{19}{15}$
9. $\dfrac{15}{32}$
10. $\dfrac{5}{9}$
11. $\dfrac{12}{5} = 2\dfrac{2}{5}$
12. $\dfrac{6}{5} = 1\dfrac{1}{5}$
13. $\dfrac{3}{32}$
14. $\dfrac{9}{8} = 1\dfrac{1}{8}$
15. $\dfrac{71}{50} = 1\dfrac{21}{50}$
16. $18\dfrac{9}{20}$
17. $\dfrac{81}{200}$
18. $3\dfrac{1}{9}$
19. $18\dfrac{1}{20}$
20. $\dfrac{256}{27} = 9\dfrac{13}{27}$

Additional Exercises, 1.3
Form III

1. $7\dfrac{34}{135}$
2. $\dfrac{2}{75}$
3. $30\dfrac{5}{6}$
4. 63
5. $1\dfrac{7}{15}$
6. $\dfrac{11}{35}$
7. $3\dfrac{1}{7}$
8. $\dfrac{1}{2}$
9. $5\dfrac{3}{5}$
10. $\dfrac{1}{25}$
11. $72\dfrac{1}{20}$
12. $84\dfrac{2}{15}$
13. $75\dfrac{17}{28}$ sq. ft.
14. $1\dfrac{3}{32}$ sq. cm.
15. $142\dfrac{4}{5}$
16. $\dfrac{11}{99} = \dfrac{1}{9}$
17. $\dfrac{9}{99} = \dfrac{1}{11}$
18. $\dfrac{22}{99} = \dfrac{2}{9}$

Additional Exercises, 1.4
Form I
1. 625
2. $\dfrac{1}{9}$
3. $\dfrac{64}{125}$
4. 1
5, 0.132651
6. 52
7. 17.
8. $\dfrac{5}{12}$
9. 45
10. $\dfrac{5}{9}$
11. 0
12. 30
13. 1
14. 1
15. 24
16. True
17. True
18. False
19. False
20. True

Additional Exercises, 1.4
Form II
1. $\dfrac{125}{64}$
2. 125
3. 0.001
4. 33
5. 48
6. 47
7. 2
8. 2
9. $\dfrac{1}{3}$
10. 11
11. 13
12. F
13. F
14. $x+4$
15. $2x-3$
16. $x-6=12$
17. $2x+14=56$
18. $x-16=23$
19. $\dfrac{x}{4}=3^2$
20. $3x+15=-45$

Additional Exercises, 1.4
Form III
1. 55
2. 35
3. 21
4. 27
5. p=38 cm; A=70 cm^2
6. p=20 in, A=21 in^2
7. p= 40 in A=100 in^2
8. p=50yd.; A=150 yd^2
9. $2+2\cdot 40\div(7+3)$
10. Two times a number divided by seven. (expression)
11. When two times a number is subtracted from five, the result is 15. (equation)
12. If four is multiplied times the difference of a number and 3, the result is 12. (equation)
13. Yes
14. No
15. $\dfrac{35}{36}$
16. 2
17. $-\dfrac{5}{2}$
18. 0
19. $\dfrac{4}{3}$
20. 121

Additional Exercises, 1.5
Form I
1. -28
2. -8
3. 4
4. 0
5. -40
6. 2
7. -56
8. -13
9. 40
10. -28
11. $\dfrac{13}{14}$
12. $-|-22| = -22$
13. 0
14. 9
15. -9
16. -9
17. 90 feet
18. ` $-\$2.0$ million
19. $6x$
20. $-6x$

Additional Exercises, 1.5
Form II
1. -10
2. -32
3. $-6\dfrac{5}{7}$
4. $-\dfrac{2}{3}$
5. 4
6. $-\dfrac{1}{125}$
7. 19
8. -45.3
9. -15
10. 0.45
11. $-\left|-\dfrac{3}{4}\right|$
12. $\dfrac{3}{4}$
13. 0
14. $\dfrac{9}{10}$
15. 4
16. Positive number
17. Negative number
18. $\$339$
18. $\$235$
20. 230

Additional Exercises, 1.5
Form III
1. 0
2. $-\dfrac{8}{17}$
3. 26
4. 44 points
5. $46°$
6. Negative seven added to the absolute value of negative seven is zero.
7. If we add the absolute value of negative three to fifteen, and then add in negative 16 and negative nine, we get our answer, If we work this out we get -7.
8. When we add the fractions $-\dfrac{12}{7}+\dfrac{9}{14}+\left(-\dfrac{1}{2}\right)$, we must get common denominators. So
$-\dfrac{24}{14}+\dfrac{9}{14}+\left(-\dfrac{7}{14}\right)=\dfrac{-22}{14}=-\dfrac{11}{7}$
9. When adding the negative absolute value of negative two thirds to the absolute value of one-half plus the sum of negative five-sixths and one-ninth, we get negative eight-ninths
10. When we add negative four and forty-four hundredths, and the sum of the absolute value of fifteen and eight tenths and negative twenty-two and three tenths, we get two and six hundredths.
11. $-\left|-\dfrac{1}{3}\right|$
12. $\left|-\dfrac{1}{3}\right|$
13. On the third floor.
14. 550 feet below sea level
15. 984 years
16. The melting point of alcohol $-114°$ is $75°$colder than the melting point of mercury17..
17. $-2 = -2$
18. $-\dfrac{11}{10} < -\dfrac{4}{5}$
19. $-16 < 16$
20. $2 > 1$

Additional Exercises, 1.6
Form I
1. -25
2. -15
3. -20
4. 23
5. 3
6. 39
7. 72
8. 0
9. 100
10. $-3-(-15)=-3+15=12$
11. $-44-18=-44+(-18)=-62$
12. -75
13. -7.9
14. $-\dfrac{83}{60}=-1\dfrac{23}{60}$
15. 39
16. 18
17. -1
18. -20
19. $\dfrac{14}{20}=\dfrac{7}{10}$
20. 0

Additional Exercises, 1.6
Form II
1. -29
2. -15
3. 9
4. -47
5. No
6. Yes
7. No
8. Yes
9. $108°$
10. $18°$
11. -14
12. 36
13. 1
14. 44
15. $49°$
16. $203.7°$
17. False
18. False
19. False
20. False

Additional Exercises, 1.6
Form III
1. 3
2. -1
3. 6.1
4. $-\dfrac{25}{48}$
5. $\dfrac{2}{3}$
6. 0
7. 11
8. 6
9. Negative
10. Negative
11. -9
12. $-\dfrac{1}{7}$
13. 0.2
14. -1
15. 7000 meters
16. 72 years
17. $-10°$ or a drop of $10°$
18. $-25°$ or a drop of $25°$

Additional Exercises, 1.7
Form I
1. Positive
2. Negative
3. 15
4. −32
5. −32
6. 0
7. −32
7. $\dfrac{1}{7}$
8. 9.02
9. 16
10. −16
11. $\dfrac{16}{49}$
12. $-\dfrac{1}{3}$
13. $\dfrac{12}{5}$
14. −4
15. $-\dfrac{5}{3}$
16. $\dfrac{5}{6}$
17. Undefined
18. 0
19. 5
20. −67

Additional Exercises, 1.7
Form II
1. −11
2. −2
3. 5
4. −1
5. −32
6. 0.0001
7. 6
8. $-\dfrac{2}{3}$
9. Yes
10. No
11. No
12. Yes
13. $-4(-3+9) = -24$
14. $3(14-(-7)) = 63$
15. −14
16. $\dfrac{1}{6}$
17. Undefined

Additional Exercises, 1.7
Form III
1. d
2. b
3. a
4. c
5. $-\dfrac{18}{5}$
6. $-\dfrac{1}{15}$
7. −30.818
8. $-\dfrac{7}{27}$
9. $-\dfrac{15}{3(-2)} \div \left(-\dfrac{3}{2}\right) = -\dfrac{5}{3}$
10. $\dfrac{-2-4^2}{3(-6)} = 1$
11. $-\dfrac{4}{5} \cdot \left(-\dfrac{8}{5}\right) = \dfrac{32}{25}$
12. $3(-16-(-23)) = 21$
13. $\dfrac{1}{4}\left(-\dfrac{2}{5}\right) \div \left(-\dfrac{5}{6}\right) = \dfrac{6}{50}$
14. 0
15. $-\dfrac{38}{27}$
16. 3

Additional Exercises, 1.8
Form I

1. $a \cdot (-4)$

2. $y + 4$

3. $x \cdot (yz)$

4. $(3x + y) + 4$

5. $(5 + 12) + x$

   $x + (5 + 12)$

6. $\left(-\dfrac{8}{7} \cdot \dfrac{7}{8}\right) \cdot r$

   $\left(-\dfrac{7}{8} \cdot r\right) \cdot \dfrac{8}{7}$

7. $= 2 \cdot 3x + 2(-7)$

   $= 6x - 14$

8. $= -5 \cdot x + (-5)(-4)$

   $= -5x + 20$

9. $= -\dfrac{1}{2} \cdot 10 + (-\dfrac{1}{2})(-16z)$

   $= -5 - 8z$

10. $= -4 \cdot x + (-4) \cdot 3 - 14$

    $= -4x - 12 - 14$

    $= -4x - 26$

11. $3(x + y)$

12. $-\dfrac{2}{7}$

13. $\left|-5\right|$

14. $\dfrac{14}{3}$

15. $-\dfrac{3}{5}$

16. Multiplicative Identity

17. Zero Product Property

18. Associative Property for Multiplication

19. Associative Property for Addition

20. Distributive Property of Multiplication over Addition

Additional Exercises, 1.8
Form II

1. Multiplicative Reciprocal Property

2. Additive Identity Property

3. Commutative Property for Multiplication

4. Commutative property for Addition

5. Commutative property for Multiplication

6. $-\dfrac{1}{2} \cdot 3x + \left(-\dfrac{1}{2}\right) \cdot 2$

   $= -\dfrac{3}{2}x - 1$

7. $-4 \cdot x + (-4) \cdot (-3y)$

   $= -4x + 12y$

8. $-x + y - z - y$

   $= -x - z$

9. $\dfrac{1}{3} \cdot 9x + \dfrac{1}{3} \cdot (-12) + 4$

   $= 3x - 4 + 4$

   $= 3x$

10. $-12 \cdot x + (-12) \cdot (-4) - 18$

    $= -12x + 48 - 18$

    $= -12x + 30$

11. $-x + 3y + 3 \cdot x + 3 \cdot 2y$

    $= -x + 3y + 3x + 6y$

    $= 2x + 9y$

12. $-5 \cdot 3x + (-5)(-y) + (-5) \cdot 7 + 42$

    $-15x + 5y - 35 + 42$

    $-15x + 5y + 7$

13. $-\dfrac{3}{4}(4x) + (-\dfrac{3}{4})(-16) + \dfrac{1}{2}$

    $= -3x + 12 + \dfrac{1}{2}$

    $= -3x + \dfrac{25}{2}$

14. $1.7(-0.1x) + 1.7(-0.3)$

    $\quad + (-5.4)$

    $-0.17x - 0.51$

    $\quad + (-5.4)$

    $-0.17x - 5.91$

15. $x + 2 - 5$

    $= x - 3$

16. Multiplicative reciprocal property

17. Commutative property for addition

18. Zero Property

19. Additive Identity

20. Distributive Property

Additional Exercises, 1.8
Form III

1a. Commutative Property for Addition

  b. Commutative Property for Addition

  c, Associative Property for Addition

2a. Commutative Property for Multiplication

  b. Associative Property for Multiplication

  c. Commutative Property for Multiplication

3. False

4. True

5. False

6. False

7. True

8. $-5x + 10y - 15 + 15$

   $= -5x + 10y$

9. $-\dfrac{1}{5}a + \dfrac{3}{5} + \left(-\dfrac{7}{5}\right)$

   $= -\dfrac{1}{5}a - \dfrac{4}{5}$

10. $-x - 2y + 7 + 14$

    $= -x - 2y + 21$

11. $8x + 8y - 12 + 9$

    $= 8x + 8y - 3$

12. $-12\triangle\blacktriangleleft + 8\triangle\ast)$

13. $x - \dfrac{1}{7} - \dfrac{5}{7}$

    $= x - \dfrac{6}{7}$

14. $-\dfrac{6}{5}x + \dfrac{1}{5}$

15. $\dfrac{1}{5} + 0(-14x) + 0(8)$

    $= \dfrac{1}{5}$

Chapter 2 Answers

Additional Exercises, 2.1
Form I

1. -1

2. Alike

3. $16k$

4. $-5y$

5. $10x + 13$

6. $0.9w - 2.0$

7. $10y + 80$

8. $-50x - 70$

9. $-4m^2 + n - 7$

10. $-18x + 36y + 27$

11. $8x - 28$

12. $6y + 42$

13. $9x + 13$

14. $0.5m + 3.2$

15. $12x - 8$

16. $12m + 4$

17. $5x - 11$

18. $7x - (-6 + 8x)$
$= 7x + 6 - 8x$
$= -x + 6$

19. $6(x + 9) + 4x$
$= 6x + 54 + 4x$
$= 10x + 54$

20. $(3x - 8) + (2x - 9) + 7$
$= 3x - 8 + 2x - 9 + 7$
$= 5x - 10$

Additional Exercises, 2.1
Form II

1. $6x - 22$

2. $-6x - 2y + 3$

3. $19y + 10$

4. $13x - 1$

5. $3y - 39$

6. $-20x$

7. $-2m^2 - 3n - 8$

8. $-15x^2 + 6y^3 - 15x$

9. $16x - 34$

10. $20y - 4$

11. $3x + 168$

12. $0.2x - 3.0$

13. $4x + 1$

14. $-3b - 12$

15. $6x - 23$

16. $2x + 28$

17. $10x - 4$

18. $\dfrac{17}{10}x - \dfrac{1}{6}$

Additional Exercises, 2.1
Form III

1. $2x^2y + 9y - 6$

2. $14a^2b + 6ab^2$

3. $-36x + 48y$

4. $14x - 12$

5. $\dfrac{1}{12}x^2 - \dfrac{41}{12}x + \dfrac{1}{12}$

6. $3.2w - 2.08$

7. $10y + 80$

8. $-10x - 70$

9. $-m^2 - 2n + 14$

10. $-19x - 19$

11. $\dfrac{1}{12}y + \dfrac{13}{6}$

12. $-0.9y - 0.14$

13. $9x^2 + 40x + 13$

14. -5.94

15. $2x^2 - 10x - 5$

16. $3x^2 + 4x + 3$

17. $5(x + 2) - 11(x - 7)$
$= -6x + 87$

18. $-3(x - 14) + 2(2(x + 1))$
$= x + 46$

19. $-2(x - 1) + 5x$
$= 3x + 2$

20. $2(3x + 2) + (x + 3)$
$7x + 7$

Additional Exercises, 2.2

Form I

1. Yes
2. $x = 4$
3. $y = 26$
4. $x = -0.4$
5. $k = -\dfrac{1}{8}$
6. $x = -11$
7. $x = -9$
8. $x = 9$
9. $x = -7$
10. $3 = x$
11. $x = -9$
12. $y = \dfrac{3}{5}$
13. $x = 0$
14. $x = 25$
15. $x = -1$
16. $x = -8$
17. $y = \dfrac{3}{5}$
18. 1st $= x°$
    2nd $= (150 - x)°$
19. 1st $= x$ ft.
    2nd $= (15 - x)$ ft.
20. $m =$ mi to Gastonia
    $m + 15 =$ mi to Charlotte

Additional Exercises, 2.2
Form II

1. No
2. $x = \dfrac{13}{12}$
3. $y = 8$
4. $x = 0.3$
5. $k = \dfrac{7}{5}$
6. $x = -25$
7. $x = -10$
8. $x = 15$
9. $x = -19$
10. $x = 7$
11. $x = -16$
12. $y = 0.5$
13. $x = 2$
14. $x = 7$
15. $x = 12$
16. $x = 9$
17. $y = \dfrac{3}{5}$
18. 1st angle $= (x - 3)°$
    2nd angle $= 90° - (x - 3)°$
    $= (87 - x)°$
19. $(40 - 2x)$ ft.
20. $(3x + 4)$ mi

Additional Exercises, 2.2
Form III

1. $x = \dfrac{7}{20}$
2. $y = -0.7$
3. $x = 0.4$
4. $k = -25$
5. $x = 9$
6. $x = -19$
7. $x = 26$
8. $x = -9$
9. $x = 12$
10. $x = -21$
11. $y = \dfrac{13}{5}$
12. $x = -8$
13. $x = 15$
14. $x = 8$
15. $x = -7$
16. $x = \dfrac{7}{20}$
17. $x = 33$
18.
    $y° =$ 1st angle
    $(5y+3)° =$ 2nd angle
    3rd angle
    $= (180 - y - (5y+3))°$
    $= (177 - 6y)°$
19. 1st piece
    x ft.
    2nd piece:
    $(x + 3)$ ft.
    3rd piece:
    $(15 - x - (x + 3))$ ft.
    $(18 - 2x)$ ft.
20. $-5(x + 1) + 4(2x - 3)$
    $= 2(x + 2) - 8$
    $x = 13$

Additional Exercises, 2.3
Form I

1. Lowest Common Denominator
2. $x = 3$
3. $x = 0$
4. $x = -16$
5. $x = \dfrac{5}{3}$
6. $x = 3$
7. $x = 26$
8. $y = \dfrac{11}{12}$
9. $x = 30$
10. $x = \dfrac{22}{15}$
11. $y = \dfrac{10}{3}$
12. $z = -\dfrac{5}{2}$
13. $a = 2$
14. $x = -15$
15. $y = -6$
16. $y = -3$
17. $x = 12$
18. $x = -7$
19. $y = \dfrac{21}{13}$
20. $x = 4$, so the lengths of the 4 sides are 4 cm, 8 cm, 13 cm. and 4 cm.

Additional Exercises, 2.3
Form II

1. $x = -5$
2. $x = 10.5$
3. $n = 2$
4. $x = 17$
5. $x = 2.6$
6. $x = -2$
7. $x = -4$
8. $a = -\dfrac{12}{13}$
9. $x = 2$
10. $y = -16$
11. $x = -15$
12. $k = -3$
13. $x = 16$
14. $y = 300$
15. $y = 12$
16. $x = \dfrac{7}{5}$
17. No solution
18. $x = -\dfrac{41}{48}$
19. All Real Numbers
20. $x = 5$, so the lengths of the sides are 5 cm, 16 cm, and 15 cm.

Additional Exercises, 2.3
Form III

1. $x = 0$
2. $x = -\dfrac{7}{12}$
3. $x = -1$
4. $x = 4$
5. $x = \dfrac{1}{26}$
6. $x = -8$
7. $x = -4$
8. $a = -10$
9. $x = -\dfrac{15}{2}$
10. $y = -\dfrac{8}{3}$
11. $x = 4$
12. $k = \dfrac{5}{3}$
13. $x = 91.2$
14. $y = 100$
15. $y = \dfrac{14}{43}$
16. $x = -\dfrac{1}{4}$
17. $x = -10$
18. $x = 8$
19. $t = 15$
20. $5x + 10$

Additional Exercises, 2.4
  Form I

1. $x = -\dfrac{15}{2}$

2. $x = 3$

3. $x = -10$

4. $x = 4$

5. $x = \dfrac{1}{26}$

6. No Solution

7. All Real Numbers

8. All Real Numbers

9. $x = 0$

10. $y = -5$

11. No Solution

12. No Solution

13. $x = \dfrac{3}{4}$

14. No Solution

15. $a = 0$

16. $x = 8$

17. All Real Numbers

18. False

19. True

20. No Solution, Null Set, Empty Set, $\varnothing$, { }

Additional Exercises, 2.4
  Form II

1. $x = 2$

2. $x = \dfrac{9}{10}$

3. $y = -\dfrac{1}{5}$

4. No Solution

5. No Solution

6. All Real Numbers

7. $x = 6$

8. No Solution

9. All Real Numbers

10. $z = -4$

11. $h = 9.9$

12. All Real Numbers

13. All Real Numbers

14. $x = 0$

15. $x = -\dfrac{3}{4}$

16. $x = -4$

17. $z = \dfrac{5}{2}$

18. No Solution

19. $x = -\dfrac{1}{9}$

20. No Solution

Additional Exercises, 2.4
  Form III

1. $x = 11$

2. $y = 38,961$

3. All Real Numbers

4. $y = 168$

5. $x = 24$

6. $x = -6$

7. $x = 18$

8. No Solution

9. $x = 1$

10 No Solution

11. No Solution

12. No Solution

13. All Real Numbers

14. $x = 1$

15. $x = \dfrac{4}{25}$

16. No Solution

17. $y = -12.8$

18. $t = 9$

19. $x = -\dfrac{64}{11}$

20. $x = \dfrac{66}{7}$

**Additional Exercises, 2.5
Form I**

1. The number is 85.
2. The lengths of the rope are 23 feet and 74 feet.
3. The number is 4.
4. The number is 60.
5. The number is 6.
6. The shorter piece is 9 feet, and the longer piece is 12 feet.
7. Tom's salary is $26,000 and Sue's salary is $52,000.
8. Dorothy won three U.S Figure Skating Championships, and Peggy won five.
9. The two board are 10 inches and 20 inches.
10. It took the carpenter approximately 15 hours to complete the job.
11. The total cost for repairing the television was $194.
12. The mechanic charged $22 an hour.
13. The two consecutive integers are 29 and 30.
14. The two angles have measures of 36° and 144°.
15. The two complementary angles have measures of 24° and 66°
16. The measures of the three consecutive angles are 59°, 60°, and 61°.
17. The measures of the angles of the trapezoid are 87°, 89°, 91°, and 93°.
18. The measure of the three consecutive integers are -30°, -28°, and -26°.
19. The license plate number is 57911
20. The angles in the four sided polygon are 30°, 30°, 150°, and 150°.

**Additional Exercises, 2.5
Form II**

1. The number is 7.
2. The three consecutive even integers are 90.92 feet and 94.
3. The number is 20.
4. The numbers are 15 and 17.
5. The numbers are 32, 34, and 36.
6. The two supplementary angles have measures 100° and 80°.
7. The string is cut into pieces that are 7 inches, 21 inches, and 39 inches.
8. Martina Navratilova won 9 single titles at Wimbledon, and Billie Jean King won 6 single titles at Wimbledon.
9. The number is $\frac{7}{50}$.
10. The measures of the angles of the triangles are 31°, 25°, and 124°.
11. The integer is -16.
12. The number is -13.
13. The number is 7.
14. The consecutive even integers are 6, 8, and 10.
15. The consecutive even integers are 10, 12, and 14.
16. The three consecutive even integers are $-2, 0$, and 2.
17. The three consecutive odd integers are 29, 31, and 33.
18. The width of the rectangle is 17 inches, and the length of the rectangle is 32 inches.
19. The two non-parallel sides of the trapezoid are 9 meters. The top base is 18 meters, and the bottom base is 27 meters..
20. The two equal sides of the isosceles triangle are 37 inches long, and the third side is 18 inches in length

**Additional Exercises, 2.5
Form III**

1. The number is 35.
2. The lengths of the four pieces of rope are 47, 49, and 51, and 53 feet.
3. The number is 240.
4. The original number is 60.
5. The number is 16.
6. The lengths of the pieces are 12 in, 12 in, 11 in, 19 in, and 41 in.
7. The width is 37 centimeters, and the length is 47 centimeters.
8. Since the winners scored one point more than the Pythons, then the Pythons scored 9 goals. So Katie scored 6 points, and Austin scored 3 points.
9. The integers are 51, 53, and 55.
10. The materials for the job cost $650.
11. Garrett was paid $10 an hour.
12. The width is 12 yards, and the length is 27 yards.
13. One angle is 135°and the other angle is 45°.
14. One angle is 25° and the other is 65°.
15. The integers are 80, 82, and 84

Additional Exercises, 2.6
Form I

1. $h = 18$
2. $r = 50$
3. $w = 8$
4. $h = 20$
5. $h = 14$
6. $m = -\dfrac{10}{3}$
7. $m = 2$
8. $m = 0$
9. Undefined
10. $p = 92$ ft.

    A=520 sq. ft.

    We would need to know the perimeter of the room for the purchase of the wallpaper.
11. It would take 2.4 hours, or 2 hours 24 minutes.
12. $68°$ F
13. $w = \dfrac{A}{l}$
14. $w = \dfrac{V}{lh}$
15. $a = c - 2b$
16. $b = \dfrac{c - a}{2}$
17. $h = \dfrac{2A}{b}$
18. $y = -2x + 5$
19. $y = 2x - 4$
20. $y = \dfrac{3}{2}x - 3$

Additional Exercises, 2.6
Form II

1. $y_2 = 0$
2. $h = 5$
3. $V = 3052.08$
4. $b = 5$
5. $t = 3$ years
6. $m = \dfrac{2}{9}$
7. $V \approx 129.81$
8. $S = 602.88$
9. $25°$ C
10. $131°$ F
11. They must purchase 3 bags.
12. 4 hours
13. The sides are 20 cm, 10 cm, 40 cm, 30 cm, and 30 cm.
14. $9:49$ am
15. $d = P - a - b - c$
16. $y = \dfrac{1}{7}x - 2$
17. $A = \dfrac{3V}{h}$
18. $l = \dfrac{S - 2hw}{4w}$
19. $y = \dfrac{-Ax + C}{B}$
20. $x = \dfrac{-By + C}{A}$

Additional Exercises, 2.6
Form III

1. $h = 5$
2. $V = 14,130$
3. $y_2 = 11$
4. $l = 11$ in.
5. $b = 16$ mi.
6. $P = \$30,000$
7. The sides of the triangle are 9 feet, 28 feet, and 27 feet.
8. $-81.4°$ F
9. $37°$ C
10. 6 bags of grass seed
11. 3.7 mi
12. The width is 30 meters, and the length is 105 meters.
13. 25 goldfish could be put into the tank.
14. You could put 41 piranhas in the tank.
15. Two 15 inch pizzas is more pizza.
16. 26,376 miles
17. $b = \dfrac{2A}{h}$
18. $w = \dfrac{4}{3}(z - 15)$ or

    $w = \dfrac{4}{3}z - 20$
19. $y = x + 10$
20. $A = \dfrac{3V}{h}$

Additional Exercises, 2.7
Form I
1. 44.64
2. 733.04
3. 60%
4. 34
5. 80
6. 15
7. 50.75
8. 610
9. 7000
10. 40%
11. 12%
12. 467.46
13. $169.63
14. 35% increase
15. The original price was $245.
16. Last year's salary was $38,000.
17. 10 lbs of the Mystery Nut Mix
18. $233\frac{1}{3}$ % increase
19. She bought the game system for $48.00.
20. Decrease in price is $297; sale price is $693.

Additional Exercises, 2.7
Form II
1. 299.2
2. 47.25
3. 22%
4. 66%
5. 4550
6. 15,400
7. 10%
8. $3.96 billion
9. $840 million
10. Discount was $37.50; sale price was $112.50.
11. 35%
12. $92.29
13. $47,520
14. $51,000
15. Old salary was $50,000; raise was $3000.
16. 45 liters
17. 120%
18. 36%
19. $75.00
20. 20 gallons

Additional Exercises, 2.7
Form III
1. 103.2
2. 500%
3. 150%
4. Rate of discount was 35%; discounted price was $140.
5. The rate of increase is approximately 72%.
6. The total cost for the dinner was $13,970.
7. There was an 18% rate of decrease.
8. Danielle's original salary before the raise was $66,000, and the she received a 12.5% increase.
9. The original asking price was $195,000 and the discounted price was $181,350.
10. 12 liters of the 3% solution must be added to the 8% solution to obtain 20 liters of 6% saline solution.
11. $269.64 was the total price after the discount and tax.
12. The amount of the discount was 70%.

13. Answers will vary.
14. Answers will vary.
15. It would take 9 cubic centimeters of the 30% solution.

Additional Exercises, 2.8
Form I
1. $0.01x$
2. $0.10y$
3. $0.25z$
4. $5(5x)$
5. $20(30-x)$
6. $100(25-z)$
7. 240 miles
8. $6\frac{2}{3}$ hours
9. 110 miles
10. 15 quarters and 180 dimes
11. $20,000 at 6% and $10,000 at 9%
12. 270 adults and 230 children
13. Jeff was hiking at 4 mph and Adrianna was hiking at 2 mph.
14. 280 miles at 70 miles per hour and 30 miles at 60 miles per hour.
15. Forty $10 bills and eighty $20 bills

Additional Exercises, 2.8
Form II
1. $15,000 invested at 5% and $21,000 invested at 8%
2. $6000 invested at 12% and $4000 invested at 15%
3. One-hundred forty $100 bills
   One-hundred fifty $20 bills
   Fifty $10 bills
4. Thirteen $20 bills and sixteen $5 bills
5. Stocks $340,000 at 12%
   Bonds $160,000 at 8%
6. Five hundred $20 bills and four-hundred $50 bills
7. Fifteen $20 bills and twenty-five $50 bills and forty $100 bills
8. $15,000 at 8% and $27,000 at 10%
9. 24 hours
10. 15 quarters and 180 dimes
11. $20,000 at 6% and $10,000 at 9%
12. 270 adults and 230 children
13. Jeff was hiking at 4 mph and Adrianna was hiking at 2 mph.
14. 280 miles at 70 miles per hour and 30 miles at 60 miles per hour.
15. forty $10 bills and eighty $20 bills

Additional Exercises, 2.8
Form III
1. 103.2
2. 500%
3. 150%
4. Amount of discount $140
   Percent of discount 35%
5. 72%
6. $13,970
7. 18%
8. Old salary $66,000
   Percent of raise 12.5%
9. Original price $195,000
   Discounted price $181,350
10. 8 liters of 3% saline solution; 12 liters of 8% saline solution
11. $269.64
12. 70% rate of discount
13. Answers will vary
14. Answers will vary
15. 9 cc of 30% antibiotic solution

Additional Exercises, 2.9
Form I

1.

2.

3.

4.

5.
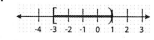

6.
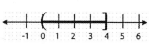

7. $x \geq 7$
8. $x > -5$
9. $x < 1$
10. $x \leq -3$
11. $x < 3$
12. $x \leq 2$
13. $x < -1$
14. $x > -3$
15. $x \geq -2$
16. $x \geq -1$
17. $x \geq -\dfrac{7}{2}$
18. $x > -7$
19. The score on the third test must be greater than or equal to 92.
20. The maximum length the garden can have is 30 yards.

Additional Exercises, 2.9
Form II

1.
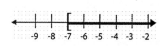

2.
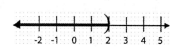

3.
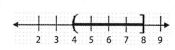

4. $x < 11$
5. $x < -3$
6. $x \geq -5$
7. $x < 8$
8. $x > 0$
9. $x \geq -10$
10. $x < -\dfrac{1}{4}$
11. $y > -1.6$
12. $x \leq -\dfrac{1}{3}$
13. $x \leq \dfrac{1}{2}$
14. $x < -3.7$
15. $x \leq 0.68$
16. $x < \dfrac{4}{9}$
17. The maximum lengths are 18 meters and 54 meters.
18. It would take three days – two days at the full 40 minutes and the third day 21.6 minutes.
19. They could invite 170 people.
20. She would need to have a score of 94 or above.

Additional Exercises, 2.9
Form III

1. $x \leq 13$
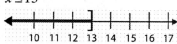

2. $x < -6$
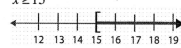

3. $x \geq 15$

4. $x \leq 98$
5. $x > \dfrac{9}{4}$
6. $x < -\dfrac{1}{6}$
7. $x > \dfrac{16}{5}$
8. $x < -8$
9. $x \leq 0$
10. $x \leq \dfrac{3}{2}$
11. $y < -22$
12. $x \leq -\dfrac{11}{5}$
13. $x > -\dfrac{3}{4}$
14. $x \leq 12$
15. $x \geq 77$
16. score ≥ 47

Chapter 3 Answers

Additional Exercises, 3.1
Form I

1. CSI

2. Dancing with the Stars

3. 21 million

4. 17.5 million

5. 3.5 million

6.
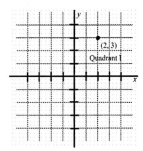

7.

8.
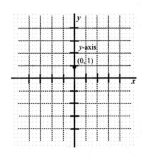

9.
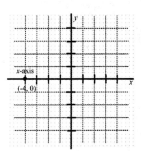

10. (−3,−4) Quadrant III

11 (4,−1) Quadrant IV

12. (−2,0) x-axis

13. (1,3) Quadrant I

14. (2,12)

15. $\left(\dfrac{2}{3},7\right)$

16.

x	y
0	−4
2	0
3	2

17.

x	y
2	0
0	$\dfrac{3}{2}$
−2	3

18.

x	y
−2	0
−2	−4
−2	3

19.

x	y
0	0
−4	1
4	−1

20.

x	y
0	6
2	7
6	9
8	10

Additional Exercises, 3.1
Form II

1. 1900 Galveston

2. More than 7000 people

3.

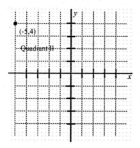

4.

5.

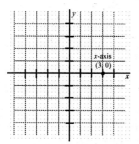

6.

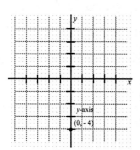

7.

8.

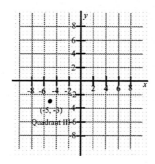

9. A (2,1) Quadrant I

10. B (−2,−3) Quadrant III

11 (3.5,0) x-axis

12. (−3,3) Quadrant II

13.

x	y
0	−2
$\frac{2}{7}$	0
$\frac{1}{7}$	−1

14.

x	y
0	−4
−4	−4
5	−4

15.

x	y

16.

0	−8
8	0
14	6

x	y
6	0
0	−4
$\frac{3}{2}$	−3

17.

x	y
0	0
0	0
4	−2
−8	4

18.

x	y
6	0
0	−2
24	6
33	9

19.

x	y
0	−5
0	0
0	2

20.

x	y
−4	0
0	0
2	0

Additional Exercises, 3.1
Form III

1.

x	y
0	0
0	0
−6	3
6	−3

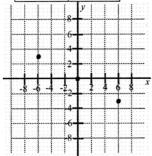

2.

x	y
0	4
2	0
2	0
−1	6

3.

x	y
−6	−5
−6	0
−6	1
−6	6

4.

x	y
−6	−5
0	−5
1	−5
6	−5

5. $-y = 2x + 1$

x	y
2	−5
−2	3
−4	7
$-\dfrac{1}{2}$	0

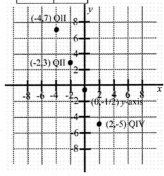

6. $x - \dfrac{1}{2}y = 2$

x	y
0	−4
2	0
4	4
6	8

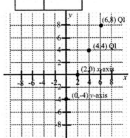

7. $y - x = 5$

x	y
0	5
−5	0
−3	2
2	7

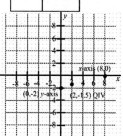

8. $\frac{1}{2}x - 2y = 4$

x	y
0	−2
8	0
16	2
2	$-\frac{3}{2}$

9. $(-1, -1)$ QIII

10. $(4, 3)$ QI

11. $(-4, 4)$ QII

12. $(0, 3)$ y − axis

13. $(3, 0)$

14. $(-2, 3)$

15. $(6, 2)$

16. $(0, -5)$

17. $(-5, 0)$

18. $(2, 4)$

19. 28 units

20. 49 sq. units

Additional Exercises, 3.2
Form I

1. $x + y = 8$

x	y
0	8
6	2
8	0

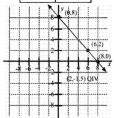

2. $x - y = 7$

x	y
0	-7
3	-4
7	0

3. $y = -3x$

x	y
0	0
2	-6
-1	3

4. $y = \dfrac{1}{4}x$

x	y
0	0
-4	-1
8	2

5. $y = -2x + 8$

x	y
0	8
1	6
5	-2

6. $7x - y = 7$

x	y
0	-7
1	0
2	7

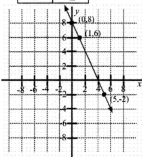

7. $x + y = -4$
   (Answers will vary.)

x	y
0	-4
-4	0
-2	-2

8. $x - y = 8$
   (Answers will vary.)

x	y
0	-8
8	0
4	-4

9. $-x + 2y = 6$
   (Answers will vary.)

x	y
0	3
-6	0
2	4

10. $y = -2x + 5$

(Points will vary.)

x	y
0	5
$\frac{5}{2}$	0
2	1

11. $y = 6x$

(Points will vary.)

x	y
0	0
0	0
6	1
−6	−1

12. $y = -2x$

(Points will vary.)

x	y
0	0
1	−2
2	−4

13. $x + 2y = 8$

(Points will vary.)

x	y
0	4
8	0
4	2

14. $y = \frac{2}{3}x - 4$

(Points will vary.)

x	y
0	−4
6	0
3	−2

15. $5y = 3x + 15$

(Points will vary.)

x	y
0	3
−5	0
−2	1.8

16. $x = 6y$

(Points will vary.)

x	y
0	0
3	0.5
6	1

17. $2x - 5y = 10$

(Points will vary.)

x	y
0	−2
5	0
−5	−4

18. $x = -\frac{2}{3}y$

(Points will vary.)

x	y
0	0
−2	3
4	−6

19. $y = x - 6$

(Points will vary.)

x	y
0	−6
6	0
2	−4

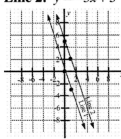

20. $x + y = 4$

(Points will vary.)

x	y
0	4
4	0
−2	6

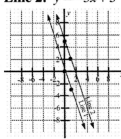

**Additional Exercises, 3.2
Form II**

1. Line 1 $\quad y = -\dfrac{3}{4}x$

    Line 2 $\quad y = -\dfrac{3}{4}x + 2$

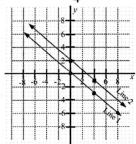

<u>Alike:</u> Line 1 and Line 2 appear to be parallel; <u>Different</u> Line 2 goes through the y-axis at 2, Line 1 goes through the y-axis at 0

2. **Line 1** $\quad y = \dfrac{3}{4}x$

    Line 2: $y = \dfrac{3}{4}x - 4$

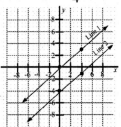

<u>Alike:</u> Line 1 and Line 2 appear to be parallel; <u>Different</u> Line 2 goes through the y-axis at -4, Line 1 goes through the y-axis at 0

3. **Line 1:** $y = -3x$
    Line 2: $y = -3x + 5$

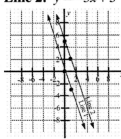

<u>Alike:</u> Line 1 and Line 2 appear to be parallel; <u>Different</u> Line 2 goes through the y-axis at 5, Line 1 goes through the y-axis at 0.

4. Line 1: $y = -\dfrac{1}{3}x$

    Line 2: $y = -\dfrac{1}{3}x + 3$

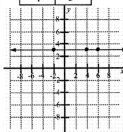

<u>Alike:</u> Line 1 and Line 2 appear to be parallel. <u>Different:</u> Line 1 goes through the y-axis at the origin, and Line 2 goes through at 3.

5. $y = 3$

x	y
−2	3
6	3
4	3

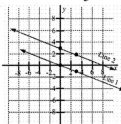

6. $x = -4$

x	y
−4	−4
−4	0
−4	6

7. $x + y = -4$

x	y
0	−4
−4	0
2	−6

8. $x - y = 8$

x	y
0	−8
8	0
4	−4

9. $-x + 2y = 6$

x	y
0	3
−6	0
4	5

10. $y = -2x + 5$

x	y
0	5
2	1
1	3

11. $y = 6x$

x	y
0	0
1	6
−1	−6

12. $y = -2x$

x	y
0	0
3	−6
−3	6

13. $x + 2y = 8$

x	y
0	4
8	0
4	2

14. $y = \dfrac{2}{3}x - 2$

x	y
0	−2
3	0
−3	−4

15. $y = 3x - 2$

x	y
0	−2
2	4
−2	−8

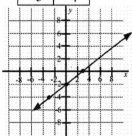

16. $x = -\dfrac{1}{2}y$

x	y
0	0
−2	4
4	−8

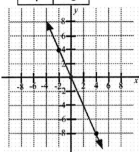

17. $2x - y = 4$

x	y
0	−4
2	0
−2	−8

18. $x = -\dfrac{3}{4}y$

x	y
0	0
−3	4
3	−4

19. $y = x + 2$

x	y
0	2
−4	−2
4	6

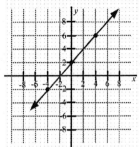

20. $x + y = 4$

x	y
0	4
4	0
2	2

Additional Exercises, 3.2
Form III

1. $2x + 3y = 6$

x	y
0	2
6	−2
3	0

2. $\dfrac{1}{2}x - y = 4$

x	y
0	−4
4	−2
8	0

3. $y = -\dfrac{5}{4}x$

x	y
0	0
4	−5
−4	5

4. $y = -1.5x + 2$

x	y
0	2
−4	8

6	-7

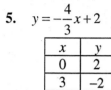

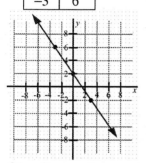

5. $y = -\dfrac{4}{3}x + 2$

x	y
0	2
3	-2
-3	6

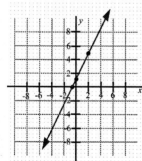

6. $2(x-3) = y-7$

x	y
0	1
$-\dfrac{1}{2}$	0
2	5

7. $2x - (y+2) = -4$

x	y
0	2
-1	0
2	6

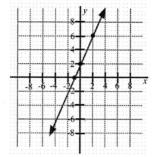

8. $y = -y + 8$

x	y
0	4
3	4
-3	4

9. $x - 2(x+3) = 6$

x	y
-12	-4
-12	0
-12	4

10. $-y = -x - 4$

x	y
0	4
-4	0
2	6

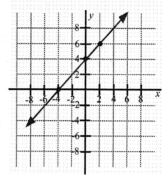

11. $y = \dfrac{5}{2}$

x	y
-2	$\dfrac{5}{2}$
0	$\dfrac{5}{2}$
2	$\dfrac{5}{2}$

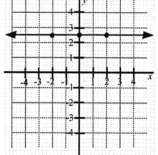

12. $x = 0$

x	y
0	-4
0	0
0	4

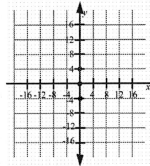

13. $y = 0$

x	y
-4	0
0	0
4	0

14. $6.60
15. Five years
16. $51,477

**Additional Exercises, 3.3
Form I**

1. x – intercepts

$(-4, 0)$ and $(4, 0)$

y – intercept

$(0, -4)$

2. x – intercept

$(-4, 0)$

y – intercept

$(0, 2)$

3. x – intercepts

$(-1.8, 0)$ and $(1.8, 0)$

y – intercept

$(0, -3)$

4.

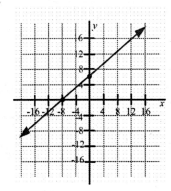

5. $x - y = 5$

x	y
0	-5
5	0
2	-3

6. $x = 3y - 6$

x	y
0	2
-6	0
-3	1

7. $x + 2y = 7$

x	y
0	$\frac{7}{2}$
7	0
1	3

8. $3x - 6y = 18$

x	y
0	-3
6	0
2	-2

9. $x = -6$

x	y
-6	-4
-6	0
-6	4

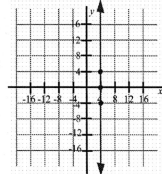

10. $y = 5$

x	y
-4	5
0	5
4	5

11. $x - 4 = 0$

x	y
4	-4
4	0
4	4

12. $y + 8 = 0$

x	y
-4	-8
0	-8
4	-8

13. B

14. C

15. A

16.

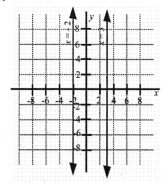

17. $(0, 50)$ If no beds are manufactured during the five hours, then they can produce 50 chests.

18. $(80, 0)$ If no chests are manufactured during the five hours, then they can manufacture 80 beds.

19.

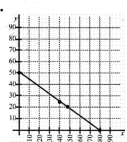

20. 40 beds

Additional Exercises, 3.3 Form II

1. x-intercept: $(-3, 0)$

y-intercepts
$(0, -2)$ and $(0, 2)$

2. x-intercept:
$(-1.5, 0)$ and $(1.5, 0)$

y-intercept $(0, 3)$

3. x-intercepts: $(2, 0)$

y-intercept $(0, 6)$

4.

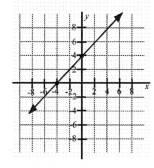

5. $4x + y = -1$

x	y
0	-1
$-\dfrac{1}{4}$	0
-1	3

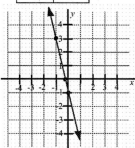

6. $3y = x - 6$

x	y
0	-2
6	0
3	-1

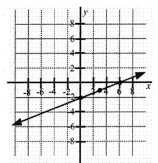

9. $2 - x = -3$

x	y
5	-4
5	0
5	4

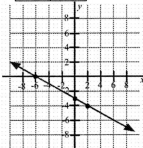

12. $2y + 8 = 12$

x	y
-4	2
0	2
4	2

7. $-x - 2y = 6$

x	y
0	−3
−6	0
−4	-1

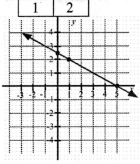

10. $-y - 4 = 2$

x	y
-4	-6
0	-6
4	-6

13.

$y = -x$		$y = -x - 4$	
x	y	x	y
0	0	0	-4
-4	4	-4	0
4	-4	2	-6

The lines are alike because they both fall from left to right, and appear to be parallel. The lines are different because they have different y-intercepts and x-intercepts.

8. $2x + 4y = 10$

x	y
0	$\frac{5}{2}$
5	0
1	2

11. $3x + 6 = -6$

x	y
-4	-4
-4	0
-4	4

14.

$3x = -6$		$-3x = -9$	
x	y	x	y
-2	-4	3	-4
-2	0	3	0
-2	4	3	-4

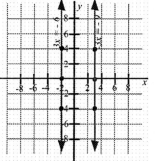

The lines are alike because they are both horizontal and appear to be parallel. Neither lines cross the x-axis. The lines are different because they cross the y-axis at different points

15.

$-y + 2 = -1$		$-2y - 2 = 4$	
x	y	x	y
-4	3	-4	-3
0	3	0	-3
4	3	4	-3

The lines are alike because they are both vertical and appear to be parallel. Neither lines cross the y-axis. The lines are different because they cross the x-axis at different points

Additional Exercises, 3.3 Form III

1. x-intercepts at, $(-1,0)$, $(2,0)$, and $(3,0)$
   y-intercept at $(0,6)$
2. x-intercepts at, $(-3,0)$ and $(3,0)$
   y-intercepts at $(0,3)$ and $(0,-3)$
3. y-intercept at $(0,-7)$
   No x-intercepts
4.

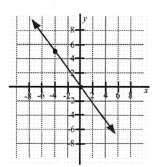

5.

$2x + y = 5$		Second line	
x	y	x	y
0	5	0	7
$\frac{5}{2}$	0	$\frac{7}{2}$	0
2	1		

6.

$y = -x - 3$		Second line	
x	y	x	y
0	-3	0	-1
-3	0	-1	0
-4	1		

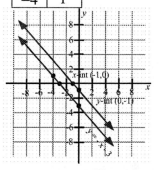

7.

$-y + 3 = 7$		Second line	
x	y	x	y
-4	-4	-4	-2
0	-4	0	-2
4	-4	4	-2

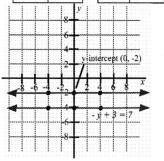

E-377

8.

$4x = -4$	
x	y
-1	-4
-1	0
-1	4

$x = 3$	
x	y
3	-4
3	0
3	4

The second line is the line $x = 3$.

9.

$3y = -9$	
x	y
-4	-3
0	-3
4	-3

$y = 5$	
x	y
-4	5
0	5
4	5

10. The x-intercept for the equation $4x = -4$ is $(-1, 0)$ and there is no y-intercept.

11. There is no x–intercept for the equation $3y = -9$, but the y-intercept is the point $(0, -3)$.

12. The x-intercept for the line $-x + 4 = 4$ is the point $(0,0)$. This line is vertical, and lies on the y-axis.

13. There is no x-intercept for the line $3y - 3 = -12$. It is a horizontal line that has the y-intercept $(0, -3)$.

14. The line $-x - y = -3$ has an x-intercept $(3,0)$ and y-intercept $(0,3)$. The line is neither vertical nor horizontal.

15. The line $-x - y = -x - 2$ has a y-intercept $(0, 2)$ and is horizontal. The line has no x-intercept.

Additional Exercises, 3.4 Form I

1. The slope is positive.
2. The slope is zero.
3. The slope is undefined.
4. $m = 2$
5. $m = -\dfrac{3}{2}$
6. $m = $ undefined
7. $m = \dfrac{1}{3}$
8. The slope of line 1 is positive, and the slope of line 2 is negative. Since any positive number is greater than a negative number, the slope of line 1 is greater than the slope of line 2.
9. The slope of the line $y = -12x + 5$ is -12.
10. The slope of the line $4x - 7y = 11$ is $\dfrac{4}{7}$.
11. The slope of the line $y + 5 = 0$ is zero.
12. The slope of the line $x = -8y$ is $-\dfrac{1}{8}$.
13. The slope of the line $x = -8x + 18$ is undefined.
14. The two points are (-3,-3) and (2,2). The slope is $m = 1$
15. The two points are (-3,2) and (-3,-3). The slope is $m = $ undefined

Additional Exercises, 3.4
Form II

1. $(-2,-1)$ and $(2,2)$

   $m = \dfrac{3}{4}$

2. $(-2,4)$ and $(2,-1)$

   $m = -\dfrac{5}{4}$

3. $(-3,2)$ and $(-3,-2)$

   $m = $ undefined

4. $m = $ undefined

5. $m = 0$

6. $m = \dfrac{5}{2}$

7. $m = -2$

8. $m = -\dfrac{1}{3}$

9. The slope of line 1 is positive, and the slope of line 2 is negative. Since any positive number is greater than a negative number, the slope of line 1 is greater than the slope of line 2.

10. $m = -2$

11. $m = \dfrac{1}{3}$

12. $m = 0$

13. $m = -\dfrac{1}{2}$

14. $m_{\text{line 1}} = -3$

    $m_{\text{line 2}} = \dfrac{1}{3}$

    The lines are perpendicular.

15. $m_{\text{line 1}} = \dfrac{1}{4}$

    $m_{\text{line 2}} = \dfrac{1}{4}$

    The lines are parallel.

16. $m_{\text{line 1}} = -\dfrac{1}{5}$

    $m_{\text{line 2}} = \dfrac{1}{5}$

    The lines are neither parallel nor perpendicular.

17. $m = \dfrac{1}{2}$

    a. The slope of a line parallel to the line containing these points is $m = \dfrac{1}{2}$.

    b. The slope of the line perpendicular is $m = -2$.

18. $m = \dfrac{5}{4}$

    a. The slope of a line parallel to the line containing these points is $m = \dfrac{5}{4}$,

    b. The slope of the line perpendicular is $m = -\dfrac{4}{5}$.

19. $m = \dfrac{5}{14}$

20. $m = \dfrac{7}{50}$

    $= 14\%$

Additional Exercises, 3.4
Form III

1. $m = $ undefined
2. $m = -2$
3. $m = 2$
4. $m = 0$
5. $m = \dfrac{5}{3}$
6. $m = \dfrac{2}{-3} = -\dfrac{2}{3}$
7. $m = \dfrac{3}{7}$
8. $m = \dfrac{1}{3}$
9. $m = -1$
10. $m = -12$
11. $m = \dfrac{4}{7}$
12. $m = -\dfrac{1}{8}$
13. $m = -1$
14. Perpendicular
15. Parallel
16. Parallel
17. $33\dfrac{1}{3}\%$
18. 50%
19. Yes
20. a. $m = 1$, Parallel slope is $m = 1$,

    b. Perpendicular slope is $m = -1$.

Additional Exercises, 3.5
Form I

1. $y = \dfrac{2}{3}x - 4$
   $2x + 3y = 12$

2. $y = \dfrac{7}{12}x$
   $-7x + 12y = 0$

3. $y = -\dfrac{1}{8}x + 4$
   $x + 8y = 32$

4. $y = -9$

5. $y = -2x + 3$

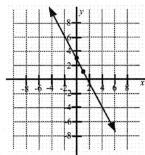

6. $y = \dfrac{3}{5}x - 2$

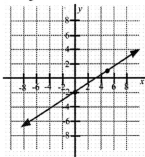

7. $3x + y = 4$
   $y = -3x + 4$

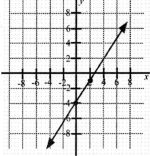

8. $3x - 2y = 8$
   $y = \dfrac{3}{2}x - 4$

9. $y = 9x - 26$
   $-9x + y = -26$

10. $y = -5x + 17$
    $5x + y = 17$

11. $y = -7x - 13$
    $7x + y = -13$

12. $y = \dfrac{4}{5}x - 20$
    $4x + 5y = -100$

13. $y = -\dfrac{1}{8}x + 3$
    $x + 8y = 24$

14. $y = 5x - 13$
    $-5x + y = -13$

15. $y = \dfrac{2}{3}x - 9$
    $-2x + 3y = -27$

16. $y = -\dfrac{2}{9}x$
    $2x + 9y = 0$

17. $y = 4x + 14$
    $-4x + y = 14$

18. $y = \dfrac{7}{8}x - \dfrac{3}{4}$
    $-7x + 8y = -6$

19. $y = \dfrac{1}{2}x$
    $-x + 2y = 0$

20. $y = -3x - 6$
    $3x + y = -6$

Additional Exercises, 3.5
Form II

1. $x = 5$
2. $y = 2$
3. $x = 2$
4. $y = -6$
5. $y = -\dfrac{1}{3}x + 5$
   $x + 3y = 15$
6. $y = -\dfrac{7}{3}x + \dfrac{25}{6}$
   $14x + 6y = 25$
7. $y = -\dfrac{3}{5}x + \dfrac{28}{5}$
   $3x + 5y = 28$
8. $y = 3$
9. $x = 2$
10. $y = -2$
11. $x = -5$
12. $y = -\dfrac{1}{5}x + 4$
    $x + 5y = 20$
13. $y = 2x - \dfrac{2}{3}$
    $-6x + 3y = -2$
14. $y = -x + 4$
    $x + y = 4$
15. $y = 9x + 5$
    $-9x + y = 5$

Additional Exercises, 3.5
Form III

1. $y = 0$

2. $y = \dfrac{5}{3}x - \dfrac{1}{4}$

   $-20x + 12y = -3$

3. $y = -\dfrac{2}{3}x - 5$

   $2x + 3y = -15$

4. $y = 5$

5. $y = \dfrac{1}{4}x + \dfrac{27}{4}$

   $-x + 4y = 27$

6. $y = \dfrac{3}{2}x + 3$

   $-3x + 2y = 6$

7. $y = -\dfrac{2}{3}x + \dfrac{7}{3}$

   $2x + 3y = 7$

8. $x = \dfrac{1}{2}$

9. $y = -\dfrac{2}{3}$

10. $x = -6$

11. $y = -4$

12. $y = -7$

13. $x = 5$

14. $y = 4$

15. $x = 4$

Additional Exercises, 3.6
Form I

1. Domain = $\{-9, 0, 3, 12\}$

   Range = $\{-15, 8, 12, 15\}$

2. Domain = $\{-7, -5, 4,\}$

   Range = $\{-7, 17\}$

3. Domain = $\{-9, 0, 3, 12\}$

   Range = $\{-15, 8, 12, 15\}$

4. Domain = $\{-2, 12\}$

   Range = $\{-4, 4, 14\}$

5. Function

6. Function

7. Function

8. Not a function

9. Not a function

10. Function

11. Function

12. $f(-1) = 13$

13. $f(2) = -14$

14. $f(0) = 4$

15. $g(0) = -7$

16. $g(-5) = 18$

17. $g(2) = -3$

18. $h(0) = 8$

19. $h(11) = 3$

20. $h(9) = 1$

Additional Exercises, 3.6
Form II

1. Domain = $\{-1\}$

   Range = $\{-4, -2, 0, 2\}$

2. Domain = $\{1, 3, 5, 7\}$

   Range = $\{-1\}$

3. Not a function

4. Function

5. Function

6. Not a function

7. Not a function

8. Function

9. $f(-2) = 12$

10. $f(0) = 0$

11. $f(2) = -4$

12. $g(0) = 1$

13. $g(-5) = -24$

14. $g(3) = -8$

15. $9000

16. $10,000

17. Yes, vertical line test

18. $12,500

19. Domain = $(-\infty, 4]$

   Range = $(-\infty, 3]$

Additional Exercises, 3.6
Form III

1. $(-\infty, \infty)$

2. $(-\infty, 7) \cup (7, \infty)$

3. $(-\infty, 5) \cup (5, \infty)$

4. $(-\infty, 0) \cup (0, \infty)$

5. $(-\infty, \infty)$

6. Domain $= (-\infty, \infty)$
   Range $= \{3\}$

7. Domain $= (-\infty, \infty)$
   Range $= (-\infty, \infty)$

8. Domain $= [-1, \infty)$
   Range $= [0, \infty)$

9. Domain $= (-\infty, \infty)$
   Range $= [0, \infty)$

10. $f(-2) = 8$
    $f(0) = 2$
    $f(2) = -4$

11. $g(-2) = 1$
    $g(0) = 5$
    $g(2) = 1$

12. $h(-2) = 4$
    $h(0) = 4$
    $h(2) = 4$

13. $f(-2) = 5$
    $f(0) = -1$
    $f(2) = 1$

14. $g(-2) = 6$
    $g(0) = 0$
    $g(2) = 6$

15. $h(-2) = 0$
    $h(0) = 4$
    $h(2) = 0$

16. $y = \dfrac{1}{3}x + 4$

17. **a.** 156.02 centimeters
    b. 176.74 centimeters

Chapter 4 Answers
Additional Exercises, 4.1
Form I

1. No
2. Yes
3. No
4. Yes
5. $\{(2,-1)\}$
6. $\{(2,1)\}$
7. $\{(3,-2)\}$
8. $\{(-3,-1)\}$
9. $\{(-2,-2)\}$
10. $\{(0,-4)\}$
11. $\{(-1,3)\}$
12. $\{(4,-3)\}$
13. No Solution
14. Infinite solution
15. $\{(3,1)\}$
16. $\{(3,3)\}$
17. $\{(1,1)\}$
18. $\{(2,2)\}$
19. 20
20. 8th year

Additional Exercises, 4.1
Form II

1. Yes
2. No
3. No
4. Yes
5. $\{(3,1)\}$
6. $\{(2,-3)\}$
7. $\{(-2,-4)\}$
8. $\{(-1,-5)\}$
9. $\{(3,0)\}$
10. $\{(-1,-4)\}$
11. $\{(-2,1)\}$
12. $\{(-2,1)\}$
13. $\{(0,-1)\}$
14. $\{(2,-2)\}$
15. Infinite solutions
16. Infinite solutions
17. No solutions
18. No solutions
19. 6th year
20. 4th year

Additional Exercises, 4.1
Form III

1. Yes
2. No
3. Yes
4. No
5. $\{(1,4)\}$
6. $\{(-2,3)\}$
7. $\{(2,6)\}$
8. $\{(-4,1)\}$
9. $\{(4,0)\}$
10. $\{(7,-3)\}$
11. $\{(-2,2)\}$
12. $\{(-5,-6)\}$
13. Infinite solution
14. $\{(4,3)\}$
15. $\{(2,3)\}$
16. $\{(3,-4)\}$
17. No solution
18. $\{(1,1)\}$
19. Answers may vary
20. Answers may vary

Additional Exercises, 4.2
Form I

1. $\{(8,-16)\}$

2. $\{(-6,2)\}$

3. $\{(2,-4)\}$

4. $\{(12,4)\}$

5. $\{(-14,2)\}$

6. $\{(0,3)\}$

7. $\{(3,-1)\}$

8. $\{(-7,-4)\}$

9. $\{(-2,3)\}$

10. $\{(-3,-1)\}$

11. $\{(2,-5)\}$

12. Infinite solutions

13. $\{(2,9)\}$

14. No solution

15. $\{(3,2)\}$

16. $\{(-1,0)\}$

17. $\left\{\left(\dfrac{2}{3},-\dfrac{4}{3}\right)\right\}$

18. $\{(4,-1)\}$

19. $\{(5,3)\}$

20. No solution

Additional Exercises, 4.2
Form II

1. $\{(4,8)\}$

2. $\{(1,4)\}$

3. $\{(8,3)\}$

4. $\{(2,1)\}$

5. $\{(11,2)\}$

6. $\{(0,1)\}$

7. $\{(7,0)\}$

8. $\{(9,1)\}$

9. $\{(-4,-3)\}$

10. No solution

11. $\{(14,-33)\}$

12. $\{(0,3)\}$

13. Infinite solutions

14. $\{(-10,-13)\}$

15. No solution

16. $\left\{\left(\dfrac{5}{2},-\dfrac{1}{2}\right)\right\}$

17. $\left\{\left(\dfrac{5}{3},\dfrac{2}{3}\right)\right\}$

18. Infinite solutions

19. \$30.00

20. 90 tons

Additional Exercises, 4.2
Form III

1. $\{(-5,-11)\}$

2. Infinite solutions

3. $\{(-4,6)\}$

4. $\{(0,2)\}$

5. $\left\{\left(-\dfrac{5}{2},2\right)\right\}$

6. $\{(1,1)\}$

7. $\{(0,-5)\}$

8. $\{(-3,2)\}$

9. $\left\{\left(\dfrac{5}{2},-2\right)\right\}$

10. Infinite solutions

11. $\left\{\left(-5,\dfrac{3}{2}\right)\right\}$

12. No solution

13. $\{(3,1)\}$

14. $\left\{\left(-\dfrac{1}{3},\dfrac{5}{3}\right)\right\}$

15. $\{(6,3)\}$

16. No solution

17. $\{(-5,-6)\}$

18. $\{(-4,-2)\}$

19. \$75.00

20. 375 tons

Additional Exercises, 4.3
Form I

1. {(5,0)}
2. $\left\{\left(2, -\frac{3}{2}\right)\right\}$
3. {(-2,4)}
4. {(3,2)}
5. {(2,3)}
6. {(5,1)}
7. {(4,3)}
8. {(1,3)}
9. {(4,3)}
10. {(0,1)}
11. {(-3,1)}
12. {(-2,1)}
13. {(2,2)}
14. {(3,-2)}
15. {(-1,3)}
16. {(8,1)}
17. No solution
18. {(1,-5)}
19. $2.80
20. 1.2 million pounds

Additional Exercises, 4.3
Form II

1. {(2,-1)}
2. {(-5,3)}
3. {(0,6)}
4. {(8,1)}
5. {(1,-3)}
6. {(3,4)}
7. {(2,3)}
8. {(-2,4)}
9. {(6,0)}
10. {(5,-1)}
11. {(0,-2)}
12. No solution
13. Infinite solutions
14. {(-6,-4)}
15. $\left\{\left(\frac{18}{17}, -\frac{22}{17}\right)\right\}$
16. {(-1,-2)}
17. No solution
18. Infinite solutions
19. $2.00
20. 2 million pounds

Additional Exercises, 4.3
Form III

1. {(1,-1)}
2. $\left\{\left(\frac{9}{2}, 3\right)\right\}$
3. {(4,-1)}
4. {(2,0)}
5. {(-10,-5)}
6. {(33,-27)}
7. {(-1,4)}
8. $\left\{\left(-\frac{3}{2}, 2\right)\right\}$
9. $\left\{\left(-\frac{1}{2}, 2\right)\right\}$
10. No solution
11. {(5,2)}
12. {(-2,5)}
13. {(0,-5)}
14. {(7,0)}
15. {(5,9)}
16. {(-59,36)}
17. {(-8,6)}
18. $\left\{\left(3, -\frac{3}{2}\right)\right\}$
19. $\left\{\left(2, -\frac{3}{4}\right)\right\}$
20. $\left\{\left(\frac{11}{28}, -\frac{37}{28}\right)\right\}$

Additional Exercises, 4.4
Form I

1. 35, 10

2. 42, 10

3. 8, 15

4. Records cost $11,
   Tapes cost $6

5. Class picture $6,
   Wallets $2

6. $200 in 9% stock,
   $300 in 10% stock

7. Adult 270, Child 250

8. 80mph, 84mph

9. 430mph

10. 10mph

11. 20 ml of 40%,
    10 ml of 70%

12. 25 ml of 20%,
    15 ml of 60%

13. Length = 29 cm
    Width = 8 cm

14. Length = 17 in
    Width = 12 in

15. 40°

16. 18 dimes, 41 quarters

17. 32°, 58°

18. 27°, 63°

19. 50°, 130°

Additional Exercises, 4.4
Form II

1. 30, 26

2. 13, 31

3. 24, 8

4. Records cost $5,
   Tapes cost $7

5. Class picture $5,
   Wallets $1.40

6. $3000 in 9% stock,
   $1500 in 6% stock

7. Adult 1520, Child 250

8. 720 km

9. 60 miles

10. Lucy swims 8 km/hr in
    still water, the current
    runs 1km/hr

11. 75 ml of 10%,
    25 ml of 50%

12. 20 ml of 20%,
    80 ml of 60%

13. 10 cm, 17 cm

14. 6 in, 23 in

15. 5 in, 12 in

16. 12 dimes, 15 quarters

17. 16°, 74°

18. 36°, 54°

19. 65°, 115°

Additional Exercises, 4.4
Form III

1. 12, 34

2. 18.6, 69.4

3. 38, 75

4. Records cost $7,
   Tapes cost $4

5. Class picture $7,
   Wallets $0.50

6. $500 in 10% stock,
   $800 in 12% stock

7. Adult 3000, Child 2000

8. Pretzel cost $1.15
   Coke cost $0.75

9. 55 mph

10. 10

11. 7.5 ml of 30%,
    2.5 ml of 70%

12. 12 ml of 50%,
    20 ml of 90%

13. 6 cm, 19 cm

14. 7 cm, 12 cm

15. 3, 4

16. 30 pennies, 90nickels

17. 24°, 66°

18. 30°, 60°

19. 30°, 150°

Additional Exercises, 4.5
Form I

1. Yes

2. No

3. No

4. No

5. Yes

6. Yes

7. No

8. Yes

9.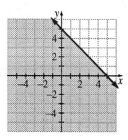

10.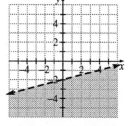

11.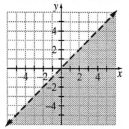

12.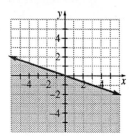

13.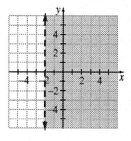

14.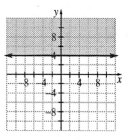

15.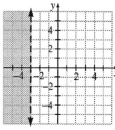

Additional Exercises, 4.5
Form II

1. Yes

2. No

3. No

4. Yes

5. Yes

6. No

7. Yes

8. No

9.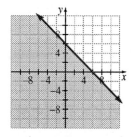

10.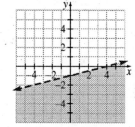

11.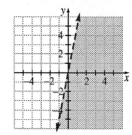

12.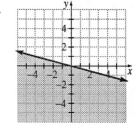

13.

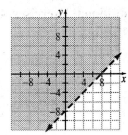

14.

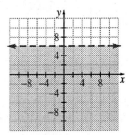

15.

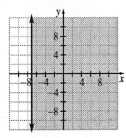

Additional Exercises, 4.5
Form III

1. No

2. No

3. Yes

4. No

5. Yes

6. No

7. No

8. Yes

9.

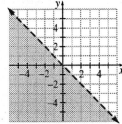

10.

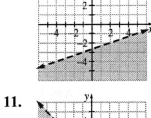

11.

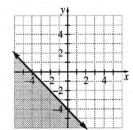

12.

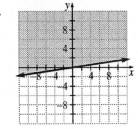

13.

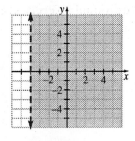

14.

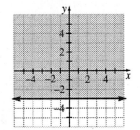

15.

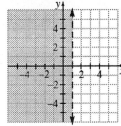

Additional Exercises, 4.6
Form I

1.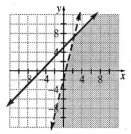

2.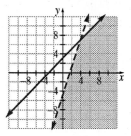

3.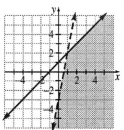

4.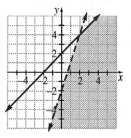

5.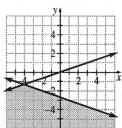

6.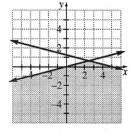

7.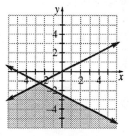

8.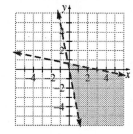

9.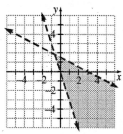

10.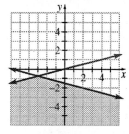

Additional Exercises, 4.6
Form II

1.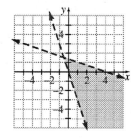

2.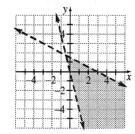

3.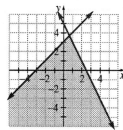

4.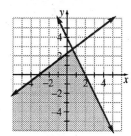

5.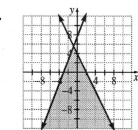

6.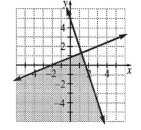

7.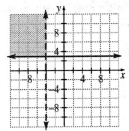

8.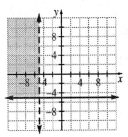

9.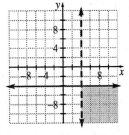

10.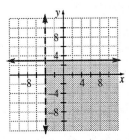

Additional Exercises, 4.6
Form III

1.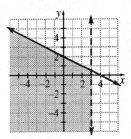

2.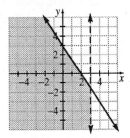

3.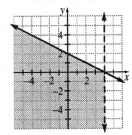

4.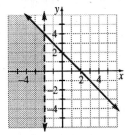

5.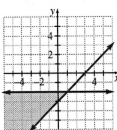

6.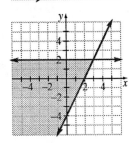

7.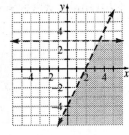

8.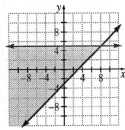

9. ∅ ; inconsistent; no shaded region in common

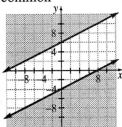

10. ∅ ; inconsistent; no shaded region in common

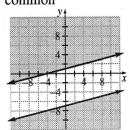

E-390

Chapter 5 Answers
Additional Exercises, 5.1
Form I

1. $6; -3x^2; 1; -8$
2. First degree; Binomial
3. Third degree; Trinomial
4a. 2
4b. -8
5a. 0
5b. 15
6. $19x^3$
7. $-11x^2 + x$
8. $2xy + 2y$
9. $7; 6; 5; 7^{th}$ degree
10. $18y + 14$
11. $a^2 - 4a - 13$
12. $2x^2$
13. $9a^2 - 8a + 10$
14. $x - 7y + 14$
15. $x^2 + \dfrac{2}{5}y^2 - 6$
16. $-9x^2y^2 - 2x^2y - 7xy - 5$
17. $6x^2 - 14x - 5$
18. $3y^2 - 9y + 2$
19. $(4x^2 - 7x + 15)$ inches
20. $(4y^2 - 3y + 12)$ meters

Additional Exercises, 5.1
Form II

1. $5; -4x^2; -1; -7$
2. First degree; Binomial
3. second degree; Trinomial
4a. -4
4b. -7
5a. 2
5b. 9
6. $21x^3$
7. $-10x^2 + 6x$
8. $-2xy + y$
9. $6; 0; 6; 4; 6^{th}$ degree
10. $19y + 12$
11. $-2a^2 - 5a - 11$
12. $x^2 - 4x - 2$
13. $13a^2 - 10a + 11$
14. $8x - 6y + 13$
15. $-\dfrac{1}{9}x^2 - \dfrac{1}{12}y^2 - 6$
16. $-3x^2y - 7xy - 16x^2y^2 - 6$
17. $6x^2 - 15x - 5$
18. $3y^2 - 6y + 7$
19. $(2x^2 - 6x + 16)$ inches
20. $(5y^2 - 4y + 15)$ meters

Additional Exercises, 5.1
Form III

1. $8, -6x^2, 1, -6$
2. First degree; Binomial
3. 7th degree; Monomial
4a. 6
4b. -10
5a. -2
5b. 10
6. $17x^3$
7. $3x^2 + 5x$
8. $2xy + 4y$
9. $9; 0; 5; 3; 9^{th}$ degree
10. $13y + 13$
11. $4a - 10$
12. $3x^2 - 4x - 13$
13. $11a^2 - 9a$
14. $9x - 8y + 12$
15. $\dfrac{1}{9}x^2 - \dfrac{1}{3}y^2 + 2$
16. $7x^2y^2 + x^2y - 6xy - 6$
17. $8x^2 - 10x - 6$
18. $5y^2 - 5y + 3$
19. $(7x^2 + 17x + 6)$ inches
20. $(4y^2 - 2y + 9)$ meters

Additional Exercises, 5.2
Form I

1. $72x^3$

2. $16x^7$

3. $\dfrac{1}{6}y^8$

4. $-24x^{10}$

5. $14y^3 - 42y^2 - 28y$

6. $-16a^3b + 20a^2b - 32a^3$

7. $2a^3b^2 - 6a^5b^4 - 7ab^7$

8. $y^2 - 7y - 44$

9. $x^2 - \dfrac{9}{25}$

10. $6x^2 + 34x - 12$

11. $15x^4 + 7x^2 - 36$

12. $25y^2 - 30y + 9$

13. $y^3 - 8y^2 + 17y - 10$

14. $4x^3 - 2x^2 - 8x - 8$

15. $4x^2 + 39x + 56$

16. $(20x^2 - 5x)$ sq in

17. $(5x^2 + 39x - 110)$ sq ft

18. $(64x^2 - 112x + 49)$ sq m

Additional Exercises, 5.2
Form II

1. $30x^3$

2. $-10.4x^7$

3. $\dfrac{2}{49}y^6$

4. $-35x^{10}$

5. $10y^3 - 35y^2 - 15y$

6. $-5a^3b + 35a^2b - 30a^3$

7. $12a^4b^2 - 36a^3b^4 - 40ab^5$

8. $y^2 - 12y - 45$

9. $x^2 - \dfrac{1}{45}x - \dfrac{2}{45}$

10. $20x^2 + 23x - 21$

11. $10x^4 - 15x^2 - 70$

12. $36y^2 - 132y + 121$

13. $y^3 - 13y^2 + 48y - 64$

14. $2x^3 - 3x^2 - 32x - 15$

15. $6x^2 + 19x + 15$

16. $(12x^2 + 32x)$ sq in

17. $(8x^2 - 22x - 21)$ sq ft

18. $(9x^2 - 30x + 25)$ sq m

Additional Exercises, 5.2
Form III

1. $40x^3$

2. $-12.6x^7$

3. $\dfrac{1}{6}y^{11}$

4. $-40x^{10}$

5. $24y^3 - 48y^2 - 40y$

6. $-15a^3b + 9a^2b - 21a^3$

7. $20a^4b^2 - 35a^3b^4 - 45ab^5$

8. $y^2 - 9y - 36$

9. $x^2 + \dfrac{1}{2}x - \dfrac{3}{16}$

10. $14x^2 + 27x - 20$

11. $12x^4 + 23x^2 - 24$

12. $49y^2 - 28y + 4$

13. $y^3 - 11y^2 + 31y - 21$

14. $3x^3 - 7x^2 - 19x - 4$

15. $4x^2 + 33x + 54$

16. $27x^2 - 3x$

17. $2x^2 - 13x - 45$

18. $x^2 - 10x + 25$

Additional Exercises, 5.3
Form I

1. $x^2 + 11x + 18$

2. $4x^2 + 13x - 66$

3. $3x^2 - 19x + 26$

4. $2y^4 + 5y^2 - 63$

5. $x^2 - \dfrac{1}{10}x - \dfrac{3}{50}$

6. $8 - 24a + 18a^2$

7. $3x^2 + 20xy - 32y^2$

8. $x^2 + 24x + 144$

9. $100a^2 - 60a + 9$

10. $y^2 - \dfrac{6}{5}y + \dfrac{9}{25}$

11. $4y^2 - 52y + 169$

12. $x^2 - 121$

13. $16x^2 - 100$

14. $9y^2 - 25$

15. $9x^2 - \dfrac{1}{36}$

16. $(7x^2 + 22x - 24)$ sq ft

17. $(9x^2 - 6x + 1)$ sq m

18. $(2x^2 - 9x - 56)$ sq in

Additional Exercises, 5.3
Form II

1. $x^2 + 9x + 8$

2. $3x^2 + 2x - 40$

3. $5x^2 - 17x + 12$

4. $3y^3 - 8y^2 + 27y - 72$

5. $x^2 - \dfrac{1}{3}x - \dfrac{5}{144}$

6. $15 - 41a + 28a^2$

7. $4x^2 + 31xy - 45y^2$

8. $x^2 + 20x + 100$

9. $121a^2 - 44a + 4$

10. $y^2 - \dfrac{10}{7}y + \dfrac{25}{49}$

11. $9y^2 - 72y + 144$

12. $x^2 - 100$

13. $25x^2 - 144$

14. $49y^4 - 16$

15. $16x^2 - \dfrac{4}{25}$

16. $(9x^2 - 38x - 35)$ sq ft

17. $(49x^2 - 28x + 1)$ sq m

18. $(16x^2 - 25)$ sq in

Additional Exercises, 5.3
Form III

1. $x^2 + 10x + 21$

2. $5x^2 + 4x - 33$

3. $4x^2 - 21x + 27$

4. $4y^5 - 7y^3 + 24y^2 - 42$

5. $x^2 - \dfrac{11}{72}x - \dfrac{1}{12}$

6. $3 - 19a + 20a^2$

7. $5x^2 + 29xy + 42y^2$

8. $x^2 + 28x + 196$

9. $144a^2 - 120a + 25$

10. $y^2 - \dfrac{8}{9}y + \dfrac{16}{81}$

11. $16y^2 - 104y + 169$

12. $x^2 - 81$

13. $9x^2 - 121$

14. $16y^4 - 49$

15. $4x^2 - \dfrac{9}{49}$

16. $(8x^2 + 15x - 27)$ sq ft

17. $(64x^2 - 48x + 9)$ sq m

18. $(20x^2 + 9x - 18)$ sq in

Additional Exercises, 5.4
Form I

1. $x^2 + 10x + 16$

2. $2x^2 + x - 45$

3. $4x^2 - 32x + 60$

4. $3y^3 - 7y^2 + 24y - 56$

5. $x^2 - \dfrac{4}{11}x - \dfrac{5}{121}$

6. $12 - 25a + 7a^2$

7. $4x^2 + 37xy - 30y^2$

8. $x^2 + 26x + 169$

9. $196a^2 - 84a + 9$

10. $y^2 - \dfrac{9}{7}y + \dfrac{9}{49}$

11. $4y^2 - 44y + 121$

12. $x^2 - 64$

13. $9x^2 - 169$

14. $81y^2 - 16$

15. $4x^2 - \dfrac{1}{25}$

16. $(5x^2 + 13x - 28)$ sq ft

17. $(25x^2 - 30x + 9)$ sq m

Additional Exercises, 5.4
Form II

1. $x^2 + 5x + 4$

2. $3x^2 - 5x - 22$

3. $4x^2 - 33x + 65$

4. $y^3 - 8y^2 + 7y - 56$

5. $x^2 - \dfrac{1}{2}x - \dfrac{7}{144}$

6. $10 - 41a + 40a^2$

7. $3x^2 + 16xy - 35y^2$

8. $x^2 + 200x + 10,000$

9. $225a^2 - 60a + 4$

10. $y^2 - \dfrac{10}{9}y + \dfrac{25}{81}$

11. $25y^2 - 120y + 144$

12. $x^2 - 400$

13. $36x^2 - 1$

14. $64y^4 - 25$

15. $49x^2 - \dfrac{4}{49}$

16. $(7x^2 + 16x - 15)$ sq ft

17. $(64x^2 - 16x + 1)$ sq m

Additional Exercises, 5.4
Form III

1. $x^2 + 15x + 56$

2. $5x^2 + 9x - 44$

3. $6x^2 - 17x + 11$

4. $a^3 + a^2b + ab^2 + b^3$

5. $x^2 - \dfrac{6}{13}x - \dfrac{7}{169}$

6. $9 - 36a + 32a^2$

7. $3x^2 + 25xy - 50y^2$

8. $x^2 + 21x + 110.25$

9. $169a^2 - 168a + 49$

10. $y^2 - \dfrac{3}{7}y + \dfrac{9}{196}$

11. $25y^2 - 80y + 64$

12. $x^2 - 49$

13. $9x^2 - 225$

14. $81y^4 - 4$

15. $25x^2 - \dfrac{9}{64}$

16. $(4x^2 + 19x - 63)$ sq ft

17. $(25x^2 - 20x + 4)$ sq m

Additional Exercises, 5.5
Form I

1. $\dfrac{1}{16}$

2. 16

3. $\dfrac{8}{15}$

4. p^6

5. $\dfrac{1}{81x^4}$

6. $\dfrac{y^{30}}{x^{27}}$

7. 18

8. x^3

9. $16a^5b^{16}c^3$

10. $\dfrac{y^6}{-64x^4}$

11. 1.5×10^7

12. 4.2×10^{-4}

13. 0.00000753

14. 305,100,000

15. 255,000,000,000

16. 70,000

Additional Exercises, 5.5
Form II

1. $\dfrac{1}{25}$

2. 81

3. $\dfrac{9}{20}$

4. p^7

5. $\dfrac{1}{64x^3}$

6. $\dfrac{1}{x^{14}y^{12}}$

7. 48

8. $\dfrac{1}{x^7}$

9. $9a^6b^{14}c^4$

10. $-\dfrac{y^{10}}{125x^2}$

11. 1.2×10^{10}

12. 3.1×10^{-4}

13. 0.000000784

14. 6,052,000

15. 427,000,000

16. 3000

Additional Exercises, 5.5
Form III

1. $\dfrac{1}{27}$

2. $\dfrac{125}{8}$

3. $\dfrac{10}{21}$

4. p^9

5. $625x^4$

6. $\dfrac{y^{45}}{x^{50}}$

7. 32

8. x^{13}

9. $\dfrac{64b^{18}c^5}{a^{37}}$

10. $\dfrac{1}{49x^{19}y^{10}}$

11. 1.35×10^{10}

12. 8.71×10^{-6}

13. 0.0843

14. 807,200

15. 49,700,000,000

16. 74

Additional Exercises, 5.6
Form I

1. $2x^2 - 6x - 11$

2. $a^3 - a^2b^4$

3. $8p^4 - 2p$

4. $a^2 - 4a + 3$

5. $-2x^3 + 3x^2 - 1$

6. $7x^2y^3 - 12y^4 - x$

7. $x + 1$

8. $x - 5$

9. $7x - 2$

10. $7a^2 + 3a - 5$

11. $x^2 + 2x + 4$

12. $3b - 8 + \dfrac{17}{b+2}$

13. $7x + 11 + \dfrac{18}{x-2}$

Additional Exercises, 5.6
Form II

1. $6x^2 - 4x - 3$

2. $a^2 - ab^3$

3. $6p^2 - 3p$

4. $4a^2 - 3a + 2$

5. $x^2 - 2x + 4$

6. $9xy^2 - 11y^3 - 14x$

7. $5x + 3$

8. $x + 3$

9. $4x + 1$

10. $3a^2 + 5a - 4$

11. $x^2 - 5x + 25$

12. $2b - 1 + \dfrac{3}{3b-1}$

13. $4x + 5$

Additional Exercises, 5.6
Form III

1. $2x^2 - 3x - 11$

2. $a^6b^2 - a^3b^4$

3. $7p^5 - 3p^2$

4. $a - 5 + \dfrac{2}{a}$

5. $-2x + \dfrac{4}{5x} - \dfrac{2}{x^5}$

6. $4x^4y^2 - 12y^6 - 18x$

7. $x + 5$

8. $x - 8$

9. $x - 3$

10. $4a^2 - 5a + 5 - \dfrac{3}{a+7}$

11. $9x^2 + 12x + 16$

12. $x + 2$

13. $4x + 3$

Chapter 6 Answers

Additional Exercises, 6.1
Form I

1. 5

2. a^4

3. $7x^2y$

4. $4(x-3)$

5. $5x(xy+y^2+1)$

6. $3xy(x^2+2xy+9)$

7. $3(y^4+2y^3+5y^2-y+7)$

8. $a^3b^2(3a-2b+5)$

9. $3(x^2y+2x+1)$

10. $6y^2(2y^3+y-3)$

11. $7x^2y(x^3y^3-2x-3y)$

12. $4(a^4+3a^2-2a+2)$

13. $(x+3)(y+2)$

14. $(a-3)(b^2+2)$

15. $(x-5)(y+1)$

16. $(x+5)(3+y)$

17. $(y-3)(3+x)$

18. $(x-3y)(4x-7)$

19. $(3x-5)(x-2y)$

20. $(4x+7)(3x^2-5)$

Additional Exercises, 6.1
Form II

1. 6

2. xy

3. 6

4. $3a(a+4)$

5. $5x(xy+2y+5)$

6. $3xy(x^3y+3x^2y+10)$

7. $4(y^4+2y^3+3y^2-y+6)$

8. $a^3b^2(3a-2b+5)$

9. $4(x^2y+2x+1)$

10. $4y^2(3y^3+y-4)$

11. $6x^2y(x^3y^4-2x-3y)$

12. $4(a^4+4a^2-3a+3)$

13. $(x+2)(y+4)$

14. $(c-3)(a^2+5)$

15. $(x-4)(y+2)$

16. $(x+4)(3+y)$

17. $(y-2)(3+x)$

18. $(x-4y)(4x-3)$

19. $(x-2y)(3x-5)$

20. $(4x+9)(5x^2-3)$

Additional Exercises, 6.1
Form III

1. 23

2. a^3b

3. $9y$

4. $3ab(a+5)$

5. $7x(xy+3y+1)$

6. $9xy(x^2+7xy+2)$

7. $3(2y^4+4y^3+5y^2-y+8)$

8. $a^3b^2(4a-5b+7)$

9. $7(x^2y+6x+1)$

10. $11y^2(y^3+2y-5)$

11. $8x^2y(x^3y^4-2xz-8yz)$

12. $abc(a^3b^2c+a^2b-a+1)$

13. $(x+5)(y+7)$

14. $(a-4)(b^2+9)$

15. $(x-5)(y+8)$

16. $(x+4)(5+4y)$

17. $(y-9)(7+x)$

18. $(x-4y)(9x-10)$

19. $(4a-3b)(3a^2-2b^2)$

20. $(4x^2-3)(2x^2-5)$

Additional Exercises, 6.2
Form I

1. $(x+4)(x+9)$

2. $(x-7)(x-8)$

3. $(x+3)(x-9)$

4. $(x+12)(x-9)$

5. Prime

6. $(x-5)(x+2)$

7. $(x+5)(x+11)$

8. $(x-3)(x-7)$

9. $(x-8)(x+3)$

10. $(x+9)(x-7)$

11. Prime

12. $(x+4)(x-3)$

13. $5(x+4)(x+3)$

14. $2(8-x)(2-x)$

15. $2(x+8)(x-1)$

16. $x(x-5)(x+1)$

17. $y(y-7)(y+3)$

18. $3x(x-7)(x-5)$

19. $2y^2(y-8)(y-2)$

20. $3y^2(y-6)(y+3)$

Additional Exercises, 6.2
Form II

1. $(x+14)(x-3)$

2. $(x+7)(x-8)$

3. $(x+5)(x-6)$

4. $(x+5)(x-4)$

5. $(x+1)(x+9)$

6. Prime

7. $(x+6)(x-4)$

8. $(x+4)(x-7)$

9. $(x-2)(x+9)$

10. $(x-9)(x+7)$

11. Prime

12. $(x+5y)(x+9y)$

13. $5(x+2)(x-3)$

14. $3(7-x)(5-x)$

15. $2(x+6)(x+1)$

16. $x(x-6)(x+1)$

17. $x(x-11)(x+4)$

18. $4x^3(x+2)(x+5)$

19. $xy(x-5y)(x-y)$

20. $2y^3(-8+5y+y^2)$

Additional Exercises, 6.2
Form III

1. $(x+14)(x-3)$

2. $(x+7)(x-8)$

3. $(x+5)(x-6)$

4. $(x+5)(x-4)$

5. $(x+9)(x+1)$

6. Prime

7. $(x+6)(x-4)$

8. $(x+4)(x-7)$

9. $(x+9)(x-2)$

10. $(x-9)(x+7)$

11. Prime

12. $(x+5y)(x+9y)$

13. $5(x-3)(x+2)$

14. $3(7-x)(5-x)$

15. $2(x+6)(x+1)$

16. $x(x-6)(x+1)$

17. $x(x-11)(x+4)$

18. $4x^3(x+5)(x+2)$

19. $xy(x-5y)(x-y)$

20. $2y^3(-8+5y+y^2)$

Additional Exercises, 6.3
Form I

1. $(y+3)$

2. $(y-1)$

3. $(2y+5)$

4. $(y-2)$

5. $(2x+1)(x+3)$

6. $(3x+2)(x+4)$

7. $(2x-3)(3x+2)$

8. $(5x-2)(x-4)$

9. $(4x-1)(2x-7)$

10. $(2a+1)(a+4)$

11. $(2x+5)(3x+2)$

12. Prime

13. $(3a+4)(a-2)$

14. $3(x+6)(x-5)$

15. $2(2x-1)(2x+5)$

16. $2(3x+2)(3x-7)$

17. $(x+9)^2$

18. $(a-12)^2$

19. $(3n+2)^2$

20. $(a-5)^2$

Additional Exercises, 6.3
Form II

1. $(2y-1)$

2. $(2y+1)$

3. $(y-5)$

4. $(3y-1)$

5. $(5x-1)(3x+2)$

6. $(4x-3)(2x-1)$

7. $(2x-5)(3x+2)$

8. $(3x+2)(3x+4)$

9. $(7x-1)(3x-2)$

10. $(6a-5)(3a+2)$

11. $(4x+3)(3x-5)$

12. $(3a-2)(5a+2)$

13. $(7a+2)(2a-7)$

14. $-4(x-3)(x+2)$

15. $7(2x+1)(3x+5)$

16. $5(5x-y)(2x+3y)$

17. $(x+4)^2$

18. $(5n+3)^2$

19. $2(x-6)^2$

20. $(8x+y)^2$

Additional Exercises, 6.3
Form III

1. $(x+2)$

2. $(y+1)$

3. $(4y+3)$

4. $(3x+4)$

5. $(3x-1)(2x-3)$

6. $(9x-2)(x+5)$

7. $(4x-3)(2x-1)$

8. $(3x-2)(x+5)$

9. $(2x-3)(x+6)$

10. $(9a-4)(a+6)$

11. $(5x-3)(3x-2)$

12. Prime

13. $-1(2a-5)(a+4)$

14. $5x(x-2)(2x+1)$

15. $3(2x-5)(x+4)$

16. $5(x+7)(x-3)$

17. $(x-3)^2$

18. $(2+9x)^2$

19. $(6x-7)^2$

20. $(8a+b)^2$

Additional Exercises, 6.4
Form I

1. $(x+3)(x+7)$

2. $(x-4)(x-9)$

3. $(2x+1)(x-5)$

4. $(2x-1)(3x-4)$

5. $(7x-2)(x-4)$

6. $(4x-1)(x-6)$

7. $(2n-3)(n+8)$

8. $(3x+4)(x-1)$

9. $(2n+3)(2n-1)$

10. $3(m+5)(m+2)$

11. $6m(m+2)(m+1)$

12. $(3m-11)(m-1)$

13. $(2m+3)^2$

14. $(2x+7)(x+8)$

15. $x(3x+2)(3x-4)$

16. Prime

17. $(2x-y)(3x-y)$

18. $(2x+5)(3x+2)$

19. $(2x+9)(x+8)$

20. $(7x+5)(x+2)$

Additional Exercises, 6.4
Form II

1. $(7x+1)(3x+2)$

2. $(3x-1)(x-5)$

3. $(n-1)(5n+1)$

4. $(6x+1)(x+3)$

5. $(3x+1)(x+2)$

6. $(7x-2)(x-1)$

7. $(5n+1)(2n+3)$

8. $(5x+1)(x-2)$

9. $(3n+1)(3n+4)$

10. $(4m-9)(m-2)$

11. $(3m-10)(m+3)$

12. $(5m-9)(2m+3)$

13. $(7m-2)(2m-5)$

14. $(9m+7)(7m+9)$

15. $2x(2x+3)(3x+1)$

16. $3m(5m+3)(m+1)$

17. $6m(5m-1)(2m-1)$

18. $2x(9x-7)(x+7)$

19. $5x(2x-1)(x+7)$

20. $y(3x-1)(2x+5)$

Additional Exercises, 6.4
Form III

1. $(x+5)(x+12)$

2. $(x-2)(x-8)$

3. $(n-3)(7n^2-10)$

4. $(4x-1)(6x^2-5)$

5. $(3x+2)(x+4)$

6. $(2x+3)^2$

7. $(10n+3)(n-2)$

8. $(6m-1)(m-3)$

9. $(2n-5)(2n+3)$

10. $(7m+5)(m+8)$

11. $(6x+5y)(x+2y)$

12. $(7m-8)(2m+3)$

13. Prime

14. $4(2m-5)(m+6)$

15. $2(4x+3y)(3x+y)$

16. $2m(5m-1)(m+1)$

17. $(4m+3)(5m+6)$

18. $(9x-4)(4x+9)$

19. $(5x+4)(4x+5)$

20. $(3x-8)(8x-5)$

Additional Exercises, 6.5
Form I

1. $(a-5)(a+5)$

2. $(x-7)(x+7)$

3. $(x-8)(x+8)$

4. $(2x-9)(2x+9)$

5. $(3x-4)(3x+4)$

6. Prime

7. $(a-10b)(a+10b)$

8. $(1-5x)(1+5x)$

9. $2x(3x-1)(3x+1)$

10. $5(x-5)(x+5)$

11. $\left(x-\dfrac{2}{3}\right)\left(x+\dfrac{2}{3}\right)$

12. $(x^2-y^3)(x^2+y^3)$

13. $(y-2)(y^2+2y+4)$

14. $(x+3)(x^2-3x+9)$

15. $(a+4)(a^2-4a+16)$

16. $(x+1)(x^2-x+1)$

17. $(2y-3)(4y^2+6y+9)$

18. $(1+5x)(1-5x+25x^2)$

19. $(x^2-2y)(x^4+2xy+4y^2)$

20. $\left(x-\dfrac{1}{2}\right)\left(x^2+\dfrac{1}{2}x+\dfrac{1}{4}\right)$

Additional Exercises, 6.5
Form II

1. $(1-3x)(1+3x)$

2. $(2x-y)(2x+y)$

3. $(11-ab)(11+ab)$

4. $(xy-10)(xy+10)$

5. $(a^2b-3)(a^2b+3)$

6. $(a^3-12)(a^3+12)$

7. $(4x-11)(4x+11)$

8. $(x^4-13)(x^4+13)$

9. $(15x-29y)(15x+29y)$

10. $9x(x-2)(x+2)$

11. $\left(y-\dfrac{4}{9}\right)\left(y+\dfrac{4}{9}\right)$

12. $ab(4ab-7)(4ab+7)$

13. $\left(\dfrac{2}{7}x-\dfrac{1}{5}\right)\left(\dfrac{2}{7}x+\dfrac{1}{5}\right)$

14. $(1-6x)(1+6x)$

15. $(x+y)(x^2-xy+y^2)$

16. $(3x-2y)(9x^2+6xy+4y^2)$

17. $(xy+6)(x^2y^2-6xy+36)$

18. $(a-7b)(a^2+7ab+49b^2)$

19. $(2a+8b)(4a^2-16ab+64b^2)$

20. $\left(n-\dfrac{2}{3}\right)\left(n^2+\dfrac{2}{3}n+\dfrac{4}{9}\right)$

Additional Exercises, 6.5
Form III

1. $(a-25)(a+25)$

2. $(ab-cd)(ab+cd)$

3. $(a^5-5)(a^5+5)$

4. $(7a-10b)(7a+10b)$

5. $(ab-14)(ab+14)$

6. Prime

7. $(3-8a)(3+8a)$

8. $\left(a-\dfrac{9}{10}\right)\left(a+\dfrac{9}{10}\right)$

9. $\left(\dfrac{2}{5}a-\dfrac{3}{4}\right)\left(\dfrac{2}{5}a+\dfrac{3}{4}\right)$

10. $3x(x-6)(x+6)$

11. $x^3y(xy-8)(xy+8)$

12. $3(x-10)(x+10)$

13. $4x(x-9)(x+9)$

14. Prime

15. $(a-9)(a^2+9a+81)$

16. $(xy-10)(x^2y^2+10xy+100)$

17. $\left(a-\dfrac{5}{6}\right)\left(a^2+\dfrac{5}{6}a+\dfrac{25}{36}\right)$

18. Prime

19. $(11a-b)(121a^2+11ab+b^2)$

20. $y(y^2-2)(y^4+2y^2+4)$

Additional Exercises, 6.6
Form I

1. $x = -10, 3$

2. $x = \dfrac{1}{2}, -\dfrac{1}{3}$

3. $x = \dfrac{3}{2}, -\dfrac{3}{2}$

4. $x = -5, 0, 5$

5. $x = 1, 3$

6. $x = -7, 0, \dfrac{5}{3}$

7. $x = -5, 4$

8. $x = -5, 9$

9. $x = -\dfrac{3}{2}, 7$

10. $y = -\dfrac{4}{3}, \dfrac{4}{3}$

11. $x = -\dfrac{5}{2}, -\dfrac{5}{3}$

12. $b = -\dfrac{7}{6}, 1$

13. $n = -4, 12$

14. $m = 0, 9$

15. $x = -6, 3$

16. $y = -\dfrac{5}{2}, \dfrac{5}{2}$

17. $p = -6, \dfrac{5}{2},$

18. $n = -5, -3, 0$

19. $y = -\dfrac{1}{4}, 0, \dfrac{1}{4}$

20. $w = -2, -\dfrac{1}{3}, 0$

Additional Exercises, 6.6
Form II

1. $x = -11, 2$

2. $x = \dfrac{2}{5}, -\dfrac{1}{3}$

3. $x = \dfrac{2}{3}, -\dfrac{2}{3}$

4. $x = -2, 0, \dfrac{1}{5}$

5. $x = 7, \dfrac{5}{2}$

6. $x = -\dfrac{7}{3}, 0, 5$

7. $x = -0.5, 0.3$

8. $x = -6, 1$

9. $x = -1, \dfrac{5}{2}$

10. $y = -\dfrac{5}{2}, \dfrac{5}{2}$

11. $x = -\dfrac{5}{2}$

12. $b = -2, \dfrac{5}{3}$

13. $n = 3, 7$

14. $m = 0, 11$

15. $x = -8, 4$

16. $y = -\dfrac{4}{3}, \dfrac{4}{3}$

17. $p = \dfrac{8}{5}, 3$

18. $n = -6, -2, 0$

19. $y = -\dfrac{1}{2}, 0, \dfrac{1}{2}$

20. $w = 0, 4$

Additional Exercises, 6.6
Form III

1. $x = -10, 3$

2. $x = \dfrac{1}{2}, -\dfrac{1}{3}$

3. $x = \dfrac{3}{2}, -\dfrac{3}{2}$

4. $x = -5, 0, 5$

5. $x = 1, 3$

6. $x = -7, 0, \dfrac{5}{3}$

7. $x = -5, 4$

8. $x = -5, 9$

9. $x = -\dfrac{3}{2}, 7$

10. $y = -\dfrac{4}{3}, \dfrac{4}{3}$

11. $x = -\dfrac{5}{2}, -\dfrac{5}{3}$

12. $b = -\dfrac{7}{6}, 1$

13. $n = -4, 12$

14. $m = 0, 9$

15. $x = -6, 3$

16. $y = -\dfrac{5}{2}, \dfrac{5}{2}$

17. $p = -6, \dfrac{5}{2},$

18. $-5, -3, 0$

19. $y = -\dfrac{1}{4}, 0, \dfrac{1}{4}$

20. $w = -2, -\dfrac{1}{3}, 0$

**Additional Exercises, 6.7
Form I**

1. 4 in^2

2. 11 cm, 5 cm

3. 20 ft

4. 15 in, 25 in

5. 3 sec

6. 12, 13, 5

7. 5, 12, 13

8. 25 ft

9. 12 cm, 16 cm

10. -3, 3

11. 6, 12

12. 6, 8

13. 4 and 5 or -4 and -5

14. 8, 9, 10

15. 18

**Additional Exercises, 6.7
Form II**

1. 8, 3

2. 10, 7

3. 12, 6

4. 30 ft, 36ft

5. 2 sec

6. 6m, 8m, 10m

7. 5ft, 12ft, 13ft

8. 20 ft

9. 10m, 24m

10. 2 or 4

11. 5 or -3

12. 5 and 7

13. 5, 6, 7

14. 3 and 5

15. 7 in

**Additional Exercises, 6.7
Form III**

1. 5 in^2

2. 11 ft , 16 ft

3. 15 ft

4. 8m

5. 5 sec

6. 8, 15, 17

7. 6, 4, 10

8. 8 ft

9. 6in, 8 in

10. -2, 2

11. 2, 5

12. 7, 9

13. 16, 17, 18

14. 7 cm

15. 6m by 8m

Chapter 7 Answers
Additional Exercises, 7.1
Form I

1. $-\dfrac{1}{2}$

2. $-\dfrac{25}{24}$

3. $\dfrac{61}{7}$

4. 4

5. none

6. **0**

7. $3k^2$

8. -9

9. $\dfrac{1}{5x+2}$

10. $-\dfrac{5}{3}$

11. 4x-7

12. $\dfrac{11x}{6}$

13. $y^2+4y+16$

14. $x+2$

15. $\dfrac{3(x+2)}{4}$

16. $x-2$

17. $\dfrac{-y+12}{y+17}, \dfrac{-(y-12)}{y+17},$
    $\dfrac{y-12}{-y-17}, \dfrac{y-12}{-(y+17)}$

18. $300

19. $255

20. 26.78

Additional Exercises, 7.1
Form II

1. -7

2. $-\dfrac{4}{9}$

3. $\dfrac{7}{2}$

4. 0

5. 10

6. none

7. $\dfrac{1}{2x-3}$

8. $\dfrac{3}{5}$

9. 1

10. –1

11. -8

12. $\dfrac{1}{x-8}$

13. $x+5$

14. $\dfrac{x+8}{x-9}$

15. $\dfrac{x+6}{3}$

16. $4+y$

17. $\dfrac{-y+2}{y+7}, \dfrac{-(y-2)}{y+7},$
    $\dfrac{y-2}{-y-7}, \dfrac{y-2}{-(y+7)}$

18. $270

19. $216

20. 19.04

Additional Exercises, 7.1
Form III

1. $\dfrac{1}{8}$

2. $-\dfrac{81}{80}$

3. -29

4. 2

5. none

6. **0**

7. $5k^2$

8. 9

9. $\dfrac{1}{5x+2}$

10. 1

11. $\dfrac{-7}{3}$

12. 9x-7

13. $\dfrac{11x}{4}$

14. $y^2+5y+25$

15. $\dfrac{5(x+5)}{6}$

16. $m-5$

17. $\dfrac{-y+13}{y+25}, \dfrac{-(y-13)}{y+25},$
    $\dfrac{y-13}{-y-25}, \dfrac{y-13}{-(y+25)}$

18. $125

19. $102.50

20. 39.41

Additional Exercises, 7.2
Form I

1. $\dfrac{-4}{x+8}$

2. $\dfrac{8}{x}$

3. $14z$

4. $\dfrac{x^3}{2}$

5. $\dfrac{5y}{6}$

6. $\dfrac{9p}{4}$

7. $\dfrac{x}{x-2}$

8. $\dfrac{8}{9x^2(x-11)}m^2$

9. $\dfrac{x^2}{x^4-18x^2+81}$

10. x^{11}

11. $\dfrac{20}{49c^2}$

12. $x^7(x+3)$

13. $\dfrac{1}{6}$

14. $\dfrac{(x-y)^2}{2}$

15. $\dfrac{x+4}{-(x+1)}$

16. $\dfrac{2(x-8)}{x-5}$

17. $\dfrac{(x-y)(x+y)}{x^2}$

18. $\dfrac{4}{11}$

19. $\dfrac{5x^4}{16(6x+7)}$

20. 682 mph

Additional Exercises, 7.2
Form II

1. $\dfrac{-5}{3x+7}$

2. $\dfrac{15x}{7}$

3. x

4. $\dfrac{-a}{6}$

5. $\dfrac{x^2}{35}$

6. $4x$

7. $\dfrac{y-2}{y}$

8. $\dfrac{2}{7(x-7)}$

9. $\dfrac{9}{(4x-9)}m^2$

10. $\dfrac{3x^7}{2}$

11. $\dfrac{8x}{y^3}$

12. $\dfrac{3x(x+12)}{2}$

13. $\dfrac{1}{26}$

14. $\dfrac{(a-b)^2}{2}$

15. $-\dfrac{x+2}{x-7}$

16. $\dfrac{5}{9}$

17. $\dfrac{x(x+2y)}{5(5x+y)}$

Additional Exercises, 7.2
Form II (continue)

18. $-\dfrac{3x(x-5)}{2}$

19. $-\dfrac{(x-4)^2}{(3x+1)^2}$

20. **0.1023** mph

Additional Exercises, 7.2
Form III

1. $\dfrac{-6}{2x-7}$

2. $\dfrac{24}{x}$

3. $8z$

4. $\dfrac{x^4}{6}$

5. $\dfrac{3y}{4}$

6. $\dfrac{20p}{7}$

7. $\dfrac{x}{x-9}$

8. $\dfrac{10}{9x^2(x-7)}m^2$

9. $\dfrac{9x^2}{256x^4-800x^3+625x^2}$

10. x^{11}

11. $\dfrac{35}{16n^2}$

12. $x^6(x-9)$

13. $\dfrac{1}{3x}$

14. z^2-b^2

15. $\dfrac{x-2}{x+7}$

16. $\dfrac{5(x-2)^2}{24}$

17. $\dfrac{x(x+4y)}{3(3x-y)}$

18. $-\dfrac{(x-3)}{(x+3)}$

19. $\dfrac{8x^4}{25(6x+7)}$

20. 1364 mph

Additional Exercises, 7.3
Form I

1. $\dfrac{5m}{4n}$

2. $\dfrac{5m}{n}$

3. 5

4. $\dfrac{x+5}{13+x}$

5. 2

6. $\dfrac{1}{x+12}$

7. $\dfrac{1}{x+4}$

8. $36x^2y$

9. $8x(x+2)$

10. $x(x+3)^2$

11. $(x-2)\,or\,(2-x)$

12. $(x+6)(x+3)(x+5)$

13. $\dfrac{20x}{16x^2}$

14. $4xy+y$

15. $18y-2$

16. $\dfrac{x(x+14)(x+12)}{x(16x+4)(x+12)(x+20)}$

17. $\dfrac{21(x-4)}{x(x+8)(x-4)}$

18. $\dfrac{28}{x+5}\,m$

19. $\dfrac{2x+13}{x+5}\,in$

Additional Exercises, 7.3
Form II

1. $\dfrac{a+11}{17}$

2. $\dfrac{6m}{n}$

3. 5

4. $\dfrac{x+10}{15+x}$

5. 2

6. $\dfrac{1}{x+6}$

7. $\dfrac{1}{x-4}$

8. $15y^7$

9. $3y(3y-5)$

10. $9(x-2)^2$

11. $x-y$

12. $(x+7)(x+5)(x+4)$

13. $\dfrac{24y^3}{48y^5}$

14. $\dfrac{b(7a+3)}{3b(3a+1)}$

15. $\dfrac{3(11y-4)}{36x^2-45}$

16. $\dfrac{10(x+4)}{(x+8)(x-4)(x+4)}$

17. $\dfrac{(x-7)(x+4)}{x(x+4)(x-6)(x+3)}$

18. $\dfrac{36}{x-15}\,ft$

19. $\dfrac{3x+11}{x+6}\,m$

Additional Exercises, 7.3
Form III

1. $\dfrac{3m}{4n}$

2. $\dfrac{7m}{n}$

3. 4

4. $\dfrac{x+10}{11+x}$

5. 2x-5

6. $\dfrac{1}{x+12}$

7. $\dfrac{1}{x+7}$

8. $30x^2y$

9. $y(y-2)$

10. $2(x+9)(x+2)$

11. $(x-17)\,or\,(17-x)$

12. $(x+2)(x-5)(x-6)$

13. $\dfrac{12x}{20x^2}$

14. $9ab+2b$

15. $24x+9$

16. $\dfrac{-11(x-3)}{x(x-6)(x-3)}$

17. $\dfrac{x(x+3)(x+20)}{x(10x+2)(x+20)(x+5)}$

18. $\dfrac{44}{x+5}\,m$

19. $\dfrac{2x+15}{x+5}\,in$

Additional Exercises, 7.4
Form I

1. $\dfrac{33}{10x}$

2. $\dfrac{15}{x}$

3. $\dfrac{75w+3a^2}{5a}$

4. $\dfrac{9-3x}{x^2}$

5. $\dfrac{19}{5(x+4)}$

6. $\dfrac{7+56x-x^3}{x^2(8x+1)}$

7. $\dfrac{4-9x}{x}$

8. $\dfrac{x^2-4x+20}{(x-4)(x+4)(x+1)}$

9. $\dfrac{-62x-51}{9x}$

10. $-\dfrac{19}{x-8}$

11. $\dfrac{-25(x-6)}{x(x+5)(x-5)}$

12. $\dfrac{-a+15}{5(a+2)}$

13. $\dfrac{30x-48}{x(x-4)}$

14. $\dfrac{3x-42}{(x+6)(x-6)}$

15. $\dfrac{4(x-12)}{(x+8)(x-8)}$

Additional Exercises, 7.4
Form II

1. $\dfrac{47}{20x}$

2. $\dfrac{32n+3m^2}{8m}$

3. $\dfrac{12x+2}{3x^2}$

4. $\dfrac{4}{x-2}$

5. $\dfrac{16x+36}{7(x+4)(x-4)}$

6. $\dfrac{6y+2-y^3}{y^2(3y+1)}$

7. $\dfrac{8}{x-9}$

8. $\dfrac{4+5x}{x}$

9. $\dfrac{3x-11}{x-7}$

10. $\dfrac{5x^4-2}{x}$

11. $\dfrac{(x+5)}{(x+6)^2}$

12. $\dfrac{20x+46}{(x-4)^2(x+10)}$

13. $\dfrac{5x+66}{(x+2)(x-10)(x+10)}$

14. $\dfrac{8x^2-5x-100}{x}$, $15,994.95$

15. $\dfrac{4x-36}{(x+6)(x-6)}$

Additional Exercises, 7.4
Form III

1. $\dfrac{196}{143x}$

2. $\dfrac{10}{x}$

3. $\dfrac{77y+3x^2}{7x}$

4. $\dfrac{2-6x}{x^2}$

5. $\dfrac{23}{6(x+8)}$

6. $\dfrac{7+21x-x^3}{x^2(3x+1)}$

7. $\dfrac{2-5x}{x}$

8. $\dfrac{x^2-7x+32}{(x-4)(x+4)(x+1)}$

9. $\dfrac{-67x+30}{9x}$

10. $-\dfrac{3}{x-7}$

11. $\dfrac{(x+2)}{(x+3)^2}$

12. $-\dfrac{6x+31}{(x-7)(x+8)}$

13. $\dfrac{26x-40}{x(x-4)}$

14. $\dfrac{-2x-30}{(x+5)(x-5)}$

15. $\dfrac{6}{(x+8)}$

**Additional Exercises, 7.5
Form I**

1. 28

2. 0

3. $\dfrac{80}{3}$

4. -21

5. -30

6. **-15**

7. 6

8. 3

9. 1

10. -8

11. 3

12. -7

13. $\dfrac{ab}{a+b}$

14. $\dfrac{A-P}{Pt}$

15. $124°, 56°$

16. $20°, 70°$

**Additional Exercises, 7.5
Form II**

1. 14

2. 2

3. -7

4. -14

5. 5

6. 2, 3

7. 10

8. 1, -12

9. 12, -3

10. $\dfrac{1}{3}$

11. No solution

12. -8

13. $\dfrac{2A}{b}$

14. $\dfrac{2A-bh}{h}$

15. $35°, 145°$

16. $70°, 110°$

**Additional Exercises, 7.5
Form III**

1. 42

2. 0

3. 432

4. $-\dfrac{35}{3}$

5. 76

6. $-\dfrac{39}{2}$

7. 44

8. 6

9. 1

10. --8

11. 3

12. -7

13. $V = NG - RG$

14. $\dfrac{A-P}{Pt}$

15. $124°, 56°$

16. $\dfrac{330°}{7}, \dfrac{300°}{7}$

Additional Exercises, 7.6
Form I

1. 2

2. -6

3. $\dfrac{17}{6}$

4. $\dfrac{5}{2}$

5. $-\dfrac{13}{5}$

6. 15

7. $2\dfrac{2}{5}$

8. $6\dfrac{2}{3}$

9. Jenny – 25 min
 Shauna - 100 min

10. 5 mph

11. 20 mph

12. $1\dfrac{9}{11}$ mph

13. 12 minutes

14. 12

15. 5.5

Additional Exercises, 7.6
Form II

1. 12

2. $\dfrac{8}{7}$

3. 13

4. 9

5. 1

6. 3, -3

7. $1\dfrac{5}{7}$

8. $1\dfrac{3}{5}$

9. 12 minutes
 24 minutes

10. 16 mph

11. 4 and 6 mph

12. 3 and 4 mph

13. 35 mph in mountains
 63 mph level road

14. 2.5

15. 1.4

Additional Exercises, 7.6
Form III

1. 10

2. -6

3. $-\dfrac{1}{3}$

4. $\dfrac{5}{2}$

5. $\dfrac{24}{5}$

6. 19

7. $4\dfrac{4}{9}$

8. $13\dfrac{1}{5}$

9. Mary – 35 min
 Kate - 140 min

10. 5 mph

11. 20 mph

12. $1\dfrac{1}{2}$ mph

13. 4 minutes

14. 10.5

15. x = 2.5 in; y = 2 in

**Additional Exercises, 7.7
Form I**

1. direct

2. inverse

3. direct

4. $y = -\dfrac{1}{2}x$

5. $y = -\dfrac{1}{4}x$

6. $y = 8x$

7. $y = \dfrac{9}{x}$

8. $y = \dfrac{26}{x}$

9. $w = ks$

10. $a = \dfrac{k}{b}$

11. $a = \dfrac{k}{s}$

12. $y = 342$

13. $x = 9$

14. $y = 144$

15. $x = 100$

16. 28 gallons

17. 156.8 meters

**Additional Exercises, 7.7
Form II**

1. direct

2. inverse

3. direct

4. $y = \dfrac{1}{4}x$

5. $y = 8x$

6. $y = 2x$

7. $y = \dfrac{12}{x}$

8. $y = \dfrac{0.3}{x}$

9. $s = kt$

10. $t = k\sqrt{x}$

11. $t = \dfrac{k}{x^3}$

12. 27

13. 2.25

14. 2

15. $\dfrac{5}{9}$

16. $166.75

17. 1.25

**Additional Exercises, 7.7
Form III**

1. direct

2. inverse

3. direct

4. $y = -\dfrac{1}{2}x$

5. $y = \dfrac{1}{2}x$

6. $y = 9x$

7. $y = \dfrac{7}{x}$

8. $y = \dfrac{20}{x}$

9. $y = kt$

10. $a = kb$

11. $b = \dfrac{k}{y}$

12. 110

13. 4

14. 81

15. 96

16. 50 gallons

17. 156.8 meters

Additional Exercises, 7.8
Form I

1. $\dfrac{20}{39}$

2. $\dfrac{3}{10}$

3. $\dfrac{x(x+3)}{63}$

4. $\dfrac{x+1}{x-1}$

5. $\dfrac{k-6}{5}$

6. $\dfrac{3}{5}$

7. $\dfrac{2-7y}{7y}$

8. $\dfrac{3}{2x}$

9. $\dfrac{16}{x}$

10. $\dfrac{1+a}{1-a}$

11. $\dfrac{2-3r}{3r}$

12. $\dfrac{1+a}{1-a}$

13. $\dfrac{13}{24}$

14. $\dfrac{3n+5}{2n^2}$

15. $\dfrac{3f_1 f_2}{3f_1+3f_2}$

Additional Exercises, 7.8
Form II

1. $-\dfrac{5}{12}$

2. $\dfrac{7}{12}$

3. $-\dfrac{3}{5}$

4. $\dfrac{4}{45}$

5. 1

6. $\dfrac{x^2-6x}{4x^2+6}$

7. $\dfrac{2}{y-1}$

8. $\dfrac{2}{x+y}$

9. $2a(a-3)$

10. $\dfrac{5x^2+1}{5x^2-x}$

11. $\dfrac{11+6x}{-6x+4}$

12. $\dfrac{a}{a-b}$

13. $\dfrac{17}{40}$

14. $\dfrac{7n+4}{2n^2}$

15. $\dfrac{f_1 f_2}{f_1+f_2}$

Additional Exercises, 7.8
Form III

1. $\dfrac{55}{18}$

2. $\dfrac{24}{19}$

3. $\dfrac{x(x+5)}{6}$

4. $\dfrac{5+14x}{5-14x}$

5. $\dfrac{y-2}{5}$

6. $\dfrac{35}{54}$

7. $\dfrac{2-7y}{7y}$

8. $\dfrac{1}{2}$

9. $\dfrac{36}{x}$

10. $\dfrac{1+a}{1-a}$

11. $\dfrac{2-5r}{5r}$

12. $\dfrac{1+a}{1-a}$

13. $\dfrac{31}{48}$

14. $\dfrac{4(2+3n)}{n^2}$

15. $\dfrac{5f_1 f_2}{5f_1+5f_2}$

Chapter 8 Answers
Additional Exercises, 8.1
Form I

1. 2

2. $\dfrac{1}{9}$

3. -3

4. Not a real number

5. $\dfrac{10}{7}$

6. 7

7. -9

8. 2

9. 6

10. Not a real number

11. -2

12. 2.236

13. 9.695

14. 27 sq ft

15. w^7

16. $2x^7$

17. $\dfrac{7z^{14}}{3}$

18. $-2x^2y^4$

19. 0, 1, 2. $\sqrt{7} \approx 2.65$, 3

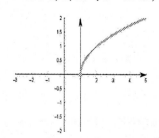

Additional Exercises, 8.1
Form II

1. 9

2. $\dfrac{1}{7}$

3. -6

4. Not a real number

5. $\dfrac{11}{2}$

6. 20

7. -4

8. -4

9. 3

10. Not a real number

11. -2

12. 6.782

13. 13.342

14. 862 sq ft

15. n^2

16. $4y^3$

17. $9z^{10}$

18. $-5xy^5$

19. 0, 1, 2. $\sqrt{6} \approx 2.45$, 3

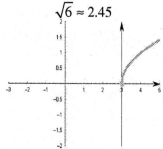

Additional Exercises, 8.1
Form III

1. 5

2. $\dfrac{1}{11}$

3. -6

4. Not a real number

5. $\dfrac{9}{4}$

6. 6

7. -2

8. -4

9. 4

10. Not a real number

11. -4

12. 1.732

13. 8.426

14. 22

15. n^{13}

16. $8x^3$

17. $\dfrac{11z^9}{7}$

18. $-8x^3y^6$

19. 0, 1, $\sqrt{2} \approx 1.41$, 2,
    $\sqrt{6} \approx 2.45$

Additional Exercises, 8.2
Form I

1. $3\sqrt{2}$

2. $2\sqrt{7}$

3. $2\sqrt{33}$

4. $\dfrac{7}{6}$

5. $\dfrac{5\sqrt{13}}{7}$

6. $-\dfrac{2\sqrt{17}}{9}$

7. $\dfrac{\sqrt{17}}{9}$

8. $y^3\sqrt{y}$

9. $9x\sqrt{6}$

10. $2x^3y^4\sqrt{31x}$

11. $\dfrac{\sqrt{15}}{x^2}$

12. $\dfrac{7\sqrt{5}}{x}$

13. $\dfrac{x^4\sqrt{x}}{7}$

14. $2\sqrt[3]{2}$

15. $4\sqrt[3]{2}$

16. $\dfrac{2\sqrt[3]{6}}{x^2}$

17. $9xy\sqrt[3]{xy^2}$

18. $5\sqrt[3]{2}$

19. $10\sqrt{15}$

Additional Exercises, 8.2
Form II

1. $5\sqrt{3}$

2. $3\sqrt{11}$

3. $6\sqrt{2}$

4. $\dfrac{3\sqrt{5}}{8}$

5. $-\dfrac{2\sqrt{21}}{5}$

6. $\dfrac{5\sqrt{3}}{9}$

7. $\dfrac{4\sqrt{3}}{15}$

8. $x^3\sqrt{x}$

9. $2y^6\sqrt{13}$

10. $3x^3y^4\sqrt{5}$

11. $\dfrac{2\sqrt{14}}{y^2}$

12. $\dfrac{7y\sqrt{2}}{x^5}$

13. $\dfrac{x^4\sqrt{x}}{y^{10}}$

14. 30

15. $2\sqrt{7}$

16. $\dfrac{\sqrt[3]{14}}{5}$

17. $3x^3y\sqrt[3]{13x}$

18. $3\sqrt[3]{10}$

19. $10\sqrt{13}$

Additional Exercises, 8.2
Form III

1. $5\sqrt{6}$

2. $5\sqrt{7}$

3. $2\sqrt{35}$

4. $\dfrac{5}{8}$

5. $\dfrac{17\sqrt{3}}{11}$

6. $-\dfrac{5\sqrt{23}}{8}$

7. $\dfrac{\sqrt{3}}{7}$

8. $y^5\sqrt{y}$

9. $8x\sqrt{7}$

10. $5x^3y^2\sqrt{2x}$

11. $\dfrac{\sqrt{46}}{x^5}$

12. $\dfrac{11y\sqrt{5}}{x^4}$

13. $\dfrac{x^3\sqrt{x}}{5y^{15}}$

14. $16\sqrt[3]{2}$

15. $5\sqrt[3]{2}$

16. $\dfrac{3\sqrt[4]{10}}{x^6}$

17. $5xy\sqrt[3]{xy^2}$

18. $2\sqrt[3]{11}$

19. $30\sqrt{3}$

Additional Exercises, 8.3
Form I

1. $7\sqrt{6}$

2. $16\sqrt{2}$

3. $52\sqrt{5}$

4. $-19\sqrt{3}$

5. $\dfrac{47\sqrt{2}}{30}$

6. $94\sqrt{2}$

7. $-2y + 4\sqrt{y}$

8. $\sqrt{x}$

9. $2x^2$

10. $\dfrac{16\sqrt{5}}{63}$

11. $66\sqrt{3x}$

12. $26x\sqrt{3x}$

13. $-3x^5\sqrt{x} + x\sqrt{x}$

14. $3x\sqrt{10} + 8x\sqrt{3}$

15. $2\sqrt[3]{y} - 3\sqrt[3]{2y}$

16. $21\sqrt[3]{x}$

17. $13x\sqrt{5} - 3\sqrt[3]{2}$

18. $\left(4\sqrt{6} + 20\right)$ ft

19. $6\sqrt{5}$ m

20. $11 + 3\sqrt{6}$ ft

Additional Exercises, 8.3
Form II

1. $-3\sqrt{7}$

2. $2\sqrt{10}$

3. $-7\sqrt{19}$

4. $9\sqrt{2}$

5. $-2\sqrt{5}$

6. $2\sqrt{6} - \sqrt{2}$

7. $3\sqrt{y} - 6y$

8. 0

9. $2x\sqrt{x}$

10. $\dfrac{3\sqrt{13}}{10}$

11. $-\sqrt{x}$

12. $15z\sqrt{10y}$

13. $3x\sqrt{5x} - 6x\sqrt{3}$

14. $10x\sqrt{2x} + 7\sqrt{x}$

15. $6\sqrt[3]{25} - \sqrt[3]{4}$

16. $6\sqrt[3]{2y}$

17. $12\sqrt[3]{x}$

18. $\left(16 + 4\sqrt{5}\right)$ ft

19. $12\sqrt{7}$ m

20. $71\sqrt{3}$ ft

Additional Exercises, 8.3
Form III

1. $-3\sqrt{3}$

2. $14\sqrt{11}$

3. $38\sqrt{10}$

4. $-19\sqrt{5}$

5. $\dfrac{28\sqrt{5}}{15}$

6. $47\sqrt{2}$

7. $-22\sqrt{3}$

8. $-3\sqrt{x}$

9. $-6x\sqrt{7x}$

10. $\dfrac{2\sqrt{13}}{3}$

11. $-37\sqrt{2a}$

12. $34x\sqrt{3x}$

13. $5x^2\sqrt{10} - x^3\sqrt{5x}$

14. $9x^3\sqrt{6x} - \sqrt{5y}$

15. $2\sqrt[3]{y} - 4\sqrt[3]{2y}$

16. $28\sqrt[3]{x}$

17. $9x\sqrt{5} - 2\sqrt[3]{3}$

18. $6\sqrt{3} + 14$ ft

19. $10\sqrt{7}$ m

20. $6\sqrt{5} + 24$ ft

Additional Exercises, 8.4
Form I

1. $\sqrt{10}$

2. $2\sqrt{7}$

3. 60

4. $3y$

5. $36y$

6. $2\sqrt{6xy}$

7. $2x\sqrt{5xy}$

8. $21+7\sqrt{3}$

9. $\sqrt{65}+\sqrt{15}-\sqrt{39}-3$

10. $626+54\sqrt{11}$

11. $180+16\sqrt{11}$

12. $4x-32\sqrt{x}+64$

13. 5

14. $2\sqrt{7}$

15. $3x^2 y\sqrt{7x}$

16. $\dfrac{\sqrt{143}}{13}$

17. $\dfrac{\sqrt{15}}{10}$

18. $2\sqrt{17}+8$

19. $3+\sqrt{6}+\sqrt{3}+\sqrt{2}$

20. $48\sqrt{6}$ sq in

Additional Exercises, 8.4
Form II

1. 10

2. 14

3. $3\sqrt{11}$

4. $17x$

5. $49x$

6. $5\sqrt{2xy}$

7. $2xy\sqrt{3y}$

8. $\sqrt{35}+\sqrt{5}$

9. -9

10. $\sqrt{35}+\sqrt{30}-\sqrt{42}-6$

11. $x-8\sqrt{x}+16$

12. $3y+4\sqrt{3y}+4$

13. 2

14. $3\sqrt{2}$

15. $2xy\sqrt{3x}$

16. $\dfrac{\sqrt{70}}{7}$

17. $\dfrac{\sqrt{6y}}{6y}$

18. $\dfrac{9\sqrt{x}+54}{x-36}$

19. $2\sqrt{2}-\sqrt{3}$

20. $45\sqrt{91}$ sq in

Additional Exercises, 8.4
Form III

1. $\sqrt{6}$

2. $5\sqrt{2}$

3. 42

4. $21y$

5. $121y$

6. $2\sqrt{5xy}$

7. $xy^2\sqrt{42x}$

8. $10+5\sqrt{2}$

9. $\sqrt{35}+\sqrt{65}-\sqrt{91}-13$

10. $308+52\sqrt{17}$

11. $460+96\sqrt{11}$

12. $36x-24\sqrt{x}+4$

13. 4

14. $2\sqrt{5}$

15. $2x^2 y\sqrt{7x}$

16. $\dfrac{\sqrt{15}}{3}$

17. $\dfrac{\sqrt{14}}{35}$

18. $6\sqrt{26}+30$

19. $6+\sqrt{30}+\sqrt{6}+\sqrt{5}$

20. $75\sqrt{2}$ sq in

Additional Exercises, 8.5
Form I

1. 625

2. 34

3. 9

4. 289

5. 7

6. 7

7. $\frac{8}{3}$

8. $\frac{22}{3}$

9. $\frac{6}{7}$

10. 9

11. 4

12. 2

13. 0, -5

14. 9

15. 64

16. no real solution

17. 9

18. $\frac{47}{2}$

Additional Exercises, 8.5
Form II

1. 49

2. 79

3. 9

4. 16

5. 25

6. no real solution

7. 7

8. 9

9. 3

10. 2

11. 4

12. 5

13. 7

14. 0, -4

15. 16

16. 4

17. 3

18. 9

Additional Exercises, 8.5
Form III

1. 1296

2. 2

3. 2

4. 49

5. $\frac{44}{3}$

6. $\frac{73}{5}$

7. 4

8. 3

9. $\frac{17}{5}$

10. $\frac{7}{3}$

11. 2

12. 2

13. 0, -4

14. 4

15. 36

16. no solution

17. 49

18. $\frac{2}{5}$

**Additional Exercises, 8.6
Form I**

1. 25

2. $5\sqrt{7} \approx 13.23$

3. $\sqrt{13} \approx 3.61$

4. 20

5. $\sqrt{31} \approx 5.57$

6. $2\sqrt{85} \approx 18.44$

7. 18

8. $\sqrt{22} \approx 4.7$

9. 6.71 ft

10. 27.86 ft

11. 13 ft

12. 29 ft

13. 12 in

14. 44 mph

15. $2\sqrt{13} \approx 7.21$

16. $5\sqrt{5} \approx 11.18$

17. $2\sqrt{10} \approx 6.32$

**Additional Exercises, 8.6
Form II**

1. $3\sqrt{13} \approx 10.82$

2. $\sqrt{30} \approx 5.48$

3. $2\sqrt{10} \approx 6.32$

4. $5\sqrt{2} \approx 7.07$

5. $\sqrt{109} \approx 10.44$

6. $3\sqrt{5} \approx 6.71$

7. $4\sqrt{5} \approx 8.94$

8. $3\sqrt{6} \approx 7.35$

9. 8.54 ft

10. 7.81 ft

11. 8 ft

12. 19 ft

13. 13.4 in

14. 45 mph

15. $\sqrt{185} \approx 13.6$

16. $5\sqrt{2} \approx 7.07$

17. $2\sqrt{26} \approx 10.2$

**Additional Exercises, 8.6
Form III**

1. $7\sqrt{2} \approx 9.9$

2. $\sqrt{181} \approx 13.45$

3. 20

4. 8

5. $\sqrt{22} \approx 4.7$

6. $\sqrt{317} \approx 17.8$

7. 17

8. $\sqrt{31} \approx 5.57$

9. 7.21 ft

10. 15.23 ft

11. 15 ft

12. 25 ft

13. 16.6 in

14. 49 mph

15. $5\sqrt{5} \approx 11.18$

16. $3\sqrt{5} \approx 6.71$

17. $2\sqrt{5} \approx 4.47$

Additional Exercises, 8.7
Form I

1. 9

2. 5

3. -3

4. -2

5. $\dfrac{3}{4}$

6. $-\dfrac{3}{4}$

7. 81

8. 32

9. $\dfrac{1}{9}$

10. $\dfrac{1}{216}$

11. $\dfrac{121}{81}$

12. $\dfrac{1}{4}$

13. 5

14. $\sqrt[3]{2}$

15. $\dfrac{1}{2}$

16. $\sqrt{c}$

17. $x^{1/4}$

Additional Exercises, 8.7
Form II

1. 12

2. 4

3. -2

4. -3

5. $\dfrac{2}{3}$

6. $-\dfrac{2}{3}$

7. 256

8. 243

9. $\dfrac{1}{4}$

10. $\dfrac{1}{512}$

11. 25

12. $\dfrac{1}{3}$

13. 2

14. $4^{3/4}$

15. $\dfrac{1}{5^{7/4}}$

16. $\dfrac{1}{\sqrt{y}}$

17. $\dfrac{9m^{1/3}n^2}{16}$

Additional Exercises, 8.7
Form III

1. 8

2. 6

3. -4

4. -2

5. $\dfrac{3}{2}$

6. $\dfrac{1}{8}$

7. $\dfrac{1}{2}$

8. $\dfrac{1}{125}$

9. $\dfrac{27}{125}$

10. $\dfrac{1}{125}$

11. $\dfrac{27}{8}$

12. $\dfrac{1}{12}$

13. 7

14. $5xy^2z^3$

15. $y^{4/3}$

16. $\dfrac{2z^3}{w}$

17. $\dfrac{y^9}{x^8}$

Chapter 9 Answers
Additional Exercises, 9.1
Form I

1. 7, -7

2. 6, -6

3. 12, -12

4. $\pm\sqrt{15}$,

5. $\pm\dfrac{1}{6}$

6. No real solution

7. $\pm\dfrac{\sqrt{170}}{10}$

8. $\pm\sqrt{17}$

9. $\pm\sqrt{13}$

10. 10, -10

11. 6, -12

12. 7, -9

13. $5\pm\sqrt{71}$

14. $0, \dfrac{1}{4}$

15. $\dfrac{4}{3}, -4$

16. $\dfrac{2}{5}, -2$

17. $-\dfrac{2}{3}, 2$

18. $6\pm\sqrt{15}$

Additional Exercises, 9.1
Form II

1. 11, -11

2. 4, -4

3. 5, -5

4. $\pm7\sqrt{2}$

5. $\pm\dfrac{1}{8}$

6. No real solution

7. $\pm\dfrac{\sqrt{30}}{10}$

8. $\pm\dfrac{5\sqrt{6}}{6}$

9. $\pm\sqrt{11}$

10. $\pm2\sqrt{7}$

11. 10, -2

12. -5, -11

13. $12\pm\sqrt{3}$

14. $0, \dfrac{1}{2}$

15. 3, 8

16. $\dfrac{6\pm3\sqrt{6}}{5}$

17. $\dfrac{7\pm4\sqrt{5}}{4}$

18. 4.47 m

Additional Exercises, 9.1
Form III

1. 13, -13

2. 5, -5

3. 14, -14

4. $-\sqrt{13}, \sqrt{13}$

5. $\dfrac{1}{4}, -\dfrac{1}{4}$

6. No real solution

7. $\dfrac{\sqrt{22}}{2}, -\dfrac{\sqrt{22}}{2}$

8. $\dfrac{\sqrt{406}}{14}, -\dfrac{\sqrt{406}}{14}$

9. $\sqrt{14}, -\sqrt{14}$

10. $\dfrac{\sqrt{145}}{5}, -\dfrac{\sqrt{145}}{5}$

11. 0, -4

12. -2, -14

13. $2+\sqrt{89}, 2-\sqrt{89}$

14. $0, -\dfrac{2}{7}$

15. No real solution

16. $\dfrac{-3+3\sqrt{5}}{5}, \dfrac{-3-3\sqrt{5}}{5}$

17. $-\dfrac{2}{5}, 2$

18. 24.75 m

Additional Exercises, 9.2
Form I

1. 1, 7

2. $1 \pm \sqrt{5}$

3. $3 \pm \sqrt{13}$

4. $\dfrac{-9 \pm \sqrt{101}}{2}$

5. 0, 20

6. -4, 1

7. $-\dfrac{5}{4}, \dfrac{1}{4}$

8. 3, 2

9. 2, -3

10. 3, 5

11. -4, 1

12. -3, 4

13. No real solution

14. $\dfrac{5}{2}, -2$

15. $\dfrac{5 \pm \sqrt{89}}{4}$

16. $\dfrac{2 \pm \sqrt{13}}{3}$

17. $\dfrac{7}{4}, -1$

18. No real solution

Additional Exercises, 9.2
Form II

1. -3, -9

2. 8, -2

3. $-2 \pm \sqrt{11}$

4. $-4 \pm 2\sqrt{7}$

5. 0, 10

6. $\dfrac{-3 \pm \sqrt{33}}{2}$

7. $\dfrac{9 \pm \sqrt{97}}{2}$

8. $\dfrac{7 \pm \sqrt{37}}{2}$

9. -2, -9

10. No real solution

11. 1, -6

12. 10, -3

13. 6, -2

14. $-1 \pm \dfrac{2\sqrt{7}}{7}$

15. $\dfrac{5 \pm \sqrt{39}}{2}$

16. $\dfrac{3 \pm \sqrt{14}}{2}$

17. No real solution

18. $h = -14$

Additional Exercises, 9.2
Form III

1. 1, 5

2. $\dfrac{-9 \pm \sqrt{89}}{2}$

3. $\dfrac{-2 \pm \sqrt{13}}{3}$

4. 0, 5

5. 1, 5

6. $5 \pm \sqrt{29}$

7. $\dfrac{-9 \pm 3\sqrt{5}}{2}$

8. 2, 6

9. $\dfrac{-3 \pm \sqrt{37}}{2}$

10. $\dfrac{-9 \pm \sqrt{69}}{2}$

11. -5, 3

12. -5, -3

13. 3, 6

14. $1 \pm \sqrt{3}$

15. $\dfrac{3 \pm \sqrt{17}}{2}$

16. $\dfrac{7}{2}, -1$

17. $-\dfrac{7}{6}, \dfrac{1}{6}$

18. $h = 24$

Additional Exercises, 9.3
Form I

1. 1, -8

2. $\dfrac{4}{3}, -1$

3. $\dfrac{1 \pm \sqrt{21}}{4}$

4. Not a real number

5. $\pm \dfrac{2}{5}$

6. $\pm\sqrt{7}$

7. $7 \pm \sqrt{19}$

8. $3 \pm \sqrt{2}$

9. 2, -13

10. $\dfrac{-3 \pm \sqrt{3}}{2}$

11. $\pm \dfrac{1}{2}$

12. $\dfrac{-3 \pm \sqrt{21}}{2}$

13. $-3 \pm \sqrt{15}$

14. $1 \pm \sqrt{7}$

15. $\dfrac{7}{2}, -\dfrac{1}{2}$

Additional Exercises, 9.3
Form II

1. -1, 7

2. 3, -2

3. $-1, -\dfrac{2}{5}$

4. $\dfrac{-5 \pm \sqrt{19}}{2}$

5. $\pm \dfrac{1}{6}$

6. 8, -7

7. $\dfrac{9 \pm \sqrt{77}}{2}$

8. $4 \pm \sqrt{5}$

9. Not a real number

10. $\dfrac{-1 \pm \sqrt{65}}{4}$

11. $\pm\sqrt{2}$

12. Not a real number

13. $\dfrac{-1 \pm \sqrt{17}}{8}$

14. $\dfrac{2}{3}, -\dfrac{1}{5}$

15. $\dfrac{3 \pm \sqrt{13}}{8}$

Additional Exercises, 9.3
Form III

1. -2, -4

2. Not a real number

3. $-\dfrac{1}{5}, -1$

4. Not a real number

5. $\pm \dfrac{1}{10}$

6. $3 \pm \sqrt{3}$

7. $-1, -\dfrac{5}{4}$

8. $\dfrac{5 \pm \sqrt{37}}{2}$

9. -4, 13

10. $\dfrac{-4 \pm 2\sqrt{10}}{3}$

11. $\pm 2\sqrt{2}$

12. $\dfrac{6}{5}, -\dfrac{1}{3}$

13. $1 \pm \sqrt{6}$

14. $1 \pm \sqrt{19}$

15. $-\dfrac{1}{4}, -\dfrac{1}{2}$

Additional Exercises, 9.4
Form I

1. $3i$

2. $2i$

3. $4i\sqrt{6}$

4. $11+i$

5. $-18-16i$

6. $-17i$

7. $-23+5i$

8. $-15-24i$

9. $79+52i$

10. 90

11. $-77+36i$

12. $13-4i$

13. $\dfrac{101}{130}+\dfrac{37}{130}i$

14. $-9\pm 8i$

15. $\dfrac{1\pm 2i\sqrt{2}}{9}$

16. $-1\pm 5i$

17. $8i,-8i$

18. $\dfrac{1}{4}\pm\dfrac{i\sqrt{79}}{4}$

Additional Exercises, 9.4
Form II

1. $9i$

2. $12i$

3. $4i\sqrt{7}$

4. $6+i$

5. $-9+i$

6. -9

7. $-3i$

8. $-28-28i$

9. $69+45i$

10. 89

11. $-17+144i$

12. $3-3i$

13. $\dfrac{3}{10}+\dfrac{1}{10}i$

14. $-6\pm 4i$

15. $\dfrac{1\pm 3i\sqrt{3}}{3}$

16. $-2\pm 3i$

17. $2i,-2i$

18. $\dfrac{1}{4}\pm\dfrac{i\sqrt{23}}{4}$

Additional Exercises, 9.4
Form III

1. $11i$

2. $5i$

3. $6i\sqrt{5}$

4. $7+i$

5. $-7+7i$

6. $9+7i$

7. $-14-17i$

8. $-9-9i$

9. $63-3i$

10. 145

11. $-15+112i$

12. $-2+2i$

13. $\dfrac{27}{25}+\dfrac{11}{25}i$

14. $-7\pm 8i$

15. $\dfrac{1\pm 2i\sqrt{2}}{2}$

16. $-2\pm 4i$

17. $10i,-10i$

18. $\dfrac{3}{4}\pm\dfrac{i\sqrt{39}}{4}$

**Additional Exercises, 9.5
Form I**

1.

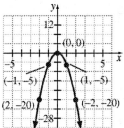

2.

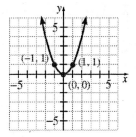

3.

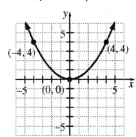

4.

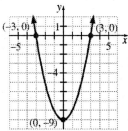

5.

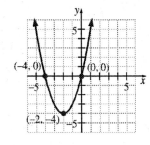

6.

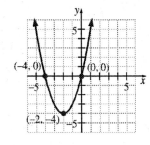

7.

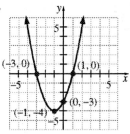

8.

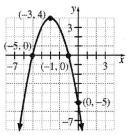

9.

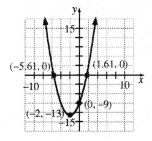

10.

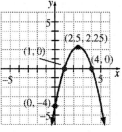

11.

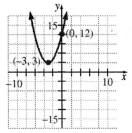

12.

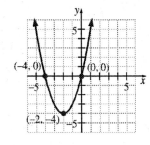

13.

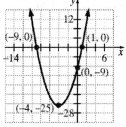

**Additional Exercises, 9.5
Form II**

1.

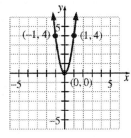

2.

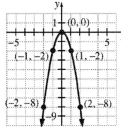

3.

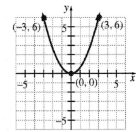

4.

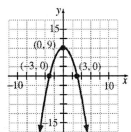

5.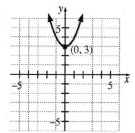

6.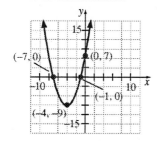

7.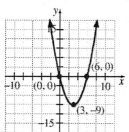

8.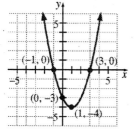

9.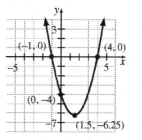

10.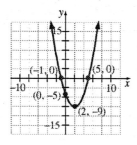

11.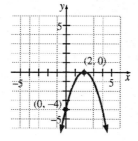

12.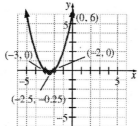

13.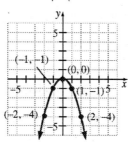

Additional Exercises, 9.5
Form III

1.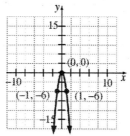

2.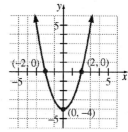

3.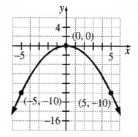

4.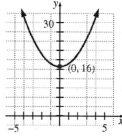

5.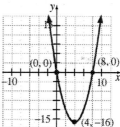

6.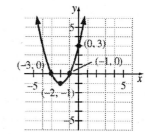

7.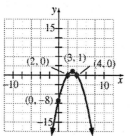

8.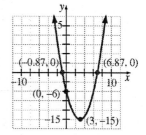

9.

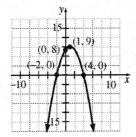

10.

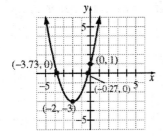

11.

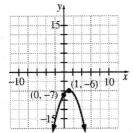

12.

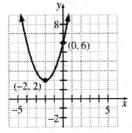

13.

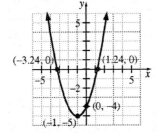

Small Group Formats

I. Structures. Many researchers agree that assigning a task to each student in a cooperative learning group assists in the learning process of the group. The following list describes various group structures and provides possible task assignments. Feel free to photocopy and distribute this list to the students.

    A. Small group of 3 students. Assign one of the following tasks to each member of the group.

        1. Recorder: This person is responsible for recording the group's answers on the worksheet.

        2. Supervisor: This person is responsible for making certain that the group stays on task and is discussing information relevant to the problem at hand.

        3. Reader/Question Interpreter: This person is responsible for reading the question aloud and making certain that the group understands what is being asked. If the group has questions, this person will contact the instructor and explain the group's questions.

    B. Small group of 4 students. Assign the following tasks to each member of the group.

        1. Recorder: same as above

        2. Supervisor: same as above

        3. Reader/Question Interpreter: same as above

        4. Quality Assurance/Reporter: This person is responsible for making certain that the recorded answer is as accurate as possible and that if a verbal explanation of the answer is required, this person will present it. (This task may be handled by the recorder in the 3-person group setting.)

    C. Think and Pair (2 students). Students are asked (usually during lecture) to work a problem or two on their own. When completed, they share their answer with the person next to them and come to a consensus on what the correct answer is. The instructor may then ask certain pairs to verbally share their answers with the class or present them more formally on the board. This method assists in class discussion as a whole, and works well if the instructor would like the students to have the time to work some problems on their own, but not take the time to get the class into a formal group setting.

II. Game Formats.

A. "The Math is Right" game format. Objective of the game is to provide students with a fun way to learn algebraic skills. The game is most useful for sections of the text where learning drill and practice techniques are essential for student success. Group structure A or B listed earlier would be appropriate for this game. The following points are guidelines for "The Math is Right."

- Provide one sheet of exercises with answer blanks per group. (Have students use separate sheets of scratch paper.) The instructor will announce when the groups may begin.

- When a group is finished with all exercises, have the Reporter call the instructor over to the group to check all answers.

- After the instructor does a quick visual check of the answers, the instructor will report to the group how many answers they have correct. However the instructor will not indicate which answers are incorrect.

- The group will then have another try at the exercises and attempt to locate the errors before having the chance to resubmit their work. First group to get all exercises correct is the winner. (Perhaps this team will get 10 points, the second team to finish may get 8 points, etc. or this activity may be used for one or two extra credit points on a Chapter Test.)

B. Relay Race. Divide the class in groups of five. One or two groups can have less than five, but none should have more than five. Students in each group should be in a row, they will not work together. Give the first student problem number 1. When he obtains his answer, he will write it on a piece of paper and give his answer to the next student. The second student's problem will contain instructions on what to do with the number or expression received from the first student. The second student will obtain his answer and write it on a piece of paper and hand it to the third student. The first group with the correct answer after problem 5 is the winner. (If a group has four students, the first student will work the first problem and the fifth problem.)

Section 1.3 Fractions

Objective: Understand the concepts of fractions.
Suggested Format: Group A Structure A
Time: 15 minutes

Find the indicated fractional portion of each word and record it in the corresponding blank. Compose a hidden message by reading down the columns when you have finished.

First $\dfrac{1}{2}$ of will   _____   First $\dfrac{3}{8}$ of sentence   _____

Last $\dfrac{1}{3}$ of length   _____   Last $\dfrac{1}{3}$ of redeem   _____

First $\dfrac{1}{2}$ of Friday   _____   Last $\dfrac{3}{7}$ of parties   _____

Last $\dfrac{2}{3}$ of trends   _____   First $\dfrac{1}{2}$ of jump   _____

First $\dfrac{1}{3}$ of linear   _____   First $\dfrac{1}{3}$ of liable   _____

Last $\dfrac{1}{2}$ of bike   _____   First $\dfrac{1}{3}$ usable   _____

Last $\dfrac{4}{9}$ of determine   _____   First $\dfrac{2}{7}$ of capable   _____

First $\dfrac{2}{5}$ of which   _____   First $\dfrac{1}{4}$ of estimate _____

Last $\dfrac{1}{7}$ of multiplication   _____   Last $\dfrac{2}{7}$ of popular   _____

Last $\dfrac{3}{4}$ of need   _____

The message is _____

Sections 1.5 Adding Real Numbers & 1.6 Subtracting Real Numbers

Objective: Application of Real Numbers.
Suggested Format: Group A Structure A
Time: 15 minutes

Find the balance of the checking account after each activity.

Action	Amount	Balance
Beginning Balance		$865.34
Deposit Paycheck	$462.83	
Pay Rent	$450.00	
Pay Electronic Bill	$75.29	
Pay Telephone Bill	$57.81	
Write a check for cash	$150.00	

Section 2.1 Simplifying Algebraic Expressions

Objective: Combining like terms.
Suggested Format: Relay Race
Time: 15 minutes

(Instructors: Make enough copies for each group. Cut the problems apart and hand a copy of problem one to the first student in each group, problem 2 to the second student, etc.)

Problem 1: $3x - 7x - 6 + 8$

Write your answer on a sheet of paper and hand it to the next student.

Problem 2: Add the expression you were given to $3x - 12$

Write your answer on a sheet of paper and hand it to the next student.

Problem 3: Subtract the expression you were given from $3x - 6$

Write your answer on a sheet of paper and hand it to the next student.

Problem 4: Add the expression you were given to $-5x + 8$

Write your answer on a sheet of paper and hand it to the next student.

Problem 5: Subtract $5x - 8$ from the expression you were given.

When you have your answer, raise your hand and the instructor will see if it is correct.

Section 2.4 Solving Linear Equations

Objective: Practice in using techniques for solving equations.
Suggested Format: Group Structure B
Time: 20 minutes

I. Solve each equation. Write the answer in the box that corresponds to the letter in the equation.

$3a + 5 = 4a + 1$ $2b - b = 9$

$3c + 4 = 2c + 3c$ $4(d - 1) = d + 5$

$5(e - 6) + 8 = e - 2$ $2(f - 3) + 7 = 3f - 6$

$\dfrac{1}{2}g + 1 = \dfrac{1}{4}g + 3$ $3h - 6 = 2h - 5$

$\dfrac{1}{2}i = 3$

$a =$	$b =$	$c =$
$d =$	$e =$	$f =$
$g =$	$h =$	$i =$

II. Look at just the numbers in the box. (Ignore the letters). Do you notice any pattern?

Section 3.1 Reading Graphs and the Rectangular Coordinate System

Objective: Interpret Real Data.
Suggested Format: Group Structure A or B
Time: 15 minutes

Enrollment at William's College, 2008

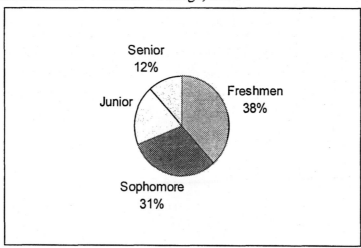

Use the graph to answer the following questions.

1. What percent of the total student body were Freshmen?   _____

2. What percent of the total student body were Sophomores?   _____

3. What percent of the total student body were Juniors?   _____

4. What percent of the total student body were Seniors?   _____

The total enrollment was 8,480.

5. How many students were Freshmen?   _____

6. How many students were Sophomores?   _____

7. How many students were Juniors?   _____

8. How many students were Seniors?   _____

Section 3.4 Slope and Rate of Change

Objective: Find the slope of a line for a practical application.
Suggested Format: Group Structure A
Time: 10 minutes

Use the information in each stated problem to write two points then use the two points to find the slope of a line going through those two points.

1. A business had 580 employees in 2003 and 780 employees in 2008. Find the rate of change (the slope of the line). HINT: Let y by the number of employees. If you let $x = 0$ represent the year 2003, 2008 will be $x = ?$ Explain what the slope means.

2. A piece of office equipment cost $20,000 new. In ten years it will be worth $5000. Find the rate of depreciation (slope). HINT: Let $y =$ the value of the machine. Let $x = 0$ be the year the machine was purchased. Explain what the slope means.

Section 3.5 Equations of Lines

Objective: Provide a practical application of equations of lines.
Suggested Format: Group Structure B
Time: 20 minutes

1. A business had 580 employees in 2003 and 780 employees in 2008. Find the rate of change (the slope of the line). HINT: Let y by the number of employees. If you let $x = 0$ represent the year 2003, 2008 will be $x = ?$
   (a) Find the slope of the line and the equation that represents the data.

   (b) How many employees will the business have in 2010?

   (c) In what year will the number of employees be 980?

2. A piece of office equipment cost $20,000 new. In ten years it will be worth $5000. Find the rate of depreciation (slope). HINT: Let $y =$ the value of the machine. Let $x = 0$ be the year the machine was purchased.
   (a) Find the slope of the line and the equation that represents the data.

   (b) What will be the value of the equipment in 5 years?

   (c) After how many years will the value of the equipment be $15,500?

A-9

Section 4.4 Systems of Linear Equations and Problem Solving

Objective: Provide a practical application of systems of equations of lines..
Suggested Format: Group Structure B
Time: 15 minutes

To encourage car pooling, a toll road decided to charge less for vehicles with 3 or more passengers. The toll is normally $3 per vehicle, but the toll for a car with 3 or more passengers is reduced to $2 per vehicle.

The first day the new prices went in to effect, the supervisor told Anne to count how many vehicles of each type went through her toll booth. Anne knew that an automatic counter kept track of the total number of vehicles that went by her booth, so she did count the number of each type of vehicle that went by. At the end of her shift, she had collected $2150 and the automatic counter told her that a total of 800 vehicles had passed by. Write a system of equations and solve so Anne can tell her supervisor how many vehicles she charged $3 and how many she charged $2.

Section 4.6 Systems of Linear Inequalities

Objective: Provide a practical application of systems of inequalities.
Suggested Format: Group Structure B
Time: 20 minutes

Jan make bracelets and necklaces to sell at an arts and crafts fair. She has 20 hours at most to work on making more jewelry. It takes her 4 hours to make 1 bracelet and 1 hour to make 1 necklace. The only needs 11 more pieces to fill her display, so she wants to make 11 or less pieces.

Write a system of inequalities to model what she needs (remember x and y need to positive). Then graph the system.

	Bracelets x	Necklaces y	
Hours			≤ 20
Number of items			≤ 11
	x		≤ 0
		y	≤ 0

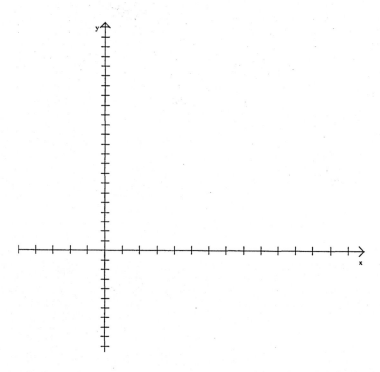

Find a point that satisfies the condition. Explain what that point represents.

Section 5.2 Adding and Subtracting Polynomials

Objective: Provide practice with adding and subtracting polynomial expressions.
Suggested Format: The Math is Right Game
Time: 15 minutes

Express the perimeter of each figure as a polynomial expression.

1.

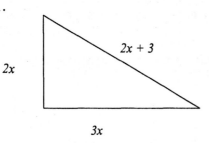

2.

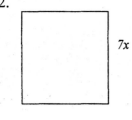

3.

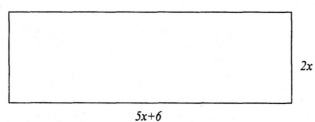

4.

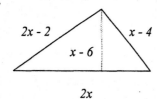

Section 5.3 Multiplying Polynomials

Objective: Provide practice with multiplying polynomial expressions.
Suggested Format: The Math is Right Game
Time: 15 minutes

Express the area of each figure as a polynomial expression.

1.

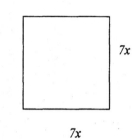

2.

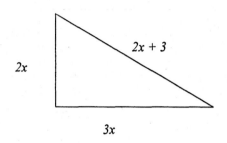

3.

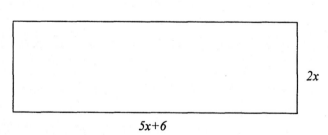

4.

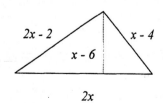

Chapter 6 Integrated Review – Choosing a Factoring Strategy

Objective: Provide practice with deciding on a factoring strategy.
Suggested Format: Group A or B
Time: 20 minutes

I. Factor the polynomials the find an expression for the width and an expression for the length. The use the length and the width to find an expression for the perimeter of each figure.

1. $A = x^2 + 2x - 15$ $l = \underline{\hspace{1cm}}$ $w = \underline{\hspace{1cm}}$ $P = \underline{\hspace{1cm}}$

2. $A = x^2 - 49$ $l = \underline{\hspace{1cm}}$ $w = \underline{\hspace{1cm}}$ $P = \underline{\hspace{1cm}}$

3. $A = 6x^2 + 7x - 20$ $l = \underline{\hspace{1cm}}$ $w = \underline{\hspace{1cm}}$ $P = \underline{\hspace{1cm}}$

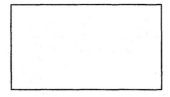

4. $A = 6x^2 - x - 15$ $l = \underline{\hspace{1cm}}$ $w = \underline{\hspace{1cm}}$ $P = \underline{\hspace{1cm}}$

5. $A = 9x^2 + 12x + 4$ $s = \underline{\hspace{1cm}}$ $P = \underline{\hspace{1cm}}$

Section 6.6 Solving Quadratic Equations by Factoring

Objective: Discover rules about the solutions to quadratic equations.
Suggested Format: Group A or B
Time: 20 minutes

I. Solve each of the following quadratic equations by factoring. Write both answers in
   column A.

	A	B	C	D	E
$x^2 + 3x - 10 = 0$					
$x^2 + x - 6 = 0$					
$2x^2 + 5x - 3 = 0$					
$3x^2 - 10x - 8 = 0$					
$x^2 - 3x - 18 = 0$					
$6x^2 + 23x - 4 = 0$					
$x^2 - 7x - 12 = 0$					
$6x^2 - 11x - 10 = 0$					
$5x^2 - 13x - 6 = 0$					
$7x^2 - 11x - 6 = 0$					

II. Add the two solutions to each equation. Write the sum in column B.

III. Each equation is written in the form $ax^2 + bx + c = 0$. Find the quotient $\dfrac{b}{a}$ for each
   equation and write that value in column C.

IV. Write the product of the two solutions in column D.

V. Each equation is written in the form $ax^2 + bx + c = 0$. Find the quotient $\dfrac{a}{c}$ for each
   equation and write that value in column C.

Study columns B and C. Can you define the relationship between the sum of the answers
and the quotient $\dfrac{b}{a}$?

Study columns D and E. Can you define the relationship between the product of the
answer and the quotient $\dfrac{a}{c}$

Chapter 7 Integrated Review – Summary on Rational Expressions

Objective: Provide practice adding and multiplying radical expressions.
Suggested Format: Group A or B
Time: 20 minutes

Find an expression for the perimeter and area of each figure.

1. $P =$ _____ $A =$ _____

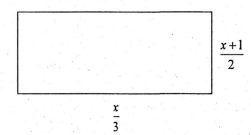

2. $P =$ _____ $A =$ _____

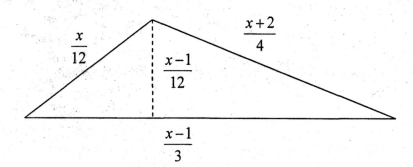

3. $P =$ _____ $A =$ _____

Section 7.6 Proportion and Problem Solving with Rational Equations

Objective: Provide a better understanding of problem solving.
Suggested Format: Group A or B
Time: 15 minutes

Divide each group into two smaller group.

First Group:
A. Solve the following problem.
    An airplane can fly 500 miles with the wind in 2 hours. In the same amount of time, it flies 300 miles against the wind. Find the air speed of the plane in still air and the wind speed.

B. Write a problem about an airplane flying with the wind and against the wind. Use problem A as an example. (Hint: start by deciding on what the answers will be and then write the problem.)

C. Give the problem you wrote to the second group and have them solve it.

Second Group:
A. Solve the following problem.
    A boat goes upstream 9 miles in one hour. In the same amount of time it goes 11 miles downstream. Find the speed of the boat in still water and the speed of the current in the river.

B. Write a problem about a boat going upstream and downstream. Use problem A as an example. (Hint: start by deciding on what the answers will be and then write the problem.)

C. Give the problem you wrote to the first group and have them solve it.

Section 8.2 Simplifying Radicals

Objective: Use radicals to find the distance between two points.
Suggested Format: Group A or B
Time: 10 minutes

The distance formula can be used to find the distance between and two points (x_1, y_1) and (x_2, y_2).

Distance formula: $D = \sqrt{(x_2 - x_1) + (y_2 - y_1)}$

Calculate the distances between the following points. Give an exact answer and then give an approximate answer to the nearest hundredth of a unit.

1. $(-2, 5)$ and $(-6, 3)$

2. $(0, 3)$ and $(-2, 4)$

Section 8.6 Radical Equations and Problem Solving

Objective: use the Pythagorean Theorem.

Suggested Format: Group B

Time: 20 minutes

Find the hypotenuse of each right triangle using the Pythagorean Theorem.

1. $a = 4$, $b = 3$, $c =$ _____

2. $a = 8$, $b = 6$, $c =$ _____

3. $a = 12$, $b = 9$, $c =$ _____

4. $a = 16$, $b = 12$, $c =$ _____

Study the previous problems and see if you can solve the next problem without using the Pythagorean Theorem.

5. $a = 20$, $b = 15$, $c =$ _____

Section 9.3 Solving Quadratic Equations by the Quadratic Formula

Objective: Derive the Quadratic Formula.
Suggested Format: Group A
Time: 15 minutes

Study the example where your textbook derived the quadratic formula. Shut your book and notes. Complete the square to derive the quadratic formula.

$$ax^2 + bx + c = 0$$

Section 9.5 Graphing Quadratic Equations

Objective: Seeing patterns in the graphs of quadratic equations.
Suggested Format: Group B
Time: 20 minutes

Have each member of the group graph one of the following quadratic equations.

1. $y = x^2$

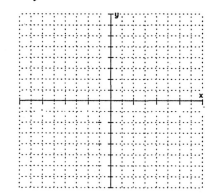

2. $y = x^2 + 2$

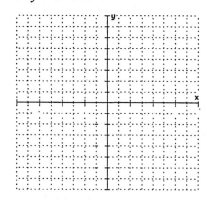

3. $y = x^2 - 2$

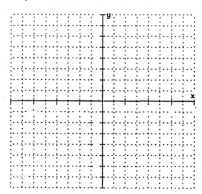

4. $y = x^2 + 3$

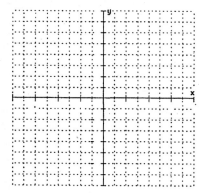

Compare the four graphs. Can you sketch the graph of $y = x^2 - 3$ without finding any points?

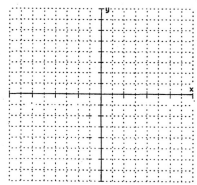

Group Activity Answers

Group Activity 1.3
With friends like mine who needs enemies, Julius Caesar

Group Activity 1.5 and 1.6
Balance
1328.17
878.17
802.88
745.07
595.07

Group Activity 2.1
1. $-4x+2$
2. $-x-10$
3. $4x+4$
4. $-x+12$
5. $-6x+20$

Group Activity 2.4

4	9	2
3	5	7
8	1	6

Group Activity 3.1
1. 38%
2. 31%
3. 19%
4. 12%
5. 3222
6. 2629
7. 1611
8. 1018

Group Activity 3.4
1. 40 new employees per year
2. $-\$1500$ per year

Group Activity 3.6
1a. $y = 40x + 580$
   b. 860 new employees
   c. 2013

2a. $y = -1500x + 20000$
   b. 12,500
   c. in 3 years

Group Activity 4.4
$x + y = 800$

$3x + 2y = 2150$
250 at \$2, 550 at \$3

Group Activity 4.6

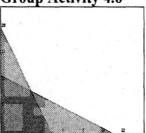

(x, y), any point that satisfies the conditions
Make x bracelets and y necklaces.

Group Activity 5.2
1. $P = 7x + 3$
2. $P = 28x$
3. $P = 14x + 12$
4. $P = 5x - 6$

Group Activity 5.3
1. $A = 3x^2$
2. $A = 49x^2$
3. $A = 10x^2 + 12x$
4. $A = x^2 - 6x$

Group Activity 6, Integrated Review
1. $l = x + 5, w = x - 3,$
   $P = 4x + 4$
2. $l = x + 7, w = x - 7,$
   $P = 4x$
3. $l = 2x + 5, w = 3x - 4,$
   (the length and width could be reversed)
   $P = 10x + 2$
4. $l = 2x + 3, w = 3x - 45$
   (the length and width could be reversed)
   $P = 10x - 4$
5. $s = 3x + 2, P = 12x + 8$

Group Activity 6.6

	A	B	C	D	E
1.	$-5, 2$	-3	3	-10	-10
2.	$2, -3$	-1	1	-6	-6
3.	$-3, \dfrac{1}{2}$	$-\dfrac{5}{2}$	$\dfrac{5}{2}$	$-\dfrac{3}{2}$	$\dfrac{3}{2}$
4.	$-\dfrac{2}{3}, 4$	$\dfrac{10}{3}$	$-\dfrac{10}{3}$	$-\dfrac{8}{3}$	$\dfrac{8}{3}$
5.	$6, -3$	3	-3	-18	-18
6.	$\dfrac{1}{6}, -4$	$-\dfrac{23}{6}$	$\dfrac{23}{6}$	$-\dfrac{2}{3}$	$\dfrac{2}{3}$
7.	$3, 4$	7	-7	12	12
8.	$\dfrac{5}{2}, -\dfrac{2}{3}$	$\dfrac{11}{6}$	$-\dfrac{11}{6}$	$-\dfrac{5}{3}$	$\dfrac{5}{3}$
9.	$3, -\dfrac{2}{5}$	$\dfrac{13}{5}$	$-\dfrac{13}{5}$	$\dfrac{6}{5}$	$-\dfrac{6}{5}$
10.	$2, -\dfrac{3}{7}$	$\dfrac{11}{3}$	$-\dfrac{11}{7}$	$-\dfrac{6}{7}$	$-\dfrac{6}{7}$

The sum of the two solutions to any quadratic equation in the form $ax^2 + bx + c = 0$ is equal to $-\dfrac{b}{a}$.

The product of the two solutions is equal to ac.

Group Activity 7, Integrated Review

1. $P = \dfrac{5x+3}{3}$, $A = \dfrac{x^2 + x}{6}$

2. $P = \dfrac{4x+1}{6}$, $A = \dfrac{x^2 - 2x + 1}{72}$

3. $P = \dfrac{10x+30}{(x+3)(x-3)(x+6)}$

$A = \dfrac{6}{(x+6)(x-3)^2(x+3)}$

Group Activity 7.6

1st Group
A. Plane 200 mph, wind 50 mph

2nd Group
A. Boat 10 mph, Current 1 mph

Group Activity 8.2

1. $2\sqrt{5}$, 4.47
2. $\sqrt{5}$, 2.24

Group Activity 8.6

1. 5
2. 10
3. 15
4. 20
5. 25

Group Activity 9.5

1.
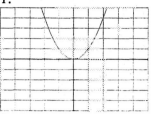

2.
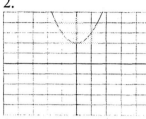

3.
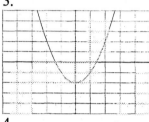

4.
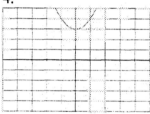

5.
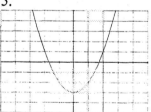

Chapter 1 Test Form A

Translate each statement into symbols. Let *x* represent the unknown number if needed.

1. Negative eight is greater than negative twelve.

1. _____

2. The absolute value of negative three is greater than two.

2. _____

3. Tell which set of numbers − 3 belongs to: whole numbers, integers, rational numbers, irrational numbers, real numbers

3. _____

4. Insert <, >, or = to make a true statement:

4. $|-12|$ _____ 6

Simplify.

5. $-14 + 3$

5. _____

6. $8 + (-12)$

6. _____

7. $(-6)(-3)$

7. _____

8. $(-2)^3$

8. _____

9. $\dfrac{1}{4} + \dfrac{2}{3}$

9. _____

10. $-\dfrac{1}{2} \div \dfrac{1}{4}$

10. _____

11. $\dfrac{3^2}{18}$

11. _____

12. $6 - 8(2 - 4)$

12. _____

13. $\dfrac{3+6}{24-6}$

13. _____

14. $6 - 2^2 + 8$

14. _____

15. $\dfrac{-15 + 2 \cdot 5}{24 - 6}$

15. _____

Chapter 1 Test Form A *cont'd*

Evaluate each expression for the values given.

16. $2x - y$ when $x = 3$ and $y = -2$ 16. _____

17. $3x - 2y$ when $x = -3$ and $y = -4$ 17. _____

18. $x^2 - 2y$ when $x = -2$ and $y = -3$ 18. _____

Name the property illustrated.

19. $2 \cdot (3 \cdot x) = (2 \cdot 3) \cdot x$ 19. _____

20. $3 \cdot 6 = 6 \cdot 3$ 20. _____

21. Find the opposite of –6.   21. _____

22. Find the reciprocal of $\dfrac{1}{4}$.   22. _____

23. A football team gained 6 yards, lost 3 yards,   23. _____
and gained 4 yards on one series of downs.
What was the total gain or loss?

Use the table to answer the following questions.

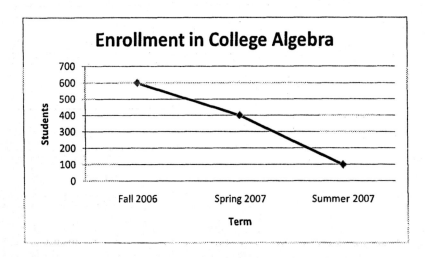

24. How many students were enrolled in Fall 2006?   24. _____

25. Find the decrease in enrollment from Fall 2006   25. _____
to Spring 2007.

Chapter 1 Test Form B

Translate each statement into symbols. Let *x* represent the unknown number if needed.

1. Six is less than the absolute value of negative ten.   **1.** _____

2. The absolute value of eight is equal to the absolute   **2.** _____
value of negative eight.

3. Tell which set of numbers $\sqrt{2}$ belongs to: **3.** _____
whole numbers, integers, rational numbers,
irrational numbers, real numbers

4. Insert <, >, or = to make a true statement: **4.** $|-6|$ _____ $|-18|$

Simplify.

5. $\dfrac{1}{2} + 1\dfrac{1}{3}$ **5.** _____

6. $-7 + (-3)$ **6.** _____

7. $-5 + 4$ **7.** _____

8. $(-4)(-3)$ **8.** _____

9. $(-2)(3)(0)(-4)$ **9.** _____

10. $-\dfrac{1}{3} \div \left(-\dfrac{1}{6}\right)$ **10.** _____

11. $-12 - (-10)$ **11.** _____

12. $-2 - (7 - 9)$ **12.** _____

13. $\dfrac{2+5}{2 \cdot 4 + 2}$ **13.** _____

14. $2 - 2^2 + 3 - 8$ **14.** _____

15. $\dfrac{-24 - 3^2}{11}$ **15.** _____

Chapter 1 Test Form B *cont'd*

Evaluate each expression for the values given.

16. $x + 2y$ when $x = -2$ and $y = -4$ 16. _____

17. $x^2 - 3y$ when $x = -4$ and $y = 4$ 17. _____

18. $x^2 - y^2$ when $x = -2$ and $y = 3$ 18. _____

Name the property illustrated.

19. $0 + 3 = 3$ 19. _____

20. $6 \cdot \dfrac{1}{6} = 1$ 20. _____

21. Find the opposite of $-\dfrac{1}{2}$.   21. _____

22. Find the reciprocal of $-\dfrac{1}{2}$.   22. _____

24. A stock rose $1\dfrac{1}{8}$ points, fell 2 points, and rose   23. _____

$2\dfrac{1}{4}$ points. What was the total gain or loss?

Use the graph to answer the following questions. The net income for a new business is shown.

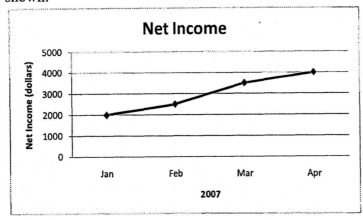

24. What is the approximate net income for February? 24. _____

25. Find the increase in net income from January to April. 25. _____

Chapter 1 Test Form C

Translate each statement into symbols. Let x represent the unknown number if needed.

1. Negative three is less than or equal to zero.

1. _____

2. The absolute value of negative ten is greater than two.

2. _____

3. Tell which set of numbers $\frac{2}{7}$ belongs to: whole numbers, integers, rational numbers, irrational numbers, real numbers

3. _____

4. Insert <, >, or = to make a true statement:

4. $|{-13}|$ _____ $|13|$

Simplify.

5. $1\frac{1}{2} + 2\frac{1}{4}$

5. _____

6. $-9 - (-4)$

6. _____

7. $-2 + (-3)$

7. _____

8. $-2(-2)$

8. _____

9. $3(-2)(-1)(4)$

9. _____

10. $-\frac{3}{4} \div \frac{1}{8}$

10. _____

11. $\dfrac{-2^3}{16}$

11. _____

12. $-8 + 6 - 4$

12. _____

13. $\dfrac{2+6}{12-8}$

13. _____

14. $3 - 2^2 - 2 \cdot 4$

14. _____

15. $\dfrac{-5+3}{2 \cdot 4}$

15. _____

Chapter 1 Test Form C *cont'd*

Evaluate each expression for the values given.

16. $2x - y$ when $x = -1$ and $y = -3$ 16. _____

17. $3x + y$ when $x = -2$ and $y = 4$ 17. _____

18. $3x^2 - 3xy$ when $x = 2$ and $y = -3$ 18. _____

Name the property illustrated.

19. $1 \cdot (-3) = -3$ 19. _____

20. $2 + (3 + 5) = (2 + 3) + 5$ 20. _____

21. Find the opposite of $\frac{1}{8}$.   21. _____

22. Find the reciprocal of $\frac{1}{8}$.   22. _____

25. Anne went on a multilevel dive in scuba class,   23. _____
She dove 60 feet, then rose 20 feet, than dove
10 feet and finally rose 20 feet for the rest of her
dive. What was the depth for the final part of the
dive?

The temperatures for one morning in March were recorded and shown on the following graph.

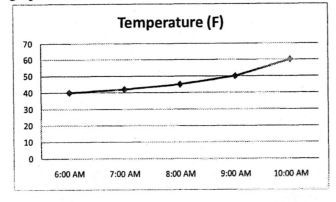

24. What is the approximate temperature at 7 a.m.?   24. _____

25. The temperature rose the most in which one hour   25. _____
period?

Chapter 1 Test Form D

Circle the correct answer.

Translate each statement into symbols. Let x represent the unknown number if needed.

1. Six is greater than negative 6.

    a. $x < 6$ **b.** $6 \geq -6$ **c.** $6 > -6$ **d.** $6 < -6$

2. The absolute value of six is equal to six.

    a. $|6| = 6$ **b.** $|-6| = 6$ **c.** $|6| = |-6|$ **d.** $|6| = |6|$

3. Which number is a rational number and a real number?

    a. $\sqrt{5}$ **b.** π **c.** -1.2 **d.** $\sqrt{3}$

4. Which of the following would be inserted to make a true statement? $|-2| \_\_\_ 2$

    a. $<$ **b.** $>$ **c.** $=$ **d.** $\leq$

Simplify each expression.

5. $\dfrac{1}{3} - \dfrac{4}{5}$

    a. $-\dfrac{3}{5}$ **b.** $-\dfrac{3}{2}$ **c.** $-\dfrac{7}{15}$ **d.** $-\dfrac{1}{5}$

6. $-4 + 6 - 3$

    a. -1 **b.** -7 **c.** -5 **d.** -13

7. $-20 + 8$

    a. -12 **b.** 12 **c.** -28 **d.** -13

8. $(-8)(-5)(2)(-1)$

    a. 80 **b.** -80 **c.** -40 **d.** 40

9. $(-0.5)(-0.2)$

    a. 0.1 **b.** -0.1 **c.** 1 **d.** -1

Chapter 1 Test Form D *cont'd*

10. $\dfrac{2}{3} \div \left(-\dfrac{1}{6}\right)$

    a. $-\dfrac{1}{9}$ **b.** $\dfrac{1}{9}$ **c.** $-\dfrac{1}{4}$ **d.** -4

11. $-6-(-3)$

    a. -3 **b.** 3 **c.** -9 **d.** 9

12. $\dfrac{2^5-8}{6+2}$

    a. $-\dfrac{2}{3}$ **b.** 0 **c.** 3 **d.** undefined

13. $\dfrac{4+(-2)^2}{2^3}$

    a. 1 **b.** 2 **c.** 0 **d.** undefined

14. $6-|-4|-2$

    a. 8 **b.** 0 **c.** 12 **d.** -4

15. $\dfrac{20+2\cdot3}{5+2}$

    a. $3\dfrac{5}{7}$ **b.** $\dfrac{1}{2}$ **c.** $\dfrac{17}{5}$ **d.** 1

Evaluate each expression for the values given.

16. $2x-y$ when $x=-2$ and $y=1$.

    a. 5 **b.** -1 **c.** -5 **d.** 7

17. $\dfrac{3x-y}{2x}$ when $x=-2$ and $y=1$.

    a. $\dfrac{7}{4}$ **b.** 5 **c.** -5 **d.** 0

18. x^2-y^2 when $x=-2$ and $y=3$.

    a. 25 **b.** -5 **c.** -13 **d.** 13

Chapter 1 Test Form D *cont'd*

Name the property illustrated.

19. $7 + 0 = 7$
    a. Commutative Property   **b.** Identity Property
    c. Associative Property   **d.** Distributive Property

20. $8 + 2 = 2 + 8$
    a. Commutative Property   **b.** Identity Property
    c. Associative Property   **d.** Distributive Property

21. Find the opposite of $\frac{5}{2}$.
    a. $-\frac{5}{2}$ **b.** $\frac{5}{2}$ **c.** $-\frac{2}{5}$ **d.** $\frac{2}{5}$

22. Find the reciprocal of $\frac{5}{2}$.
    a. $-\frac{5}{2}$ **b.** $\frac{5}{2}$ **c.** $-\frac{2}{5}$ **d.** $\frac{2}{5}$

23. Your stock posted a fall of $1\frac{1}{8}$ points, rose $\frac{1}{4}$, and fell $\frac{3}{4}$. What is the overall change?
    a. $+2\frac{1}{8}$ **b.** $-1\frac{5}{8}$ **c.** $-2\frac{1}{8}$ **d.** $\frac{5}{8}$

The graph shows the enrollment of a small junior college.

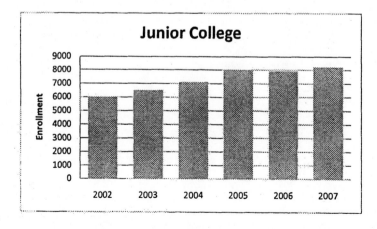

24. What was the approximate enrollment in 2003?
    a. 6500   **b.** 6000   **c.** 7000   **d.** 8000

25. In what year did the enrollment fall from the previous?
    a. 2002   **b.** 2003   **c.** 2007   **d.** 2006

Chapter 1 Test Form E

Circle the correct answer.

Translate each statement into symbols. Let x represent the unknown number if needed.

1. Negative six is greater than negative 8.

    a. $-6 < -8$ **b.** $-6 > -8$ **c.** $-8 > -6$ **d.** $-6 \geq -8$

4. The absolute value of negative seven is less than or equal to seven.

    a. $|-7| = 7$ **b.** $|-7| < 7$ **c.** $|-7| \leq 7$ **d.** $|-7| > 7$

5. Which number is an integer, a rational number, and a real number?

    a. -5 **b.** $\dfrac{1}{2}$ **c.** $\sqrt{5}$ **d.** $-\dfrac{1}{3}$

4. Which of the following would be inserted to make a true statement? $|-5|$ _____ -3

    a. $<$ **b.** $>$ **c.** $=$ **d.** none

Simplify each expression.

5. $\dfrac{2}{3} + \dfrac{1}{4}$

    a. $\dfrac{11}{12}$ **b.** $\dfrac{3}{7}$ **c.** $\dfrac{1}{4}$ **d.** $\dfrac{5}{12}$

6. $-8 - (-3)$

    a. -11 **b.** 11 **c.** -5 **d.** 5

7. $-37 - 15$

    a. -22 **b.** 22 **c.** -52 **d.** 52

8. $(-0.03)(0.4)$

    a. -0.12 **b.** -0.012 **c.** -1.2 **d.** 0.12

9. $(2)(-4)(-3)(-2)(-1)$

    a. -48 **b.** 48 **c.** 28 **d.** -28

Chapter 1 Test Form E *cont'd*

10. $-\dfrac{3}{5} \div \left(-\dfrac{3}{10}\right)$

    a. $\dfrac{1}{2}$ **b.** $-\dfrac{1}{2}$ **c.** $-\dfrac{9}{50}$ **d.** 2

11. $\dfrac{2^4}{8}$

    a. 1   **b.** 2   **c.** $\dfrac{1}{2}$ **d.** $\dfrac{1}{4}$

12. $-7 + [-1 - 3) + 4]$

    a. 1   **b.** -15 **c.** -7 **d.** -1

13. $\dfrac{5 + (-3)^2}{3 - 10}$

    a. $-\dfrac{11}{7}$ **b.** $\dfrac{11}{7}$ **c.** $\dfrac{4}{7}$ **d.** -2

14. $3 - 6(4 - 2)$

    a. 6   **b.** -6 **c.** -9 **d.** 9

15. $\dfrac{-5 + 2 \cdot 4}{6}$

    a. -2 **b.** 2   **c.** $-\dfrac{1}{2}$ **d.** $\dfrac{1}{2}$

Evaluate each expression for the values given.

16. $2x - y$ when $x = 7$ and $y = -7$.

    a. 7   **b.** 21   **c.** -7 **d.** -49

17. $\dfrac{5 - y}{x - 7}$ when $x = -3$ and $y = -4$.

    a. $-\dfrac{8}{11}$ **b.** $-\dfrac{9}{10}$ **c.** $-\dfrac{8}{3}$ **d.** $-\dfrac{2}{11}$

Chapter 1 Test Form E *cont'd*

18. $-x^2 + 2y$ when $x = -1$ and $y = 4$.
    a. 3   **b.** 7   **c.** 9   **d.** 4

Name the property illustrated.

19. $7 - (x+1) = (7-x) + 1$
    a. Commutative Property   **b.** Identity Property
    c. Associative Property   **d.** Distributive Property

20. $7(x+1) = 7x + 7$
    a. Commutative Property   **b.** Identity Property
    c. Associative Property   **d.** Distributive Property

21. Find the opposite of $-\dfrac{1}{3}$.

    a. $\dfrac{1}{3}$ **b.** $-\dfrac{1}{3}$ **c.** -3 **d.** 3

22. Find the reciprocal of -5.

    a. $-\dfrac{1}{5}$ **b.** 5   **c.** $\dfrac{1}{5}$ **d.** -5

23. Yesterday your stock posted a change of $-1\dfrac{3}{4}$ points, but today it showed a

    change of $\dfrac{1}{8}$. What is the overall change for the two days?

    a. $1\dfrac{5}{8}$ **b.** $-1\dfrac{5}{8}$ **c.** $-1\dfrac{7}{8}$ **d.** $-1\dfrac{1}{2}$

A football team was 19 yards from the goal when the following series of plays occurred.

	Gains or Losses in Yards
First Down	−2
Second Down	5
Third Down	−10
Fourth Down	25

24. During which down did the greatest loss of yardage occur?
    a. First   **b.** Second   **c.** Third   **d.** Fourth

25. After the first four downs, how far was the football from their starting position?
    a. 1 yard   **b.** 18 yards   **c.** 42 yards   **d.** 37 yards

Chapter 1 Test Form F

Circle the correct answer.

Translate each statement into symbols. Let x represent the unknown number if needed.

1. Three times a number subtracted from twenty is negative ten.

    a. $3x - 20 = -10$ **b.** $20 - 3x = -10$

    c. $-10 - 3x = 20$ **d.** $10 - 3x = -20$

21. The absolute value of negative seven is less than or equal to nine.

    a. $-|7| \leq 9$ **b.** $-|7| \geq 9$ **c.** $|-7| \leq 9$ **d.** $|-7| \geq 9$

22. Which number is a natural number, integer, rational number, and real number?

    a. -5 **b.** $\dfrac{1}{2}$ **c.** $\sqrt{5}$ **d.** 6

4. Which of the following would be inserted to make a true statement? $|-7|$ _____ 7

    a. $<$ **b.** $>$ **c.** $=$ **d.** none

Simplify each expression.

5. $1\dfrac{1}{2} - \dfrac{3}{4}$

    a. $-\dfrac{1}{2}$ **b.** 1 **c.** $\dfrac{1}{2}$ **d.** $\dfrac{3}{4}$

6. $(-8) - (-3)$

    a. -11 **b.** -5 **c.** 5 **d.** 11

7. $-17 - (-25)$

    a. 8 **b.** -8 **c.** 42 **d.** -42

8. $(0.4)(-0.5)$

    a. -2 **b.** -0.2 **c.** -0.02 **d.** -20

9. $(-3)(-2)(2)(-1)$

    a. -12 **b.** 12 **c.** 13 **d.** -13

Chapter 1 Test Form F *cont'd*

10. $-\dfrac{3}{7} \div \left(\dfrac{6}{28} \right)$

     a. $\dfrac{9}{28}$ **b.** $-\dfrac{9}{98}$ **c.** -2 **d.** $-\dfrac{1}{2}$

11. $\dfrac{3^3 - 2^3}{3^2 - 2^2}$

     a. 1 **b.** -1 **c.** $\dfrac{19}{5}$ **d.** $\dfrac{3}{2}$

12. $-6 + [(3 - 4) + 5]$

     a. 0 **b.** 12 **c.** -1 **d.** -2

13. $\dfrac{4 + (-1)^2}{(-1)^3 - 2}$

     a. $-\dfrac{5}{3}$ **b.** -3 **c.** -5 **d.** -1

14. $(4 - 6)^2$

     a. 4 **b.** 2 **c.** 20 **d.** -4

15. $\dfrac{-8 + 2 \cdot 3}{-8 - 2 \cdot 3}$

     a. $\dfrac{1}{7}$ **b.** $\dfrac{6}{5}$ **c.** $-\dfrac{1}{7}$ **d.** $-\dfrac{6}{5}$

Evaluate each expression for the values given.

16. $2x - 3y$ when $x = -1$ and $y = -1$.

     a. 0 **b.** -2 **c.** 1 **d.** -1

17. $\dfrac{6 - y}{x + 6}$ when $x = -3$ and $y = -4$.

     a. $\dfrac{7}{2}$ **b.** $3\dfrac{1}{3}$ **c.** $\dfrac{2}{5}$ **d.** -2

Chapter 1 Test Form F *cont'd*

18. $x^2 - 4y^2$ when $x = 3$ and $y = -2$.
    a. 7   **b.** -7   **c.** 1   **d.** -1

Name the property illustrated.

19. $[4 + (-2)] - 3 = [(-2) + 4] - 3$
    a. Commutative Property   **b.** Identity Property
    c. Associative Property   **d.** Distributive Property

20. $4(3 - 2) = 4(3) + 4(-2)$
    a. Commutative Property   **b.** Identity Property
    c. Associative Property   **d.** Distributive Property

21. Find the opposite of $-\dfrac{5}{3}$.

    a. $\dfrac{3}{5}$ **b.** $-\dfrac{3}{5}$ **c.** $\dfrac{5}{3}$ **d.** $-\dfrac{5}{3}$

22. Find the reciprocal of -5.

    a. $-\dfrac{1}{5}$ **b.** 5   **c.** $\dfrac{1}{5}$ **d.** -5

23. The temperature at 5:00 was -2° F. By 11:00 , the temperature dropped 7 degrees. What was the temperature at 11:00?
    a. -9°   **b.** -5°   **c.** 5°   **d.** 9°

The chart shows a deposit and several checks written against a checking account in one day, beginning with a balance of $1083.50.

Activity	Amount
Check	$10.00
Deposit	$200.00
Check	$20.50
Check	$180.00

24. What was the total of the checks?

    a. $180.00   **b.** $200.50   **c.** $210.50   **d.** $420.50

25. What was the balance of the account at the end of the day?

    a. $1073.00   **b.** $1094.00   **c.** 41494.00   **d.** $1473.00

Chapter 2 Test Form A

Simplify each of the following expressions.

   1. $6x - 8 - 3x + 4$ **1.** _____

   2. $6x + 2 - 5.2x - 7.3$ **2.** _____

   3. $2(x - 3) + 3(x + 4)$ **3.** _____

   4. Subtract $-2x + 4$ from $7x - 3$.   **4.** _____

Solve each of the following.

   5. $-5x = -25$ **5.** _____

   6. $\dfrac{2}{3}x = 18$ **6.** _____

   7. $5x - 3 = 6x$ **7.** _____

   8. $7x - 3 + 8 = 6x$ **8.** _____

   9. $-2(x + 3) = 3(x - 7)$ **9.** _____

   10. $\dfrac{2}{3} - x + 5x = \dfrac{1}{2}x$ **10.** _____

   11. $-0.2(3x - 8) = 1.6 + 2x$ **11.** _____

   12. $3(x - 5) = 2(x + 5) + x$ **12.** _____

   13. $4(3 - 6x) = -2(x + 5)$ **13.** _____

   14. The sum of two consecutive integers is 135.   **14.** _____
       Find the two integers.

   15. A mechanic charges $50 an hour plus parts.   **15.** _____
       If a bill was $450 that included $150 in parts,
       how many hours did the job take?

Chapter 2 Test Form A *cont'd*

16. A lab has a 20% acid solution and a 50% acid solution. How many liters of each are required to obtain 600 liters of a 30% acid solution?

16. _____

17. Two trains leave Chicago at the same time traveling in opposite directions. One is going 60 miles per hour and the other is going 65 miles per hour. How long before they are 375 miles a part?

17. _____

18. Substitute the given values into the formula and and solve for the unknown variable.

$V = \frac{1}{3}\pi r^2 h$; $\pi = 3.14$, $V = 56.62$, $r = 3$

18. _____

19. Solve the formula for the indicated variable.
$P = 2a + 2b$ for b

19. _____

20. Solve the formula for the indicated variable.
$A = lwh$ for h.

20. _____

Solve the inequalities.

21. $3 - x \le 2x - 7$

21. _____

22. $\dfrac{2(3-x)}{4} \le 10$

22. _____

23. $5 - 3x \le -10$

23. _____

24. $8 < x - 5 < 21$

24. _____

25. $-5 < 2x + 7 \le 13$

25. _____

Chapter 2 Test Form B

Simplify each of the following expressions.

1. $8x-3-9x-5$

1. _____

2. $7.5x-2.8+2x-3.5$

2. _____

3. $4(3x-6)+2(8-3x)$

3. _____

4. Subtract $3x-4$ from $-2x+5$.

4. _____

Solve each of the following.

5. $4x+3=27$

5. _____

6. $-\dfrac{2}{5}x=-30$

6. _____

7. $8x-4=10x+6$

7. _____

8. $5x-3-2x=2(x+4)$

8. _____

9. $\dfrac{2(x-3)}{4}=4x-3$

9. _____

10. $\dfrac{1}{2}-x+7=\dfrac{3}{4}+2x$

10. _____

11. $5(x-3)=2(3x+8)$

11. _____

12. $-0.2(x-6)+x=0.3(4-x)$

12. _____

13. $3x+5=2(x-5)+x$

13. _____

14. Two angles are complementary angles if their sum is 90°. Find two complementary angles if the second angle is twice the first.

14. _____

Chapter 2 Test Form B *cont'd*

15. Yohannes invested $24,000 in two money market   15. _____
    funds. The first paid 5% interest per year and the
    second paid 3% interest per year. He earned a
    total profit of $1120 in one year. How much did
    he invest in each rate?

16. The sum of three consecutive numbers is 255.   16. _____
    Find the three numbers.

17. A number plus one half of the number is 48.   17. _____
     Find the number.

18. Substitute the given values into the formula and   18. _____
    and solve for the unknown variable.
    $P = 2a + 2b$;$a = 12, P = 46$

19. Solve the formula for the indicated variable.   19. _____

    $V = \dfrac{1}{3}\pi r^2 h$ for π

20. Solve the formula for the indicated variable.   20. _____
    $Ax + By + C = 0$ for y

Solve the inequalities.

21. $7 - 6x \le 8 - 5x$ 21. _____

22. $\dfrac{2(2x-1)}{5} \ge -3$ 22. _____

24. $7 - 3x \ge -20$ 23. _____

24. $-4 < 2x + 8 < 20$ 24. _____

25. $0 < 3x - 6 < 12$ 25. _____

Chapter 2 Test Form C

Simplify each of the following expressions.

1. $8x - 5 + 2x - 8$

1. _____

2. $2.3x - 7.1 + 0.3x + 5$

2. _____

3. $2(x-5) - 2(2x+4)$

3. _____

4. Subtract $2x - 8$ from $7x + 4$.

4. _____

Solve each of the following.

5. $5x + 2 = 17$

5. _____

6. $-\dfrac{2}{7}x = 28$

6. _____

7. $8x - 12 = 6x$

7. _____

8. $3x - 2 + 4x = 3(2x - 1)$

8. _____

9. $\dfrac{4(x+2)}{5} = 2x - 8$

9. _____

10. $\dfrac{1}{2} - 2x + 3 = \dfrac{1}{4} + x$

10. _____

11. $-2.6x(x-2) + 3x = 1.2$

11. _____

12. $3(2x-7) - (x+5) = -6$

12. _____

13. $4(x-3) = 2(2x-7)$

13. _____

14. The sum of the measures of the three angles of triangle is 180°. Find the three angles of a triangle if two angles are the same the third angle is 60° more than each of the other two.

14. _____

15. If sales tax is 8%, what will be the total cost of a shirt that costs $24?

15. _____

Chapter 2 Test Form C *cont'd*

16. Pablo invested $45,000 in two bonds. The first bond paid 3% interest per year and the second paid 8% per year. The total interest Pablo received in one years was $2850. How much did he invest in each bond?

16. _____

17. Linda drove from Philadelphia to New York City at the rate of 50 miles per hour. She made the trip from New York City to Philadelphia, along the same route traveling 40 miles per hour. Her total driving time was 3.6 hours. Find the distance between Philadelphia and New York.

17. _____

18. Substitute the given values into the formula and and solve for the unknown variable.
$V = lwh$; $w = 6, h = 12, V = 576$

18. _____

19. Solve the formula for the indicated variable.
$y = mx + b$ for x

19. _____

20. Solve the formula for the indicated variable.
$2xy - 3y = 7$ for x.

20. _____

Solve the inequalities.

21. $3x - 8 < 2x - 12$

21. _____

22. $\dfrac{2(5-x)}{5} < -2$

22. _____

23. $4 - 5x \le 24$

23. _____

24. $-6 < 2x - 4 < 18$

24. _____

25. $0 < x + 4 < 12$

25. _____

Chapter 2 Test Form D

Circle the correct answer.

Simplify each of the following expressions.

1. $5x - 8 - 3x - 4$

   a. $2x + 12$ b. $2x - 4$ c. $2x - 12$ d. $8x - 4$

2. $4x - 9 - 6x + 9$

   a. $-2x$ b. $-2x - 18$ c. $2x$ d. $2x + 18$

3. $4(2x - 3) - 2(x + 5)$

   a. $6x - 22$ b. $2x - 17$ c. $10x - 22$ d. $6x - 17$

4. Subtract $3.1x + 1.8$ from $4x - 5$

   a. $0.9x - 3.2$ b. $0.9x - 6.8$ c. $-0.9x + 6.8$ d. $-0.9x - 3.2$

Solve each of the following equations.

5. $\dfrac{4}{7}x = 28$

   a. 49 b. 16 c. 7 d. $\dfrac{1}{7}$

6. $-5x = \dfrac{1}{3}$

   a. $\dfrac{1}{15}$ b. $-\dfrac{1}{15}$ c. $-\dfrac{5}{3}$ d. $\dfrac{5}{3}$

7. $21x - 8 = 17x$

   a. 2 b. 1 c. -1 d. -2

8. $3x + 4 - 4x = 2(3x - 5)$

   a. 3 b. -1 c. -3 d. 2

Chapter 2 Test Form D *cont'd*

9. $\dfrac{3(2x+3)}{5} = 7$

    a. $\dfrac{13}{3}$ **b.** 4   **c.** -4 **d.** $\dfrac{1}{3}$

10. $0.2(x-3) - x = 0.2$

    a. -10 **b.** 1   **c.** -1 **d.** No solution

11. $3x - 6 = 4(x-2) - x$

    a. -4 **b.** 2   **c.** $\dfrac{1}{2}$ **d.** No solution

12. $3x - 2(x+4) = 7$

    a. -1 **b.** 15   **c.** 3   **d.** No solution

13. $4x + 3 = 2(2x+3) - 7$

    a. -7 **b.** 4   **c.** 3   **d.** No solution

14. Substitute the given values into the given formula and solve for the unknown variable.
$2x + 3y = 12$; $x = 3$

    a. 2   **b.** $\dfrac{3}{2}$ **c.** $\dfrac{7}{3}$ **d.** -3

15. Solve for the indicated variable. $x = 3a + 2b + c$ for b

    a. $b = \dfrac{x}{3a+c}$ **b.** $b = \dfrac{x-3a-c}{2}$

    c. $b = x - 3a - c$ **d.** $b = x - 3a - c - 2$

16. Solve for l. $V = lwh$

    a. $l = v - 2h$ **b.** $l = \dfrac{V}{wh}$ **c.** $l = \dfrac{wh}{V}$ **d.** $l = Vwh$

Chapter 2 Test Form D *cont'd*

Solve the following applications.

17. David invested $23,000 in two certificates. One certificate paid 6% per year and the other paid 3% per year. He earned $1230 interest in one year. How much did he invest in the 3% certificate?

    a. $8000   **b.** $5000   **c.** $18,000   **d.** $11,500

18. Ann Marie wishes to mix peanuts worth $1.38 a pound with cashews worth $2.10 a pound to get 8 pounds of mixture worth $1.65 a pound. How many pounds of peanuts does she need?

    a. 5   **b.** 4   **c.** 3   **d.** 7

19. A $400 television set is on sale 40% off. What will be the sales price?

    a. $360   **b.** $160   **c.** $240   **d.** $560

20. The length of a rectangle is 4 feet less than 3 times the width. The perimeter is 16 feet. Find its length.

    a. 5 feet   **b.** 6 feet   **c.** 3 feet   **d.** 2 feet

Solve the inequalities.

21. $3x - 6 < 5x - 8$

    a. $x < 1$ **b.** $x > -1$ **c.** $x < -1$ **d.** $x > 1$

22. $5 - x < 30$

    a. $x < 25$ **b.** $x > 25$ **c.** $x < 35$ **d.** $x > -25$

23. $\dfrac{3(2x-5)}{2} < 8$

    a. $x < \dfrac{31}{6}$ **b.** $x < \dfrac{13}{6}$ **c.** $x < \dfrac{23}{6}$ **d.** $x < \dfrac{7}{3}$

24. $-3 < 5 - x < 8$

    a. $-8 < x < 3$ **b.** $-3 < x < 8$ **c.** $8 < x < -3$ **d.** $-3 < x < 3$

25. $0 < 3x - 6 < 6$

    a. $0 < x < 6$ **b.** $2 < x < 6$ **c.** $2 < x < 4$ **d.** $0 < x < 4$

Chapter 2 Test Form E

Circle the correct answer.

Simplify each of the following expression.

1. $7y - 3 - 4y - 6$

    a. $11y - 9$ **b.** $11y - 3$ **c.** $3y - 3$ **d.** $3y - 9$

2. $8.2x - 14 - 3.7x + 5.1$

    a. $4.5x - 8.9$ **b.** $4.5x - 19.1$ **c.** $11.9x - 8.9$ **d.** $11.9x - 19.1$

3. $8(3y - 5) - 6(5y - 2)$

    a. $54y - 28$ **b.** $54y - 52$ **c.** $-6y - 28$ **d.** $-6y - 52$

4. Subtract $2x - 8$ from $4x + 6$

    a. $6x - 2$ **b.** $2x + 14$ **c.** $-2x - 14$ **d.** $2x - 2$

Solve each of the following equations.

5. $8 - x = 15$

    a. 7   **b.** 23   **c.** -7 **d.** -23

6. $5x - 6 = 4(x + 3)$

    a. 18   **b.** 9   **c.** 6   **d.** 12

7. $\dfrac{2}{3}x = 14$

    a. $\dfrac{3}{28}$ **b.** 21   **c.** $\dfrac{28}{3}$ **d.** $\dfrac{1}{21}$

8. $6x - 9 = 3x + 12$

    a. 7   **b.** 14   **c.** 4   **d.** -7

Chapter 2 Test Form E *cont'd*

9. $17y - 6 - 20y = 8(3y - 1)$

     a. $-\dfrac{2}{27}$ **b.** $\dfrac{2}{27}$ **c.** $-\dfrac{5}{27}$ **d.** $\dfrac{5}{27}$

10. $\dfrac{7(2y + 5)}{3} = 3y + 7$

     a. $-\dfrac{56}{5}$ **b.** $\dfrac{56}{5}$ **c.** $-\dfrac{14}{5}$ **d.** $\dfrac{14}{5}$

11. $\dfrac{3}{8} - 2x + 5x = \dfrac{9}{8} + 6x$

     a. $\dfrac{1}{2}$ **b.** $-\dfrac{1}{2}$ **c.** $\dfrac{1}{4}$ **d.** $-\dfrac{1}{4}$

12. $0.6(2y - 6) = -0.4(3y - 4)$

     a. $\dfrac{13}{6}$ **b.** $\dfrac{52}{19}$ **c.** $-\dfrac{52}{19}$ **d.** No solution

13. $5x + 3 = 2(x - 7) + 3x$

     a. 17   **b.** −17   **c.** −11   **d.** No solution

Solve the following applications.

14. How many pounds of red grapes worth $0.95 per pound does Nina need to mix with green grapes worth $1.25 per pound to have a mixture of 12 pounds of grapes worth $1.15 per pound?

     a. 8 pounds   **b.** 4 pounds   **c.** 6 pounds   **d.** 7 pounds

15. The perimeter of a rectangle is 84 feet. The length of the rectangle is 3 feet less than 2 times its width. What is the length of the rectangle?

     a. 9 feet   **b.** 18 feet   **c.** 15 feet   **d.** 27 feet

16. The sum of three consecutive even numbers is 138. What is the middle number?

     a. 41   **b.** 46   **c.** 40   **d.** 44

Chapter 2 Test Form E *cont'd*

17. Maurice spent $20 to join a video club and rent six video tapes. If the membership fee is $5, how much does it cost to rent each video tape?

    a. $4   **b.** $2.80   **c.** $2.50   **d.** $2.25

18. A $32 shirt is on sale for 15% off. Find the sales price.

    a. $4.80   **b.** $27.20   **c.** $37.65   **d.** $17

19. Substitute the given values into the formula and solve for the unknown variable.
    $y = mx + b$; $x = 10, b = 4, y = 9$

    a. $m = \dfrac{2}{3}$ **b.** $m = -\dfrac{2}{3}$ **c.** $m = \dfrac{1}{2}$ **d.** $m = -\dfrac{1}{2}$

20. Solve the formula for the indicated variable. $A = p + prt$ for r

    a. $r = \dfrac{A-p}{pt}$ **b.** $r = \dfrac{A}{pt} - p$ **c.** $r = A - p - pt$ **d.** $r = \dfrac{A}{p+pt}$

Solve the following inequalities.

21. $12x - 9 < 15x - 3$

    a. $x > -2$ **b.** $x < -2$ **c.** $x > 2$ **d.** $x < 2$

22. $5 - x \geq 17$

    a. $x \geq 12$ **b.** $x \leq 12$ **c.** $x \geq -12$ **d.** $x \leq -12$

23. $-10 < 2x - 5 < 3$

    a. $\dfrac{5}{2} < x < 4$ **b.** $-1 < x < \dfrac{5}{2}$ **c.** $-\dfrac{5}{2} < x < 4$ **d.** $-\dfrac{5}{2} < x < -1$

24. $\dfrac{2(2x-3)}{3} < 2$

    a. $x > 3$ **b.** $x < 3$ **c.** $x > -3$ **d.** $x < -3$

25. $0 < 3 - x < 8$

    a. $-3 < x < 5$ **b.** $3 < x < -5$ **c.** $-5 < x < 3$ **d.** $5 < x < 3$

Chapter 2 Test Form F

Circle the correct answer.

Simplify each of the following expression.

1. $6x-12-8x+4$

    a. $-2x+8$ **b.** $2x-8$ **c.** $-2x-16$ **d.** $-2x-8$

2. $10.2y-0.1-3.6y+5.2$

    a. $6.6y+5.1$ **b.** $6.6y+3.9$ **c.** $13.8y-14.3$ **d.** $13.8y+14.3$

3. $6(8x-3)-9(4-x)$

    a. $57x-18$ **b.** $39x-54$ **c.** $57x-54$ **d.** $39x-18$

4. Subtract $2.6x+5$ from $4x-2.5$.

    a. $6.6x+2.5$ **b.** $1.4x-7.5$ **c.** $-1.4x+7.5$ **d.** $-6.6x-2.5$

5. Write the algebraic expression for the quotient of 3 times a number and 5 less than the number.

    a. $\dfrac{x-5}{3x}$ **b.** $\dfrac{5-x}{3x}$ **c.** $\dfrac{3x}{x-5}$ **d.** $\dfrac{3x}{5-x}$

Solve each of the following equations.

6. $8-x=12$

    a. 4 **b.** -4 **c.** -20 **d.** 20

7. $-\dfrac{5}{6}x-7=18$

    a. -30 **b.** 30 **c.** $-\dfrac{66}{5}$ **d.** $\dfrac{66}{5}$

8. $14x-7=7$

    a. 2 **b.** -1 **c.** 1 **d.** -2

Chapter 2 Test Form F *cont'd*

9. $4x + 9 - 14x = 3(4x - 7)$

   a. $-\dfrac{15}{11}$ **b.** $\dfrac{15}{11}$ **c.** 6 **d.** -6

10. $\dfrac{5(x-6)}{7} = 3x + 4$

   a. $-\dfrac{29}{8}$ **b.** $\dfrac{29}{13}$ **c.** $-\dfrac{5}{8}$ **d.** $-\dfrac{1}{13}$

11. $\dfrac{4}{11} - 2y + 5y = \dfrac{9}{11} + y$

   a. 10 **b.** $\dfrac{13}{11}$ **c.** $\dfrac{5}{11}$ **d.** $\dfrac{5}{22}$

12. $12(5 - 3x) = 9(7 - 4x)$

   a. $\dfrac{1}{24}$ **b.** -3 **c.** 3 **d.** No solution

13. Substitute the given values into the given formula and solve for the unknown variable. $V = lwh$ for $V = 48, w = 3, h = 8$

   a. 4 **b.** 2 **c.** 6 **d.** 16

14. Solve for the indicated variable. $P = 2(l + w)$ for w

   a. $w = 2P - l$ **b.** $w = \dfrac{2P}{l}$

   c. $w = \dfrac{P}{2} - l$ **d.** $w = \dfrac{P - l}{2}$

15. Solve for π. $V = \dfrac{1}{3}\pi r^3$

   a. $\pi = \dfrac{V}{r^3}$ **b.** $\pi = \dfrac{3V}{r^3}$ **c.** $\pi = 3Vr^3$ **d.** $\pi = \dfrac{V}{3r^3}$

Chapter 2 Test Form F *cont'd*

Solve the following applications.

16. A plumber charges $78 to unstop a drain. This fee includes $14 in parts and $32 an hour for labor. How many hours did the plumber work?
    a. 1 hour   **b.** 2 hours   **c.** 3 hours   **d.** 4 hours

17. A restaurant increased the price of Tayla's favorite dinner from $6.95 to $7.50. Find the percent increase in the price.
    a. 55%   **b.** 0.55%   **c.** 75   **d.** 8%

18. Abraham invested $42,000 in two accounts. The first paid 8% interest per year and the second paid 3% per year. He earned a total of $2960 in one year. How much did he invest at 8%?
    a. $8000   **b.** $34,000   **c.** $38,000   **d.** $21,000

19. The sum of three consecutive numbers is 246. What is the middle number?
    a. 82   **b.** 43   **c.** 85   **d.** 81

20. The length of a rectangle is 4 feet less than 3 times the width. The perimeter is 16 feet. Find its length.
    a. 5 feet   **b.** 6 feet   **c.** 3 feet   **d.** 2 feet

Solve the following inequalities.

21. $17x - 5 \le 19x + 1$
    a. $x \le -3$ **b.** $x \ge -3$ **c.** $x \le 3$ **d.** $x \ge 3$

22. $5 - x < 12$
    a. $x < 7$ **b.** $x < -7$ **c.** $x > 7$ **d.** $x > -7$

23. $-9 \le 4x + 7 < 11$
    a. $-4 \le x < 1$ **b.** $-4 < x \le 1$ **c.** $-\dfrac{1}{2} \le x < 1$ **d.** $-\dfrac{1}{2} < x \le 1$

24. $3 \le 4 - x \le 10$
    a. $-1 \le x \le -6$ **b.** $1 \le x \le -6$ **c.** $-6 \le x \le 1$ **d.** $1 \le x \le 14$

25. $\dfrac{6(2x-1)}{5} \le -6$
    a. $x \ge -2$ **b.** $x \ge 2$ **c.** $x \le -2$ **d.** $x \le 2$

Chapter 3 Test Form A

Graph the following.

1. $x = 3y - 6$

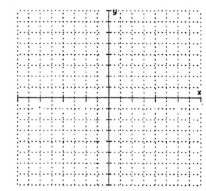

2. $2x - y = -2$

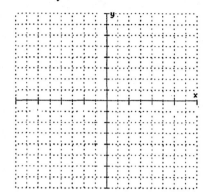

3. $y = \dfrac{2}{3}x + 4$

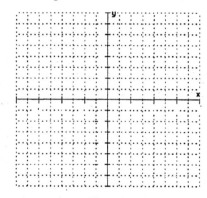

4. $y = 2$

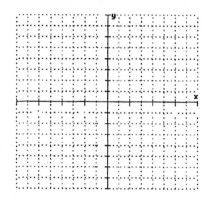

Find the slopes of the following lines.

5.

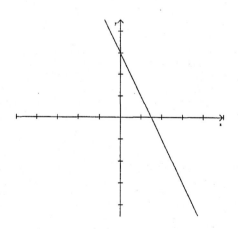

5. _____

Chapter 3 Test Form A *cont'd*

6. through $(-2, 4)$ and $(-6, 5)$

6. _____

7. $3x + 2y = 6$

7. _____

8. $y = 5$

8. _____

9. Determine the slope and y-intercept of the line $2x + y = 3$

9. _____

10. Determine whether the graphs of the lines would be parallel, perpendicular, or neither.
$$y = 3x - 6$$
$$x + 3y = 9$$

10. _____

Find the equations of the following lines. Write the equation in the from $Ax + By = C$.

11. with slope $-\dfrac{1}{3}$, through $(-2, 4)$

11. _____

12. through the origin and $(5, -6)$

12. _____

13. through $(-3, 5)$ and $(4, 2)$

13. _____

14. with slope 6 and y-intercept -3

14. _____

Determine which of the following are functions.

15.

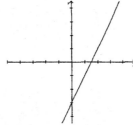

15. _____

16.

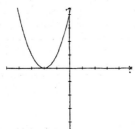

16. _____

Chapter 3 Test Form A *cont'd*

Use the function $f(x) = 3x^2 - 7$ for problems 17 – 19.

17. Find $f(1)$.   17. _____

18. Find $f(-2)$ 18. _____

19. Find $f\left(\dfrac{1}{3}\right)$ 19. _____

Use the following graph for problems 20 – 21.

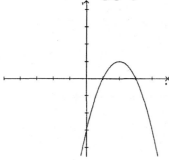

20. Find the domain.   20. _____

21. Find the range.   21. _____

22. Find the domain of the function $y = \dfrac{1}{2x-1}$.   22. _____

The following graph shows the height in feet of a ball thrown in the air by a small child.

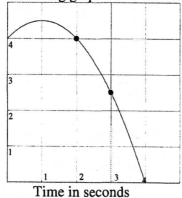

Time in seconds

23. How high is the ball after 2 seconds?   23. _____

24. What is the approximate height of the ball at its highest point?   24. _____

25. After how many seconds does the ball hit the ground?   25. _____

Chapter 3 Test Form B

Graph the following.

1. $2x - y = 2$

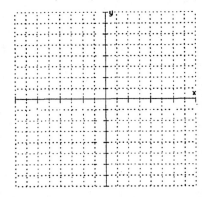

2. $x - 2y = 4$

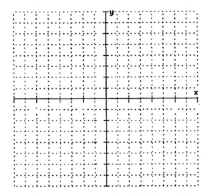

3. $y = 2x - 3$

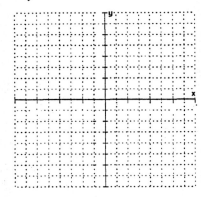

4. $x = -2$

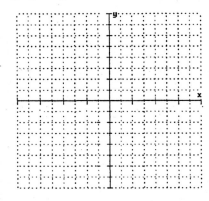

Find the slopes of the following lines.

5.

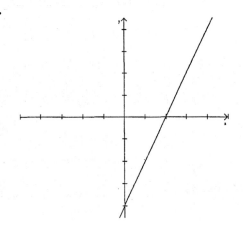

5. _____

Chapter 3 Test Form B *cont'd*

6. through $(-6, -4)$ and $(0, 8)$ 6. _____

7. $2x - 5y = 10$ 7. _____

8. $x = 4$ 8. _____

9. Determine the slope and y-intercept of the line   9. _____
     $3x + 2y = 4$

10. Determine whether the graphs of the lines would   10. _____
      parallel, perpendicular, or neither.
      $6x + 2y = 12$
         $y = -3x + 4$

Find the equations of the following lines. Write the equation in the from $Ax + By = C$.

11. with slope $\dfrac{2}{3}$, through $(-1, -4)$ 11. _____

12. through $(-4, 5)$ and $(-2, -3)$ 12. _____

13. through $(3, -4)$ and $(4, -4)$ 13. _____

14. with slope $-\dfrac{2}{3}$ and y-intercept 6   14. _____

Determine which of the following are functions.

15. $\{(-2, 0), (-1, 4), (1, 3), (2, 3)\}$ 15. _____

16.   16. _____

Chapter 3 Test Form B *cont'd*

Use the function $f(x) = 3x - 6$ for problems 17 – 19.

17. Find $f(2)$.   17. _____

18. Find $f(-2)$ 18. _____

19. Find $f(0)$ 19. _____

Use the following graph for problems 20 – 21.

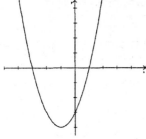

20. Find the domain.   20. _____

21. Find the range.   21. _____

22. Find the domain of the function $y = \dfrac{2}{2x-4}$.   22. _____

The following graph shows the height in feet of a diver above the water after x seconds.

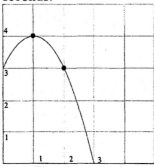

Time in seconds

23. What is the height above the water at the highest   23. _____
point?

24. After how many seconds was the highest point   24. _____
reached?

25. After how many seconds did the diver hit the   25. _____
water?

Chapter 3 Test Form C

Graph the following.

1. $2x + y = 5$

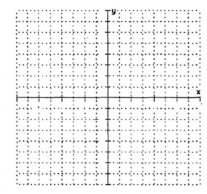

2. $y = 2x + 3$

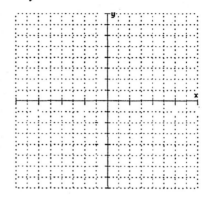

3. $x = 3$

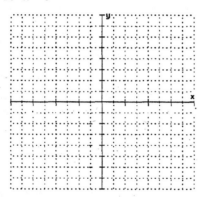

4. $x - 3y = 6$

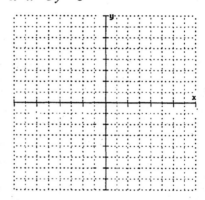

Find the slopes of the following lines.

5.

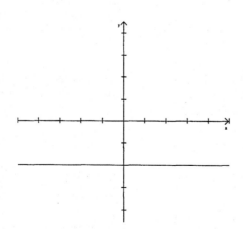

5. _____

Chapter 3 Test Form C *cont'd*

6. through $(-2, -5)$ and $(-3, 8)$ 6. _____

7. $x - 4y = 7$ 7. _____

8. $y = 5$ 8. _____

9. Determine the slope and y-intercept of the line   9. _____
 $3x - y = 4$

10. Determine whether the graphs of the lines would   10. _____
 parallel, perpendicular, or neither.
 $2x - y = 3$

$$y = \frac{1}{2}x - 4$$

Find the equations of the following lines. Write the equation in the from $Ax + By = C$.

11. with slope $-\frac{2}{5}$, through $(2, 0)$ 11. _____

12. through the $(0, -2)$ and $(4, -7)$ 12. _____

13. through $(-5, 4)$ and $(-6, 4)$ 13. _____

14. with slope $\frac{3}{5}$ and y-intercept 4   14. _____

Determine which of the following are functions.

15. $\{(1, 3), (-1, 3), (2, 3)\}$ 15. _____

16.   16. _____

Chapter 3 Test Form C *cont'd*

Use the function $f(x) = \frac{2}{3}x - 6$ for problems 17 – 19.

    17. Find $f(6)$.

    17. _____

    18. Find $f(-3)$

    18. _____

    19. Find $f(2)$

    19. _____

Use the following graph for problems 20 – 21.

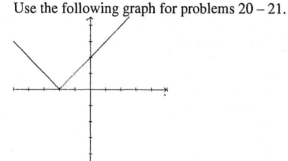

    20. Find the domain.

    20. _____

    21. Find the range.

    21. _____

    22. Find the domain of the function $y = \dfrac{x+2}{x-3}$.

    22. _____

The following graph shows the height in feet of a ball as it is dropped and then bounces up, after x seconds.

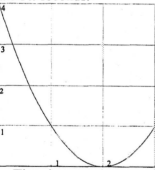

Time in seconds

    23. After how many seconds does the ball hit the ground?

    23. _____

    24. At what two times is the ball 1 foot off the ground?

    24. _____

    25. How high was the ball after 1 second?

    25. _____

Chapter 3 Test Form D

Match the correct equation to the given graph.

1.

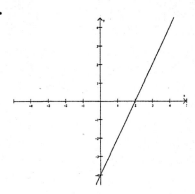

    a. $2x + y = -4$ **b.** $2x + y = 0$ **c.** $2x - y = 4$ **d.** $2x + y = 4$

2.

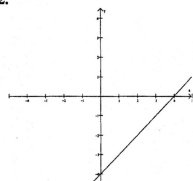

    a. $x + y = 4$ **b.** $x - y = 4$ **c.** $x + y = -4$ **d.** $x - y = -4$

3.

    a. $y = \dfrac{2}{3}x + 5$ **b.** $y = -\dfrac{2}{3}x + 5$ **c.** $y = 2x + 5$ **d.** $2x - 3y = 5$

Chapter 3 Test Form D *cont'd*

4.

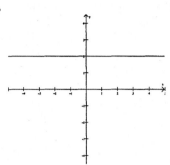

    a. $y = 2$ **b.** $x = 2$ **c.** $y = -2$ **d.** $x = -2$

Find the slopes of the following lines.

5.

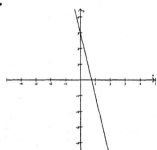

    a. $m = -\dfrac{1}{4}$ **b.** $m = \dfrac{1}{4}$ **c.** $m = 4$ **d.** $m = -4$

6. through $(3, -4)$ and $(-6, 4)$

    a. $m = 0$ **b.** $m = -\dfrac{8}{11}$ **c.** $m = -\dfrac{8}{9}$ **d.** $m = \dfrac{8}{9}$

7. $3x - 5y = 8$

    a. $m = -\dfrac{5}{3}$ **b.** $m = \dfrac{5}{3}$ **c.** $m = \dfrac{3}{5}$ **d.** $m = -\dfrac{3}{5}$

8. $x = -4$

    a. $m = -4$ **b.** $m = 4$ **c.** $m = 0$ **d.** m is undefined

9. Write in the slope-intercept form. $3x - 4y = 4$

    a. $y = -\dfrac{3}{4}x + 1$ **b.** $y = \dfrac{3}{4}x - 1$ **c.** $y = 3x + 6$ **d.** $y = -3x - 2$

10. Are the graphs of the following lines parallel, perpendicular, or neither.

$$y = 2x - 5$$

$$4x - 2y = 6$$

a. parallel   **b.** perpendicular   **c.** neither

Find the equation of the following lines.

11. with slope $\dfrac{2}{3}$, through (0, 5)

    a. $2x - 3y = -15$ **b.** $2x + 3y = 15$

    c. $2x + 3y = -15$ **d.** $3x - 2y = 15$

12. through (2, 6) and (−3, 5)

    a. $x + y = 8$ **b.** $x + 5y = 28$ **c.** $x - y = -8$ **d.** $x - 5y = -28$

13. through (−4, −3) and (4, −6)

    a. $3x - 8y = 12$ **b.** $9x + 8y = -12$ **c.** $3x + 8y = -36$ **d.** $9x + 8y = 24$

14. with slope $\dfrac{3}{5}$ and *y*-intercept −4

    a. $3x - 5y = 20$ **b.** $3x + 5y = -20$ **c.** $5x - 3y = 12$ **d.** $5x + 3y = -12$

15. Determine which one is a function.

    a. {(1, 3), (−1, 2), (2, 4), (−2, −3)}   **b.** {(−2, 0), (1, 0), (1, 2), (2, −4)}

    c. {(1, 3), (1, 2), (2, 4), (2, −3)}   **d.** {(0, 3), (0, 4), (0, 6)}

16. Determine which one is not a function.

a.

b.

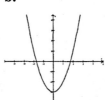

c.

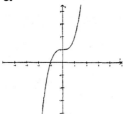

d.

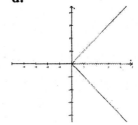

Chapter 3 Test Form D *cont'd*

Use the function $f(x) = 3x - 7$, for problems 17 – 19.

17. Find $f(2)$.

    a. 1   **b.** −1   **c.** −2   **d.** 2

18. Find $f(0)$.

    a. 4   **b.** −4   **c.** −7   **d.** 7

19. Find $f\left(-\dfrac{1}{2}\right)$.

    a. $-\dfrac{17}{2}$ **b.** −2   **c.** 2   **d.** $\dfrac{11}{2}$

Use the following graph for problems 20 and 21.

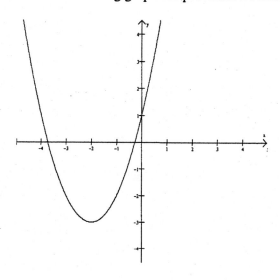

20. Give the domain.

    a. $(-\infty, \infty)$ **b.** $[-2, -4]$ **c.** $[-2, \infty)$ **d.** $[-4, \infty)$

21. Give the range.

    a. $(-\infty, \infty)$ **b.** $[-2, -4]$ **c.** $[-2, \infty)$ **d.** $[-3, \infty)$

Chapter 3 Test Form D *cont'd*

22. Give the domain: $\dfrac{x-5}{x+3}$

    a. all real numbers except −3   **b.** $(-\infty, 3]$

    c. $(3, \infty)$ **d.** all real numbers except 3

The following graph shows the height of a diver in feet above the water x seconds after the dive begins.

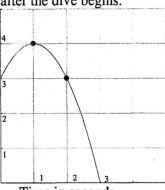

Time in seconds

23. What was the divers highest point above the water?

    a. 1 foot   **b.** 2 feet   **c.** 3 feet   **d.** 4 feet

24. After how many seconds did the diver reach the highest point?

    a. 1 second   **b.** 2 second   **c.** 3 seconds   **d.** 4 seconds

25. After how many seconds did the diver hit the water?

    a. 1 second   **b.** 2 second   **c.** 3 seconds   **d.** 4 seconds

Chapter 3 Test Form E

Match the correct equation to the given graph.

1.

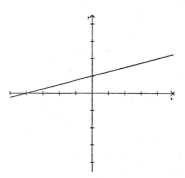

a. $x + 4y = 4$ **b.** $4x + y = 4$ **c.** $x + y = 4$ **d.** $x - 4y = -4$

2.

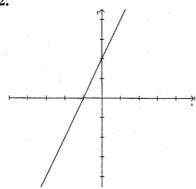

a. $x - 2y = -2$ **b.** $x + 2y = -2$ **c.** $2x - y = -2$ **d.** $2x + y = -2$

3.

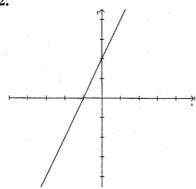

a. $y = \frac{2}{3}x - 1$ **b.** $y = -\frac{2}{3}x + 1$ **c.** $y = \frac{2}{3}x + 1$ **d.** $2x + 3y = 1$

Chapter 3 Test Form E *cont'd*

4.

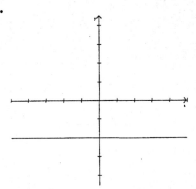

    a. $y = 2$ **b.** $x = 2$ **c.** $y = -2$ **d.** $x = -2$

Find the slopes of the following lines.

5.

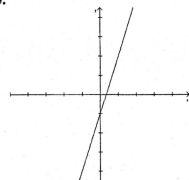

    a. $m = -3$ **b.** $m = \dfrac{1}{3}$ **c.** $m = 3$ **d.** $m = -\dfrac{1}{3}$

6. through (3, 5) and (6, 2)

    a. $m = 3$ **b.** $m = -1$ **c.** $m = \dfrac{1}{3}$ **d.** $m = -3$

7. $3x - 4y = 6$

    a. $m = -\dfrac{3}{4}$ **b.** $m = \dfrac{3}{4}$ **c.** $m = -4$ **d.** $m = -3$

8. $x = -4$

    a. $m = -4$ **b.** $m = 4$ **c.** $m = 0$ **d.** m is undefined

Chapter 3 Test Form E *cont'd*

9. Determine the slope and the *y*-intercept. $3x - y = 4$

    a. $m = 3, b = 4$ **b.** $m = -3, b = 4$ **c.** $m = 3, b = -4$ **d.** $m = -3, b = -4$

10. Are the graphs of the following lines parallel, perpendicular, or neither.

$2x - 3y = 6$

$2x + 3y = 9$

    a. parallel   **b.** perpendicular   **c.** neither

Find the equation of the following lines.

11. with slope $\dfrac{1}{2}$, through $(-1, 3)$

    a. $x - 2y = 7$ **b.** $x - 2y = -7$ **c.** $x + 2y = 7$ **d.** $x + 3y = -7$

12. through $(-2, 0)$ and $(3, 1)$

    a. $x - 5y = -2$ **b.** $x - y = -2$ **c.** $x + y = 4$ **d.** $x + 5y = 2$

13. through $(3, -2)$ and $(-4, 1)$

    a. $3x - 5y = 19$ **b.** $3x + 7y = -5$ **c.** $7x - 3y = 3$ **d.** $2x + 9y = -7$

14. with slope $\dfrac{4}{3}$ and *y*-intercept -3

    a. $3x - 4y = -12$ **b.** $4x + 3y = -9$ **c.** $4x - 3y = 9$ **d.** $3x - 4y = 12$

15. Determine which one is not a function.

    a. $\{(-3, 2), (-2, 1), (-1, 0 \quad)\}$ **b.** $\{(3, 0), (-2, 0), (5, 0)\}$

    c. $\{(2, 1), (1, 2), (0, 1)\}$ **d.** $\{(-1, 3), (4, -1), (4, 3)\}$

16. Determine which one is a function.

    a.   **b.**

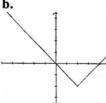

    c.   **d.**

 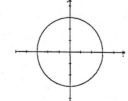

Chapter 3 Test Form E *cont'd*

Use the function $f(x) = 3x - 5$, for problems 17 – 19.

17. Find $f(4)$.

    a. 7   **b.** 2   **c.** −7   **d.** −2

18. Find $f(-1)$.

    a. −2   **b.** −8   **c.** 8   **d.** 2

19. Find $f\left(\dfrac{2}{3}\right)$.

    a. 4   **b.** 13   **c.** 3   **d.** −3

Use the following graph for problems 20 and 21.

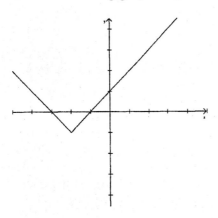

20. Give the domain.

    a. $(-\infty, \infty)$ **b.** $(-\infty, -1]$ **c.** $[-1, \infty)$ **d.** $[-1, 2]$

21. Give the range.

    a. $(-\infty, \infty)$ **b.** $(-\infty, -1]$ **c.** $[-1, \infty)$ **d.** $[-1, 2]$

22. Give the domain: $y = \dfrac{3}{x+2}$

    a. $(-\infty, -2)$ **b.** all real numbers except −2
    c. $(-2, \infty)$ **d.** all real numbers except 2

Chapter 3 Test Form E *cont'd*

The following graph represents the height in feet of a football after it is thrown when it is yards away from the quarterback.

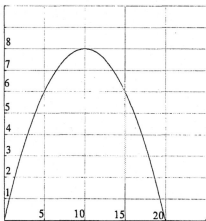

Distance away from the quarterback in yards

23. What is the highest the football goes?
    a. 4 feet   **b.** 6 feet   **c.** 8 feet   **d.** 2 feet

24. How far from the quarterback is the ball when it is at the highest point?

    a. 5 yards   **b.** 10 yards   **c.** 15 yards   **d.** 20 yards

25. How far from the quarterback is the ball when it hits the ground?

    a. 5 yards   **b.** 10 yards   **c.** 15 yards   **d.** 20 yards

Chapter 3 Test Form F

Match the correct equation to the given graph.

1.

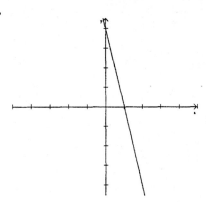

    a. $x + 4y = 4$ **b.** $4x + y = 4$ **c.** $x + y = 4$ **d.** $x - 4y = -4$

2.

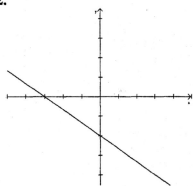

    a. $x - 2y = -2$ **b.** $x + 2y = -2$ **c.** $2x - y = -2$ **d.** $2x + y = -2$

3.

    a. $y = \dfrac{2}{3}x - 1$ **b.** $y = -\dfrac{2}{3}x + 1$ **c.** $y = \dfrac{2}{3}x + 1$ **d.** $y = -\dfrac{1}{3}x + 3$

Chapter 3 Test Form F *cont'd*

4.

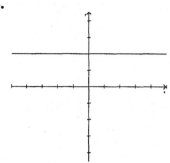

   a. $y = 2$ **b.** $x = 2$ **c.** $y = -2$ **d.** $x = -2$

Find the slopes of the following lines.

5.

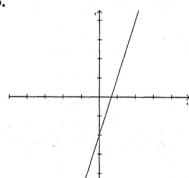

   a. $m = 3$ **b.** $m = -3$ **c.** $m = \dfrac{1}{3}$ **d.** $m = -\dfrac{1}{3}$

6. through $(-1, -9)$ and $(4, -2)$

   a. $m = \dfrac{5}{7}$ **b.** $m = -\dfrac{11}{3}$ **c.** $m = \dfrac{7}{5}$ **d.** $m = -\dfrac{3}{11}$

7. $4x - 6y = -36$

   a. $m = \dfrac{2}{3}$ **b.** $m = -\dfrac{2}{3}$ **c.** $m = 0$ **d.** undefined

8. $4y + 3 = 9$

   a. $m = -3$ **b.** $m = \dfrac{4}{3}$ **c.** $m = 0$ **d.** m is undefined

Chapter 3 Test Form F *cont'd*

9. Determine the slope and the *y*-intercept. $3x + y = -4$

   a. $m = 3, b = 4$ **b.** $m = \dfrac{1}{3}, b = 4$ **c.** $m = -3, b = -4$ **d.** $m = -\dfrac{1}{3}, b = 4$

10. Are the graphs of the following lines parallel, perpendicular, or neither.
$$y = -\frac{2}{5}x - 3$$
$$2x + 5y = 10$$

   a. parallel   **b.** perpendicular   **c.** neither

Find the equation of the following lines.

11. with slope $-\dfrac{3}{7}$, through (0, –5)

   a. $3x + 7y = -5$ **b.** $3x + 7y = -35$ **c.** $-3x + 7y = -5$ **d.** $-3x + 7y = -35$

12. with slope 4 and *x*-intercept –3

   a. $4x + y = -12$ **b.** $4x - y = -12$ **c.** $4x - 3y = 12$ **d.** $4x + 3y = 12$

13. with undefined slope through (3, –1)
   a. $x = 3$ **b.** $y = -1$ **c.** $3x - y = 0$ **d.** $3x - y = -3$

14. through (7, –4) and (–1, –5)

   a. $3x - 2y = 28$ **b.** $2x - 3y = 28$ **c.** $x - 8y = 39$ **d.** $x - 8y = 25$

15. Determine which one is a function.

   a. {(–1, 1), (1, 1), (–2, 2), (2, 2)}   **b.** {(1,1), (1, –1), (4, 2), (4 –2)}
   c. {(1, –1), (1,1), (2, –2), (2, 2)}   **d.** {(0, 1), (0, 2), (0, 3), (0, 4)}

Chapter 3 Test Form F *cont'd*

16. Determine which one is a function.

a.

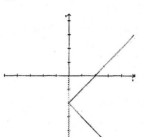

b.

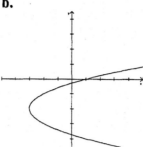

c.

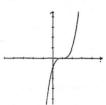

d.

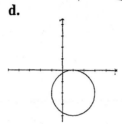

Use the function $f(x) = -\dfrac{9}{2}x + 4$, for problems 17 – 19.

17. Find $f(2)$.

   a. −13   b. 13   c. −5   d. −14

18. Find $f(-2)$.

   a. −13   b. 13   c. 5   d. 14

19. Find $f(4)$.

   a. −22   b. 0   c. −32   d. −14

Chapter 3 Test Form F *cont'd*

Use the following graph for problems 20 and 21.

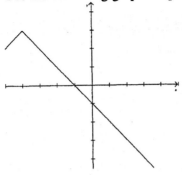

20. Give the domain.

    a. $(-\infty, \infty)$ **b.** $[-3, 4]$ **c.** $(-\infty, 4]$ **d.** $[3, \infty)$

21. Give the range.

    a. $(-\infty, \infty)$ **b.** $[-3, 4]$ **c.** $(-\infty, 3]$ **d.** $[3, \infty)$

22. Give the domain: $y = \dfrac{1}{x+5}$

    a. $(-\infty, -5)$ **b.** all real numbers except -5

    c. $(-5, \infty)$ **d.** all real numbers except 5

The graph shows the height in feet of a toy rocket seconds after it has been fired.

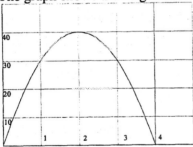

Time in seconds after fired

23. What is the highest the rocket goes?

    a. 10 feet   **b.** 20 feet   **c.** 30 feet   **d.** 40 feet

24. How long does it take the rocket to reach its highest point?

    a. 1 second   **b.** 2 seconds   **c.** 3 seconds   **d.** 4 seconds

25. At what two times is the rocket 30 feet high?

    a. 0 and 2 seconds   **b.** 1 and 2 seconds

    c. 1 and 3 seconds   **d.** 2 and 4 seconds

Chapter 4 Test Form A

Determine whether the ordered pair satisfies the system of linear equation..

1. $x - 2y = 4$ $(2,1)$
   $3x + y = 5$

   1. _____

2. $x + y = 3$ $(2,1)$
   $2x - y = 3$

   2. _____

3. $x + 2y = 5$ $(1,4)$
   $2x - y = -2$

   3. _____

Solve each system of equations by graphing.

4. $y = 3x - 1$
   $y = -3x + 3$

5. $2x - y = 4$
   $6x - 3y = 8$

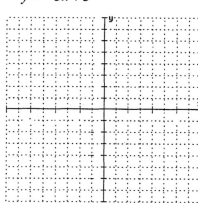
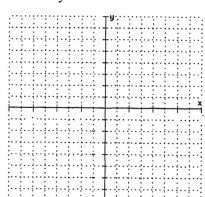

Solve each system of equations by substitution.

6. $2x - 3y = -8$
   $x - y = -2$

   6. _____

7. $2x + y = 5$
   $3x - 2y = 4$

   7. _____

8. $y = 3x - 2$
   $2x + y = 8$

   8. _____

9. $3x - y = 2$
   $2x - y = 0$

   9. _____

Chapter 4 Test Form A *cont'd*

10. $3x + y = 5$
$2x - y = 10$

10. _____

Solve each system of equations by addition.

11. $3x - 2y = 6$
$x + 2y = 2$

11. _____

12. $\dfrac{x}{4} + \dfrac{3y}{4} = 2$
$\dfrac{x}{2} + \dfrac{y}{4} = -1$

12. _____

13. $x + 2y = -2$
$3x - 4y = -6$

13. _____

14. $2x + 4y = 12$
$3x + 6y = 10$

14. _____

15. $2x + 3y = -1$
$x + 4y = 7$

15. _____

Solve by substitution or addition.

16. $y = -2x$
$2x + y = 0$

16. _____

17. $3x + y = 5$
$6x - y = -2$

17. _____

18. $\dfrac{1}{2}x + y = \dfrac{7}{2}$
$\dfrac{1}{2}x - \dfrac{1}{2}y = -1$

18. _____

19. One number is 2 more than another number. Their sum is 8. Find the two numbers.

19. _____

20. Basketball tickets at a high school sell for $5 and $2 for students. $900 was made in sales for one game and a total of 270 tickets were sold. How many of each type ticket were sold?

20. _____

Chapter 4 Test Form A *cont'd*

Graph each inequality.

21. $y < 2x + 3$

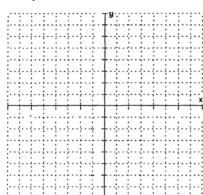

22. $2x + y \le 3$

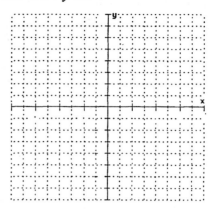

Graph the solutions to each system of inequalities.

23.
$x + y \le 3$
$2x - y > 5$

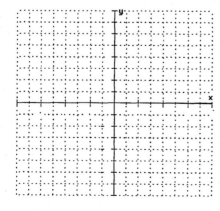

24.
$x \le 3$
$x + 4y > 5$

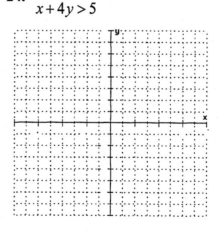

25.
$y < 2x + 5$
$x + y < 6$

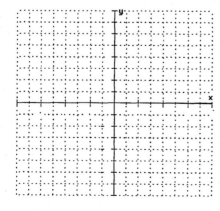

Chapter 4 Test Form B

Determine whether the ordered pair satisfies the system of linear equation..

1. $2x + y = 3$ $\quad(2,-1)$
$\quad x - y = 3$

1. _____

2. $3x - y = 8$ $\quad(3,1)$
$\quad x + y = 0$

2. _____

3. $4x + 2y = 6$ $\quad(1,1)$
$\quad 6x + 3y = 9$

3. _____

Solve each system of equations by graphing.

4. $y = 2x - 3$
$\quad y = x - 2$

5. $x + y = 1$
$\quad x - y = -7$

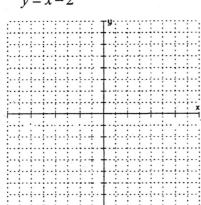
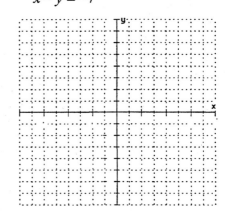

Solve each system of equations by substitution.

6. $x = 3 - 2y$
$\quad -x + 2y = 13$

6. _____

7. $x + 4y = 11$
$\quad 2x - 3y = 0$

7. _____

8. $y = 3x$
$\quad 2x - y = 5$

8. _____

9. $4x + 2y = 3$
$\quad y = 6 - 2x$

9. _____

Chapter 4 Test Form B *cont'd*

10. $\begin{aligned} 2x - y &= 4 \\ x + y &= 1 \end{aligned}$

10. _____

Solve each system of equations by addition.

11. $\begin{aligned} 3x - 2y &= -7 \\ 5x + 3y &= 20 \end{aligned}$

11. _____

12. $\begin{aligned} 5x - y &= 3 \\ x + 2y &= 16 \end{aligned}$

12. _____

13. $\begin{aligned} 4x - y &= 5 \\ 3x - 2y &= 0 \end{aligned}$

13. _____

14. $\begin{aligned} 4x + y &= 3 \\ 8x - y &= 0 \end{aligned}$

14. _____

15. $\begin{aligned} 4x - 8y &= 6 \\ 5x - 10y &= 15 \end{aligned}$

15. _____

Solve by substitution or addition.

16. $\begin{aligned} 2x + 2y &= 4 \\ x - y &= 4 \end{aligned}$

16. _____

17. $\begin{aligned} x + y &= 5 \\ x + 2y &= 10 \end{aligned}$

17. _____

18. $\begin{aligned} \frac{1}{2}x + y &= -1 \\ \frac{1}{2}x + \frac{3}{4}y &= 1 \end{aligned}$

18. _____

19. One number is twice another number. Their sum is 9. Find the two numbers.

19. _____

20. How much 20% solution needs to be added to 60% solution to make 400 ml of a 40% solution?

20. _____

Chapter 4 Test Form B *cont'd*

Graph each inequality.

21. $y \leq 3$

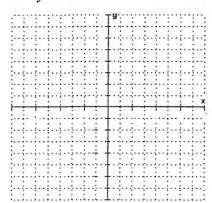

22. $3x + y > 4$

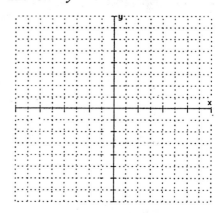

Graph the solutions to each system of inequalities.

23.
$x + y < 3$
$2x - y > 5$

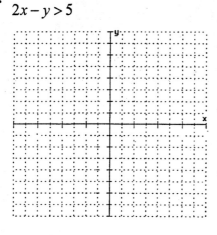

24.
$y < 2x + 5$
$2 + y < 6$

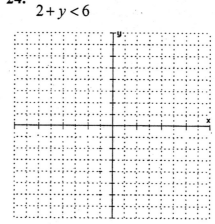

25.
$x \leq 3$
$x + 4y > 5$

Chapter 4 Test Form C

Determine whether the ordered pair satisfies the system of linear equation..

1. $3x - y = 8 \quad (1,5)$
   $6x + y = 1$

   1. _____

2. $2x - 3y = -8 \quad (2,4)$
   $3x + y = 10$

   2. _____

Solve each system of equations by graphing.

3. $y = x - 2$
   $y = 3x - 8$

4. $x + 2y = 6$
   $x + y = 2$

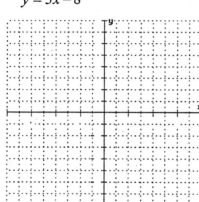
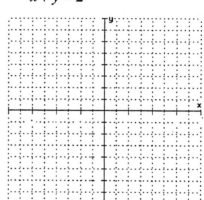

Solve each system of equations by substitution.

5. $y = -x + 5$
   $2x - 3y = -5$

   5. _____

6. $2x + y = 10$
   $3x - 4y = 26$

   6. _____

7. $x - y = 4$
   $2x + y = 2$

   7. _____

8. $y = 2x + 3$
   $3x + 2y = 6$

   8. _____

9. $y = -2x + 3$
   $8x + 4y = 12$

   9. _____

Chapter 4 Test Form C *cont'd*

Solve each system of equations by addition.

10. $3x - 2y = 6$
$4x + 2y = 8$

10. _____

11. $3x - 6y = 5$
$2x - 4y = 8$

11. _____

12. $\dfrac{x}{3} - \dfrac{y}{6} = 1$

$x + \dfrac{y}{4} = \dfrac{3}{2}$

12. _____

13. $3x - 6y = 12$
$2x - 4y = 7$

13. _____

14. $2x + y = 6$
$3x - y = -1$

14. _____

15. $-x + y = -2$
$3x - 2y = 6$

15. _____

Solve by substitution or addition.

16. $2x - y = 4$
$3x - 2y = 4$

16. _____

17. $x + 2y = 2$
$2x - 2y = 1$

17. _____

18. $x + \dfrac{1}{3}y = \dfrac{7}{3}$

$x - \dfrac{1}{2}y = 4$

18. _____

19. The sum of two numbers is 20. Their difference is 4. Find the two numbers.

19. _____

20. A boat travels 100 miles downstream in the same length of time it travels 50 miles upstream. If the boat's speed in still water is 30mph, find The speed of the current of the river.

20. _____

Chapter 4 Test Form C *cont'd*

Graph each inequality.

21. $2x - y \geq 3$

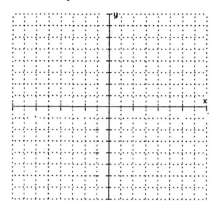

22. $x > -2$

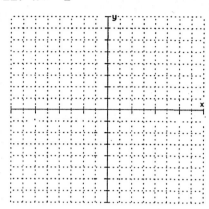

Graph the solutions to each systems of inequalities.

23. $\begin{aligned} x + y &\leq 3 \\ x - y &> 5 \end{aligned}$

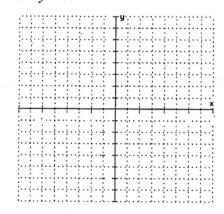

24. $\begin{aligned} 2x + y &< 3 \\ x - 3y &\geq 8 \end{aligned}$

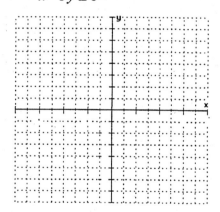

25. $\begin{aligned} x + y &> 4 \\ x &\geq 3 \end{aligned}$

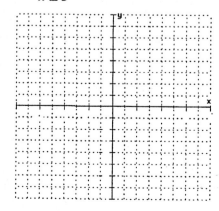

Chapter 4 Test Form D

Choose the correct answer to each problem.

1. Which point is a solution to the following system? $\begin{aligned} 2x + 4y &= 6 \\ x - 2y &= 7 \end{aligned}$

      a. $(5, -1)$ **b.** $(-3, 2)$ **c.** $(3, -2)$ **d.** $(-3, 1)$

Use the following system of equations for problems 2 and 3. Solve by graphing.

$$y = x + 2$$
$$y = 2x + 1$$

2. Find the correct graph for the system.

    a.   **b.**

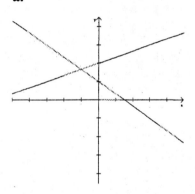
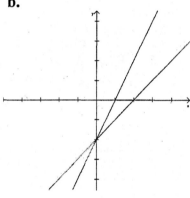

    c.   **d.**

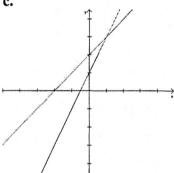
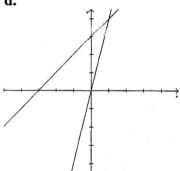

3. Find the solution to the system.

      a. $(-3, 2)$ **b.** $(2, -2)$ **c.** $(1, 3)$ **d.** $(1, 4)$

Chapter 4 Test Form D *cont'd*

Use the following system of equations for problems 4 and 5. Solve by graphing.

$$x + 2y = 4$$
$$2x - 3y = 1$$

4. Find the correct graph for the system.

a.

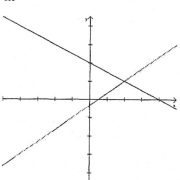

b.

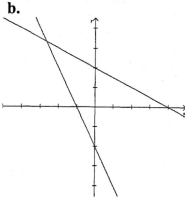

c.

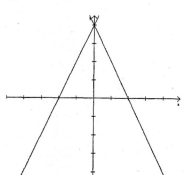

d.

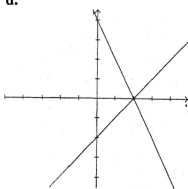

5. Find the solution to the system.

a. $(2, 1)$ **b.** $(2, -2)$ **c.** $(1, 3)$ **d.** $(1, 4)$

Solve by substitution.

6.
$$4x - 2y = 6$$
$$y = 2x - 3$$

a. $(2, -1)$ **b.** $(0, -3)$ **c.** infinite solutions   **d.** no solution

Chapter 4 Test Form D *cont'd*

Use the following system of equations for problems 7 and 6. Solve by substitution.

$3x - y = -2$

$x + 2y = 4$

7. Which of the following shows a substitution that could be used to solve the system?

   a. $x + 2(-3x - 2) = 4$ b. $x + 2(3x + 2) = 4$

   c. $x + 2(-3x + 2) = 4$ d. $x + 2(3x - 2) = 4$

8. Find the solution to the system.

   a. $(1, 5)$ b. $(0, 2)$ c. $(4, 0)$ d. no solution

Use the following system of equations for problems 9 and 10. Solve by addition.

$3x - 6y = 8$

$4x - 8y = 12$

9. Which of the following is the result of multiplying the first equation by -4 and the second equation by 3 and adding the results?

   a. $2y = -2$ b. $6y = 6$ c. $0 = 0$ d. $0 = 4$

10. Find the solution to the system.

    a. $(1, -1)$ b. $(3, 0)$ c. infinite solutions   d. no solution

Use the following system of equation for problems 11, 12 and 13. Solve by addition.

$3x + y = 4$

$x + \dfrac{1}{2}y = \dfrac{3}{2}$

11. Which of the following represents the second equation after the fraction has been eliminated?

    a. $x + y = 3$ b. $2x + y = 3$ c. $2x + 2y = 6$ d. $4x + 4y = 12$

12. Which of the following is the result of subtracting the second equation from the first?

    a. $2x = 1$ b. $x = 1$ c. $x - y = -2$ d. $y = 1$

13. Find the solution to the system.

    a. $(1, 1)$ b. $(0, 4)$ c. $\left(2, -\dfrac{1}{3}\right)$ d. $\left(\dfrac{3}{4}, 1\right)$

Chapter 4 Test Form D *cont'd*

Use the following system of equations for problems 14 and 15. Solve by addition.
$$3x - 2y = -14$$
$$5x + 3y = 2$$

14. Which of the following is the result of multiplying the first equation by 5 and the second equation by -3 and adding the results?

    a. $-y = -64$ **b.** $-19y = -76$ **c.** $12y = -12$ **d.** $-11y = -77$

15. Find the solution to the system.

    a. $(-2, -10)$ **b.** $(-2, 4)$ **c.** $(1, -1)$ **d.** $(0, 7)$

Solve each of the following by substitution or addition.

16.
$$2x + 2y = 4$$
$$x + 2y = 1$$

    a. $(1, 1)$ **b.** $(0, 2)$ **c.** $(3, -1)$ **d.** $(1, 0)$

17.
$$2x + y = -2$$
$$x + 2y = -4$$

    a. $(-2, -1)$ **b.** $(2, -6)$ **c.** $(2, -4)$ **d.** $(0, -2)$

18.
$$x + y = 1$$
$$2x - 2y = 10$$

    a. $(3, -2)$ **b.** $(0, 1)$ **c.** $(-5, -6)$ **d.** $(3, -4)$

19. The sum of two numbers is 68. One number is 4 more than the other. Find the two numbers.

    a. 34, 30   **b.** 34, 34   **c.** 8, 60   **d.** 32, 36

20. The perimeter of a rectangle is 36 feet. The length is twice the width. Find the dimensions of the rectangle.

    a. 12 ft, 24 ft   **b.** 6 ft, 12 ft   **c.** 8 ft, 16 ft   **d.** 18 ft, 18 ft

Chapter 4 Test Form D *cont'd*

Match the graph to the inequality.

21. $2x - 3y > 2$

a.
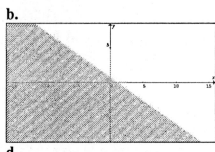

b.
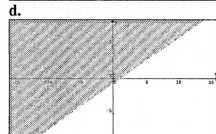

c.
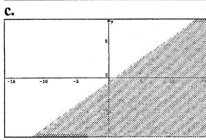

d.
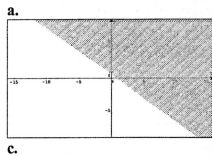

22. $x < -2$

a.
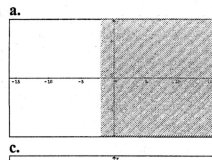

b.
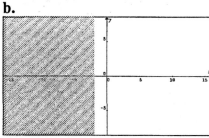

c.
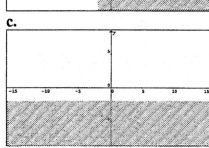

Time in seconds

d.
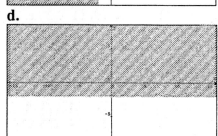

Chapter 4 Test Form D *cont'd*

23. $x + 3y \leq 6$
    $2x - y > 3$

a.

b.
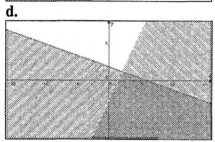

c.
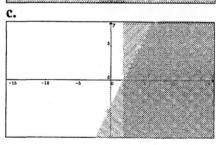

d.

24. $x < 2$
    $2x - y > 4$

a.

b.

c.

d.
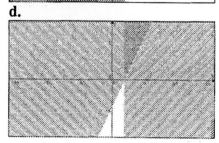

Chapter 4 Test Form D *cont'd*

25.
$$x - y < 3$$
$$2x + y > 6$$

a.

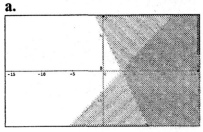

b.

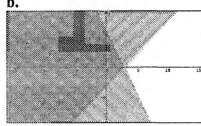

c.

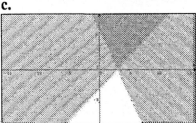

d.

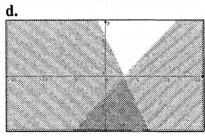

Chapter 4 Test Form E

Choose the correct answer to each problem.

1. Which point is a solution to the following system? $\begin{array}{l} 2x - y = 1 \\ x + 2y = 8 \end{array}$

    a. $(1, 1)$ **b.** $(2, 3)$ **c.** $(5, 7)$ **d.** $(1, 3)$

2. Which point is a solution to the following system? $\begin{array}{l} x - 2y = -12 \\ 2x + 9y = 2 \end{array}$

    a. $(-8, 2)$ **b.** $(0, 6)$ **c.** $(-4, 4)$ **d.** $(4, 8)$

Use the following system of equations for problems 3 and 4. Solve by graphing.
$$y = x - 3$$
$$y = -2x + 3$$

3. Find the correct graph for the system.

    a.

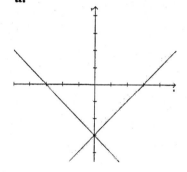

    b.

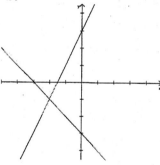

    c.

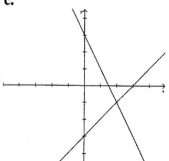

    d.

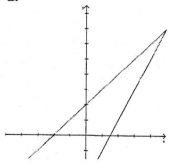

4. Find the solution to the system.

    a. $(0, 3)$ **b.** $(-2, -1)$ **c.** $(5, 7)$ **d.** $(2, -1)$

Chapter 4 Test Form E *cont'd*

Use the following system of equations for problems 5 and 6. Solve by graphing.

$$2x - y = -4$$

$$x - 3y = 3$$

5. Find the correct graph for the system.

a. 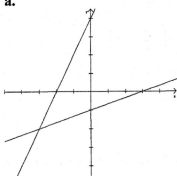   b.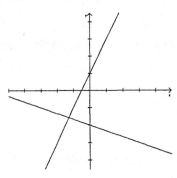

c. 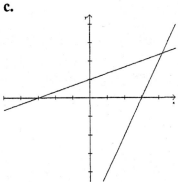   d.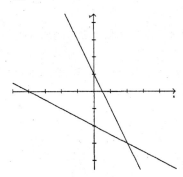

6. Find the solution to the system.

   a. $(-2, 3)$ b. $(3, 2)$ c. $(2, -3)$ d. $(-3, -2)$

Use the following system of equations for problems 7 and 8. Solve by substitution.

$$2x + y = 12$$

$$3x - y = 13$$

7. Which of the following shows a substitution that could be used to solve the system?

   a. $3x - (2x - 12) = 13$ b. $3x - (12 - 2x) = 13$

   c. $2x + (13 - 3x) = 12$ d. $2x - (3x - 13) = 12$

8. Find the solution to the system.

   a. $(3, 6)$ b. $(0, 12)$ c. $(5, 2)$ d. $(1, -10)$

Chapter 4 Test Form E *cont'd*

Use the following system of equations for problems 9 and 10. Solve by substitution.

$x - 3y = 8$

$-2x + 6y = 20$

9. Which of the following shows a substitution that could be used to solve the system?

   a. $-2(8 + 3y) + 6y = 20$ b. $-2(8 - 3y) + 6y = 20$

   c. $-2 + 8 + 3y + 6y = 2-$ d. $-2 - 3y + 8 + 6y = 20$

10. Find the solution to the system.

   a. $(14, 6)$ b. $(5, -1)$ c. infinite solutions   d. no solution

Use the following system of equation for problems 11and 12. Solve by addition.

$4x + 5y = 6$

$-4x + 12y = -40$

11. Which of the following is the result of adding the two equations?

   a. $17y = -46$ b. $17y = -34$ c. $7y = -46$ d. $7y = -34$

12. Find the solution to the system.
   a. $(4, -2)$ b. $(2, -5)$ c. $(4, 2)$ d. $(6, -1)$

Use the following system of equations for problems 13 and 14. Solve by

$6x - 2y = -19$

addition. $\dfrac{1}{2}x + \dfrac{1}{3}y = \dfrac{1}{6}$

13. Which of the following is the result of multiplying the second equation by 6 and then adding that result to the first equation?

   a. $8x = 16$ b. $9x = -12$ c. $9x = -18$ d. $9x = 8$

14. Find the solution to the system.

   a. $\left(\dfrac{4}{3}, \dfrac{27}{2}\right)$ b. $\left(-2, \dfrac{7}{2}\right)$ c. $(2, 16)$ d. $\left(-2, \dfrac{5}{3}\right)$

Chapter 4 Test Form E *cont'd*

Solve each of the following by substitution or addition.

15. $2x + 4y = 6$
    $3x + 6y = 8$

    a. $(1, 1)$ **b.** $(-2, 0)$ **c.** infinite solutions   **d.** no solution

16. $2x + y = 5$
    $x + y = 2$

    a. $(3, -1)$ **b.** $(2, 1)$ **c.** $(1, 3)$ **d.** $(0, 2)$

Use the following information to solve problems 17 and 18.

The difference of two numbers is 2. The larger is 3 less than 6 times the smaller number. Find the numbers.

17. Which of the following system of equations could be used to solve the problem?

    a. $x - y = 2$ **b.** $x - y = 2$ **c.** $x - y = 2$ **d.** $x - y = 2$
    $x = 6y - 3$ $y = 6x - 3$ $x = 3 - 6y$ $y = 3 - 6x$

18. Find the two numbers.

    a. $3, 1$ **b.** $4, 2$ **c.** $5, 3$ **d.** $-1, 1$

Use the following information for problems 19 and 20.

Maria invested $8000 for one year. Part of the money was invested at 8% and the rest and 9%. If the total interest earned for one year was $670, how much was invested at each rate.

19. Which of the following systems of equations could be used to solve the problem?

    a. $x + y = 8000$ **b.** $x + y = 8000$
    $8x + 9y = 670$ $0.8x + 0.9y = 670$

    c. $8x + 9y = 8000$ **d.** $x + y = 8000$
    $x + y = 670$ $0.08x + 0.09y = 670$

20. How much was invested at each rate?

    a. $3000 at 8% and $5000 at 9%   **b.** $5000 at 8% and $3000 at 9%
    c. $4000 at 8% and $4000 at 9%   **d.** $2500 at 8% and $5500 at 9%

Chapter 4 Test Form E *cont'd*

Match the graph to the inequality.

21. $2x + 3y < 3$

a.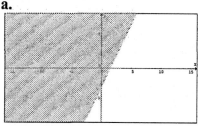

b.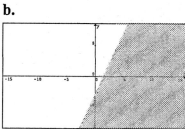

c.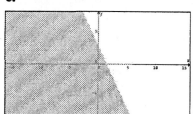

d.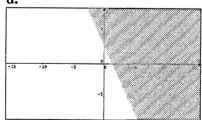

22. $x > -3$

a.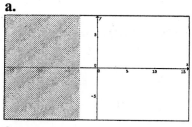

b.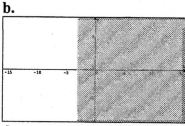

c.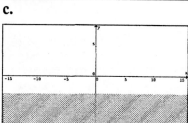

d.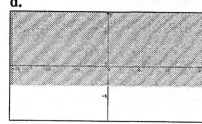

Chapter 4 Test Form E *cont'd*

23. $x + y \leq 4$
    $2x - y \geq 2$

a.
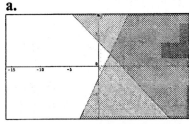

b.
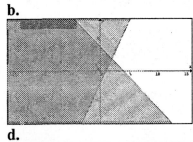

c.
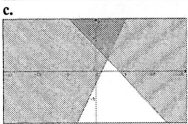

d.
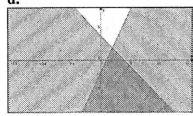

24. $y \geq 3$
    $2x + y \leq 5$

a.
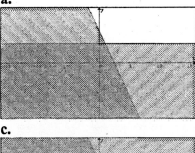

b.
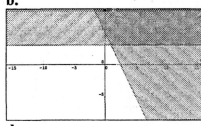

c.
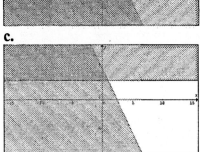

d.
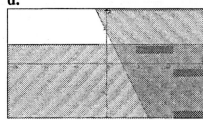

Chapter 4 Test Form E *cont'd*

25. $x - 2y \le 4$
$3x + 2y \ge 4$

a.

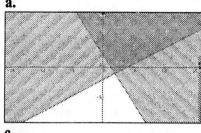

b.

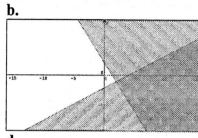

c.

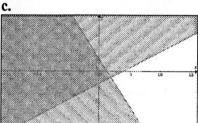

d.

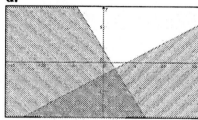

Chapter 4 Test Form F

Choose the correct answer to each problem.

1. Which point is a solution to the following system? $\begin{array}{l} x - y = 0 \\ 2x + y = -12 \end{array}$

   a. $(-4, 4)$ b. $(-4, -4)$ c. $(2, -2)$ d. $(-6, 0)$

2. Which point is a solution to the following system? $\begin{array}{l} x - 3y = 10 \\ x + y = -14 \end{array}$

   a. $(-8, -6)$ b. $(-7, -7)$ c. $(1, -3)$ d. $(2, 2)$

Use the following system of equations for problems 3 and 4. Solve by graphing.
$$x + 2y = 7$$
$$y = x - 1$$

3. Find the correct graph for the system.

   a.

   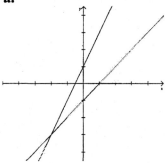

   b.

   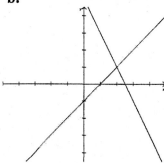

   c.

   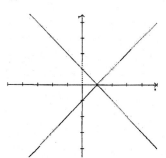

   d.

   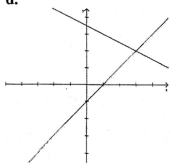

4. Find the solution to the system.

   a. $(-2, -3)$ b. $(-1, -2)$ c. $(3, 2)$ d. $(2 , 1)$

Chapter 4 Test Form F *cont'd*

Use the following system of equations for problems 5 and 6. Solve by graphing.

$$y = -2x - 3$$
$$2x + y = 4$$

5. Find the correct graph for the system.

a.

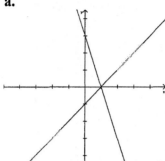

b.

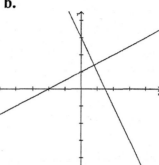

c.

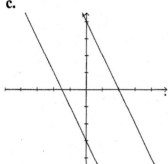

d.

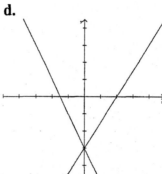

6. Find the solution to the system.

    a. $(0, -3)$ **b.** $(1, 0)$ **c.** $(1, 1)$ **d.** no solution

Use the following system of equations for problems 7 and 8. Solve by substitution.
$$x - y = 1$$
$$y = -3x - 5$$

7. Which of the following shows a substitution that could be used to solve the system?

    a. $x - 3x - 5 = 1$ **b.** $-3x - 5 - 1 = x$
    c. $x + 3x + 5 = 1$ **d.** $x + 3x - 5 = 1$

8. Find the solution to the system.

    a. $(-1, -2)$ **b.** $(-1, 1)$ **c.** $(1, 0)$ **d.** $(1, 2)$

Chapter 4 Test Form F *cont'd*

Use the following system of equations for problems 9 and 10. Solve by substitution.

$2x - 3y = -9$

$4x - y = 7$

9. Which of the following shows a substitution that could be used to solve the system?

   a. $2x - 3(4x - 7) = -9$

   b. $2x - 3(4x + 7) = -9$

   c. $2x - 3(4x - y - 7) = -9$

   d. $2(4x - y) - 3y = -9$

10. Find the solution to the system.

    a. $(-1, 3)$ b. $(-3, 19)$ c. $(3, 5)$ d. no solution

Use the following system of equations for problems 11 and 13. Solve by addition.

$x - 2y = 2$

$3x + 2y = -2$

11. Which of the following is the result of adding the two equations?

    a. $2x = -4$ b. $2x = 0$ c. $4x = -4$ d. $4x = 0$

12. Find the solution to the system.
    a. $(0, 1)$ b. $(0, -1)$ c. $(0, 4)$ d. $(0, -4)$

Use the following system of equations for problems 13 and 14. Solve by

$3x - y = 10$

addition. $\dfrac{2}{3}x + \dfrac{1}{6}y = \dfrac{2}{3}$

13. Which of the following is the result of multiplying the second equation by 6 and then adding that result to the first equation?

    a. $10x = 12$ b. $7x = 16$ c. $7x = 6$ d. $7x = 14$

14. Find the solution to the system.

    a. $(-1, -7)$ b. $(-2, -4)$ c. $(2, -4)$ d. $(1, -13)$

Chapter 4 Test Form F *cont'd*

Solve each of the following by substitution or addition.

15. $\begin{aligned} x + y &= -1 \\ 2x + y &= 2 \end{aligned}$

    a. $(2, -3)$ **b.** $(3, -4)$ **c.** $(-1, 1)$ **d.** $(1, 2)$

16. $\begin{aligned} x + y &= -2 \\ 2x - 4y &= 8 \end{aligned}$

    a. $(0, -2)$ **b.** $(2, 3)$ **c.** $(-2, 0)$ **d.** $(3, 1)$

Use the following information to solve problems 17 and 18.

At a high school football game, student tickets cost $2 each and adult tickets cost $3. A total of 1957 tickets were sold and a total of $5035 was collected. How many of each type of ticket were sold?

17. If x represents the number of student tickets and y represents the number of adult tickets, which of the following system of equations could be used to solve the problem?

    a. $\begin{aligned} x + y &= 1957 \\ 2x + 3y &= 5035 \end{aligned}$ **b.** $\begin{aligned} x + y &= 5035 \\ 2x + 3y &= 1957 \end{aligned}$

    c. $\begin{aligned} 2x + 3y &= 1957 \\ 2x + 3y &= 5035 \end{aligned}$ **d.** $\begin{aligned} 2x &= 1957 \\ 3y &= 5035 \end{aligned}$

18. Solve the system. How many tickets of each type were sold?

    a. 926 student tickets, 1021 adult tickets
    b. 836 student tickets, 1121 adult tickets
    c. 1036 student tickets, 921 adult tickets
    d. 1136 student tickets, 821 adult tickets

Chapter 4 Test Form F *cont'd*

Use the following information for problems 19 and 20.

Frank invested $8000 for one year. Part of the money was invested at 4% and the rest and 5%. If the total interest earned for one year was $350, how much was invested at each rate.

19. Which of the following systems of equations could be used to solve the problem?

a.
$$x + 0.04x = 350$$
$$y + 0.05y = 8000$$

b.
$$0.04x + 0.05y = 8000$$
$$x + y = 350$$

c.
$$4x + 5y = 350$$
$$x + y = 8000$$

d.
$$0.04x + 0.05y = 350$$
$$x + y = 8000$$

20. How much was invested at each rate?

a. $3000 at 4% and $5000 at 5% **b.** $2000 at 4% and $6000 at 5%
c. $3500 at 4% and $4500 at 5% **d.** $5000 at 4% and $3000 at 5%

Match the graph to the inequality.

21. $2x + 3y > 3$

a.
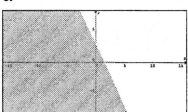

b.
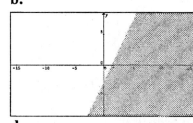

c.

d.
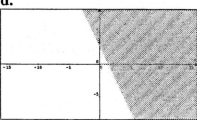

Chapter 4 Test Form F *cont'd*

22. $y < -3$

a.

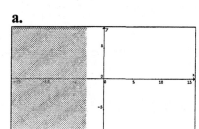

b.

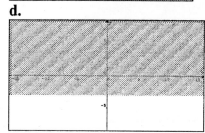

c.

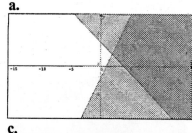

d.

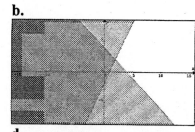

23. $x + y \geq 4$
    $2x - y \geq 2$

a.

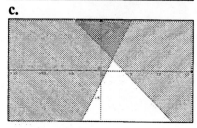

b.

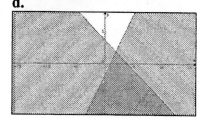

c.

d.

Chapter 4 Test Form F *cont'd*

24. $\quad y \geq 3$
$\quad\quad 2x + y \geq 5$

a.

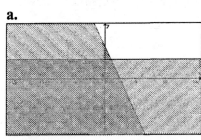

b.

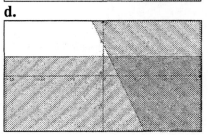

c.

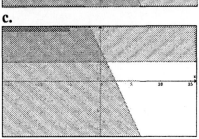

d.

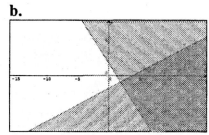

25. $\quad x - 2y \geq 4$
$\quad\quad 3x + 2y \leq 4$

a.

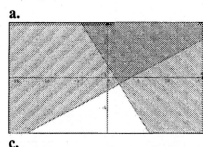

b.

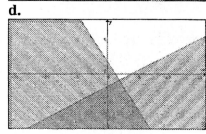

c.

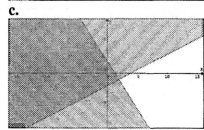

d.

Chapter 5 Test Form A

Evaluate.

1. $(-2)^3$

1. _____

2. -2^4

2. _____

3. 4^{-2}

3. _____

Simplify. Use only positive exponents in the final answer.

4. $(4x^3)(2x^5)$

4. _____

5. $(-4x^5)(5x^6)$

5. _____

6. $\dfrac{a^6 b^5}{a^3 b^2}$

6. _____

7. $(3x^4 y^3)^0$

7. _____

8. $\left(-\dfrac{1}{3}\right)^{-2}$

8. _____

9. $\left(\dfrac{x^{-2} y}{x^{-3} y^5}\right)^{-2}$

9. _____

10. Express in scientific notation. 5,723,000

10. _____

11. Express in standard form. 7.94×10^{-6}

11. _____

12. Perform the indicated operation and express the answer in scientific notation.
$(2.4 \times 10^3) \times (3.8 \times 10^5)$

12. _____

13. Find the degree of the following polynomial.
$4x^5 + 2x^3 - 3x^2 + 4x - 6$

13. _____

Perform the indicated operation.

14. $(3x^2 - 7x - 9) + (3x^2 - 9x)$

14. _____

Chapter 5 Test Form A *cont'd*

15. $\left(3x^2 - 7x - 5\right) + \left(2x^2 - 8x - 4\right)$ 15. _____

16. $\left(5x^2 - 3x - 5\right) - \left(7x^2 - 4x + 4\right)$ 16. _____

17. $\left(4a^2 - 3ab + 5b^2\right) - \left(3a^2 - 3ab + 4b^2\right)$ 17. _____

18. $\left(-\dfrac{2}{3}x^5\right)\left(\dfrac{5}{6}x^8\right)$ 18. _____

19. $-2x^3\left(3x^4 - 2x^2 + 4\right)$ 19. _____

20. $\left(3x - 5\right)\left(2x + 3\right)$ 20. _____

21. $\left(3x + 2\right)^2$ 21. _____

22. $\left(2x - 5\right)\left(2x + 5\right)$ 22. _____

23. $\dfrac{4x^5 - 16x^3 - 8x^2}{4x^2}$ 23. _____

24. $\dfrac{x^2 + 5x - 24}{x + 8}$ 24. _____

25. The area of a rectangle is $x^2 - x - 6$. Find   25. _____
    the length if the width is $x - 3$.

Chapter 5 Test Form B

Evaluate.

1. $(-2)^4$ 1. _____

2. 2^{-4} 2. _____

3. $(-3)^{-2}$ 3. _____

Simplify. Use only positive exponents in the final answer.

4. $\dfrac{x^{16}}{x^4}$ 4. _____

5. $\left(\dfrac{a^3b^5}{a^6b^4}\right)^3$ 5. _____

6. $(-2x^5)(4x^3y^2)$ 6. _____

7. $\left(\dfrac{x^{-3}y^4}{x^{-4}y^{-3}}\right)^{-2}$ 7. _____

8. Express in scientific notation. 0.00000236 8. _____

9. Express in standard form. 4.29×10^6 9. _____

10. Perform the indicated operation and express   10. _____
    the answer in scientific notation.
    $(3.1\times10^3)(4.6\times10^8)$

11. Find the degree of the following polynomial.   11. _____
    $6x^2y^3 - 8xy^7 + 3xy$

Perform the indicated operation.

12. $3x - 4x^3 + 2x + 5x^3 + 8$ 12. _____

13. $(2x^2 + 3x - 7) + (4x^2 - 3x + 9)$ 13. _____

Chapter 5 Test Form B *cont'd*

14. $\dfrac{\substack{x^4 - 4x^3 + 2x - 8}}{-\left(3x^4 + 2x^3 - 3x - 5\right)}$

14. _____

15. Subtract $\left(3x^2 - 8\right)$ from $4x^2 - 2x + 3$

15. _____

16. $-3x\left(4x^2 - 5x + 6\right)$

16. _____

17. $\left(3x - 6\right)\left(4x + 5\right)$

17. _____

18. $\left(2x - 3\right)\left(3x^2 - 4x + 5\right)$

18. _____

19. $\left(3x - 4\right)\left(2x + 5\right)$

19. _____

20. $\left(3x - 5\right)^2$

20. _____

21. $\left(7x - 3\right)\left(7x + 3\right)$

21. _____

22. $\left(3x^2 - 5y^3\right)^2$

22. _____

23. $\dfrac{4x^3 + 8x^2 - 2x}{2x}$

23. _____

24. $\dfrac{x^3 - 8}{x - 2}$

24. _____

25. The area of a square if each side is $x - 4$.

25. _____

Chapter 5 Test Form C

Evaluate.

1. $(-2)^3$ 1. _____

2. -3^0 2. _____

3. -2^4 3. _____

Simplify. Use only positive exponents in the final answer.

4. $\dfrac{a^{27}}{a^{13}}$ 4. _____

5. $\dfrac{12x^7y^3}{6x^3y}$ 5. _____

6. $\dfrac{3^5 x^4 y^{-2}}{3^3 x^6 y^{-8}}$ 6. _____

7. $\left(\dfrac{x^{-4}y^2}{x^4 y^{-3}}\right)^{-2}$ 7. _____

8. Express in scientific notation. 0.000094   8. _____

9. Express in standard form. 7.29×10^6 9. _____

10. Perform the indicated operation and express   10. _____
    the answer in scientific notation.
    $(5.6 \times 10^3)(4 \times 10^5)$

11. Find the degree of the following polynomial.   11. _____
    $3x^2 y + 4x^5 y^3 - 7x^2$

Perform the indicated operation.

12. $3x^2 - 2x + 5 + 4x^2 - 5x$ 12. _____

13. $(3x^2 - 2x + 8) + (4x^2 - 5)$ 13. _____

Chapter 5 Test Form C *cont'd*

14. $\left(3x^2 - 4x - 7\right) - \left(2x^2 - 4x + 8\right)$

14. _____

15. Subtract $\left(3x^2 - 7\right)$ from $\left(2x^2 - 7x + 5\right)$

15. _____

16. $2x^3\left(-3x^2 - 4x + 5\right)$

16. _____

17. $\left(2x - 5\right)\left(x + 4\right)$

17. _____

18. $\left(2x - 3\right)\left(4x^2 - 7x + 5\right)$

18. _____

19. $\left(4x + 2\right)\left(7x - 3\right)$

19. _____

20. $\left(4x - 3\right)^2$

20. _____

21. $\left(2x - 7\right)\left(2x + 7\right)$

21. _____

22. $\left(x^2 - 4y^5\right)\left(3x^2 - 2y^5\right)$

22. _____

23. $\dfrac{7x^2 - 4xy + 7}{7x^2}$

23. _____

24. $\dfrac{8x^3 - 27}{2x - 3}$

24. _____

25. A building is 540 feet high. Neglecting air resistance, the height of an object dropped from the top of this building at time t is given by the polynomial $-16t^2 + 540$. Find the height of the object after 5 seconds.

25. _____

Chapter 5 Test Form D

Evaluate.

1. -4^2

    a. 16   **b.** -16 **c.** 8   **d.** $\dfrac{1}{16}$

2. 7^0

    a. 7   **b.** 0   **c.** 1   **d.** $\dfrac{1}{7}$

3. 4^{-2}

    a. 16   **b.** -16 **c.** 8   **d.** $\dfrac{1}{16}$

Simplify. Use only positive exponents in the final answer.

4. $\dfrac{x^{15}}{x^5}$

    a. x^5 **b.** x^{10} **c.** 1   **d.** $\dfrac{1}{x^5}$

5. $\left(\dfrac{5xy^3}{10x^2y^5}\right)^2$

    a. $4x^2y^4$ **b.** $\dfrac{4}{x^2y^4}$ **c.** $\dfrac{y^6}{2x^4y^{10}}$ **d.** $\dfrac{1}{4x^2y^4}$

6. $\dfrac{9^2x^{-5}y^{-3}}{9^3x^{-2}y^{-2}}$

    a. $9x^3y$ **b.** $\dfrac{1}{9x^3y}$ **c.** x^3y **d.** $\dfrac{1}{x^7y^5}$

Chapter 5 Test Form D *cont'd*

7. $\left(\dfrac{a^4 b^{-2}}{a^{-3} b}\right)^{-3}$

   a. $\dfrac{b^3}{a^{21}}$ b. $\dfrac{1}{a^3 b^3}$ c. $a^3 b^3$ d. $\dfrac{b^9}{a^{21}}$

8. Express in scientific notation. 70,400,000

   a. 7.04×10^5 b. 7.04×10^7 c. 7.4×10^5 d. 704×10^5

9. Express in standard notation. 9.02×10^{-6}

   a. $-90,200,000$ b. 0.00000902 c. 0.000000902 d. -0.000000902

10. Simplify. Write the answer in scientific notation. $\left(3.6 \times 10^5\right)\left(5.4 \times 10^{-8}\right)$

    a. 19.44×10^{-3} b. 19.44×10^{-4} c. 1.944×10^{-2} d. 19.44×10^3

11. Find the degree of the polynomial. $-18x^2 y^2 z + 8x^3 y - 5xz^3$

    a. 4   b. -18 c. 5   d. 13

Perform the indicated operations.

12. $17xy - 3x^2 + 4y - 12xy + 4x^2 - 4$

    a. $x^2 + 5xy - y$ b. $x^2 + 5xy + y$

    c. $x^2 + 5xy$ d. $x^2 + 5xy + 4y - 4$

13. $\left(-3x^4 + 2x^2 - 4x + 8\right) + \left(x^4 - 3x^2 + 2x - 7\right)$

    a. $-2x^4 - 3x^3 + 2x^2 - 2x + 1$ b. $-5x^{10} + 1$

    c. $-2x^4 - x^2 - 2x + 1$ d. $2x^4 - x^3 - 2x + 1$

14. $\left(2x - 7 + 6x^2\right) - \left(3x - 4x^2 - 8\right)$

    a. $2x^2 - x + 1$ b. $10x^2 + 5x - 15$ c. $2x^2 + 5x - 15$ d. $10x^2 - x + 1$

Chapter 5 Test Form D *cont'd*

15. Subtract $\left(3x^2 - 6\right)$ from $\left(4x^2 - 3x + 4\right)$

    a. $x^2 - 3x - 2$ **b.** $x^2 - 3x + 10$ **c.** $7x^2 - 3x - 2$ **d.** $-x^2 + 3x - 10$

16. $-2x^2\left(3x^2y - 4x + 2y\right)$
    a. $-6x^4y + 8x^3 - 4x^2y$ **b.** $-6x^4y - 8x^2 - 4x^2y$

    c. $-6x^2y^3 + 8x^3 + 4x^2$ **d.** $-6x^4y + 8x^2 - 4x^2y$

17. $\left(x - 4\right)\left(x - 6\right)$

    a. $x^2 - 24$ **b.** $x^2 - 10x - 24$ **c.** $x^2 - 10x + 24$ **d.** $x^2 - 6x - 24$

18. $\left(2x - 4\right)\left(3x^2 - 7x + 8\right)$

    a. $6x^3 - 2x^2 + 12x - 32$ **b.** $6x^3 - 26x^2 + 44x - 32$

    c. $6x^3 - 26x^2 - 12x - 32$ **d.** $6x^2 - 26x^2 - 12x - 32$

19. $\left(3x - 2\right)\left(5x + 4\right)$

    a. $15x^2 - 8$ **b.** $15x^2 - 22x + 8$ **c.** $15x^2 + 2x - 8$ **d.** $15x^2 + 120x - 8$

20. $\left(3x - 7\right)^2$

    a. $9x^2 - 21x + 49$ **b.** $9x^2 - 42x + 49$ **c.** $3x^2 - 49$ **d.** $9x^2 - 49$

21. $\left(2x - 3\right)\left(2x + 3\right)$

    a. $4x^2 - 9$ **b.** $4x^2 + 9$ **c.** $4x^2 - 12x + 9$ **d.** $4x^2 + 12x - 9$

22. $\left(7x^2 - 4y^4\right)\left(3x^2 - 2y^4\right)$

    a. $21x^2 - 26x^2y^4 + 8y^4$ **b.** $21x^4 - 26x^2y^4 - 8y^8$

    c. $21x^4 - 26x^2y^4 + 8y^8$ **d.** $21x^2 - 26x^6 - 8y^4$

Chapter 5 Test Form D *cont'd*

23. $\dfrac{15a^4 - 6a^3 + 3a}{3a}$

    a. $5a^3 - 2a^2$ **b.** $3a^4 - 2a^3$ **c.** $5a^3 - 2a^2 + 1$ **d.** $5a^3 - 2a + 1$

24. $\dfrac{9x^3 - 12x^2 + 8}{3x + 2}$

    a. $3x^2 - 6x + 4$ **b.** $3x^2 - 2x + 4$

    c. $3x^2 - 2x - 1 + \dfrac{6}{3x + 2}$ **d.** $3x^2 + 6x - 6 - \dfrac{4}{3x + 2}$

25. A rocket is fired upward from the ground with velocity of 175 feet per second. After t seconds the height of the rocket is given by $-16t^2 + 175t$. Find the height after 3 seconds.

    a. 2829 feet   **b.** 477 feet   **c.** 669 feet   **d.** 381 feet

Chapter 5 Test Form E

Evaluate.

1. $(-4)^3$

   a. -12 b. -64 c. 64 d. 12

2. 8^0

   a. 1 b. -1 c. 0 d. 8

3. 10^{-3}

   a. -30 b. -1000 c. $-\dfrac{1}{1000}$ d. $\dfrac{1}{1000}$

Simplify. Use only positive exponents in the final answer.

4. $\dfrac{y^{17}}{y^{12}}$

   a. y^{29} b. y^5 c. $\dfrac{1}{y^5}$ d. 1

5. $\left(\dfrac{9x^{12}y^5}{18x^9y^7}\right)^4$

   a. $2x^3y^2$ b. $2x^3y^{35}$ c. $\dfrac{x^3}{2y^2}$ d. $\dfrac{x^{12}}{16y^8}$

6. $\dfrac{8x^{-5}y^{-1}}{8^3x^2y^7}$

   a. $64x^7y^7$ b. $\dfrac{64}{x^3y^6}$ c. $\dfrac{1}{64x^7y^8}$ d. $64x^3y^9$

Chapter 5 Test Form E *cont'd*

7. $\left(\dfrac{a^5b^{-2}}{a^{-1}b^{-1}}\right)^{-4}$

    a. $\dfrac{a^6}{b}$ b. $\dfrac{b^4}{a^{24}}$ c. $\dfrac{a^4}{b^3}$ d. $\dfrac{b^{12}}{a^{16}}$

8. Express in scientific notation. 0.000072

    a. 7.2×10^{-4} b. 7.2×10^{-5} c. 72×10^{-4} d. 72×10^{-6}

9. Express in standard notation. 7.69×10^7

    a. 76,900,000   b. 7,690,000,000   c. 7,690,000   d. 769,000,000

10. Multiply. Write the answer in standard form. $\left(4.7\times10^{-6}\right)\left(3\times10^4\right)$

    a. 1221   b. 0.1221   c. 1410   d. 0.141

11. Find the degree of the polynomial. $15xy^2z - xy - xy^3z$
    a. 4   b. 5   c. 15   d. 7

Perform the indicated operations.

12. $9ab + 6 - 4a^2 - 11ab + a^2$

    a. $3a^2 - 20ab + 6$ b. $3a^2 - 2ab + 6$
    c. $-3a^2 - 2ab + 6$ d. $-3a^2 - 20ab + 6$

13. $\left(x^3 - 12x^2 - 5x + 3\right) + \left(4x^3 - 9x^2 - 5x\right)$

    a. $4x^3 - 8x^2 - 14x + 3$ b. $-4x^3 - 8x^2 - 14x + 3$
    c. $5x^3 - 21x^2 - 10x + 3$ d. $5x^3 + 21x^2 + 10x + 3$

14. $\left(5a^4 - 6a^2 - 7\right) - \left(3a^2 - 12a^4 - a^5 - 8\right)$

    a. $8a^4 - 18a^2 + a^5 - 15$ b. $8a^4 - 18a^2 + a^5 + 1$
    c. $a^5 + 17a^4 - 9a^2 + 1$ d. $a^5 - 7a^4 - 3a^2 - 15$

Chapter 5 Test Form E *cont'd*

15. Subtract $\left(4x^2-7x-8\right)$ from $\left(3x^2-2x+8\right)$

    a. $-x^2+5x+16$ **b.** $-x^2-9x-16$ **c.** $-x^2-9x$ **d.** $7x^2-9x$

16. $-12b\left(3ab^2-6ab-4\right)$

    a. $-36ab^2-72ab-48$ **b.** $-36ab^2+72ab+24$
    c. $-36ab^3-72ab^2-48b$ **d.** $-36ab^3+72ab^2+48b$

17. $\left(4x-7\right)\left(2x+3\right)$

    a. $8x^2-2x-21$ **b.** $8x^2-21$ **c.** $8x^2+12x-21$ **d.** $8x^2-14x-21$

18. $\left(5x-8\right)\left(x^2-10x-3\right)$

    a. $5x^2-18x^2+65x+24$ **b.** $5x^3-18x^2+55x+24$
    c. $5x^3+42x^2+65x+24$ **d.** $5x^3-58x^2+65x+24$

19. $\left(7x-3\right)\left(3x-6\right)$

    a. $21x^2-33x+18$ **b.** $21x^2-51x+18$
    c. $21x^2+22x+18$ **d.** $21x^2+51x+18$

20. $\left(5x-3\right)^2$

    a. $25x^2-30x+9$ **b.** $25x^2+9$ **c.** $25x^2+30x-9$ **d.** $25x^2-9$

21. $\left(5x-2\right)\left(5x+2\right)$

    a. $25x^2-20x-4$ **b.** $25x^2-10x+4$ **c.** $25x^2-4$ **d.** $25x^2+4$

22. $\left(11x^2-8y\right)^2$

    a. $121x^4-64y^2$ **b.** $121x^2-64y^2$
    c. $121x^4-176x^2y+64y^2$ **d.** $121x^2-176xy+64y^2$

Chapter 5 Test Form E *cont'd*

23. $\dfrac{4a^3 - 8ab^3 - 3b}{-48ab}$

    a. $-\dfrac{a^2}{12b} + \dfrac{b^2}{6} + \dfrac{1}{16a}$ **b.** $\dfrac{a^2}{12b} - \dfrac{b^2}{6} - \dfrac{1}{16a}$

    c. $\dfrac{a^2}{12b} + \dfrac{b^2}{6} + \dfrac{1}{16a}$ **d.** $\dfrac{a^2}{12b} - \dfrac{b^2}{6} - \dfrac{1}{24a}$

24. $\dfrac{4x^4 - 3x^2 + 5x - 6}{2x - 3}$

    a. $2x^3 - 3x^2 + 3x - 7$ **b.** $2x^3 + 3x^2 + 3x + 7 + \dfrac{15}{2x - 3}$

    c. $2x^3 - 3x^2 + 3x - 2 - \dfrac{12}{2x - 3}$ **d.** $2x^3 = 3x^2 - 3x + 2 + \dfrac{12}{2x - 3}$

25. A rocket is fired upward from the ground with velocity of 150 feet per second. After t seconds the height of the rocket is given by $-16t^2 + 150t$. Find the height after 2 seconds.

    a. 6 feet   **b.** 236 feet   **c.** 118 feet   **d.** 86 feet

Chapter 5 Test Form F

Evaluate.

1. -7^2

    a. -14 b. 49 c. -49 d. $\dfrac{1}{49}$

2. $\left(-36\right)^0$

    a. -1 b. 1 c. 0 d. -36

3. -3^{-4}

    a. -81 b. 81 c. $-\dfrac{1}{81}$ d. $\dfrac{1}{81}$

Simplify. Use only positive exponents in the final answer.

4. $\dfrac{h^8}{h^4}$

    a. h^2 b. h^8 c. h^4 d. 1

5. $\left(\dfrac{2x^{16}y^7}{20x^{13}y^{11}}\right)^4$

    a. $\dfrac{x^3}{10u^4}$ b. $\dfrac{x^{12}}{10,000y^{16}}$ c. $10,000x^{12}y^{16}$ d. $10x^3y^4$

6. $\dfrac{5x^{-11}y^{-3}}{5^4x^5y^{-9}}$

    a. $\dfrac{y^6}{125x^{16}}$ b. $\dfrac{x^{16}}{125y^6}$ c. $\dfrac{x^6}{125y^{12}}$ d. $\dfrac{x^{16}}{125y^{12}}$

Chapter 5 Test Form F *cont'd*

7. $\left(\dfrac{p^{-5}q^{-7}}{p^{3}q^{-2}}\right)^{-4}$

   a. $\dfrac{q^{20}}{p^{8}}$ b. $p^{8}q^{20}$ c. $\dfrac{q^{20}}{p^{32}}$ d. $p^{32}q^{20}$

8. Express in scientific notation. 0.0000000291

   a. 2.91×10^{7} b. 2.91×10^{-8} c. 2.91×10^{-7} d. 2.91×10^{8}

9. Express in standard notation. 5.04×10^{6}

   a. 504,000,000   b. 0.000504   c. 0.00000504   d. 5,040,000

10. Multiply. Write the answer in standard form. $\left(6.5\times10^{-9}\right)\left(3\times10^{3}\right)$

    a. 0.00000195   b. 0.0000195   c. 19,500,000   d. 1,905,000

11. Find the degree of the polynomial. $12a^{2}b-9ab^{3}c+7a^{2}b^{2}c$

    a. 10   b. 5   c. 6   d. 3

Perform the indicated operations.

12. $5xy-8-3x^{2}+2-xy$

    a. $-3x^{2}+4xy-6$ b. $3x^{2}-4xy-6$
    c. $-11x^{2}+4xy-6$ d. $2x^{2}-xy-6$

13. $\left(a^{3}-15a^{2}-7a+16\right)+\left(7a^{2}-3a+2a^{3}\right)$

    a. $3a^{3}-8a^{2}-10a+16$ b. $a^{3}-8a^{2}-10a+18$
    c. $8a^{3}-18a^{2}-5a+16$ d. $3a^{3}-8a^{2}-4a+16$

14. $\left(9a^{4}-5a^{2}+4\right)-\left(a^{3}-8a^{4}+16\right)$

    a. $a^{4}-a^{3}-5a^{2}-12$ b. $a^{4}-a^{3}-5a+20$
    c. $17a^{4}-a^{3}-5a^{2}-12$ d. $17a^{4}-a^{3}-5a^{2}+20$

Chapter 5 Test Form F *cont'd*

15. Subtract $\left(12x^3 - 9x^2 + 20\right)$ from $\left(3x^3 - x^2 + 4\right)$.

    a. $9x^3 - 10x^2 + 24$ **b.** $-9x^3 + 8x^2 - 16$

    c. $9x^3 - 8x^2 + 16$ **d.** $-9x^3 + 10x^2 - 24$

16. $-10y\left(3xy^3 - 9x^2 + 20\right)$

    a. $30xy^2 - 70x + 200y$ **b.** $-30xy^2 + 70x - 200$

    c. $20xy^3 - 17xy + 200y^2$ **d.** $-30xy^4 + 90x^2y - 200y$

17. $\left(a - 2\right)\left(4a + 3\right)$

    a. $4a^2 - 11a - 6$ **b.** $4a^2 + 3a - 6$ **c.** $4a^2 - 5a - 6$ **d.** $4a^2 - 8a - 6$

18. $\left(9x - 2\right)\left(x^2 - 5x - 4\right)$

    a. $9x^3 - 47x^2 - 26x + 8$ **b.** $9x^3 - 43x^2 - 46x + 8$

    c. $9x^3 - 43x^2 - 46x - 8$ **d.** $9x^3 - 5x - 8$

19. $\left(6x - 5\right)\left(4x + 3\right)$

    a. $24x^2 - 2x - 15$ **b.** $24x^2 + 18x - 15$ **c.** $24x^2 + 38x + 15$ **d.** $24x^2 + 2x - 15$

20. $\left(5x - 6\right)^2$

    a. $25x^2 - 30x + 36$ **b.** $25x^2 - 36$ **c.** $25x^2 - 60x + 36$ **d.** $5x^2 - 36$

21. $\left(7x - 8\right)\left(7x + 8\right)$

    a. $7x^2 - 64$ **b.** $49x^2 - 64$ **c.** $49x^2 - 116x + 64$ **d.** $49x^2 + 64$

22. $\left(5x^2 - 9y\right)^2$

    a. $25x^4 - 81y^2$ **b.** $25x^2 - 81y^2$

    c. $25x^4 - 90x^2y + 81y^2$ **d.** $25x^4 + 90x^2y + 81y^2$

Chapter 5 Test Form F *cont'd*

23. $\dfrac{-9x^2y+18x-27xy}{-54xy}$

     a. $\dfrac{x}{6}+\dfrac{1}{3y}-\dfrac{1}{2}$ **b.** $\dfrac{x}{6}-\dfrac{1}{3y}+\dfrac{1}{2}$ **c.** $\dfrac{x^2}{6}+\dfrac{x}{2y}-\dfrac{1}{3}$ **d.** $\dfrac{x^2}{6}-\dfrac{x}{2y}+\dfrac{1}{3}$

24. $\dfrac{64x^3-125}{4x+5}$

     a. $16x^2+20x-25$ **b.** $16x^2-20x+25$

     c. $16x^2-20x+25+\dfrac{250}{4x+5}$ **d.** $16x^2-20x+25-\dfrac{250}{4x+5}$

25. The length of a rectangle is $3x-5$ and the width is $x+2$. Find the area.

     a. $4x-3$ **b.** $2x-7$ **c.** $3x^2+x-10$ **d.** $3x^2-x-10$

Chapter 6 Test Form A

Factor each polynomial completely. If a polynomial cannot be factored, write "prime."

1. $8x^3 - 12x^2$

1. _____

2. $a(a+2) - 3(a+2)$

2. _____

3. $3x^2 + 6xy - 5x - 10y$

3. _____

4. $x^2 - x - 12$

4. _____

5. $x^2 - 11x + 30$

5. _____

6. $a^2 + 12a + 36$

6. _____

7. $x^2 - 5x + 8$

7. _____

8. $3x^2 + 2x - 8$

8. _____

9. $x^3 - 8$

9. _____

10. $6x^3 - 38x^2 + 40x$

10. _____

11. $x^3 - 16x + 2x^2 - 32$

11. _____

12. $x^5 - 4x^3 - 9x^3 + 36x$

12. _____

13. $x^2 - xy - 6y^2$

13. _____

14. $2x^2 + 5xy - 12y^2$

14. _____

Chapter 6 Test Form A *cont'd*

Solve each equation.

15. $x^2 - x - 12 = 0$ 15. _____

16. $x^2 + 4x = 12$ 16. _____

17. $x^2 + x - 30 = 0$ 17. _____

18. $15x^3 - 4x^2 - 4x = 0$ 18. _____

19. $x^3 = 9x$ 19. _____

20. $20x^2 + 7x - 6 = 9$ 20. _____

21. $4x^2 = 49$ 21. _____

22. $x^2 - 7x = 0$ 22. _____

23. A rectangle has an area of 54 square feet.   23. _____
    If the length is 3 feet more than the width,
    find the dimensions of the rectangle.

24. The sum of two numbers is 14. The sum of   24. _____
    the squares of the two numbers is 100. Find
    the two numbers.

25. The height h of a rock t seconds after it is dropped   25. _____
    off a cliff is given by the equation
    $h = -16t^2 + 400$. How many seconds after the
    rock is dropped will it hit the ground?

Chapter 6 Test Form B

Factor each polynomial completely. If a polynomial cannot be factored, write "prime."

1. $5x^4 + 10x^3$

1. _____

2. $xy + 2x - 3y - 6$

2. _____

3. $6x^2 - 4xy + 15x - 10y$

3. _____

4. $x^2 - 6x - 27$

4. _____

5. $x^2 - 11x + 24$

5. _____

6. $x^2 - 7x - 9$

6. _____

7. $x^2 + 6x + 9$

7. _____

8. $10x^2 - 11x - 6$

8. _____

9. $x^3 + 125$

9. _____

10. $5x^3 + 20x^2 - 105x$

10. _____

11. $x^2 - 64$

11. _____

12. $x^4 - 16x^2 + 3x^3 y - 48xy$

12. _____

13. $x^2 - 10xy + 24y^2$

13. _____

14. $4x^2 + 4xy - 3y^2$

14. _____

Chapter 6 Test Form B *cont'd*

Solve each equation.

15. $x^2 - x - 20 = 0$ 15. _____

16. $x^2 + 2x - 24 = 0$ 16. _____

17. $2x^2 - 15x + 7 = 0$ 17. _____

18. $3x^3 - 20x^2 + 12x = 0$ 18. _____

19. $5x^2 + 2x = 0$ 19. _____

20. $x^2 = 64$ 20. _____

21. $x(x-2) = 15$ 21. _____

22. $15x^2 - 44x + 21 = 0$ 22. _____

23. A rectangle has an area of 80 square feet.   23. _____
    If the length is 2 feet more than the width,
    find the dimensions of the rectangle.

24. A number squared minus eleven times the number   24. _____
    is equal to −28. Find two numbers that satisfy
    these conditions.

25. The height h of a rock t seconds after it is dropped   25. _____
    off a cliff is given by the equation
    $h = -16t^2 + 256$. How many seconds after the
    rock is dropped will it hit the ground?

Chapter 6 Test Form C

Factor each polynomial completely. If a polynomial cannot be factored, write "prime."

1. $6x^4 - 4x$

    1. _____

2. $6a + 3 - 2ab - b$

    2. _____

3. $2x^2 + 5xy - 10x - 25y$

    3. _____

4. $a^2 - 2a - 35$

    4. _____

5. $x^2 - 10x + 21$

    5. _____

6. $x^2 + 12x + 32$

    6. _____

7. $x^2 + 10x + 25$

    7. _____

8. $x^2 - 2x + 10$

    8. _____

9. $3x^2 + 13x - 10$

    9. _____

10. $2x^3 - 4x^2 - 30x$

    10. _____

11. $x^3 - 5x^2 - 4x + 20$

    11. _____

12. $x^3 + 1$

    12. _____

13. $2x^2 + 5xy - 12y^2$

    13. _____

14. $8x^2 - 14xy + 3y^2$

    14. _____

Chapter 6 Test Form C *cont'd*

Solve each equation.

15. $x^2 - 16x + 48 = 0$ 15. _____

16. $x^2 + 9x + 18 = 0$ 16. _____

17. $x^2 - 7x - 18 = 0$ 17. _____

18. $x(2x + 7)(3x - 1) = 0$ 18. _____

19. $x^3 - 25x = 0$ 19. _____

20. $5x^2 - 17x + 6 = 0$ 20. _____

21. $4x^2 - 20x + 25 = 0$ 21. _____

22. $x^2 - 7x = 0$ 22. _____

23. A square has an area of 225 square feet. Find   23. _____
    the length of each side.

24. The sum of two numbers is 8. The sum of   24. _____
    the squares of the two numbers is 34. Find
    the two numbers.

25. The height h of a rock t seconds after it is   25. _____
    dropped off a cliff is given by the equation
    $h = -16t^2 + 144$. How many seconds after the
    rock is dropped will it hit the ground?

Chapter 6 Test Form D

Choose the correct answer to each problem.

Factor each polynomial completely.

1. $6x^4 - 2x^3 + 12x^2$

   a. $3x(2x^3 - x^2 + 4x)$ b. $3x^2(2x^2 - x + 4)$
   c. $2x^2(3x^2 - x + 6)$ d. $x^2(6x^2 - 3x + 12)$

2. $x^2 + 5x - xy - 5y$

   a. $(x-5)(x+y)$ b. $(x+5)(x+y)$
   c. $(x-y)(x+5)$ d. $(x-5)(x-y)$

3. $x^2 + 12x + 20$

   a. $(x+2)(x+10)$ b. $(x+4)(x+5)$ c. $(x+3)(x+3)$ d. prime

4. $x^2 - x - 20$

   a. $(x-10)(x+2)$ b. $(x+5)(x-4)$ c. $(x-5)(x+4)$ d. prime

5. $x^2 + 7x + 9$

   a. $(x+3)^2$ b. $(x+3)(x-3)$ c. $(x+9)(x+1)$ d. prime

6. $3x^2 + 7x - 20$

   a. $(3x-4)(x+5)$ b. $3(x-10)(x+3)$
   c. $3(x+10)(x-3)$ d. $(3x-5)(x+4)$

7. $x^2 - 49$

   a. $(x-7)(x+7)$ b. $(x+7)^2$ c. $(x-49)(x+1)$ d. $(x-7)^2$

8. $4x^2 - 12x + 9$

   a. $(2x-3)^2$ b. $(4x-3)(x-3)$ c. $2(x-3)^2$ d. $4(x-3)^2$

Chapter 6 Test Form D *cont'd*

9. $6x^2 + 9x - 60$

    a. $(6x - 15)(x + 4)$ **b.** $(2x - 5)(3x + 12)$

    c. $3(2x - 5)(x + 4)$ **d.** $6(x - 2)(x + 5)$

10. $10x^3 - 15x^2 - 10x$

    a. $x(5x - 10)(2x + 1)$ **b.** $5x(x - 2)(2x + 1)$

    c. $5(x^2 - 2)(2x + 1)$ **d.** $5x(x + 1)(2x - 2)$

11. $y^3 + 4y^2 - 9y - 36$

    a. $(y^2 + 9)(y - 4)$ **b.** $(y^2 + 9)(y + 4)$

    c. $(y - 2)(y + 4)(y - 9)$ **d.** $(y - 3)(y + 3)(y + 4)$

12. $9x^2 - 36$

    a. $(3x - 6)(3x + 6)$ **b.** $(3x - 6)^2$

    c. $3(3x^2 - 12)$ **d.** $9(x - 2)(x + 2)$

13. $x^2 + xy - 12y^2$

    a. $(x + 3y)(x + 4y)$ **b.** $(x - 3y)(x - 4y)$

    c. $(x - 3y)(x + 4y)$ **d.** $(x + 3y)(x - 4y)$

14. $x^3 - 8$

    a. $(x^2 - 4)(x + 2)$ **b.** $(x - 2)(x^2 - 2x + 4)$

    c. $(x - 2)(x^2 + 2x + 4)$ **d.** $(x - 2)^3$

15. $x^3 + 125$

    a. $(x + 5)^3$ **b.** $(x + 5)(x^2 - 25)$

    c. $(x + 5)(x^2 - 5x + 25)$ **d.** $(x + 5)^2(x - 5)$

Chapter 6 Test Form D *cont'd*

Solve the polynomial equations.

16. $x^2 - 10x + 16 = 0$

    a. $-4, 3$ **b.** $2, 8$ **c.** 4 **d.** $2, 5$

17. $x^2 + 2x - 35 = 0$

    a. $-4, 3$ **b.** $-7, 5$ **c.** $-7, -5$ **d.** $2, 5$

18. $x^2 - 2x - 15 = 0$

    a. $-3, 5$ **b.** $3, -5$ **c.** $2, 1$ **d.** $5, 3$

19. $x(3x + 1)(5x - 2) = 0$

    a. $0, \dfrac{1}{3}, \dfrac{2}{5}$ **b.** $0, \dfrac{2}{5}, -\dfrac{1}{3}$ **c.** $0, -\dfrac{1}{3}, -\dfrac{2}{5}$ **d.** $\dfrac{2}{5}, \dfrac{1}{3}$

20. $t^3 - 6t^2 + 9t = 0$

    a. $0, 3$ **b.** $0, 3, -3$ **c.** $0, -9$ **d.** $0, -3$

21. $15x^2 - 19x + 6 = 0$

    a. $\dfrac{3}{5}, \dfrac{2}{3}$ **b.** $1, \dfrac{2}{5}$ **c.** $-\dfrac{3}{5}, -\dfrac{2}{3}$ **d.** $-1, -\dfrac{2}{5}$

22. $x^3 + 3x^2 - 10x = 0$

    a. $0, 2, -5$ **b.** $2, -5$ **c.** $-2, 5$ **d.** $0, 5, 2$

23. A rectangle has an area of 54 square inches. The length is 3 feet more than the width. Find the dimensions of the rectangle.

    a. $w = 6$ in, $l = 9$ in   **b.** $w = 7$ in, $l = 8$ in
    c. $w = 2$ in, $l = 5$ in   **d.** $w = 9$ in, $l = 12$ in

Chapter 6 Test Form D *cont'd*

24. The length of a rectangle is 4 feet more than the width. If the area of the rectangle is 45 square feet, find the dimensions.

    a. $w = 3$ feet, $l = 15$ feet   **b.** $w = 5$ feet, $l = 9$ feet

    c. $w = 8$ feet, $l = 12$ feet   **d.** $w = 6$ feet, $l = 9$ feet

25. The height of an object t seconds after it is dropped off a building is given by the equation $h = -16t^2 + 400$. How many seconds after the rock is dropped will it hit the ground?

    a. 10 seconds   **b.** 5 seconds   **c.** 20 seconds   **d.** 25 seconds

Chapter 6 Test Form E

Choose the correct answer to each problem.

Factor each polynomial completely.

1. $24x^3 - 8x^2 + 48x$

   a. $8(3x^3 - x^2 + 6x)$ b. $8x(3x^2 - x + 6)$
   c. $4x(6x^2 + 2x + 12)$ d. $4(6x^3 - 2x^2 + 12x)$

2. $15(a+11) - b(a+11)$

   a. $(15-b)(a+11)$ b. $(a+11)^2(15-b)$
   c. $15b(a+11)$ d. $(15+b)(a+11)$

3. $9x^2 - 9xy - 8x + 8y$

   a. $(9x-8)(x-y)$ b. $(9x-8)(x+y)$
   c. $(9x-y)(x-8)$ d. $(9x-y)(x+8)$

4. $x^2 - 81$

   a. $(x-3)^2$ b. $(x-1)(x-9)$ c. $(x-3)(x+3)$ d. $(x-9)(x+9)$

5. $x^2 + 3x - 70$

   a. $(x-10)(x+7)$ b. $(x+10)(x+7)$ c. $(x-7)(x+10)$ d. prime

6. $y^2 - 20y + 100$

   a. $(y+10)(y-10)$ b. $(y-10)^2$
   c. $(y+10)^2$ d. $(y-25)(y+4)$

7. $x^2 + 25$

   a. $(x+5)^2$ b. $(x+5)(x-5)$ c. $(x-5)^2$ d. prime

Chapter 6 Test Form E *cont'd*

8. $9x^2 + 50x - 24$

   a. $(9x+3)(x-8)$ **b.** $(9x-3)(x+8)$

   c. $(9x-4)(x+6)$ **d.** $(9x+4)(x-6)$

9. $5x^2 - 60x + 180$

   a. $5(x-6)^2$ **b.** $5(x-6)(x+6)$

   c. $5(x-9)(x-4)$ **d.** $(5x+6)(x-6)$

10. $6x^3 + 48x^2 - 54x$

   a. $6(x^3 + 12x^2 - 9x)$ **b.** $6x(x-3)^2$

   c. $6x(x-9)(x+1)$ **d.** $6x(x-1)(x+9)$

11. $xy^2 - 64x - 3y^2 + 192$

   a. $(x-64)(y-3)$ **b.** $(y-8)(y+8)(x-3)$

   c. $(y-8)^2(y-3)$ **d.** $(y^2+64)(x-3)$

12. $x^5 - 256x$

   a. $x(x^2-16)(x-4)(x+4)$ **b.** $x(x+4)^2(x-4)^2$

   c. $x(x^2+16)(x-4)(x+4)$ **d.** $x(x-4)^4$

13. $x^2 + 6xy - 72y^2$

   a. $(x-9y)(x+8y)$ **b.** $(x-8y)(x+9y)$

   c. $(x-12y)(x+6y)$ **d.** $(x-6y)(x+12y)$

14. $x^3 + 8$

   a. $(x+2)^3$ **b.** $(x+2)(x^2-2x+4)$

   c. $(x+2)(x^2+2x+4)$ **d.** $(x+8)(x^2-8x+64)$

Chapter 6 Test Form E *cont'd*

15. $8x^3 - 125$

    a. $(2x-5)^3$ **b.** $(2x+5)(2x-5)$

    c. $(2x-5)(4x^2+10x+25)$ **d.** $(2x-5)(2x^2-10x+25)$

Solve the polynomial equations.

16. $(x-10)(x+6)=0$

    a. $10, -6$ **b.** $10, 6$ **c.** $-10, 6$ **d.** $-10, -6$

17. $x^2+11x+28=0$

    a. $-14, -2$ **b.** $14, 2$ **c.** $-7, -4$ **d.** $7, 4$

18. $x^2+6x=40$

    a. $4, -10$ **b.** $-4, 10$ **c.** $5, -8$ **d.** $-5, 8$

19. $16x(6x-19)(5x+12)=0$

    a. $\dfrac{1}{16}, \dfrac{6}{19}, -\dfrac{5}{12}$ **b.** $0, -\dfrac{6}{19}, \dfrac{5}{12}$ **c.** $0, \dfrac{19}{6}, -\dfrac{12}{5}$ **d.** $0, -\dfrac{19}{6}, \dfrac{12}{5}$

20. $3t^3 - 192t = 0$

    a. $0, 8, -8$ **b.** $0, 24, -8$ **c.** $\dfrac{1}{3}, 8, -8$ **d.** $0, 8$

21. $60y^2 - 41y = 3$

    a. $-\dfrac{3}{4}, \dfrac{1}{15}$ **b.** $\dfrac{3}{4}, -\dfrac{1}{15}$ **c.** $-\dfrac{3}{10}, \dfrac{1}{6}$ **d.** $\dfrac{3}{10}, -\dfrac{1}{6}$

22. $x^2 - 9x = 0$

    a. 9 **b.** $0, 9$ **c.** 5 **d.** no solution

Chapter 6 Test Form E *cont'd*

23. $x^2 - 3x = 10$

    a. $5, -2$ **b.** $-5, 2$ **c.** $1, 3$ **d.** $4, -3$

24. A room is in the shape of a triangle. The length of the base of the triangle is 8 feet longer than its altitude. If the area is 120 square feet, find the length of the base.

    a. 8 feet   **b.** 80 feet   **c.** 30 feet   **d.** 20 feet

25. The length of a rectangle is 2 feet more than the length. The area is 80 feet. Find the dimensions.

    a. $w = 8$ feet, $l = 10$ feet   **b.** $w = 4$ feet, $l = 20$ feet
    c. $w = 10$ feet, $l = 12$ feet   **d.** $w = 6$ feet, $l = 8$ feet

Chapter 6 Test Form F

Choose the correct answer to each problem.

Factor each polynomial completely.

1. $22x^3 - 55x^2 + 44x$

   a. $11(2x^3 - 5x^2 + 2x)$ b. $11(2x^3 - 5x^2 + 4x)$
   c. $11x(2x^2 - 5x + 2)$ d. $11x(2x^2 - 5x + 4)$

2. $2(x-3) + y(x-3)$

   a. $(x-3)(2+y)$ b. $(x-3)^2(2+y)$
   c. $(x-3)(2-y)$ d. $2y(x-3)$

3. $6x^2 - 6xy - 5x + 5y$

   a. $(6x-5)(x+y)$ b. $(6x-5)(x-y)$
   c. $(6x-y)(x+5)$ d. $(6x-y)(x-5)$

4. $x^2 + 4x - 96$

   a. $(x-8)(x+12)$ b. $(x-12)(x-8)$
   c. $(x-4)(x+24)$ d. $(x-24)(x+4)$

5. $x^2 - 13x + 36$

   a. $(x-12)(x-3)$ b. $(x-6)(x+6)$
   c. $(x-9)(x-4)$ d. $(x-6)^2$

6. $x^2 - 24x + 144$

   a. $(x-16)(x-9)$ b. $(x-16)(x+9)$
   c. $(x-12)^2$ d. $(x-12)(x+12)$

Chapter 6 Test Form F *cont'd*

7. $2x^2 - 50$

    a. $(2x-25)(x+2)$ **b.** $2(x-5)(x-5)$

    c. $2(x-5)(x+5)$ **d.** $2x(x-25)$

8. $5x^2 - 22x + 21$

    a. $(5x-3)(x-7)$ **b.** $(5x-7)(x-3)$ **c.** $(5x+3)(x+7)$ **d.** prime

9. $8x^2 - 48x + 72$

    a. $8(x-3)^2$ **b.** $8(x+3)^2$ **c.** $4(2x-5)(x-6)$ **d.** prime

10. $6y^3 - 30y^2 - 84y$

    a. $2y(3y-7)(y+6)$ **b.** $6y(y+7)(y-2)$

    c. $6(y^2-7)(y+2)$ **d.** $6y(y-7)(y+2)$

11. $xy^2 - 36x - 2y^2 + 72$

    a. $(y^2-2)(x+36)$ **b.** $(y-6)(y+6)(x+2)$

    c. $(y-6)(y+6)(x-2)$ **d.** $(y-6)^2(x+2)$

12. $x^5 - 1296x$

    a. $x(x+6)^2(x-6)^2$ **b.** $x(x^2+36)(x-6)(x+6)$

    c. $x(x^2-36)(x-6)(x+6)$ **d.** $x(x-6)^4$

13. $x^2 - 9xy - 70y^2$

    a. $(x-5y)(x+14y)$ **b.** $(x+5y)(x-14y)$

    c. $(x-7y)(x+10y)$ **d.** $(x+7y)(x-10y)$

14. $x^3 - 8$

    a. $(x-2)(x^2+2x+4)$ **b.** $(x-2)(x^2-2x+4)$

    c. $(x-2)^3$ **d.** $(x-2)(x^2+4)$

Chapter 6 Test Form F *cont'd*

15. $x^3 - 1$

    a. $(x-1)^3$ **b.** $(x-1)(x^2+x-1)$

    c. $(x-1)(x^2+x+1)$ **d.** prime

Solve the polynomial equations.

16. $(x-18)(x+25)=0$

    a. $-25, 18$ **b.** $-18, 25$ **c.** $18, 25$ **d.** $-18, -25$

17. $x^2 + 11x + 24 = 0$

    a. $-2, 12$ **b.** $2, -12$ **c.** $3, 8$ **d.** $-3, -8$

18. $x^2 - 8x = 48$

    a. $-16, 3$ **b.** $-3, 16$ **c.** $-12, 4$ **d.** $12, -4$

19. $12x(7x-12)(6x+11)=0$

    a. $\dfrac{1}{12}, \dfrac{7}{12}, -\dfrac{6}{11}$ **b.** $12, -\dfrac{7}{12}, \dfrac{6}{11}$ **c.** $0, \dfrac{12}{7}, -\dfrac{11}{6}$ **d.** $\dfrac{2}{5}, \dfrac{1}{3}$

20. $3t^3 - 192t = 0$

    a. $\dfrac{1}{3}, 8, -8$ **b.** $0, 8, -8$ **c.** $0, 24, 8$ **d.** $0, -8$

21. $15y^2 - 17y = 18$

    a. $2, -\dfrac{3}{5}$ **b.** $-2, \dfrac{3}{5}$ **c.** $-\dfrac{9}{5}, \dfrac{2}{3}$ **d.** $\dfrac{9}{5}, -\dfrac{2}{3}$

22. $x^2 = 64$

    a. 8 **b.** $8, -8$ **c.** $4, -16$ **d.** $2, -32$

Chapter 6 Test Form F *cont'd*

23. $x(x+2)=8$

    a. $2, -4$ **b.** $4, -2$ **c.** $8, -2$ **d.** $0, -2$

24. If the sides of a square are increased by 4 inches, area becomes 121 square inches. Find the length of the sides of the original square.

    a. 7 inches   **b.** 15 inches   **c.** 11 inches   **d.** 8 inches

25. The height of an object t seconds after it is dropped off a building is given by the equation $h = -16t^2 + 576$. How many seconds after the rock is dropped will it hit the ground?

    a. 16 seconds   **b.** 6 seconds   **c.** 24 seconds   **d.** 4 seconds

Chapter 7 Test Form A

Find any real numbers for which the following expressions are undefined.

1. $\dfrac{x+6}{x-5}$

1. _____

2. $\dfrac{x-2}{x^2+6x+8}$

2. _____

Simplify.

3. $\dfrac{2x^2-6x}{2x^2+2x}$

3. _____

4. $\dfrac{x^2+3x-18}{x^2-9}$

4. _____

5. $\dfrac{2-x}{x^2+2x-8}$

5. _____

6. $\dfrac{x-2}{x^3-8}$

6. _____

7. $\dfrac{ay+3a+3y+9}{ay-4a+3y-12}$

7. _____

Perform the indicated operations. Simplify if possible.

8. $\dfrac{x^2-16}{3x-9}\cdot\dfrac{x-3}{x^2+2x-8}$

8. _____

9. $\dfrac{x^2+9x+20}{4x}\div\dfrac{5x+25}{2x^2}$

9. _____

10. $\dfrac{2}{x+3}\cdot\left(6x+18\right)$

10. _____

11. $\dfrac{x}{x-2}-\dfrac{2}{x-2}$

11. _____

Chapter 7 Test Form A *cont'd*

12. $\dfrac{3}{4x-3}-\dfrac{5}{8x-6}$

12. _____

13. $\dfrac{1}{x+2}+\dfrac{3}{x-2}$

13. _____

14. $\dfrac{x}{x^2-2x-8}+\dfrac{3}{x^2-4}$

14. _____

Solve each equation.

15. $\dfrac{3}{x-2}+\dfrac{1}{2}=\dfrac{x}{x-2}$

15. _____

16. $\dfrac{3}{x^2-x-20}=\dfrac{2}{x-5}+\dfrac{1}{x+4}$

16. _____

17. $\dfrac{3}{5x}=\dfrac{1}{x+4}$

17. _____

18. $\dfrac{x+2}{x^2-4}=\dfrac{1}{x+2}+\dfrac{2}{x+2}$

18. _____

Simplify each complex fraction.

19. $\dfrac{\dfrac{x}{3}+1}{\dfrac{x}{3}-1}$

19. _____

20. $\dfrac{\dfrac{1}{x}-\dfrac{3}{y}}{\dfrac{1}{xy}}$

20. _____

Chapter 7 Test Form A *cont'd*

Solve each problem.

21. Six times the reciprocal of a number is equal to
    4 times the reciprocal of 2. Find the number.

    21.

22. It takes John 4 hours to mow a lawn. It takes
    Maria 3 hours to mow the same lawn. How
    long would it take if they worked together?

    22.

23. Find x. The triangles are similar.

    23.

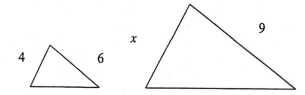

24. y varies directly as x. y is 15 when x is 5. Find
    y when x is 7.

    24.

25. y varies inversely as x squared. y is 32 when x is
    4. Find y when x is 5.

    25. _____

Chapter 7 Test Form B

Find any real numbers for which the following expressions are undefined.

1. $\dfrac{2x}{3x-2}$

1. _____

2. $\dfrac{x-3}{x^2-x-20}$

2. _____

Simplify.

3. $\dfrac{6x-3y}{9}$

3. _____

4. $\dfrac{x^2-4x-12}{x^2+8x+12}$

4. _____

5. $\dfrac{x+1}{x^2-x-2}$

5. _____

6. $\dfrac{y-x}{x^2+xy-2y^2}$

6. _____

7. $\dfrac{ay+3a+3y+9}{ay-4a+3y-12}$

7. _____

Perform the indicated operations. Simplify if possible.

8. $\dfrac{x}{x^2-3x-18}\cdot\dfrac{x^2-x-12}{x^2-4x}$

8. _____

9. $\dfrac{x^2-3x-4}{x^2-16}\cdot\dfrac{x+4}{3x-9}$

9. _____

10. $\dfrac{x-3}{x+2}\div\left(x^2-x-6\right)$

10. _____

11. $\dfrac{3x-6}{2x}+\dfrac{3x-8}{2x}$

11. _____

Chapter 7 Test Form B *cont'd*

12. $\dfrac{3}{x^2-9}+\dfrac{2}{x-3}$

12. _____

13. $\dfrac{4}{x+3}-\dfrac{6}{3x+9}$

13. _____

14. $\dfrac{x}{x+3}-\dfrac{5}{x^2-2x-15}$

14. _____

Solve each equation.

15. $\dfrac{x}{x-4}-2=\dfrac{1}{x-4}$

15. _____

16. $\dfrac{2}{9x^2-1}+\dfrac{1}{3x+1}=0$

16. _____

17. $\dfrac{5}{4x}=\dfrac{2}{x+3}$

17. _____

18. $\dfrac{x+3}{x^2-x-12}+\dfrac{2}{x+3}=\dfrac{1}{x-4}$

18. _____

Simplify each complex fraction.

19. $\dfrac{\dfrac{1}{x}-\dfrac{1}{y}}{\dfrac{3}{x}}$

19. _____

20. $\dfrac{\dfrac{3}{4}-\dfrac{1}{2}}{\dfrac{5}{4}+\dfrac{1}{2}}$

20. _____

Chapter 7 Test Form B *cont'd*

Solve each problem.

21. Twice the reciprocal of a number added to $\dfrac{3}{5}$ is equal to 1. Find the number.

21. _____

22. In the time it takes a pilot to fly 360 miles with a head wind, she can only fly 240 against the wind. If the speed of the plane in still air is 150 mph, Find the wind speed.

22. _____

23. Find x. The triangles are similar.

23. _____

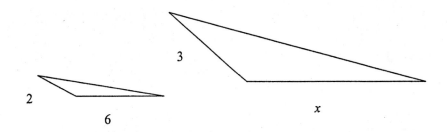

24. y varies directly as x. y is 12 when x is 8. Find y when x is 20.

24. _____

25. y varies inversely as x squared. y is 36 when x is 3. Find y when x is 5.

25. _____

Chapter 7 Test Form C

Find any real numbers for which the following expressions are undefined.

1. $\dfrac{x-7}{x+2}$

1. _____

2. $\dfrac{x+5}{x^2+3x-4}$

2. _____

Simplify.

3. $\dfrac{x^2-9}{3x-9}$

3. _____

4. $\dfrac{x^2-x-56}{x^2+14x+49}$

4. _____

5. $\dfrac{x-2}{x^2-4}$

5. _____

6. $\dfrac{3-x}{x^2+4x-21}$

6. _____

Perform the indicated operations. Simplify if possible.

7. $\dfrac{x^2-12x+35}{3x-21}\cdot\dfrac{4x-8}{x^2-3x-10}$

7. _____

8. $\dfrac{x+7}{x^2-10x+25}\div\dfrac{x^2+11x+28}{x^2-x-20}$

8. _____

9. $\dfrac{x}{2x^2-7x-15}\cdot\dfrac{x^2-3x-10}{2x^2+4x}$

9. _____

10. $\dfrac{1}{x+2}\div\dfrac{1}{x^2-4}$

10. _____

11. $\dfrac{4x}{x+2}+\dfrac{8}{x+2}$

11. _____

Chapter 7 Test Form C *cont'd*

12. $\dfrac{x}{x-5} - \dfrac{3}{x^2-3x-10}$

12. _____

13. $\dfrac{2}{x-2} + \dfrac{3}{x-2}$

13. _____

14. $\dfrac{1}{x^2-81} + \dfrac{1}{x^2-2x-63}$

14. _____

Solve each equation.

15. $\dfrac{x}{x-7} + \dfrac{1}{3} = \dfrac{4}{x-7}$

15. _____

16. $\dfrac{14}{9x^2-25} = \dfrac{3}{3x-5} + \dfrac{5}{3x+5}$

16. _____

17. $\dfrac{7}{3x} = \dfrac{4}{x-2}$

17. _____

18. $\dfrac{x-2}{x^2-5x-14} + \dfrac{2}{x-7} = \dfrac{5}{x+2}$

18. _____

Simplify each complex fraction.

19. $\dfrac{\dfrac{4}{x} - \dfrac{2}{y}}{\dfrac{6}{xy}}$

19. _____

20. $\dfrac{\dfrac{1}{6} - \dfrac{2}{3}}{\dfrac{5}{6}}$

20. _____

Chapter 7 Test Form C *cont'd*

Solve each problem.

21. Seven times the reciprocal of a number plus $\dfrac{3}{5}$ 21. _____

    is 3. Find the number.

22. One pipe fills a pool in 6 hours. A second pipe   22. _____
    can fill the same pool in 4 hours. How long
    would it take to fill the pool if both pipes were
    working at the same time?

23. Find x. The triangles are similar.   23. _____

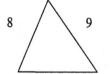

24. y varies directly as x squared. y is 24 when x is 4.   24. _____
    Find y when x is 2.

25. y varies inversely as x squared. y is 5 when x is   25. _____
    4. Find y when x is 3.

Chapter 7 Test Form D

Choose the correct answer to each problem.

Find any real numbers for which the following expressions are undefined.

1. $\dfrac{7x+2}{7x-2}$

   a. $\dfrac{2}{7}$ b. $-\dfrac{2}{7}$ c. 0 d. 1

2. $\dfrac{x-3}{x^2-3x-10}$

   a. 0 b. $5, -2$ c. $-5, 2$ d. 3

Simplify the following rational expressions.

3. $\dfrac{x^2-3x}{4x-12}$

   a. $\dfrac{x}{4}$ b. $\dfrac{x-3}{4}$ c. $\dfrac{1}{4}$ d. 0

4. $\dfrac{6x^2-x-1}{4x-2}$

   a. $\dfrac{3x-1}{2}$ b. $\dfrac{3x-1}{-2}$ c. $\dfrac{6x-1}{4}$ d. $\dfrac{3x+1}{2}$

5. $\dfrac{x+2}{x^3+8}$

   a. $\dfrac{1}{x^2+4}$ b. $\dfrac{1}{x^2-2x+4}$ c. $\dfrac{1}{x^2+2x+4}$ d. $\dfrac{1}{(x+2)^2}$

6. $\dfrac{6x^2}{3x^2-15x}$

   a. $\dfrac{2}{-15x}$ b. $\dfrac{2}{x-5}$ c. $\dfrac{2x}{x-5}$ d. 2

Chapter 7 Test Form D *cont'd*

Perform the indicated operations. Simplify if possible.

7. $\dfrac{x+2}{3x^2-2x-5}\cdot(3x-5)$

    a. 2   **b.** $\dfrac{x+2}{x+1}$ **c.** $\dfrac{x+2}{x-1}$ **d.** $x+2$

8. $\dfrac{3x}{x^2-2x-24}\div\dfrac{3x^2-6x}{x^2+2x-8}$

    a. $x-6$ **b.** $\dfrac{1}{x-6}$ **c.** $\dfrac{x+2}{x-1}$ **d.** 1

9. $\dfrac{4-x}{x+4}\cdot\dfrac{1}{2x^2-5x-12}$

    a. $\dfrac{1}{(x+4)(2x+3)}$ **b.** $\dfrac{-1}{(x+4)(2x+3)}$ **c.** $\dfrac{1}{(x-4)(2x+3)}$ **d.** $\dfrac{2x+3}{x-4}$

10. $\dfrac{x^2-x-20}{x^2-16}\cdot\dfrac{2x-8}{x^2-25}$

    a. $\dfrac{x+4}{x-4}$ **b.** $\dfrac{2x-8}{(x-4)(x+5)}$ **c.** $\dfrac{2}{x+5}$ **d.** $\dfrac{2(x-5)}{x+5}$

11. $\dfrac{x+3}{4x-12}\cdot\dfrac{x^2-9}{x^2+x-6}$

    a. $\dfrac{1}{4(x-2)}$ **b.** $\dfrac{(x+3)(x-2)}{4(x-3)^2}$ **c.** $\dfrac{x-3}{4(x-2)}$ **d.** $\dfrac{x+3}{4(x-2)}$

12. $\dfrac{x^2}{x+2}-\dfrac{4}{x+2}$

    a. $x-2$ **b.** $x+2$ **c.** x^2-4 **d.** $\dfrac{x^2-4}{x+2}$

Chapter 7 Test Form D *cont'd*

13. $\dfrac{5}{x^2-5x-14}-\dfrac{6}{x+2}$

    a. $\dfrac{-1}{x^2-5x-14}$ **b.** $\dfrac{-6x+47}{(x-7)(x+2)}$ **c.** $\dfrac{-x-42}{(x-7)(x+2)}$ **d.** $\dfrac{-1}{x+2}$

14. $\dfrac{3}{x-7}+\dfrac{5}{x+4}$

    a. $\dfrac{-8}{3}$ **b.** $\dfrac{8x-23}{(x-7)(x+4)}$ **c.** $\dfrac{8}{(x-7)(x+4)}$ **d.** $\dfrac{8x-3}{(x-7)(x+4)}$

15. $\dfrac{x}{x^2-3x-10}-\dfrac{3}{x^2-7x+10}$

    a. $\dfrac{x-3}{(x-5)(x+2)(x-2)}$ **b.** $\dfrac{x-3}{(x-5)(x+2)}$

    c. $\dfrac{x^2-5x-6}{(x-5)(x+2)(x-2)}$ **d.** $\dfrac{-2}{(x-5)(x+2)}$

Solve the each equation.

16. $\dfrac{x}{x+3}+\dfrac{x-6}{x+3}=1$

    a. 9   **b.** −3   **c.** 0   **d.** No solution

17. $\dfrac{3}{x-7}=\dfrac{3}{x^2-5x-14}$

    a. −6   **b.** 34   **c.** −1   **d.** No solution

18. $\dfrac{4}{x+2}=1$

    a. 2   **b.** −2   **c.** 4   **d.** No solution

Chapter 7 Test Form D *cont'd*

19. $\dfrac{-18}{x^2-x-20}+\dfrac{4}{x-5}=\dfrac{2}{x+4}$

   a. 6   **b.** 2   **c.** 4   **d.** No solution

Simplify the complex fractions.

20. $\dfrac{\dfrac{1}{x}}{\dfrac{4}{x}+\dfrac{3}{x}}$

   a. $\dfrac{12}{7x}$ **b.** $\dfrac{1}{7}$ **c.** 7   **d.** $\dfrac{12}{x^2}$

21. $\dfrac{\dfrac{1}{6}-\dfrac{1}{4}}{\dfrac{1}{12}-\dfrac{1}{3}}$

   a. $-\dfrac{1}{3}$ **b.** 2   **c.** $\dfrac{1}{2}$ **d.** $\dfrac{1}{3}$

Solve each problem.

22. Seven times the reciprocal of a number plus five times the reciprocal of the number equals four. Find the number.

   a. 3   **b.** 12   **c.** 4   **d.** 5

23. Don can clean a house in 3 hours. Lisa can clean the same house in 8 hours. How long would it take them to clean the house if they worked together?

   a. $5\dfrac{1}{2}$ hours **b.** $2\dfrac{2}{11}$ hours   **c.** 11 hours   **d.** $3\dfrac{1}{2}$ hours

24. *y* varies directly as *x*. *y* is 15 when *x* is 5. Find *y* if *x* is 4.

   a. 3   **b.** 12   **c.** 20   **d.** 9

25. *y* varies inversely as *x*. *y* is 4 when *x* is 16. Find *y* if *x* is 20.

   a. $\dfrac{16}{5}$ **b.** 4   **c.** 10   **d.** 16

Chapter 7 Test Form E

Choose the correct answer to each problem.

Find any real numbers for which the following expressions are undefined.

1. $\dfrac{x+2}{x-6}$

    a. 6   **b.** -2 **c.** $6, -2$ **d.** none

2. $\dfrac{x}{x^2-16}$

    a. $4, -4$ **b.** $0, 4, -4$ **c.** 16   **d.** 0

Simplify the following rational expressions.

3. $\dfrac{2x^2-6x}{x^2-3x}$

    a. 3   **b.** $\dfrac{2}{x}$ **c.** 2   **d.** $x-2$

4. $\dfrac{3x^2+3x-6}{x^2-x}$

    a. $\dfrac{3(x+1)}{x^2}$ **b.** $\dfrac{3(x-2)}{x^2}$ **c.** $\dfrac{3(x+2)}{x}$ **d.** $\dfrac{3(x+2)}{x(x+1)}$

5. $\dfrac{x^3-8}{x-2}$

    a. x^2-4 **b.** x^2+2x+4 **c.** x^2-2x+4 **d.** $x^2-8x+64$

6. $\dfrac{6x^2}{3x^2-15x}$

    a. $\dfrac{2}{-15x}$ **b.** $\dfrac{2}{x-5}$ **c.** $\dfrac{2x}{x-5}$ **d.** 2

Chapter 7 Test Form E *cont'd*

Perform the indicated operations. Simplify if possible.

7. $\dfrac{x^2-6x+9}{x-3} \div (x-3)$

    a. 1   **b.** $\dfrac{1}{(x-3)^2}$ **c.** $-2x+3$ **d.** $\dfrac{x^2-6x+9}{(x-3)^2}$

8. $\dfrac{4x}{x^2+7x+10} \div \dfrac{2x^2-10x}{x^2-25}$

    a. $\dfrac{x-5}{x+2}$ **b.** $x+2$ **c.** $\dfrac{4x}{x+2}$ **d.** $\dfrac{2}{x+2}$

9. $\dfrac{x-2}{xy-4y} \cdot \dfrac{3x-12}{4x-8}$

    a. $\dfrac{3}{4y}$ **b.** $\dfrac{3}{y}$ **c.** $\dfrac{3}{4}$ **d.** $\dfrac{x-4}{4y}$

10. $\dfrac{x^2-8x+15}{x^2-25} \cdot \dfrac{x+5}{x^2-9}$

    a. $\dfrac{1}{x-3}$ **b.** $\dfrac{x-5}{x+3}$ **c.** $\dfrac{1}{x+3}$ **d.** $\dfrac{x+5}{x-3}$

11. $\dfrac{x+2}{4x-8} \div \dfrac{x^2-7x-18}{2x-4}$

    a. $\dfrac{x+2}{4(x-9)}$ **b.** $\dfrac{1}{2(x-9)}$ **c.** $\dfrac{1}{2(x+9)}$ **d.** $\dfrac{x-2}{4(x+9)}$

12. $\dfrac{a^2}{a-3} - \dfrac{9}{a-3}$

    a. a^2-9 **b.** $a+3$ **c.** $\dfrac{a+3}{a-3}$ **d.** $\dfrac{a^2-9}{2(a-3)}$

Chapter 7 Test Form E *cont'd*

13. $\dfrac{11}{x+3} - \dfrac{4}{x^2+6x+9}$

   a. $\dfrac{11x+29}{(x+3)^2}$ b. $\dfrac{7}{(x+3)^2}$ c. $\dfrac{7}{x+3}$ d. $\dfrac{11x+37}{(x+3)^2}$

14. $\dfrac{2}{x-1} + \dfrac{3}{x-4}$

   a. $\dfrac{5}{(x-1)(x-4)}$ b. $\dfrac{5}{(x-4)}$ c. $\dfrac{5x-11}{(x-1)(x-4)}$ d. $\dfrac{5x-14}{(x-1)(x-4)}$

15. $\dfrac{x}{x^2-2x-63} - \dfrac{2}{x^2+8x+7}$

   a. $\dfrac{x-2}{(x-9)(x+7)(x+1)}$ b. $\dfrac{x^2-x+18}{(x-9)(x+7)(x+1)}$

   c. $\dfrac{x-28}{(x+9)(x-7)(x+1)}$ d. $\dfrac{x^2-x-18}{(x-9)(x+7)(x+1)}$

Solve the each equation.

16. $\dfrac{x}{x+3} + \dfrac{x-6}{x+3} = 1$

   a. -3 b. 6   c. 9   d. No solution

17. $\dfrac{2}{x-9} = \dfrac{2}{x^2-6x-27}$

   a. -2 b. -4 c. 4   d. No solution

18. $\dfrac{z-1}{z+1} = 2$

   a. -2 b. 3   c. -3 d. No solution

Chapter 7 Test Form E *cont'd*

19. $\dfrac{-21}{x^2-3x-20}+\dfrac{5}{x-5}=\dfrac{3}{x+2}$

    a. -2 **b.** 4 **c.** -5 **d.** No solution

Simplify the complex fractions.

20. $\dfrac{\dfrac{1}{x}}{\dfrac{3}{x}-\dfrac{2}{x}}$

    a. $\dfrac{1}{2}$ **b.** $\dfrac{1}{3}$ **c.** 1 **d.** x

21. $\dfrac{\dfrac{1}{5}-\dfrac{1}{4}}{\dfrac{1}{20}}$

    a. 1 **b.** -1 **c.** $\dfrac{1}{20}$ **d.** $-\dfrac{1}{20}$

Solve each problem.

22. Fourteen times the reciprocal of a number is equal to seven times the reciprocal of nine. Find the number.

    a. 18 **b.** $\dfrac{98}{9}$ **c.** $\dfrac{9}{2}$ **d.** $\dfrac{7}{9}$

23. An airplane traveled 2000 miles in the same time that a car traveled 300 miles. If the rate of the plane is 340 miles per hour greater than the rate of the car, find the rate of the car.

    a. 40 mph   **b.** 50 mph   **c.** 60 mph   **d.** 70 mph

24. y varies directly as x squared. y is 2 when x is 2. Find y if x is 4.

    a. $\dfrac{1}{2}$ **b.** 16 **c.** 8 **d.** 4

25. y varies inversely as x. y is 3 when x is 5. Find y if x is 16.

    a. 5 **b.** $\dfrac{15}{16}$ **c.** 10 **d.** 16

Chapter 7 Test Form F

Choose the correct answer to each problem.

Find any real numbers for which the following expressions are undefined.

1. $\dfrac{x-1}{x^2-13x+30}$

    a. $1, 10, 3$ **b.** $10, 3$ **c.** $1, -10, -3$ **d.** $-10, -3$

2. $\dfrac{x-3}{x^2+4x}$

    a. $-3, 4$ **b.** $-4, 0, 3$ **c.** $0, 4$ **d.** $0, -4$

Simplify the following rational expressions.

3. $\dfrac{4x-12}{x^2-3x}$

    a. $\dfrac{4}{3}$ **b.** $\dfrac{3}{4}$ **c.** $\dfrac{4}{x}$ **d.** 0

4. $\dfrac{x-2}{x^2-8x+12}$

    a. $\dfrac{x-2}{x+6}$ **b.** $\dfrac{1}{x+6}$ **c.** $-\dfrac{1}{x+6}$ **d.** $\dfrac{1}{x-6}$

5. $\dfrac{6-x}{x^2-4x-12}$

    a. $\dfrac{-1}{x+2}$ **b.** $\dfrac{1}{x-2}$ **c.** $\dfrac{-1}{x-2}$ **d.** $\dfrac{1}{x+2}$

6. $\dfrac{x^3+8}{x^2-2x+4}$

    a. $\dfrac{x+2}{2x}$ **b.** $x+2$ **c.** $x-2$ **d.** x^2-4

Chapter 7 Test Form F *cont'd*

Perform the indicated operations. Simplify if possible.

7. $\dfrac{6x^2 + 11x - 10}{3x^2 + x - 2}$

     a. $\dfrac{(2x-5)(x+4)}{(3x-2)(x+1)}$ **b.** $\dfrac{2x+5}{x+1}$ **c.** $\dfrac{3x-5}{x+1}$ **d.** $x+6$

8. $\dfrac{3x^2 + 6x}{6ax - 18a} \cdot \dfrac{9ax + 27a}{x^2 + 2x}$

     a. $-\dfrac{9}{2}$ **b.** $\dfrac{9a}{2x}$ **c.** $\dfrac{9}{2}$ **d.** $\dfrac{9(x+3)}{2x(x-3)}$

9. $\dfrac{2x}{x^2 - 3x} \cdot \dfrac{2x^2 - 9x + 9}{8x - 12}$

     a. $\dfrac{x+3}{x(x-3)}$ **b.** $\dfrac{x(x+3)}{2}$ **c.** $\dfrac{1}{2}$ **d.** $\dfrac{2x+3}{2(2x-3)}$

10. $\dfrac{6x^2 y^3}{15xy^2} \cdot \dfrac{10}{x}$

     a. $2y$ **b.** $4y$ **c.** $2xy$ **d.** $4xy$

11. $\dfrac{x^2 - 4}{3x^2 + 6x} \div \dfrac{1}{9x}$

     a. $3(x-3)$ **b.** $3x$ **c.** $x-2$ **d.** $3x(x-2)$

12. $\dfrac{x^2 - 2x - 8}{x^2 - 4} \cdot \dfrac{x^2 + 3x - 10}{x^2 + x - 20}$

     a. $\dfrac{x-4}{x+4}$ **b.** $\dfrac{(x-5)(x-4)}{(x+5)(x+4)}$ **c.** 1 **d.** $\dfrac{x-2}{x-4}$

13. $\dfrac{4x-3}{2x+7} - \dfrac{3x+8}{2x+7}$

    a. $\dfrac{x+5}{2x+7}$ **b.** $\dfrac{x-11}{2x+7}$ **c.** $\dfrac{7x+5}{2x+7}$ **d.** $\dfrac{7x-11}{2x+7}$

14. $\dfrac{1}{x+2y} + \dfrac{1}{x-2y}$

    a. $\dfrac{2x}{x^2-4y^2}$ **b.** $\dfrac{2x+4y}{x^2-4y^2}$ **c.** $\dfrac{2}{x^2-4y^2}$ **d.** $\dfrac{2}{4x^2y^2}$

15. $\dfrac{2x}{x^2-4x+4} + \dfrac{3}{x-2}$

    a. $\dfrac{2x+3}{x-2}$ **b.** $\dfrac{2x+3}{(x-2)^2}$ **c.** $\dfrac{5x-2}{(x-2)^2}$ **d.** $\dfrac{5x-6}{(x-2)^2}$

Solve the each equation.

16. $\dfrac{5}{7x-3} = \dfrac{3}{4x-5}$

    a. 16   **b.** −16   **c.** −2   **d.** No solution

17. $\dfrac{x}{x-6} - 3 = \dfrac{6}{x-6}$

    a. −12   **b.** 6   **c.** 12   **d.** No solution

18. $\dfrac{x+6}{27} = \dfrac{1}{x}$

    a. −3, 9   **b.** 3   **c.** −9, 3   **d.** No solution

19. $\dfrac{-26}{x^2+2x-35} + \dfrac{3}{x-5} = \dfrac{2}{x+7}$

    a. −7   **b.** 5   **c.** −5   **d.** No solution

Chapter 7 Test Form F *cont'd*

Simplify the complex fractions.

20. $\dfrac{\dfrac{2}{x}+\dfrac{3}{y}}{\dfrac{4}{x}-\dfrac{2}{y}}$

   a. $\dfrac{1}{4}$ b. $\dfrac{4y-2x}{2y+3x}$ c. $\dfrac{2y+3x}{4y-2x}$ d. $\dfrac{5}{2}$

21. $\dfrac{\dfrac{1}{5}-\dfrac{1}{4}}{\dfrac{1}{20}}$

   a. $\dfrac{1}{5}$ b. $\dfrac{1}{3}$ c. $\dfrac{1}{20}$ d. -1

Solve each problem.

22. It takes Sara three times as long to deliver papers as it does Jennifer. Working together they can deliver the papers in 15 minutes. How long would it take Jennifer by herself?

   a. 25 minutes   b. 20 minutes   c. 30 minutes   d. 35 minutes

23. A boat can travel 160 miles in the same time that a second boat can travel 200 miles. If the speed of the second boat is 20 miles per hour faster than the first boat, what was the speed of the first boat?

   a. 80 mph   b. 85 mph   c. 100 mph   d. 60 mph

24. y varies directly as x squared. y is 18 when x is 3. Find y if x is 4.

   a. $\dfrac{1}{2}$ b. 4   c. 32   d. 2

25. y varies inversely as x. y is 4 when x is 9. Find y if x is 6.

   a. 6   b. 36   c. 18   d. 8

Chapter 8 Test Form A

Simplify the following. Assume that all variables represent a positive number.

1. $\sqrt{100x^6}$

1. _____

2. $-\sqrt{\dfrac{16}{49}}$

2. _____

3. $(81)^{\frac{1}{4}}$

3. _____

4. $\sqrt[4]{81x^8}$

4. _____

5. $\sqrt{9x^2}$

5. _____

6. $\sqrt{\dfrac{x^6}{25}}$

6. _____

Perform the indicated operations. Simplify if possible.

7. $4\sqrt{3} - 2\sqrt{5} + 3\sqrt{3} - 4\sqrt{5}$

7. _____

8. $\sqrt{12} + \sqrt{75} - \sqrt{27}$

8. _____

9. $\sqrt{32x^4}$

9. _____

10. $\sqrt{3} \cdot \sqrt{27}$

10. _____

11. $\sqrt{2}\left(\sqrt{6} - \sqrt{8}\right)$

11. _____

12. $2\sqrt{25x}$

12. _____

13. $\sqrt{27x^5}$

13. _____

14. $\sqrt{\dfrac{1}{49}}$

14. _____

Name: **Date:**

Instructor: **Section:**

Chapter 8 Test Form A *cont'd*

Rationalize each denominator and simplify.

15. $\sqrt{\dfrac{1}{5}}$ 15. _____

16. $\dfrac{3}{\sqrt{2x}}$ 16. _____

17. $\dfrac{5}{x-\sqrt{2}}$ 17. _____

18. $\dfrac{\sqrt{6}-5}{\sqrt{6}+5}$ 18. _____

Solve the following rational equations.

19. $\sqrt{x}+5=9$ 19. _____

20. $\sqrt{3x-5}=\sqrt{2x+4}$ 20. _____

21. $\sqrt{3x-3}=2x-5$ 21. _____

Use the Pythagorean Theorem to find the unknown length for the right triangles in problems 22 and 23.

22. legs of 7 in and 4 in Find the hypotenuse.   22. _____

23. A 10-foot ladder is leaning against a building with its base 6 feet from the bottom of the building. How high up the building is the top of the ladder. Round your answer to the nearest tenth.   23. _____

24. Find the distance between the two points. $(-3, 4)$ $(-2, 6)$ 24. _____

25. Simplify. $\left(\dfrac{x^{\frac{1}{2}}}{x^{\frac{3}{4}}}\right)^4$ 25. _____

Chapter 8 Test Form B

Simplify the following. Assume that all variables represent a positive number.

1. $\sqrt{16x^4}$

1. _____

2. $\sqrt{\dfrac{49}{64}}$

2. _____

3. $\sqrt{16}$

3. _____

4. $-\sqrt[4]{16x^4}$

4. _____

5. $\sqrt{64x^8}$

5. _____

6. $\sqrt{\dfrac{x^6}{25}}$

6. _____

Perform the indicated operations. Simplify if possible.

7. $\sqrt{32x^3}$

7. _____

8. $\sqrt{32} - \sqrt{8}$

8. _____

9. $\sqrt{3} \cdot \sqrt{12}$

9. _____

10. $\sqrt{3} \cdot \sqrt{75}$

10. _____

11. $3\sqrt{8x^4}$

11. _____

12. $\sqrt{50x^5}$

12. _____

13. $\dfrac{\sqrt{40}}{\sqrt{5}}$

13. _____

14. $\sqrt{\dfrac{3}{16}}$

14. _____

Chapter 8 Test Form B *cont'd*

Rationalize each denominator and simplify.

15. $\sqrt{\dfrac{2}{3}}$

15. _____

16. $\dfrac{3}{\sqrt{2}}$

16. _____

17. $\dfrac{2}{\sqrt{3}-x}$

17. _____

18. $\dfrac{\sqrt{3}-4}{\sqrt{3}+4}$

18. _____

Solve the following rational equations.

19. $\sqrt{x}-3=2$

19. _____

20. $\sqrt{4x+7}=\sqrt{2x+9}$

20. _____

21. $\sqrt{4x+9}=x-3$

21. _____

Use the Pythagorean Theorem to find the unknown length for the right triangles in problems 22 and 23.

22. legs of 6 in and 8 in Find the hypotenuse.

22. _____

23. The sides of a square are 36 inches. Find the diagonal of the square. Round your answer to two decimal places.

23. _____

24. Find the distance between the two points.
(5, 6) (9, 3)

24. _____

25. Simplify. $\left(\dfrac{x^{\frac{3}{4}}}{x^{\frac{1}{2}}}\right)^2$

25. _____

Chapter 8 Test Form C

Simplify the following. Assume that all variables represent a positive number.

1. $\sqrt{25}$

1. _____

2. $\sqrt{\dfrac{16}{49}}$

2. _____

3. $\sqrt[3]{8}$

3. _____

4. $\sqrt[4]{x^4 y^{12}}$

4. _____

5. $\sqrt{5x^8}$

5. _____

6. $\sqrt{\dfrac{x^6}{16}}$

6. _____

Perform the indicated operations. Simplify if possible.

7. $\sqrt{24x^7}$

7. _____

8. $\sqrt{3} \cdot \sqrt{48}$

8. _____

9. $\sqrt{\dfrac{3}{49}} - \sqrt{\dfrac{3}{81}}$

9. _____

10. $\sqrt{2} \cdot \sqrt{18}$

10. _____

11. $4\sqrt{32x^3}$

11. _____

12. $\sqrt{48x^6}$

12. _____

13. $\sqrt{\dfrac{720}{9}}$

13. _____

14. $\sqrt{\dfrac{7}{25}}$

14. _____

Chapter 8 Test Form C *cont'd*

Rationalize each denominator and simplify.

15. $\sqrt{\dfrac{2}{5}}$ 15. _____

16. $\dfrac{5}{\sqrt{5x}}$ 16. _____

17. $\dfrac{4}{\sqrt{2}+x}$ 17. _____

18. $\dfrac{\sqrt{5}-3}{\sqrt{5}+3}$ 18. _____

Solve the following rational equations.

19. $\sqrt{x}-3=5$ 19. _____

20. $\sqrt{x-4}=\sqrt{2x-5}$ 20. _____

21. $\sqrt{x+3}=x-3$ 21. _____

Use the Pythagorean Theorem to find the unknown length for the right triangles in problems 22 and 23.

22. A right triangle has sides of 5 in and 5 in. Find hypotenuse.   22. _____

23. The hypotenuse of a right triangle is 70 ft and one leg is 25 ft. Find the length of the other side.   23. _____

24. Find the distance between the two points.
    $(-4, 5)$ $(-6, -8)$ 24. _____

25. Simplify. $\left(x^{\frac{3}{5}}\right)\left(x^{\frac{1}{3}}\right)$ 25. _____

Chapter 8 Test Form D

Choose the correct answer to each problem.

Simplify the following. Assume that all variables represent a positive number.

1. $\sqrt{36}$

     a. $\sqrt{6}$ **b.** 36   **c.** 6   **d.** 3

2. $\sqrt{\dfrac{121}{144}}$

     a. $\dfrac{11}{12}$ **b.** $\sqrt{23}$ **c.** $\sqrt{\dfrac{11}{12}}$ **d.** $\dfrac{12}{11}$

3. $\sqrt{x^4}$

     a. x^8 **b.** x^4 **c.** x^2 **d.** $\sqrt{x^4}$

4. $\sqrt[4]{x^8 y^4}$

     a. $x^2 y^4$ **b.** $x^2 y$ **c.** $x^4 y$ **d.** $x^8 y^4$

5. $\sqrt{9x^4}$

     a. $9x^2$ **b.** $3x^2$ **c.** $3x$ **d.** $9x$

6. $\sqrt{\dfrac{12}{3}}$

     a. 4   **b.** $\sqrt{4}$ **c.** 2   **d.** $\dfrac{\sqrt{12}}{3}$

Perform the indicated operations. Simplify if possible.

7. $\sqrt{24x^6}$

     a. $2\sqrt{6x^6}$ **b.** $12x^3$ **c.** $2x^3\sqrt{6}$ **d.** $6x^3$

Chapter 8 Test Form D *cont'd*

8. $\sqrt{27} + \sqrt{12}$

   a. $\sqrt{39}$ **b.** $3\sqrt{13}$ **c.** $5\sqrt{3}$ **d.** $13\sqrt{3}$

9. $\sqrt{2} \cdot \sqrt{8}$

   a. $2\sqrt{2}$ **b.** 16 **c.** $\sqrt{6}$ **d.** 4

10. $\sqrt{15} \cdot \sqrt{10}$

   a. 5 **b.** $5\sqrt{6}$ **c.** $5\sqrt{30}$ **d.** $10\sqrt{15}$

11. $\sqrt{3}\left(\sqrt{6} - \sqrt{12}\right)$

   a. $3\sqrt{2} - 6$ **b.** $-3\sqrt{2}$ **c.** $\sqrt{18} - 6$ **d.** $\sqrt{12}$

12. $\sqrt{72x^5}$

   a. $36x^2$ **b.** $36x^2\sqrt{x}$ **c.** $6x^2\sqrt{2x}$ **d.** $6x\sqrt{2x}$

13. $\dfrac{\sqrt{96}}{\sqrt{8}}$

   a. $2\sqrt{6}$ **b.** $\sqrt{12}$ **c.** $4\sqrt{3}$ **d.** $2\sqrt{3}$

14. $\sqrt{\dfrac{21}{16}}$

   a. $\dfrac{\sqrt{21}}{16}$ **b.** $\dfrac{\sqrt{21}}{2}$ **c.** $\dfrac{\sqrt{21}}{4}$ **d.** $\dfrac{21}{4}$

Rationalize each denominator and simplify.

15. $\sqrt{\dfrac{1}{5}}$

   a. $\dfrac{1}{5}$ **b.** $\dfrac{\sqrt{5}}{5}$ **c.** 5 **d.** $\dfrac{1}{\sqrt{5}}$

Chapter 8 Test Form D *cont'd*

16. $\dfrac{3}{\sqrt{6x}}$

   a. $\dfrac{\sqrt{6x}}{2x}$ b. $\dfrac{1}{2x}$ c. $\sqrt{3}$ d. $\dfrac{\sqrt{6}}{2x}$

17. $\dfrac{3}{\sqrt{2}-5}$

   a. -1 b. $-\sqrt{2}-5$ c. $\sqrt{2}+5$ d. $\dfrac{3\left(\sqrt{2}+5\right)}{-23}$

18. $\dfrac{x}{\sqrt{x}+4}$

   a. $\dfrac{x\left(\sqrt{x}-4\right)}{x-16}$ b. $\dfrac{x\left(\sqrt{x}+4\right)}{x+16}$ c. $\dfrac{x}{x-16}$ d. $\dfrac{x\left(\sqrt{x}-4\right)}{x-4}$

Solve the following radical equations.

19. $\sqrt{x}+2=6$

   a. 2   b. 16   c. 4   d. 64

20. $\sqrt{2x-7}=\sqrt{x+5}$

   a. 2   b. -2 c. 12   d. no solution

21. $\sqrt{2x+1}=x-1$

   a. 16   b. 4   c. 4, 0   d. 0

Chapter 8 Test Form D *cont'd*

In problems 22 and 23, use the Pythagorean theorem to find the unknown length in the right triangle.

22. One leg is 5 cm and the other leg is $\sqrt{6}$ cm. Find the exact length of the hypotenuse.

   a. $\sqrt{11}$ cm   **b.** $\sqrt{61}$ cm   **c.** $\sqrt{19}$ cm   **d.** $\sqrt{31}$ cm

23. The hypotenuse is 13 ft and one leg is 12 ft. Find the exact length of the other leg.

   a. 5 ft   **b.** 25 ft   **c.** $\sqrt{313}$ ft   **d.** 1 ft

24. Find the distance between the two points. $(3, -4)$ and $(0, 6)$

   a. 109   **b.** $\sqrt{5}$ **c.** $\sqrt{11}$ **d.** $\sqrt{109}$

25. Simplify. $\left(\dfrac{x^{\frac{2}{3}}}{x^{\frac{1}{6}}} \right)^6$

   a. $\dfrac{x^5}{x^4}$ **b.** $\dfrac{1}{x^2}$ **c.** x^3 **d.** x^4

Chapter 8 Test Form E

Choose the correct answer to each problem.

Simplify the following. Assume that all variables represent a positive number.

1. $\sqrt{25}$

    a. 5   **b.** $\sqrt{5}$ **c.** 25   **d.** 10

2. $-\sqrt{\dfrac{64}{81}}$

    a. $\dfrac{8}{9}$ **b.** $\sqrt{\dfrac{8}{9}}$ **c.** $-\dfrac{8}{9}$ **d.** $-\sqrt{\dfrac{8}{9}}$

3. $\sqrt[3]{-125}$

    a. -5 **b.** -25 **c.** 5   **d.** 25

4. $\sqrt[3]{x^6 y^6}$

    a. $x^3 y^3$ **b.** $x^2 y^2$ **c.** xy **d.** $x^6 y^6$

5. $\sqrt{100x^6}$

    a. $100x^3$ **b.** $\sqrt{10x^3}$ **c.** $10\sqrt{x^6}$ **d.** $10x^3$

6. $\sqrt{\dfrac{49}{x^4}}$

    a. $\dfrac{7}{x^2}$ **b.** $\dfrac{7}{x^4}$ **c.** $\dfrac{\sqrt{7}}{x^2}$ **d.** $\dfrac{\sqrt{7}}{x^4}$

Perform the indicated operations. Simplify if possible.

7. $\sqrt{36x^5}$

    a. $6x$ **b.** $6x^2\sqrt{x}$ **c.** $x^2\sqrt{6x}$ **d.** $6x\sqrt{x}$

Chapter 8 Test Form E *cont'd*

8. $\sqrt{75} - \sqrt{48}$

    a. $3\sqrt{3}$ **b.** $\sqrt{27}$ **c.** $9\sqrt{3}$ **d.** $\sqrt{3}$

9. $\sqrt{3} \cdot \sqrt{18}$

    a. 3 **b.** $3\sqrt{6}$ **c.** $2\sqrt{3}$ **d.** 6

10. $\sqrt{5} \cdot \sqrt{15}$

    a. $25\sqrt{3}$ **b.** $5\sqrt{3}$ **c.** $3\sqrt{5}$ **d.** 75

11. $\sqrt{5} \cdot \sqrt{20}$

    a. 4 **b.** $\sqrt{100}$ **c.** $\sqrt{10}$ **d.** 10

12. $\sqrt{75x^8}$

    a. $x^4\sqrt{75}$ **b.** $5x^2\sqrt{3}$ **c.** $5\sqrt{3x^8}$ **d.** $5x^4\sqrt{3}$

13. $\dfrac{\sqrt{75}}{\sqrt{64}}$

    a. $\dfrac{3\sqrt{5}}{8}$ **b.** $\dfrac{5\sqrt{3}}{8}$ **c.** $\dfrac{25\sqrt{3}}{64}$ **d.** $\dfrac{5\sqrt{2}}{64}$

14. $\sqrt{\dfrac{12x^3}{49}}$

    a. $\dfrac{2x\sqrt{3x}}{7}$ **b.** $\dfrac{6x}{7}$ **c.** $\dfrac{2\sqrt{3x^3}}{7}$ **d.** $\dfrac{2\sqrt{3x^3}}{\sqrt{7}}$

Chapter 8 Test Form E *cont'd*

Rationalize each denominator and simplify.

15. $\sqrt{\dfrac{2}{3}}$

    a. $\dfrac{\sqrt{2}}{3}$ **b.** $\sqrt{2}$ **c.** $\dfrac{\sqrt{6}}{3}$ **d.** $\dfrac{2}{3}$

16. $\dfrac{5}{\sqrt{15x}}$

    a. $\sqrt{3x}$ **b.** $\dfrac{\sqrt{15x}}{3x}$ **c.** $\dfrac{\sqrt{15x}}{5x}$ **d.** $\dfrac{5\sqrt{3}}{x}$

17. $\dfrac{7}{\sqrt{x}-3}$

    a. $\dfrac{7\left(\sqrt{x}-3\right)}{x-3}$ **b.** $\dfrac{7\left(\sqrt{x}+3\right)}{x-9}$ **c.** $\dfrac{7\left(\sqrt{x}-3\right)}{x-9}$ **d.** $\dfrac{7\left(\sqrt{x}+3\right)}{x-3}$

18. $\dfrac{\sqrt{3}-1}{\sqrt{3}+1}$

    a. $\dfrac{\sqrt{3}+1}{3}$ **b.** 2 **c.** $2-\sqrt{3}$ **d.** $-\dfrac{\sqrt{3}}{3}$

Solve the following radical equations.

19. $\sqrt{x}+2=4$

    a. 4   **b.** 2   **c.** 0   **d.** 16

20. $\sqrt{5x+4}=\sqrt{4x+8}$

    a. 4   **b.** 12   **c.** 6   **d.** $\dfrac{4}{3}$

21. $\sqrt{3x-2}=x-4$

    a. 5   **b.** 2   **c.** 9   **d.** 2, 9

Chapter 8 Test Form E *cont'd*

In problems 22 and 23, use the Pythagorean theorem to find the unknown length in the right triangle.

22. One leg is 4 cm and the other leg is 6 cm. Find the exact length of the hypotenuse.

   a. $\sqrt{10}$ cm   **b.** $2\sqrt{13}$ cm   **c.** $2\sqrt{6}$ cm   **d.** $13\sqrt{2}$ cm

23. Two sides of a right triangle are 6 ft and 8 ft. Find the exact length of the hypotenuse.

   a. 14 ft   **b.** 16 ft   **c.** 12ft   **d.** 10 ft

24. Find the distance between the two points. $(-3, 5)$ and $(4, -6)$

   a. 170   **b.** $\sqrt{170}$ **c.** 2   **d.** $\sqrt{2}$

25. Simplify. $\left(\dfrac{x^{\frac{2}{3}}}{x^{\frac{1}{2}}} \right)^{6}$

   a. x^3 **b.** $x^{\frac{1}{2}}$ **c.** x **d.** x^4

Chapter 8 Test Form F

Choose the correct answer to each problem.

Simplify the following. Assume that all variables represent a positive number.

1. $\sqrt{81}$

    a. 81   **b.** $\sqrt{9}$ **c.** 3   **d.** 9

2. $-\sqrt{\dfrac{16}{121}}$

    a. $-\dfrac{16}{121}$ **b.** $-\dfrac{8}{11}$ **c.** $-\dfrac{8}{121}$ **d.** $-\dfrac{4}{11}$

3. $-\sqrt[3]{27}$

    a. 3   **b.** 9   **c.** -3 **d.** -9

4. $\sqrt{25x^8}$

    a. $x^4\sqrt{5}$ **b.** $5\sqrt{x^8}$ **c.** $\sqrt{5x^4}$ **d.** $5x^4$

5. $\sqrt{49x^6}$

    a. $7x^6$ **b.** $7x^3$ **c.** $\sqrt{7x^3}$ **d.** $7\sqrt{x^6}$

6. $\sqrt{\dfrac{x^8}{9}}$

    a. $\dfrac{x^6}{3}$ **b.** $\dfrac{x^2}{3}$ **c.** $\dfrac{x^4}{\sqrt{3}}$ **d.** $\dfrac{x^4}{3}$

Perform the indicated operations. Simplify if possible.

7. $\sqrt{49x^9}$

    a. $\sqrt{7x^9}$ **b.** $7x^7$ **c.** $7\sqrt{x^9}$ **d.** $7x^4\sqrt{x}$

Chapter 8 Test Form F *cont'd*

8. $\sqrt{32} - \sqrt{48}$

    a. -4 **b.** -16 **c.** $4\sqrt{2} - 4\sqrt{3}$ **d.** $15\sqrt{2} - 16\sqrt{3}$

9. $\sqrt{3} \cdot \sqrt{27}$

    a. $3\sqrt{9}$ **b.** $3\sqrt{3}$ **c.** 81 **d.** 9

10. $\sqrt{12} \cdot \sqrt{18}$

    a. $36\sqrt{3}$ **b.** $6\sqrt{6}$ **c.** $24\sqrt{6}$ **d.** $18\sqrt{2}$

11. $3\sqrt{12x^6}$

    a. $9x^3\sqrt{4}$ **b.** $6x^3$ **c.** $12x^3\sqrt{3}$ **d.** $6x^3\sqrt{3}$

12. $\left(\sqrt{x} + 4\right)^2$

    a. $x + 16$ **b.** $x + 4\sqrt{x} + 8$ **c.** $x + 8$ **d.** $x + 8\sqrt{x} + 16$

13. $\dfrac{\sqrt{8000}}{\sqrt{20}}$

    a. 200 **b.** 400 **c.** 20 **d.** 40

14. $\sqrt{\dfrac{20x^4}{5x^3}}$

    a. $5\sqrt{x}$ **b.** $10x$ **c.** $2\sqrt{x}$ **d.** $2x$

Rationalize each denominator and simplify.

15. $\sqrt{\dfrac{2}{5}}$

    a. $\sqrt{2}$ **b.** $\sqrt{5}$ **c.** $\dfrac{\sqrt{5}}{5}$ **d.** $\dfrac{\sqrt{10}}{5}$

Chapter 8 Test Form F *cont'd*

16. $\dfrac{8y}{\sqrt{2}}$

    a. $4y\sqrt{2}$ **b.** $\dfrac{y\sqrt{2}}{4}$ **c.** $16y\sqrt{2}$ **d.** $\dfrac{y\sqrt{2}}{16}$

17. $\dfrac{6}{2+\sqrt{x}}$

    a. $12+\sqrt{x}$ **b.** $\dfrac{12+\sqrt{x}}{2+x}$ **c.** $12-\sqrt{x}$ **d.** $\dfrac{12-6\sqrt{x}}{4-x}$

18. $\dfrac{\sqrt{5}-1}{\sqrt{5}+1}$

    a. $\dfrac{2}{3}$ **b.** $\dfrac{3-\sqrt{5}}{2}$ **c.** $\dfrac{2\sqrt{5}}{3}$ **d.** $\dfrac{2-\sqrt{5}}{3}$

Solve the following radical equations.

19. $\sqrt{x}+8=10$

    a. 4   **b.** 2   **c.** 36   **d.** no solution

20. $\sqrt{x-3}=4$

    a. 19   **b.** 7   **c.** 4   **d.** no solution

21. $\sqrt{14-x}=8-x$

    a. $-5, -10$ **b.** 5   **c.** 5, 0   **d.** no solution

Chapter 8 Test Form F *cont'd*

In problems 22 and 23, use the Pythagorean theorem to find the unknown length in the right triangle.

22. One leg is 4 and the other leg is 8. Find the exact length of the hypotenuse.

    a. $4\sqrt{5}$ **b.** $2\sqrt{3}$ **c.** $5\sqrt{4}$ **d.** $4\sqrt{2}$

23. Two sides of a right triangle are 7 and 24 ft. Find the length of the hypotenuse.

    a. 25 ft   **b.** 31 ft   **c.** 23 ft   **d.** $\sqrt{31}$ ft

24. Find the distance between the two points. $(-2, 0)$ and $(-4, 6)$

    a. 40   **b.** $2\sqrt{2}$ **c.** $2\sqrt{5}$ **d.** $2\sqrt{10}$

25. Simplify. $\left(\dfrac{x^{\frac{2}{5}}}{y^{\frac{1}{3}}} \right)^{6}$

    a. $\dfrac{x^{\frac{12}{5}}}{y}$ **b.** $\dfrac{x^{\frac{12}{5}}}{y^{2}}$ **c.** $\dfrac{x}{y^{2}}$ **d.** $\dfrac{x^{12}}{y}$

Chapter 9 Test Form A

Solve using the square root property.

1. $x^2 + 4 = 29$

2. $(x - 2)^2 = 25$

3. $(2x - 3)^2 + 4 = 13$

Solve by completing the square.

4. $x^2 + 6x = 4$

5. $x^2 + 4x - 9 = 0$

6. $x^2 + 2x = 5$

Solve using the quadratic formula.

7. $x^2 + 7x - 4 = 0$

8. $3x^2 - 6x - 8 = 0$

9. $x^2 + 4x + 2 = 0$

Solve using the most appropriate method.

10. $9x^2 - 12x + 4 = 0$

11. $(2x - 4)^2 = 64$

12. $x^2 - 3x - 4 = 0$

13. $x(x - 1) = 6$

14. $(x - 2)(x - 4) = 10$

15. $x^2 - 7x + 3 = 0$

1. _____

2. _____

3. _____

4. _____

5. _____

6. _____

7. _____

8. _____

9. _____

10. _____

11. _____

12. _____

13. _____

14. _____

15. _____

Chapter 9 Test Form A *cont'd*

Simplify.

16. $\sqrt{-16}$ 16. _____

17. $\sqrt{-8}$ 17. _____

18. $(3-6i)-(5+2i)$ 18. _____

19. $(2+3i)(4-6i)$ 19. _____

20. $\dfrac{2-i}{3+2i}$ 20. _____

Graph the quadratic function. Label the vertex and any intercept points with their coordinates.

21. $y = x^2 + 4x + 4$ 22. $y = x^2 + 1$

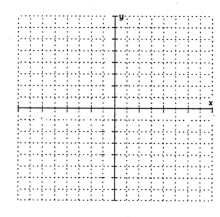 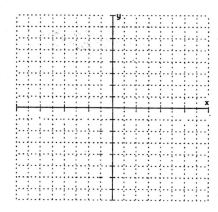

23. $y = -x^2 + 6x - 4$

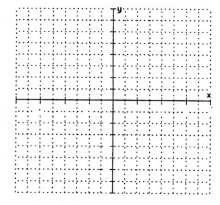

Chapter 9 Test Form A *cont'd*

Use the following information for problems 24 and 25.

A toy rocket is launched from the ground with an initial velocity of 80 feet per second. The height h of the rocket after t seconds is given by the formula $h = 80t - 16t^2$.

24. How long after it is launched will the rocket be   **24.** _____
      at its highest point?

25. What will be the highest height the rocket   **25.** _____
      will reach?

Chapter 9 Test Form B

Solve using the square root property.

1. $4x^2 = 100$

2. $(2x+3)^2 = 75$

3. $(x-3)^2 = 25$

Solve by completing the square.

4. $x^2 + 16x = -9$

5. $3x^2 - 11x = 4$

6. $x^2 + 4x = 5$

Solve using the quadratic formula.

7. $x^2 + 4x - 8 = 0$

8. $x^2 - 8x + 3 = 0$

Solve using the most appropriate method.

9. $(3x-2)(x-1) = 14$

10. $3x^2 - 48 = 0$

11. $3x^2 - 7x + 4 = 0$

12. $(2x-3)^2 = 25$

13. $5x^2 - 6x - 3 = 0$

14. $5x^3 = 20x$

15. $x^2 + 3x = 40$

1. _____

2. _____

3. _____

4. _____

5. _____

6. _____

7. _____

8. _____

9. _____

10. _____

11. _____

12. _____

13. _____

14. _____

15. _____

Chapter 9 Test Form B *cont'd*

Simplify.

16. $\sqrt{-25}$

16. _____

17. $\sqrt{-20}$

17. _____

18. $(2-3i)-(4-6i)$

18. _____

19. $(2+3i)^2$

19. _____

20. $\dfrac{2+i}{3-2i}$

20. _____

Graph the quadratic function. Label the vertex and any intercept points with their coordinates.

21. $y = x^2 - 1$

22. $y = x^2 - 2x - 8$

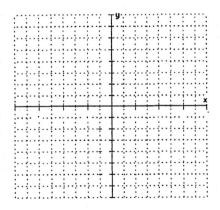

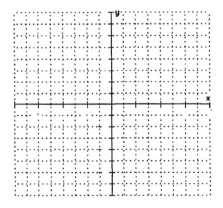

Chapter 9 Test Form B *cont'd*

23. $y = 2x^2 + 4x + 3$

24. $y = x^2 - 2x$

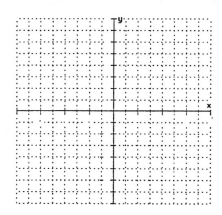
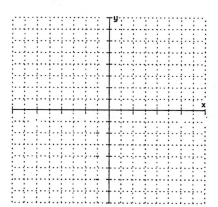

25. The length of a rectangle is 4 feet more than its width. The area of the rectangle is 96 square feet. Find the length and the width of the rectangle.

25. _____

Chapter 9 Test Form C

Solve using the square root property.

1. $3x^2 - 3 = 24$

2. $(x-4)^2 = 7$

3. $(3x-4)^2 = 5$

1. _____

2. _____

3. _____

Solve by completing the square.

4. $x^2 + 8x = -4$

5. $x^2 + x = \dfrac{3}{4}$

6. $x^2 + 3x = 6$

4. _____

5. _____

6. _____

Solve using the quadratic formula.

7. $4x^2 - 4x = 15$

8. $x^2 + 8x + 4 = 0$

9. $x^2 + 3x = 8$

7. _____

8. _____

9. _____

Solve using the most appropriate method.

10. $x^2 + 10x + 25 = 0$

11. $(2x-3)^2 = 25$

12. $x^2 - 2x - 2 = 0$

13. $x(x-4) = -3$

14. $(x-4)(x+3) = 6$

15. $3x^2 = 48$

10. _____

11. _____

12. _____

13. _____

14. _____

15. _____

Chapter 9 Test Form C *cont'd*

16. $6x^2 - 7x - 20 = 0$ 16. _____

Simplify.

16. $\sqrt{-36}$ 17. _____

18. $\sqrt{-20}$ 18. _____

19. $(3 + 2i) - (4 - 7i)$ 19. _____

20. $(2 - 3i)(4 + 2i)$ 20. _____

21. $\dfrac{1 - 3i}{4 + i}$ 21. _____

Graph the quadratic function. Label the vertex and any intercept points with their coordinates.

22. $y = -x^2 - 3x$ 23. $y = x^2 + x - 2$

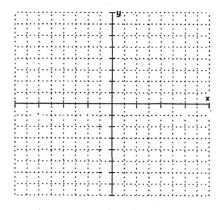   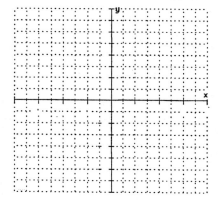

Chapter 9 Test Form C *cont'd*

24. $y = x^2 - 1$

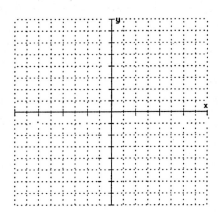

25. The area A of a circle with radius r is found by
the formula $A = \pi r^2$. If the area of a circle
is $\dfrac{9}{16}\pi$ square inches, find its radius.

25. _____

Chapter 9 Test Form D

Choose the correct answer to each problem.

Solve using the square root property.

1. $3x^2 = 48$

   a. $9, -9$ **b.** $16, -16$ **c.** $\dfrac{4\sqrt{3}}{3}, -\dfrac{4\sqrt{3}}{3}$ **d.** $4, -4$

2. $(x-3)^2 = 16$

   a. $19, -1$ **b.** 7 **c.** $7, -1$ **d.** $-4, 4$

3. $(2x-5)^2 = 7$

   a. $\dfrac{5\sqrt{7}}{2}$ **b.** $\dfrac{5 \pm \sqrt{7}}{2}$ **c.** 6 **d.** 12

Solve by completing the square.

4. $x^2 + 6x = 27$

   a. $-9, 3$ **b.** $-3, 9$ **c.** $6, -12$ **d.** $-6, 12$

5. $x^2 - x = 20$

   a. $2, -10$ **b.** $5, -4$ **c.** $3, -5$ **d.** $-3, 5$

6. $x^2 + 2x = 8$

   a. 2 **b.** $-4, 2$ **c.** $-1 \pm 2\sqrt{2}$ **d.** $\pm\sqrt{2}$

Solve using the quadratic formula.

7. $3x^2 + 10x - 8 = 0$

   a. $-2, \dfrac{4}{3}$ **b.** $2, -\dfrac{4}{3}$ **c.** $\dfrac{2}{3}, -4$ **d.** no real solutions

Chapter 9 Test Form D *cont'd*

8. $x^2 - 4x + 6 = 0$

   a. $2 \pm \sqrt{10}$ **b.** $2 \pm \sqrt{2}$ **c.** $-3, -2$ **d.** no real solutions

9. $x^2 + 5x + 3 = 0$

   a. $\dfrac{5 \pm \sqrt{37}}{2}$ **b.** $\dfrac{-5 \pm 3\sqrt{2}}{2}$ **c.** $\dfrac{-5 \pm \sqrt{27}}{2}$ **d.** $\dfrac{-5 \pm \sqrt{13}}{2}$

Solve using the most appropriate method.

10. $2x^2 + 7x - 15 = 0$

   a. $-\dfrac{5}{2}, 3$ **b.** $\dfrac{5}{2}, -3$ **c.** $-5, \dfrac{3}{2}$ **d.** $-\dfrac{3}{2}, 5$

11. $(x - 4)^2 = 25$

   a. 9   **b.** $5, -5$ **c.** $9, -1$ **d.** $20, 21$

12. $x^2 - 6x - 30 = 0$

   a. $3 \pm 4\sqrt{3}$ **b.** $3 \pm \sqrt{39}$ **c.** $6, 0$ **d.** no real solutions

13. $x(x - 3) = 10$

   a. $10, 13$ **b.** $2, -5$ **c.** $5, -2$ **d.** $5, 2$

14. $(x - 2)(x - 3) = 2$

   a. $2, 3$ **b.** $4, 5$ **c.** $4, 1$ **d.** $-4, -1$

15. $4x^2 - 20x + 25 = 0$

   a. $\dfrac{5}{2}$ **b.** $-\dfrac{5}{2}$ **c.** $\dfrac{25}{4}, 1$ **d.** $\dfrac{2}{5}$

16. $x^2 - 4x - 8 = 0$

   a. $-2, 4$ **b.** $-4, 2$ **c.** $2 \pm 2\sqrt{3}$ **d.** $2 \pm 4\sqrt{3}$

Chapter 9 Test Form D *cont'd*

17. $2x^2 + 7x - 15 = 0$

    a. $\dfrac{-7 \pm \sqrt{11}}{4}$ **b.** $\dfrac{-7 \pm \sqrt{109}}{4}$ **c.** $-\dfrac{3}{2}, 5$ **d.** $-5, \dfrac{3}{2}$

Simplify.

18. $\sqrt{-64}$

    a. 8 **b.** $8i$ **c.** -8 **d.** $-8i$

19. $\sqrt{-50}$

    a. $5i\sqrt{2}$ **b.** $2i\sqrt{5}$ **c.** $25i$ **d.** $-2i\sqrt{5}$

20. $(2 - 3i) - (4 + 2i)$

    a. $-2 - 5i$ **b.** $6 - 5i$ **c.** $-2 - i$ **d.** $6 - i$

21. $(3 - 2i)(4 + 5i)$

    a. $2 + 7i$ **b.** $22 + 7i$ **c.** $12 - 3i$ **d.** $12 + 7i$

22. $\dfrac{3}{4 - 2i}$

    a. $2 + \dfrac{1}{2}i$ **b.** $1 - \dfrac{1}{2}i$ **c.** $1 + \dfrac{1}{2}i$ **d.** $\dfrac{3}{5} + \dfrac{3}{10}i$

Chapter 9 Test Form D *cont'd*

Graph the quadratic function. Label the vertex and any intercept points with their coordinates.

23. $y = x^2 - 6x + 5$

a.

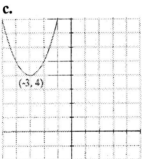

b.

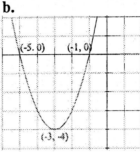

c.

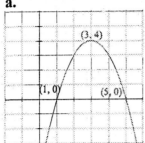

d.

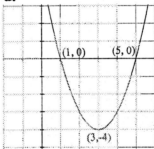

24. $y = x^2 + 2x - 1$

a.

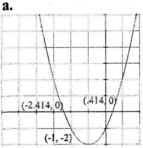

b.

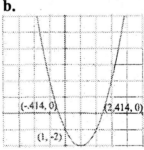

c.

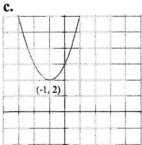

d.

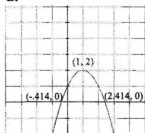

25. The area of a triangle is 24 square inches. The height is 3 times the base. Find the dimensions of the triangle.

a. base = 8 in, height = 24 in   **b.** base = 4 in, height = 12 in
c. base = 3 in, height = 6 in   **d.** base = 2 in, height = 12 in

Chapter 9 Test Form E

Choose the correct answer to each problem.

Solve using the square root property.

1. $5x^2 = 45$

    a. 3   **b.** 9   **c.** $3, -3$ **d.** $9, -9$

2. $\left(x - \dfrac{3}{4}\right)^2 = \dfrac{1}{16}$

    a. 1   **b.** $\pm\dfrac{1}{4}$ **c.** $\dfrac{1}{2}$ **d.** $1, \dfrac{1}{2}$

3. $(2x - 3)^2 = 5$

    a. $\dfrac{3\sqrt{5}}{2}$ **b.** $\dfrac{3 \pm \sqrt{5}}{2}$ **c.** 4   **d.** $\dfrac{\pm 3\sqrt{5}}{2}$

Solve by completing the square.

4. $x^2 - 8x = 5$

    a. $-2, -4$ **b.** $4 \pm \sqrt{13}$ **c.** $25, -17$ **d.** $4 \pm \sqrt{21}$

5. $x^2 + 7x = 18$

    a. $-9, 2$ **b.** $3, -6$ **c.** $9, -2$ **d.** $-3, 6$

6. $x^2 + 4x + 1 = 0$

    a. $2 \pm \sqrt{3}$ **b.** $-2 \pm \sqrt{3}$ **c.** $1, -1$ **d.** $1, -3$

Solve using the quadratic formula.

7. $2x^2 + 9x - 5 = 0$

    a. $-\dfrac{1}{2}, 5$ **b.** $\dfrac{1}{2}, -5$ **c.** $1, -\dfrac{5}{2}$ **d.** $-1, -\dfrac{5}{2}$

Chapter 9 Test Form E *cont'd*

8. $x^2 + 2x - 5 = 0$

    a. $5, -1$ **b.** $-1 \pm \sqrt{6}$ **c.** $1 \pm \sqrt{6}$ **d.** no real solutions

9. $x^2 - 4x - 2 = 0$

    a. $2 \pm \sqrt{6}$ **b.** $2 \pm 2\sqrt{6}$ **c.** $2 \pm 3\sqrt{2}$ **d.** $2 \pm 6\sqrt{2}$

Solve using the most appropriate method.

10. $x^2 - 16x + 64 = 0$

    a. $8, -8$ **b.** -8 **c.** 8 **d.** no real solutions

11. $(x - 4)^2 = 9$

    a. 7 **b.** $13, -5$ **c.** $7, 1$ **d.** no real solutions

12. $x^2 - 11x + 30 = 0$

    a. $10, -3$ **b.** $5, 6$ **c.** $-5, -6$ **d.** $-10, 3$

13. $4x^2 - 20x + 25 = 0$

    a. $\dfrac{5}{2}$ **b.** $-\dfrac{5}{2}$ **c.** $\dfrac{2}{5}$ **d.** $-\dfrac{2}{5}$

14. $2x^2 - x - 15 = 0$

    a. $-\dfrac{3}{2}, \dfrac{5}{4}$ **b.** $3, -\dfrac{5}{2}$ **c.** $\dfrac{3}{2}, -5$ **d.** no real solutions

15. $x(x - 3) = 18$

    a. 6 **b.** $-6, 3$ **c.** $6, -3$ **d.** no real solutions

16. $(x - 1)(x + 7) = 9$

    a. $1, -7$ **b.** $2, -8$ **c.** 2 **d.** no real solutions

Chapter 9 Test Form E *cont'd*

Simplify.

17. $\sqrt{-25}$

   a. 5   **b.** $5i$ **c.** -5 **d.** $\sqrt{5}$

18. $\sqrt{-24}$

   a. $12i$ **b.** $2i\sqrt{6}$ **c.** -12 **d.** $-12i$

19. $(3-4i)-(3-2i)$

   a. $6-2i$ **b.** $-6i$ **c.** $6-6i$ **d.** $-2i$

20. $(4-3i)(2+i)$

   a. $8+i$ **b.** $8-5i$ **c.** $5-2i$ **d.** $11-2i$

21. $2i(4-i)$

   a. $-2+8i$ **b.** $2+8i$ **c.** $8-2i$ **d.** $6i$

22. $\dfrac{2-i}{2-3i}$

   a. $-\dfrac{1}{5}-\dfrac{4}{5}i$ **b.** $\dfrac{1}{13}+\dfrac{4}{13}i$ **c.** $-\dfrac{7}{5}-\dfrac{4}{5}i$ **d.** $\dfrac{7}{13}+\dfrac{4}{13}i$

Chapter 9 Test Form E *cont'd*

Graph the quadratic function. Label the vertex and any intercept points with their coordinates.

23. $y = -x^2 - 4x - 5$

a.

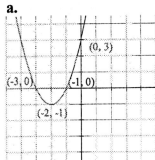

b.

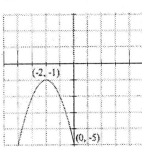

c.

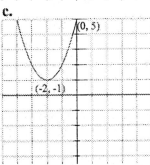

d.

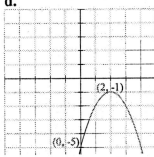

24. $y = x^2 - 2x$

a.

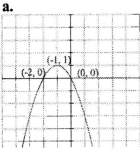

b.

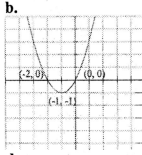

c.

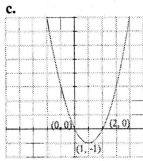

d.

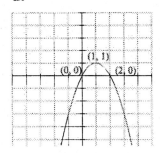

25. A triangular sail is made of 90 square feet of cloth. Its height is 5 times its base. Find the dimensions of the sail.

    a. base = 6 ft, height = 30 ft   **b.** base = 5 ft, height = 25 ft

    c. base = 4 ft, height = 20 ft   **d.** base = 3 ft, height = 15 ft

Chapter 9 Test Form F

Choose the correct answer to each problem.

Solve using the square root property.

1. $3x^2 = 12$

    a. 4 b. $2, -2$ c. $\pm 2\sqrt{3}$ d. 2

2. $\left(x + \dfrac{1}{11}\right)^2 = \dfrac{1}{121}$

    a. 0 b. $-\dfrac{2}{11}$ c. $0, -\dfrac{2}{11}$ d. no real solutions

3. $(x-2)^2 = 4$

    a. $0, 4$ b. 4 c. 6 d. 2

Solve by completing the square.

4. $x^2 + 6x = 10$

    a. $-3, 4$ b. $16, -25$ c. $-3 \pm \sqrt{19}$ d. $-3 \pm \sqrt{10}$

5. $x^2 - 7x = \dfrac{1}{4}$

    a. $7 \pm \sqrt{5}$ b. $7 \pm 5\sqrt{2}$ c. $\dfrac{7 \pm 5\sqrt{2}}{2}$ d. no real solutions

6. $x^2 + 4x = 5$

    a. $-2 \pm \sqrt{5}$ b. $2 \pm \sqrt{5}$ c. $1, -5$ d. 1

Solve using the quadratic formula.

7. $x^2 + 20x + 10 = 0$

    a. $-10 \pm 3\sqrt{10}$ b. $20, -40$ c. $-10, -1$ d. no real solutions

Chapter 9 Test Form F *cont'd*

8. $x^2 - 2x + 5 = 0$

    a. $1 \pm \sqrt{6}$ **b.** $1 \pm \sqrt{12}$ **c.** $\dfrac{2 \pm \sqrt{3}}{2}$ **d.** no real solutions

9. $10x^2 - x = 21$

    a. $\dfrac{1 \pm \sqrt{841}}{20}$ **b.** $\dfrac{1 \pm \sqrt{841}}{2}$ **c.** $\dfrac{3}{2}, -\dfrac{7}{5}$ **d.** $\dfrac{7}{5}, -\dfrac{3}{2}$

Solve using the most appropriate method.

10. $4x^2 - 12x = 0$

    a. $0, -3$ **b.** $0, 3$ **c.** $12, 4$ **d.** $-4, 12$

11. $9x^2 - 6x + 1 = 0$

    a. $\dfrac{2}{3}$ **b.** $\dfrac{1}{3}$ **c.** $-\dfrac{1}{3}$ **d.** $\dfrac{1}{3}, -\dfrac{1}{3}$

12. $x^2 - 144 = 0$

    a. 12 **b.** $12, -12$ **c.** $4, 36$ **d.** no real solutions

13. $5x^2 - 3x - 2 = 0$

    a. $-\dfrac{2}{5}, 1$ **b.** $\dfrac{2}{5}, 1$ **c.** $-\dfrac{5}{2}, 1$ **d.** no real solutions

14. $x^2 - 2x - 5 = 0$

    a. $5, -1$ **b.** $-1 \pm \sqrt{6}$ **c.** $1 \pm \sqrt{6}$ **d.** no real solutions

15. $x(3x + 2) = 1$

    a. $\dfrac{1}{3}, -1$ **b.** $0, -\dfrac{2}{3}$ **c.** $-\dfrac{1}{3}, 1$ **d.** no real solutions

16. $\dfrac{1}{2}x^2 - \dfrac{7}{2}x + 3 = 0$

    a. $\dfrac{1}{3}, 7$ **b.** $1, 6$ **c.** $\dfrac{1}{3}, 1$ **d.** no real solutions

Chapter 9 Test Form F *cont'd*

Simplify.

17. $\sqrt{-81}$

    a. 9   **b.** -9 **c.** $9i$ **d.** $-9i$

18. $\sqrt{-48}$

    a. $-2\sqrt{24}$ **b.** $2i\sqrt{24}$ **c.** $4i\sqrt{3}$ **d.** $24i$

19. $(3-2i)-(4-6i)$

    a. $7+4i$ **b.** $-1-8i$ **c.** $7-8i$ **d.** $-1+4i$

20. $(2-3i)(5+2i)$

    a. $16-11i$ **b.** $10-17i$ **c.** $10-5i$ **d.** $4-11i$

21. $\dfrac{3-2i}{4+i}$

    a. $\dfrac{10}{3}-\dfrac{11}{3}i$ **b.** $22+7i$ **c.** $\dfrac{10}{17}-\dfrac{11}{17}i$ **d.** $12+7i$

Identify the equation which the graph represents.

22.

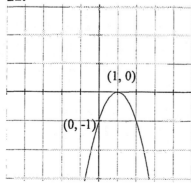

    a. $y=-x^2+2x-1$ **b.** $y=x^2-2x+1$
    c. $y=-x^2-2x-1$ **d.** $y=x^2+2x+1$

Chapter 9 Test Form F *cont'd*

23.

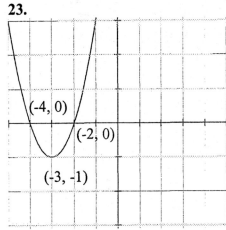

    a. $y = -x^2 - 6x - 8$ **b.** $y = x^2 - 6x + 8$

    c. $y = -x^2 + 6x - 8$ **d.** $y = x^2 + 6x + 8$

24. A ball is tossed into the air from a height of 10 feet with an initial velocity of 12 feet per second. Find the time t (in seconds) for the ball to reach the ground by solving the equation $-16t^2 + 12t + 10 = 0$.

    a. 2 sec   **b.** $1\frac{1}{4}$ sec   **c.** $\frac{1}{2}$ sec   **d.** $\frac{3}{4}$ sec

25. A ball is tossed into the air from a height of 10 feet with an initial velocity of 12 feet per second. Find the time t (in seconds) for the ball to reach maximum height using the graph of the equation $-16t^2 + 12t + 10 = h$.

    a. $\frac{3}{8}$ sec   **b.** $\frac{1}{4}$ sec   **c.** 10 sec   **d.** $\frac{3}{4}$ sec

Chapter 1 Test Answers

Test 1 – A
1. $-8 > -12$
2. $|-3| > 2$
3. integer, rational number, real number
4. $>$
5. -11
6. -4
7. 18
8. -8
9. $\dfrac{11}{12}$
10. -2
11. $\dfrac{1}{2}$
12. 22
13. $\dfrac{1}{2}$
14. 10
15. $-\dfrac{5}{18}$
16. 8
17. -1
18. 10
19. Associative property of multiplication
20. Commutative property of multiplication
21. 6
22. 4
23. gain 7 yards
24. 600
25. 200

Test 1 – B
1. $6 < |-10|$
2. $|8| = |-8|$
3. irrational, real
4. $<$
5. $1\dfrac{5}{6}$
6. -10
7. -1
8. 12
9. 0
10. 2
11. -2
12. 0
13. $\dfrac{7}{10}$
14. -7
15. -3
16. -10
17. 4
18. -5
19. Identity property of addition
20. Inverse property of multiplication
21. $\dfrac{1}{2}$
22. -2
23. rose $1\dfrac{3}{8}$ points
24. $2500
25. $2000

Test 1 – C
1. $-3 \le 0$
2. $|-10| > 2$
3. rational, real
4. $=$
5. $3\dfrac{3}{4}$
6. -5
7. -5
8. 4
9. 24
10. -6
11. $-\dfrac{1}{2}$
12. -6
13. 2
14. -9
15. $-\dfrac{1}{4}$
16. 1
17. -2
18. 30
19. Identity property of multiplication
20. Associative property of addition
21. $-\dfrac{1}{8}$
22. 8
23. 30 feet
24. $42°$
25. 9 am to 10 am

Chapter 1 Test Answers

Test 1 – D	Test 1 – E	Test 1 – F
1. c	1. b	1. b
2. a	2. c	2. c
3. c	3. a	3. d
4. c	4. b	4. c
5. c	5. a	5. d
6. a	6. c	6. b
7. a	7. c	7. a
8. b	8. b	8. b
9. a	9. b	9. a
10. d	10. d	10. c
11. a	11. b	11. c
12. c	12. c	12. d
13. a	13. d	13. a
14. b	14. c	14. a
15. a	15. d	15. a
16. c	16. b	16. c
17. a	17. b	17. b
18. b	18. b	18. b
19. b	19. c	19. a
20. a	20. d	20. d
21. a	21. a	21. c
22. d	22. a	22. a
23. b	23. b	23. a
24. a	24. c	24. c
25. d	25. b	25. a

Chapter 2 Test Answers

Test 2 – A
1. $3x - 4$
2. $0.8x - 5.3$
3. $5x + 6$
4. $9x - 7$
5. 5
6. 27
7. −3
8. −5
9. 3
10. $-\dfrac{4}{21}$
11. 0
12. No solution
13. 1
14. 67, 68
15. 6 hours
16. 400 liters of 20%, 200 liters of 50%
17. 3 hours
18. 533.3604
19. $b = \dfrac{P - 2a}{2}$
20. $h = \dfrac{A}{lw}$
21. $x \geq \dfrac{10}{3}$
22. $x \geq -17$
23. $x \geq 5$
24. $13 < x < 26$
25. $-6 < x \leq 3$

Test 2 – B
1. $-x - 8$
2. $9.5x - 6.3$
3. $6x - 8$
4. $-5x + 9$
5. 6
6. 75
7. −5
8. 11
9. $\dfrac{3}{7}$
10. $\dfrac{9}{4}$
11. −31
12. 0
13. No solution
14. 30°, 60°
15. $20,000 at 5%, $4000 at 3%
16. 84, 85, 86
17. 32
18. 11
19. $\pi = \dfrac{3V}{r^2 h}$
20. $y = \dfrac{-Ax - C}{B}$
21. $x \geq -1$
22. $x \geq -\dfrac{13}{4}$
23. $x \leq 9$
24. $-6 < x < 6$
25. $2 < x < 6$

Test 2 – C
1. $10x - 13$
2. $2.6x - 2.1$
3. $-2x - 18$
4. $5x + 12$
5. 3
6. −98
7. 6
8. −1
9. 8
10. $\dfrac{13}{12}$
11. −10
12. 4
13. No solution
14. 40°, 40°, 100°
15. $25.92
16. $15,000 at 3%, $30,000 at 8%
17. 80 miles
18. 8
19. $x = \dfrac{y - b}{m}$
20. $x = \dfrac{3y + 7}{2y}$
21. $x < -4$
22. $x > 10$
23. $x \geq -4$
24. $-1 < x < 11$
25. $-4 < x < 8$

Chapter 2 Test Answers

Test 2 – D	Test 2 – E	Test 2 – F
1. c	1. d	1. d
2. a	2. a	2. a
3. a	3. c	3. c
4. b	4. b	4. b
5. a	5. c	5. c
6. b	6. a	6. b
7. a	7. b	7. a
8. d	8. a	8. c
9. a	9. b	9. b
10. c	10. c	10. a
11. d	11. d	11. d
12. b	12. a	12. d
13. d	13. d	13. b
14. a	14. b	14. c
15. b	15. d	15. b
16. b	16. b	16. b
17. b	17. c	17. d
18. a	18. b	18. b
19. c	19. c	19. a
20. a	20. a	20. a
21. d	21. a	21. b
22. d	22. d	22. d
23. a	23. c	23. a
24. b	24. b	24. c
25. c	25. c	25. c

Test 3 – A

1.

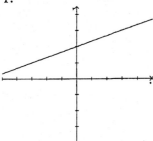

2.

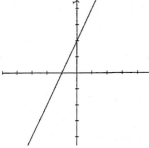

3.

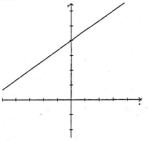

4.

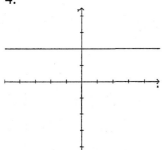

5. -2

6. $-\dfrac{1}{4}$

7. $-\dfrac{3}{2}$

8. 0

9. $m = -2, \ b = 3$

10. perpendicular

11. $x + 3y = 10$

12. $6x + 5y = 0$

13. $3x + 7y = 26$

14. $6x - y = 3$

15. Function

16. Function

17. -4

18. 5

19. $-\dfrac{20}{3}$

20. $(-\infty, \infty)$

21. $[1, \infty)$

22. all real numbers except $\dfrac{1}{2}$

23. 4 feet

24. 4.5 feet

25. 4 seconds

Test 3 – B

1.

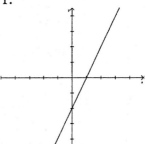

2.

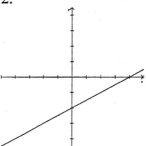

3.

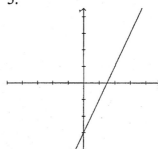

4.

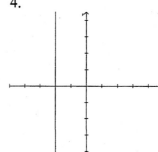

5. 2

6. 2

7. $\dfrac{2}{5}$

8. undefined

9. $m = -\dfrac{3}{2}, b = 2$

10. parallel

11. $2x - 3y = 10$

12. $4x + y = -11$

13. $y = -4$

14. $2x + 3y = 18$

15. function

16. not a function

17. 0

18. -12

19. -6

20. $(-\infty, \infty)$

21. $[-4, \infty)$

22. all real numbers except 2

23. 4 feet

24. 1 second

25. 3 seconds

Test 3 – C

1.

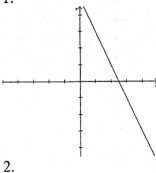

2.

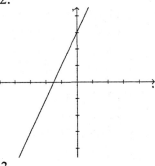

3.

4.

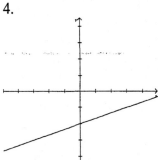

5. 0

6. -13

7. $\dfrac{1}{4}$

8. 0

9. $m = 3, \, b = -4$

10. neither

11. $2x + 5y = 4$

12. $5x + 4y = -8$

13. $y = 4$

14. $3x - 5y = -20$

15. function

16. not a function

17. -2

18. -8

19. $-\dfrac{14}{3}$

20. $(-\infty, \infty)$

21. $[0, \infty)$

22. all real numbers except 3

23. 2 seconds

24. 1 and 3 seconds

25. 1 foot

Chapter 3 Test Answers

Test 3 – D	Test 3 – E	Test 3 – F
1. c	1. d	1. b
2. b	2. c	2. c
3. b	3. a	3. d
4. a	4. c	4. a
5. d	5. c	5. a
6. c	6. b	6. c
7. c	7. b	7. a
8. d	8. d	8. c
9. b	9. c	9. c
10. a	10. c	10. a
11. a	11. b	11. b
12. d	12. a	12. b
13. c	13. b	13. a
14. a	14. c	14. c
15. a	15. d	15. a
16. d	16. b	16. c
17. b	17. a	17. c
18. c	18. b	18. b
19. a	19. d	19. d
20. a	20. a	20. a
21. d	21. c	21. c
22. a	22. b	22. b
23. d	23. c	23. d
24. a	24. b	24. b
25. c	25. d	25. c

Chapter 4 Test Answers

Test 4 – A

1. no
2. yes
3. no
4. $\left(\dfrac{2}{3}, 1\right)$
5. no solution
6. (2, 4)
7. (2, 1)
8. (2, 4)
9. (2, 4)
10. (3, −4)
11. (2, 0)
12. (−4, 4)
13. (−2, 0)
14. no solution
15. (−5, 3)
16. infinite solutions
17. $\left(\dfrac{1}{3}, 4\right)$
18. (1, 3)
19. 3 and 5
20. 120, $5 tickets
    150, $2 tickets
21.

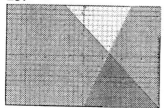

22.

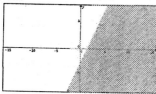

23.

24.

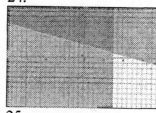

25.

Test 4 – B

1. yes
2. no
3. yes
4. (1, −1)
5. (−3, 4)
6. (−5, 4)
7. (3, 2)
8. (−5, −15)
9. no solution
10. $\left(\dfrac{5}{3}, -\dfrac{2}{3}\right)$
11. (1, 5)
12. (2, 7)
13. (2, 3)
14. $\left(\dfrac{1}{4}, 2\right)$
15. no solution
16. (3, −1)
17. (0, 5)
18. (14, −8)
19. 6, 3
20. 200 ml
21.

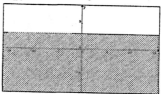

22.

23.

Chapter 4 Test Answers

Test 4 – C

24.
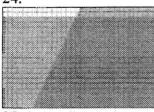

25.

1. no
2. yes
3. (3, 1)
4. (−2, 4)
5. (2, 3)
6. (6, −2)
7. (2, −2)
8. (0, 3)
9. infinite solutions
10. (2, 0)
11. no solution
12. (2, −2)
13. no solution
14. (1, 4)
15. (2, 0)
16. (4, 4)
17. $\left(1, \frac{1}{2}\right)$
18. (3, −2)
19. 8, 12
20. 10 mph

25.

21.
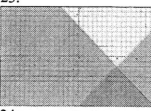

22.
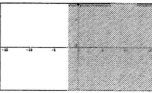

23.
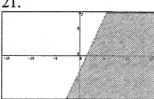

24.
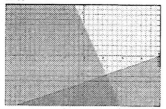

Chapter 4 Test Answers

Test 4 – D	Test 4 – E	Test 4 – F
1. a	1. b	1. b
2. c	2. a	2. a
3. c	3. c	3. d
4. a	4. d	4. c
5. a	5. a	5. c
6. c	6. d	6. d
7. b	7. b	7. c
8. b	8. c	8. a
9. d	9. a	9. a
10. d	10. d	10. c
11. b	11. b	11. d
12. b	12. a	12. b
13. a	13. c	13. d
14. b	14. b	14. c
15. b	15. d	15. b
16. c	16. a	16. a
17. d	17. a	17. a
18. a	18. a	18. b
19. d	19. d	19. d
20. b	20. b	20. d
21. c	21. c	21. d
22. b	22. b	22. c
23. d	23. d	23. a
24. a	24. c	24. b
25. c	25. a	25. d

Chapter 5 Test Answers

Test 5 – A

1. -8
2. -16
3. $\dfrac{1}{16}$
4. $8x^8$
5. $-20x^{11}$
6. a^3b^3
7. 1
8. 9
9. $\dfrac{y^8}{x^2}$
10. 5.723×10^6
11. 0.00000794
12. 9.12×10^8
13. 5
14. $6x^2-16x-9$
15. $5x^2-15x-9$
16. $-2x^2+x-9$
17. a^2+b^2
18. $-\dfrac{5}{9}x^{13}$
19. $-6x^7+4x^5-8x^3$
20. $6x^2-x-15$
21. $9x^2+12x+4$
22. $4x^2-25$
23. x^3-4x-2
24. $x-3$
25. $x+2$

Test 5 – B

1. 16
2. $\dfrac{1}{16}$
3. $\dfrac{1}{9}$
4. x^{12}
5. $\dfrac{b^3}{a^9}$
6. $-8x^8y^2$
7. $\dfrac{1}{x^2y^{14}}$
8. 2.36×10^{-6}
9. $4,290,000$
10. 1.426×10^{12}
11. 8
12. x^3+5x+8
13. $6x^2+2$
14. $-2x^4-6x^3+5x-3$
15. $x^2-2x+11$
16. $-12x^3+15x^2-18x$
17. $12x^2-9x-30$
18. $6x^3-17x^2+22x-15$
19. $6x^2+7x-20$
20. $9x^2-30x+25$
21. $49x^2-9$
22. $9x^4-30x^2y^3+25y^6$
23. $2x^2+4x-1$
24. x^2+2x+4
25. $x^2-8x+16$

Test 5 – C

1. -8
2. -1
3. -16
4. a^{14}
5. $2x^4y^2$
6. $\dfrac{9y^6}{x^2}$
7. $\dfrac{x^{16}}{y^{10}}$
8. 9.4×10^{-5}
9. $7,290,000$
10. 2.24×10^9
11. 8
12. $7x^2-7x+5$
13. $7x^2-2x+3$
14. x^2-15
15. $-x^2-7x+12$
16. $-6x^5-8x^4+10x^3$
17. $2x^2+3x-20$
18. $8x^3-26x^2+31x-15$
19. $28x^2+2x-6$
20. $16x^2-24x+9$
21. $4x^2-49$
22. $3x^4-14x^2y^5+8y^{10}$
23. $1-\dfrac{4y}{7x}+\dfrac{1}{x^2}$
24. $4x^2+6x+9$
25. 140 feet

Chapter 5 Test Answers

Test 5 – D	Test 5 – E	Test 5 – F
1. b	1. b	1. c
2. c	2. a	2. b
3. d	3. d	3. c
4. b	4. b	4. c
5. d	5. d	5. b
6. b	6. c	6. a
7. d	7. b	7. d
8. b	8. b	8. b
9. b	9. a	9. d
10. c	10. d	10. b
11. c	11. b	11. b
12. d	12. c	12. a
13. c	13. c	13. a
14. d	14. c	14. c
15. b	15. a	15. b
16. a	16. d	16. d
17. c	17. a	17. c
18. b	18. d	18. a
19. c	19. b	19. a
20. b	20. a	20. c
21. a	21. c	21. b
22. c	22. c	22. c
23. c	23. a	23. b
24. a	24. b	24. d
25. d	25. b	25. c

Chapter 6 Test Answers

Test 6 – A
1. $4x^2(2x-3)$
2. $(a-3)(x+2)$
3. $(3x-5)(x+2y)$
4. $(x-4)(x+3)$
5. $(x-6)(x-5)$
6. $(a-6)^2$
7. prime
8. $(3x-4)(x+2)$
9. $(x-2)(x^2+2x+4)$
10. $2x(x-5)(3x-4)$
11. $(x+2)(x-4)(x+4)$
12. $x(x-3)(x+3)\cdot$
    $(x-2)(x+2)$
13. $(x-3y)(x+2y)$
14. $(2x-3y)(x+4y)$
15. $-3, 4$
16. $2, -6$
17. $5, -6$
18. $0, \dfrac{2}{3}, -\dfrac{2}{5}$
19. $0, 3, -3$
20. $\dfrac{2}{5}, -\dfrac{3}{4}$
21. $\dfrac{7}{2}, -\dfrac{7}{2}$
22. $0, 7$
23. $w = 6$ ft, $l = 9$ ft
24. $6, 8$
25. 5 seconds

Test 6 – B
1. $5x^3(x+2)$
2. $(x-3)(y+2)$
3. $(2x+5)(3x-2y)$
4. $(x-9)(x+3)$
5. $(x-3)(x-8)$
6. prime
7. $(x+3)^2$
8. $(2x-3)(5x+2)$
9. $(x+5)(x^2-5x+25)$
10. $5x(x+7)(x-3)$
11. $(x-8)(x+8)$
12. $x(x+3y)\cdot$
    $(x-4)(x+4)$
13. $(x-4y)(x-6y)$
14. $(2x-y)(2x+3y)$
15. $5, -4$
16. $4, -6$
17. $7, \dfrac{1}{2}$
18. $0, 6, \dfrac{2}{3}$
19. $0, -\dfrac{2}{5}$
20. $8, -8$
21. $5, -3$
22. $\dfrac{3}{5}, \dfrac{7}{3}$
23. $w = 8$ ft, $l = 10$ ft
24. $7, 4$
25. 4 seconds

Test 6 – C
1. $2x(3x^2-2)$
2. $(3-b)(2a+1)$
3. $(x-5)(2x+5y)$
4. $(a+5)(a-7)$
5. $(x-7)(x-3)$
6. $(x+4)(x+8)$
7. $(x+5)^2$
8. prime
9. $(3x-2)(x+5)$
10. $2x(x+3)(x-5)$
11. $(x-2)(x+2)(x-5)$
12. $(x+1)(x^2-x+1)$
13. $(x+4y)(2x-3y)$
14. $(2x-3y)(4x-y)$
15. $12, 4$
16. $-6, -3$
17. $9, -2$
18. $0, -\dfrac{7}{2}, \dfrac{1}{3}$
19. $0, 5, -5$
20. $\dfrac{2}{5}, 3$
21. $\dfrac{5}{2}$
22. $0, 7$
23. 15 ft
24. $5, 3$
25. 3 seconds

Chapter 6 Test Answers

Test 6 – D	Test 6 – E	Test 6 – F
1. c	1. b	1. d
2. c	2. a	2. a
3. a	3. a	3. b
4. c	4. d	4. a
5. d	5. c	5. c
6. d	6. b	6. c
7. a	7. d	7. c
8. a	8. c	8. b
9. c	9. a	9. a
10. b	10. d	10. d
11. d	11. b	11. c
12. d	12. c	12. b
13. c	13. d	13. b
14. c	14. b	14. a
15. c	15. c	15. c
16. b	16. a	16. a
17. b	17. c	17. d
18. a	18. a	18. d
19. b	19. c	19. c
20. a	20. a	20. b
21. a	21. b	21. d
22. a	22. b	22. b
23. a	23. a	23. a
24. b	24. d	24. a
25. b	25. a	25. b

Chapter 7 Test Answers

Test 7 – A

1. 5
2. $-2, -4$
3. $\dfrac{x-3}{x+1}$
4. $\dfrac{x+6}{x+3}$
5. $\dfrac{-1}{x+4}$
6. $\dfrac{1}{x^2+2x+4}$
7. $\dfrac{y+3}{y-4}$
8. $\dfrac{x-4}{3(x-2)}$
9. $\dfrac{x(x+4)}{10}$
10. 12
11. 1
12. $\dfrac{1}{2(4x-3)}$
13. $\dfrac{4x+4}{(x+2)(x-2)}$
14. $\dfrac{x^2+x-12}{(x-4)(x+2)(x-2)}$
15. 4
16. 0
17. 6
18. 4
19. $\dfrac{x+3}{x-3}$
20. $y-3x$
21. 3
22. $1\dfrac{5}{7}$ hour
23. 6
24. 21
25. $\dfrac{512}{25}$

Test 7 – B

1. $\dfrac{2}{3}$
2. $5, -4$
3. $\dfrac{2x-y}{3}$
4. $\dfrac{x-6}{x+6}$
5. $\dfrac{1}{x-2}$
6. $\dfrac{-1}{x+2y}$
7. $\dfrac{y+3}{y-4}$
8. $\dfrac{1}{x-6}$
9. $\dfrac{x+1}{3(x-3)}$
10. $\dfrac{1}{(x+2)^2}$
11. $\dfrac{3x-7}{x}$
12. $\dfrac{2x+9}{(x+3)(x-3)}$
13. $\dfrac{2}{x+3}$
14. $\dfrac{x^2-5x-5}{(x+3)(x-5)}$
15. 7
16. no solution
17. 5
18. no solution
19. $\dfrac{y-x}{3y}$
20. $\dfrac{1}{7}$
21. 5
22. 30 mph
23. 9
24. 30
25. $\dfrac{324}{25}$

Test 7 – C

1. -2
2. $-4, 1$
3. $\dfrac{x+3}{3}$
4. $\dfrac{x-8}{x+7}$
5. $\dfrac{1}{x+2}$
6. $\dfrac{-1}{x+7}$
7. $\dfrac{4(x-2)}{3(x+2)}$
8. $\dfrac{1}{x-5}$
9. $\dfrac{1}{2(2x+3)}$
10. $x-2$
11. 4
12. $\dfrac{x^2+2x-3}{x^2-3x-10}$
13. $\dfrac{5}{x-2}$
14. $\dfrac{2x+16}{(x-9)(x+9)(x+7)}$
15. $\dfrac{19}{4}$
16. 1
17. $-\dfrac{14}{5}$
18. $\dfrac{37}{2}$
19. $\dfrac{2y-x}{3}$
20. $-\dfrac{3}{5}$
21. $\dfrac{35}{12}$
22. $2\dfrac{2}{5}$
23. $\dfrac{9}{2}$
24. 6
25. $\dfrac{80}{9}$

Chapter 7 Test Answers

Test 7 – D	Test 7 – E	Test 7 – F
1. a	1. a	1. b
2. b	2. a	2. d
3. a	3. c	3. c
4. d	4. c	4. d
5. b	5. b	5. a
6. c	6. c	6. b
7. b	7. a	7. b
8. b	8. d	8. d
9. b	9. a	9. c
10. c	10. c	10. b
11. d	11. b	11. a
12. a	12. b	12. c
13. b	13. a	13. b
14. b	14. c	14. a
15. c	15. b	15. d
16. a	16. c	16. b
17. c	17. a	17. d
18. a	18. c	18. c
19. d	19. d	19. c
20. b	20. c	20. c
21. d	21. b	21. d
22. a	22. a	22. b
23. b	23. c	23. a
24. b	24. c	24. c
25. a	25. b	25. a

Chapter 8 Test Answers

Test 8 – A

1. $10x^3$
2. $-\dfrac{4}{7}$
3. 3
4. $3x^2$
5. $3x$
6. $\dfrac{x^3}{5}$
7. $7\sqrt{3}-6\sqrt{5}$
8. $4\sqrt{3}$
9. $4x^2\sqrt{2}$
10. 9
11. $2\sqrt{3}-4$
12. $10\sqrt{x}$
13. $3x^2\sqrt{3x}$
14. $\dfrac{1}{7}$
15. $\dfrac{\sqrt{7}}{7}$
16. $\dfrac{3\sqrt{2x}}{2x}$
17. $\dfrac{5x+5\sqrt{2}}{x^2-2}$
18. $\dfrac{31-10\sqrt{6}}{-19}$
19. 16
20. 9
21. 4
22. $\sqrt{65}$ in
23. 8 ft
24. $\sqrt{5}$
25. $\dfrac{1}{x}$

Test 8 – B

1. $4x^2$
2. $\dfrac{7}{8}$
3. 4
4. $-2x$
5. $8x^4$
6. $\dfrac{x^3}{5}$
7. $4x\sqrt{2x}$
8. $2\sqrt{2}$
9. 6
10. 15
11. $6x^2\sqrt{2}$
12. $5x^2\sqrt{2x}$
13. $2\sqrt{2}$
14. $\dfrac{\sqrt{3}}{4}$
15. $\dfrac{\sqrt{6}}{3}$
16. $\dfrac{3\sqrt{2}}{2}$
17. $\dfrac{2\sqrt{3}+2x}{3-x^2}$
18. $\dfrac{19-8\sqrt{3}}{-13}$
19. 25
20. 1
21. 10, 0
22. 10 in
23. 50.91 in
24. 5
25. $\dfrac{1}{x}$

Test 8 – C

1. 5
2. $\dfrac{4}{7}$
3. 2
4. xy^3
5. $x^4\sqrt{5}$
6. $\dfrac{x^3}{4}$
7. $2x^3\sqrt{6x}$
8. 12
9. $\dfrac{2\sqrt{3}}{63}$
10. 6
11. $16x\sqrt{2x}$
12. $4x^3\sqrt{3}$
13. $4\sqrt{5}$
14. $\dfrac{\sqrt{7}}{5}$
15. $\dfrac{\sqrt{10}}{5}$
16. $\dfrac{\sqrt{5x}}{x}$
17. $\dfrac{4\sqrt{2}-4x}{2-x^2}$
18. $\dfrac{3\sqrt{5}-7}{2}$
19. 64
20. no solution
21. 6
22. $5\sqrt{2}$ in
23. $5\sqrt{171}$ in
24. $\sqrt{173}$
25. $x^{\frac{14}{15}}$

Chapter 8 Test Answers

Test 8 – D

1. c
2. a
3. c
4. b
5. b
6. c
7. c
8. c
9. d
10. b
11. a
12. c
13. d
14. c
15. b
16. a
17. d
18. a
19. b
20. c
21. b
22. d
23. a
24. d
25. c

Test 8 – E

1. a
2. c
3. a
4. b
5. d
6. a
7. b
8. d
9. b
10. b
11. d
12. d
13. b
14. a
15. c
16. b
17. b
18. c
19. a
20. a
21. c
22. b
23. d
24. b
25. c

Test 8 – F

1. d
2. d
3. c
4. d
5. b
6. d
7. d
8. c
9. d
10. b
11. d
12. d
13. c
14. c
15. d
16. a
17. d
18. b
19. a
20. a
21. b
22. a
23. a
24. d
25. b

Chapter 9 Test Answers

Test 9 – A
1. $-5, 5$
2. $-3, 7$
3. $0, 3$
4. $-3 \pm \sqrt{13}$
5. $-2 \pm \sqrt{13}$
6. $-1 \pm \sqrt{6}$
7. $\dfrac{-7 \pm \sqrt{65}}{2}$
8. $\dfrac{3 \pm \sqrt{33}}{3}$
9. $-2 \pm \sqrt{2}$
10. $\dfrac{2}{3}$
11. $-2, 6$
12. $-1, 4$
13. $-2, 3$
14. $3 \pm \sqrt{11}$
15. $\dfrac{7 \pm \sqrt{37}}{2}$
16. $4i$
17. $2i\sqrt{2}$
18. $-2 - 8i$
19. 26
20. $\dfrac{4}{13} - \dfrac{7}{13}i$
21.

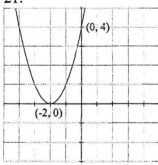

22.

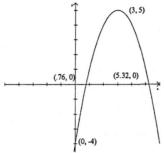

23.

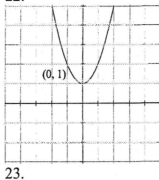

24. 2.5 seconds
25. 100 feet

Test 9 – B
1. $-5, 5$
2. $\dfrac{-3 \pm 5\sqrt{3}}{2}$
3. $-2, 8$
4. $-8 \pm \sqrt{55}$
5. $-\dfrac{1}{3}, 4$
6. $-5, 1$
7. $-2 \pm 2\sqrt{3}$
8. $4 \pm \sqrt{13}$
9. $-\dfrac{4}{3}, 3$
10. $-4, 4$
11. $1, \dfrac{4}{3}$
12. $-1, 4$
13. $\dfrac{3 \pm 2\sqrt{3}}{5}$
14. $-2, 0, 2$
15. $-8, 5$
16. $5i$
17. $2i\sqrt{5}$
18. $-2 + 3i$
19. $-5 + 12i$
20. $\dfrac{4}{13} + \dfrac{7}{13}i$
21.

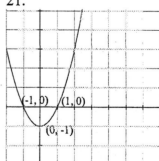

Chapter 9 Test Answers

22.

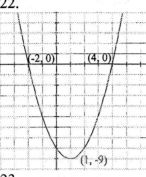

23.

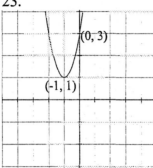

24.

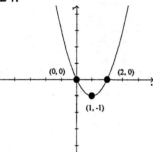

26. 8 feet, 12 feet

Test 9 – C

1. $-3, 3$
2. $4 \pm \sqrt{7}$
3. $\dfrac{4 \pm \sqrt{5}}{3}$
4. $-4 \pm 2\sqrt{3}$
5. $-\dfrac{3}{2}, \dfrac{1}{2}$
6. $\dfrac{-3 \pm \sqrt{33}}{2}$
7. $-\dfrac{3}{2}, \dfrac{5}{2}$
8. $-4 \pm 2\sqrt{3}$
9. $\dfrac{-3 \pm \sqrt{41}}{2}$
10. -5
11. $-1, 4$
12. $1 \pm \sqrt{3}$
13. $3, 1$
14. $\dfrac{1 \pm \sqrt{73}}{2}$
15. $-4, 4$
16. $-\dfrac{4}{3}, \dfrac{5}{2}$
17. $6i$
18. $2i\sqrt{5}$
19. $14 - 8i$
20. $\dfrac{1}{17} - \dfrac{13}{17}i$
21. $\dfrac{1}{15} - \dfrac{13}{15}i$
22.

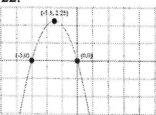

23.

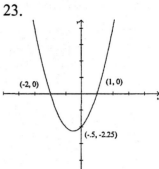

24.

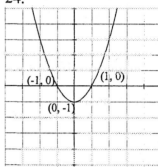

25. $\dfrac{3}{4}$ in

Chapter 9 Test Answers

Test 9 – D	Test 9 – E	Test 9 – F
1. d	1. c	1. b
2. c	2. d	2. c
3. b	3. b	3. a
4. a	4. d	4. c
5. b	5. a	5. c
6. b	6. b	6. c
7. c	7. b	7. a
8. d	8. b	8. d
9. d	9. a	9. c
10. c	10. c	10. b
11. c	11. c	11. b
12. b	12. b	12. b
13. c	13. a	13. a
14. c	14. b	14. c
15. a	15. c	15. a
16. c	16. b	16. b
17. d	17. b	17. c
18. b	18. b	18. c
19. a	19. d	19. d
20. a	20. d	20. a
21. b	21. b	21. c
22. d	22. d	22. a
23. d	23. b	23. d
24. a	24. c	24. b
25. b	25. a	25. a